The Microsc

Its History, Construction, and Application 15th ed.; Being a familiar introduction to the use of the instrument, and the study of microscopical science

Jabez Hogg

Alpha Editions

This edition published in 2023

ISBN : 9789357383752

Design and Setting By
Alpha Editions
www.alphaedis.com
Email - info@alphaedis.com

Contents

PREFACE TO THE FIFTEENTH EDITION.

THE First Edition of this work appeared in 1854, a time in the history of the Microscope when the instrument, as an aid to original scientific research, may be said to have been in its infancy. Then certainly it was seldom employed in the laboratory or the medical schools. Now, however, as I anticipated, it has asserted its proper position, and has at length become one of the most important auxiliaries to science, and a direct incentive to original work, while it has doubtless exercised considerable influence over the student's power of observation, and materially assisted in his studies, let his ultimate object and pursuits be what they may.

The greater use made of the Microscope has likewise conferred benefits of untold value upon the arts and industries of the country, thereby adding to the national prosperity in ways as manifold as unique. The Microscope has also proved of immense value in the promotion of the health of the community, and the art and science of healing, since the theory of medicine has become a science, resting on the minute microscopical examination of animal tissues.

The work of research in the sister sciences and by other methods has, during the last decade, received a corresponding impetus, while it has undoubtedly tended towards elaboration and specialisation in all departments. In consequence, the progress of microscopical science has become more dependent upon the specialist for gaining accurate knowledge and for certain important details seen to be branching out in many directions. There never was a time when the instrument was so constantly and generally resorted to and with so much confidence and advantage, as the present. It has shown itself equal to the task imposed—that of teaching the eye to see things that are new, and also, what is perhaps of more importance, to perceive things which had been entirely overlooked. The older defects, perhaps, arose from two causes; the want of more careful training of the organ of vision, and the want of sufficient power and precision in the optical part of the Microscope itself. Both of these obstacles have been to a considerable extent removed, and all educational systems are looked upon as incomplete without a knowledge of the Microscope.

A step has already been taken in another direction, that of furnishing special forms of instruments, better adapted to the uses to which they will hereafter be put, and purposely designed for chemical and analytical processes, for petrological pursuits, the geometrical measurement of crystals, for special work in connection with manufacturing industries, for the dairyman, and the farmer. For the detection of adulterations—that of butter, for example—a newer form of instrument has been devised, namely, a "Butro-refractometer," by the help of which any adulteration of this universal article of diet will at once be revealed. The form of instrument upon which the optician has expended a greater amount of skill than perhaps on any other is the Bacteriological Microscope, as may be inferred from the larger space I have devoted to this important adjunct, since by original research, there can be no doubt a still greater future is in store for science in this special department of microscopy. But perfect success in this direction remains very much with the practical optician, and the further improvements made in the optical part of the instrument, since it is admitted that the highest theoretical perfection has not yet been reached.

It is a commonplace remark that every question solved is a step towards new problems waiting solution. It is equally obvious that many difficulties must be encountered by every author who uses his best endeavours to supply a standard volume or even a fairly comprehensive text-book on the Microscope, one that will remain a sure guide for any lengthened period. Such a success I regard as scarcely possible. I may, however, notice that my earlier work has met with a great amount of appreciation, and its utility acknowledged in the past by a demand almost unprecedented, edition after edition being called for.

It is hardly necessary to add that my task has been accomplished with an earnest desire to assist in diffusing a love for an instrument which has been my constant companion for upwards of sixty years.[1] Moreover, I have a firm conviction of the real utility of the Microscope in the work of education, its practical value in many branches of science, art, and manufacturing industries. These are my chief reasons for applying myself once more to the task of revision, rewriting, and rearranging and bringing this book as far as possible into line with the knowledge gained in chemical pathology and bacteriology.

It will be noticed that in the first part, my subjects have as far as possible been treated from a historical point of view. This method has enabled me to affix dates of introduction of special inventions and improvements made in the instrument and its appliances. The enlargement of my pages has enabled me to devote more space to bacteriological processes, and by the further addition of plates and several hundred illustrations to more fully elucidate the subject matter of my text. In an Appendix I have introduced a selection of "Formulæ and Methods" of staining, mounting, etc., also tables of the "Metrical System," now in general use in the laboratory; together with comparative thermometric values, all of which I trust may prove of service to the student.

Before bringing these few prefatory remarks to a close, a pleasing duty devolves upon me—that of tendering my thanks for cordial aid received from Professor Dr. EDGAR CROOKSHANK in dealing with his special subject, Bacteriology. From his valuable "Text-Book on Bacteriology" I have extracted much useful matter. I am equally indebted to Professor MARSHALL WARD, F.R.S., Cambridge, for much information on "Economic Botany," and the great advances made in the knowledge of the uses of plants, and the industrial value of bacteria in particular. My acknowledgments are also due to the Messrs. WARNE for many illustrations placed at my disposal, and for useful facts derived from their "Royal Natural History." It will, however, be seen that the results of a large amount of independent observation have been consigned to my pages. As the references show, recourse has been had to original sources for trustworthy, reliable information on many subjects. These are constantly, almost daily, being added to, as is made manifest by the numerous periodical publications of the day devoted to this and kindred sciences; the foremost and most important among which is that almost exclusively given to microscopical science, "The Journal of the Royal Microscopical Society of London," the perusal of which I commend to my readers.

LONDON, JULY, 1898.

PREFACE TO THE FIRST EDITION.

THE Author of this Publication entered upon his task with some hesitation and diffidence; but the reasons which influenced him to undertake it may be briefly told, and they at once explain his motives, and plead his justification, for the work which he now ventures to submit to the indulgent consideration of his readers.

It had been to him for some time a subject of regret that one of the most useful and fascinating studies—that which belongs to the domain of microscopic observation—should be, if not wholly neglected, at best but coldly and indifferently appreciated by the great mass of the general public; and he formed a strong opinion that this apathy and inattention were mainly attributable to the want of some concise, yet sufficiently comprehensive, *popular* account of the Microscope, both as regards the management and manipulation of the instrument, and the varied wonders and hidden realms of beauty that are disclosed and developed by its aid. He saw around him valuable, erudite, and splendid volumes, which, however, being chiefly designed for circulation amongst a special class of readers, were necessarily published at a price that renders them practically unattainable by the great bulk of the public. They are careful and beautiful contributions to the objects of science, but they do not adequately bring the value and charm of microscopic studies home, so to speak, to the firesides of the people. Day after day, new and interesting discoveries, and amplifications of truth already discerned, have been made, but they have been either sacrificed in serials, or, more usually, devoted to the pages of class publications; and thus this most important and attractive study has been, in a great measure, the province of the few only, who have derived from it a rich store of enlightenment and gratification: the many not having, however, participated, to any great extent, in the instruction and entertainment which always follow in the train of microscopical science.[2]

The manifold uses and advantages of the Microscope crowd upon us in such profusion, that we can only attempt to enumerate them in the briefest and most rapid manner in these prefatory pages.

It is not many years since this invaluable instrument was regarded in the light of a costly toy; it is now the inseparable companion of the man of science. In the medical world, its utility and necessity are fully appreciated, even by those who formerly were slow to perceive its benefits; now, knowledge which could not be obtained even by the minutest dissection is acquired readily by its assistance, which has become as essential to the anatomist and pathologist as are the scalpel and bedside observation. The smallest portion of a diseased structure, placed under a Microscope, will tell more in one minute to the experienced eye than could be ascertained by long examination of the mass of disease in the ordinary method. Microscopic agency, in thus assisting the medical man, contributes much to the alleviation of those multiplied "ills which flesh is heir to." So fully impressed were the Council of the Royal College of Surgeons with the importance of the facts brought to light in a short space of time, that, in 1841, they determined to establish a Professorship of Histology, and to form a collection of preparations of the elementary tissues of both animals and vegetables, healthy and morbid, which should illustrate the value of microscopical investigations in physiology and medical science. From that time, histological anatomy deservedly became an important branch of the education of the medical student.

In the study of Vegetable Physiology, the Microscope is an indispensable instrument; it enables the student to trace the earliest forms of vegetable life, and the functions of the different tissues in the growth of plants. Valuable assistance is derived from its agency in the detection of adulterations. In the examination of flour, an article of so much importance to all, the Microscope enables us to judge of the size and shape of the starch-grains, their markings, their isolation and agglomeration, and thus to distinguish the starch-grains of one meal from those of another. It detects these and other ingredients, invisible to the naked eye, whether combined in atoms or aggregated in crystals, which adulterate our food, our drink, and our medicines. It discloses the lurking poison in the minute crystallisations which its solutions precipitate. "It tells the murderer that the blood which stains him is that of his brother, and not of the other life which he pretends to have taken; and as a witness against the criminal, it on one occasion appealed to the very sand on which he trod at midnight."

The zoologist finds in the Microscope a necessary coadjutor. To the geologist it reveals, among a multiplicity of other facts, "that our large coal-beds are the ruins of a gigantic vegetation; and the vast limestone rocks, which are so abundant on the earth's surface, are the catacombs of myriads of animal tribes, too minute to be perceived by the unaided vision."

By "conducting the eye to the confines of the visible form," the Microscope proves an effective auxiliary in defining the geometric properties of bodies. Its influence as an instrument of research upon the structure of bodies has been compared to that of the galvanic battery, in the hands of Davy, upon Chemistry. It detects the smallest structural difference, heretofore inappreciable, and, as an ally of Chemistry, enables us to discover the very small changes of form and colour effected by test-fluids upon solids; and dissects for us, so to speak, the most multiplex compounds. It opens out to the mind an extended and vast tract, opulent in wonders, rich in beauties, and boundless in extent.

The Microscope not only assists studies, and develops objects of profound interest, but also opens up innumerable sources of entertainment and amusement, in the ordinary conventional acceptation of these terms; disclosing to us peculiarities and attractions in abundance; impressing us with the wonderful and beautifully skilful adaptation of all parts of creation, and filling our minds with additional reverence and admiration for the beneficent and Almighty Creator.

The Author will conclude these prefatory observations with a few words in explanation of his arrangements, by way of dealing with the instrument and development of his subject. He has sought, in the volume that he now lays before the public, to point out and elucidate at once in a practical manner and in a popular style, the vast fund of utility and amusement which the Microscope affords, and has endeavoured to touch upon most of the interesting subjects for microscopic observation as fully as the restrictions of a limited space, and the nature of the succinct summary, would permit. To have dwelt upon each in complete detail would have necessitated the issue of many expensive volumes—and this would have entirely frustrated the aim which the writer had in view; he has, therefore, contented himself with the humble, but, he trusts, not useless, task of setting up a finger-post, so to say, to direct the inquirer into the wider road. In the section of the work devoted to the minuter portion of creation, he has ventured to dwell somewhat longer, in the belief that that department is more especially the province of the microscopist. He has arranged his topics under special headings, and in separate chapters, for the sake of perspicuity and precision; and has brought the ever-welcome aid of illustration to convey his explanatory remarks more vividly to the minds of his readers.

Finally, it is the Author's hope that, by the instrumentality of this volume, he may possibly assist in bringing the Microscope, and its valuable and delightful studies, before the general public in a more familiar, compendious, and economical form than he found it at the period of its publication, so that, in these days of a diffused taste for reading and the spread of cheap publications, he may thus supply further exercise for the intellectual faculties; contribute to the additional amusement and instruction of the family circle, and aid the student of nature in investigating the wonderful and exquisite works of the Almighty. If it shall be the good fortune for this work, which is now confided with great diffidence to the consideration of the public, to succeed, in however slight a degree, in furthering this design, the Author will feel fully repaid for the amount of time and labour expended.

LONDON, *May*, 1854.

PART I.

Early History of the Microscope.

The instrument known as the Microscope derives its designation from two Greek words, μικρὸς (*mikros*), *small,* and σκοπέω (*skopeo*), *to see or observe;* and is an optical instrument by means of which objects are so magnified that details invisible or indistinct to the naked eye are clearly seen. Its origin, so far as yet can be traced back, seems to be of a doubtful nature. It is tolerably certain the ancients had little or no conception of the magnifying power of lenses; this may be surmised from their writings. The elder Pliny incidentally states that the physicians of his day cauterised by means of "a globe of crystal." The learned Greek physician, Galen, however, demonstrates conclusively that in the first and second centuries of our era the use of magnifying lenses was quite unknown either to Greek or Roman. Moreover, the writings of Archimedes, Ptolemy, and other learned men, show that, although they had some idea of the action of refraction at plane surfaces, as of water, yet of the refraction at curved surfaces they had formed no conception. Indeed, they refer quite indiscriminately to the spherical form, or the disc, or the plane surface of the water, but not one of them speaks of the lenticular form, or the curvature of their surfaces.

As to the more powerful optical instruments, the telescope and microscope, although it would appear that Alhazen in the 10th or 11th century, Roger Bacon in the 13th, and Fracastoro and Baptist Porta in the 16th, had formed some idea that lenses might be made and combined so that distant objects might be seen clearer, or near ones magnified beyond the power of normal vision; yet we hold with Kepler, that no instrument analogous to our telescope was known before the early part of the 17th century.

The combination of lenses associated with the name of Galileo, was, he tells us, of Dutch origin, and of a date anterior to that of his telescope, constructed by him in 1609; and this would appear to be the probable origin of the microscope consisting of a combination of a convex object lens with a concave eye lens.[3]

It now appears almost impossible to assign the exact date of the first production of the microscope (as distinguished from the simple magnifying lens), but those who have made a special investigation, agree that it must have been invented between 1590 and 1609, and that either of the three spectacle-makers of Middelburg, Holland, Hans Janssen, his son Zacharias Janssen, and Hans Lippershey, may have been the inventor, the probabilities being in favour of the Janssens, and there the question must remain.

The history of the modern microscope, like that of nations and arts, has had its brilliant periods, in which it shone with uncommon splendour, and was cultivated with extraordinary ardour; these periods have been succeeded by intervals marked with no discovery, and in which the science seemed to fade away, or at least to lie dormant, till some favourable circumstance—the discovery of a new object, or some new improvement in the instruments of observation—awakened the attention of the curious, and reanimated the spirit of research. Thus, soon after the invention of the microscope, the field it presented to observation was cultivated by men of the first rank in science, and who enriched almost every branch of natural history by the discoveries made by means of this instrument.

The Modern Microscope.

To the celebrated Dr. Hooke belongs the honour of publishing an account of the compound instrument in 1665 in his "Micrographia." His first claim, however, is founded on the application of a lamp adjustable on a pillar, together with a glass globe of water and a deep plano-convex condensing lens. By means of this arrangement, he says, "The light can be directed more directly on the object under examination." In the further description given of his microscope, he explains: "It has four draw-tubes for lengthening the body, and a third lens to the optical combination." This, it would appear, was only brought into use when he wished to see the whole object at once: "The middle-glass lens, conveying a very great company of radiating pencils (of light) which would stray away; but when I had occasion to examine the small parts of a body, I took out the middle glass and made use of one eye-glass with the object-glass."

From Hooke's description I gather that he also introduced the ball-and-socket movement into the construction of the body of his instrument. This has found many imitators since his day; some of them have gone so far as to claim the invention as one quite new. For small accessories, where the leverage need not be considered, the ball-and-socket has proved convenient enough; but not, however, if applied to the stand of the microscope. Hooke, in his early work, expressed dissatisfaction with the English-made lenses he had in use. He complains of the "apertures of the object-glasses, which are so small that very few rays are admitted; none will admit a sufficient number of rays to magnifie the object beyond a determinate bigness." So we may take it that he thus early discovered the great importance of an increase in the aperture of his microscope. Other improvements of importance were made, and he was the first to describe a useful method of estimating the magnifying power of his lenses, and the difficulty of distinguishing between a prominence and a depression in the object under investigation, which he was made more fully aware of when preparing drawings for the illustration of his "Micrographia Illustrata"; this would be in 1664, if not earlier. His book created no little sensation on its first appearance, and it soon became scarce. Hooke (says Mr. Mayall) "must undoubtedly be credited with the first suggestion of immersion lenses." Nevertheless, in his "Lectures and Collections," published in 1676, he appears to be no longer enthusiastic over his double microscope, and once more he reverts to the simpler instrument of his earlier days. Whether this change of opinion was due to the publication of Leeuwenhoek's observations with his simple microscopes it is impossible to say.

As early as 1673 Leeuwenhoek communicated some important discoveries made by a simple microscope of his own construction to the Royal Society; he, however, gave no particulars of the construction of the instrument. Dr. Adams, writing to his friend (Sir) Hans Sloane, says: "They appear to be spherules lodged between two plates of gold or brass, in a hole whose diameter appears to be no bigger than that of a small pin's head." At his death he bequeathed to the Royal Society a cabinet containing twenty-six of these microscopes; the cabinet and the microscopes long ago disappeared, but not before they were carefully examined and described by Mr. Henry Baker, F.R.S. In his report to the Royal Society, he says: "They consisted of a series of convex-lenses, ranging in power from 1·20 to 1·5, and magnifying from 160 to 40 diameters." This must now be regarded as an eventful period in the history of the microscope, since Leeuwenhoek's discoveries created a great sensation throughout Europe. And all further improvements in compound instruments appear to have been laid aside for some considerable period in consequence: and the pocket instrument of Wilson, together with that of his scroll standard (seen on the cover of this book), and which was one of the first simple microscopes with a mirror mounted on the base in a line with the optic axis.

The discoveries once more made, and at a much later period (1738), by Dr. Nathaniel Lieberkuhn with his simple microscopes, and by means of which he discovered the minute structure of the mucous membrane of the alimentary canal, and which alone would have immortalised his name had we not preserved in use to this day an important adjunct of every modern instrument, the Lieberkuhn reflector.

In the Museum of the Royal College of Surgeons of England, there is a small cabinet of two drawers, containing a set of twelve of his simple microscopes, each being provided with an original injection. The form of the instrument is shown in Figs. 1 and 2. *a b* represents a piece of brass tubing about an inch long and an inch in diameter and provided with a cap at each extremity. The one at *a* carries a small double-convex lens of half an inch focal length; while at *b* there is fixed a condensing lens three-quarters of an inch in diameter. In Fig. 2 the instrument is seen in section, and explains itself. It is held by the handle in such a position that the rays of light, from a lamp or a white cloud, may fall on the condenser *b*, and concentrate on the speculum *l*. This again further condenses the rays on the disc *c*, where the object is held, and its adjustment made by the milled-head screw *d*, so as to bring it within the focus of the lens *a*.

Fig. 1.

From this digression I pass on to the evolution of the compound microscope. The earliest workable form known was that designed by Eustachio Divini, who brought it to the notice of the Royal Society in 1668. It consisted of two plano-convex lenses, combined with their convex surfaces retained in apposition. His idea was subsequently improved upon by a London optician. Not long afterwards, Philip Bonnani published an account of his improved compound microscope; and we are certainly indebted to him for two or more forms of the movable horizontal microscopes, and for the compound condenser fitted with focussing gear for illuminating transparent objects by transmitted light. I must, however, pass by the many changes made in the structure and form of the instrument by the celebrated Dr. Culpeper, Scarlet, Cuff, and many other inventors.

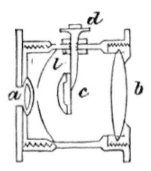

Fig. 2.—Lieberkuhn's Microscope.

Benjamin Martin's Microscope.—Benjamin Martin, about 1742, was busily engaged in making improvements in the microscope, and I may say he was certainly the first to provide accurate results for determining the exact magnifying power of any object-lens, so that the observer might state the exact amplification in a certain number of diameters. He devised numerous improvements in the mechanism and optical arrangements of the instrument; the rack and pinion focussing adjustments; the inclining movements to the pillar carrying the stage; and the rectangular mechanical motions to the stage itself. He was familiar with the principles of achromatism, since it appears he produced an achromatic objective about 1759, and he is said to have sent an achromatic objective to the Royal Society about that date. But an ingeniously constructed microscope by Martin found its way to George the Third, the grandfather of our Queen, and afterwards came into the possession of the late Professor John Quekett, of the Royal College of Surgeons, who presented it to the Royal Microscopical Society of London. This microscope will ever associate Martin's name with the earliest and best form of the instrument, even should he not receive full recognition as the inventor of the *achromatic microscope*. On this account I introduce a carefully made drawing of so singularly perfect a form of the early English microscope to the notice of my readers. (Fig. 3.) The description given of it by the late Professor Quekett is as follows:—"It stands about two feet in height, and is supported on a tripod base, A; the central part of the stem, B, is of triangular figure, having a rack at the back, upon which the stage, O, and frame, D, supporting the mirror, E, are capable of being moved up or down. The compound body, F, is three inches in diameter; it is composed of two tubes, the inner of which contains the eye-piece, and can be raised or depressed by rack and pinion, so as to increase or diminish the magnifying power. At the base of the triangular bar is a cradle joint, G, by which the instrument can be inclined by turning the screw-head, H (connected with an endless screw acting upon a worm-wheel). The arm, I, supporting the compound body, is supplied with a rack and pinion, K, by which it can be moved backwards and forwards, and a joint is placed below it, upon which the body can be turned into the horizontal position; another bar, carrying a stage and mirror, can be attached by a screw, L N, so as to convert it into a horizontal microscope. The stage, O, is provided with all the usual apparatus for clamping objects, and a condenser can be applied to its under surface; the stage itself may be removed, the arm, P, supporting it, turned round on the pivot, C, and another stage of exquisite workmanship placed in its stead, the under surface of which is shown at Q."

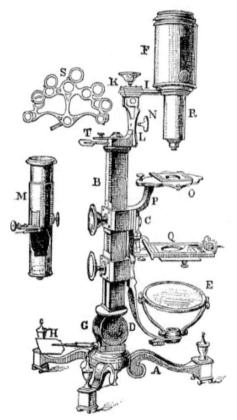

Fig. 3.—Martin's Universal Microscope. 1782.

This stage is strictly a micrometer one, having rectangular movements and a fine adjustment, the movements being accomplished by the fine-threaded screws, the milled heads of which are graduated. The mirror, E, is a double one, and can be raised or depressed by rack and pinion; it is also capable of removal, and an apparatus for holding large opaque objects, such as minerals, can be substituted for it. The accessory instruments are very numerous, and amongst the more remarkable may be mentioned a tube, M, containing a speculum, which can take the place of the tube, R, and so form a reflecting microscope. The apparatus for holding animalcules or other live objects, which is represented at S, as well as a plate of glass six inches in diameter, with four concave wells ground in it, can be applied to the stage, so that each well may be brought in succession under the magnifying power. The lenses belonging to this microscope are twenty-four in number; they vary in focal length from four inches to one-tenth of an inch; ten of them are supplied with Lieberkuhns. A small arm, capable of carrying single lenses, can be supplied at T, and when turned over, the stage of the instrument becomes a single microscope; there are four lenses suitable for this purpose, their focal length varying from one-tenth to one-fortieth of an inch. The performance of all the lenses is excellent, and no pains appear to have been spared in their construction. There are numerous other pieces of accessory apparatus, all remarkable for the beauty of their workmanship.[4]

In addition to the movements described by Quekett, the body-tube with its support can be moved in an arc concentrically with the axis of the triangular pillar, on the top of which it is fitted with a worm-wheel and endless-screw mechanism, actuated by the screw-head, T, below. It must therefore be admitted that Martin led the way far beyond his contemporaries, both in the design and the evolution of the microscope. Furthermore, in his "New Elements of Optics," 1759, he dealt with the principle of achromatism, by the construction of an achromatic telescope.

At a somewhat later period there lived in London a philosophical instrument maker of some repute, George Adams, who published in 1746 a quarto book, entitled "Micrographia Illustrata, or the Knowledge of the Microscope Explained." This work fairly well describes "the nature, uses, and magnifying powers of microscopes in general, together with full directions how to prepare, apply, examine, and preserve minute objects." Adams' book was the first of the kind published in this country, and it contributed in no small degree to the advancement of microscopical science. Adams writes: "We owe the construction of the variable microscope to the ingenuity and generosity of a noble person. The apparatus belonging to it is more convenient, more certain, and more extensive than that of any other at present extant; consequently, the advantage and pleasure attending the observations in viewing objects through it must be as extensive in proportion." This is believed to apply to Martin's several microscopes, and that especially constructed for the king, afterwards improved upon by Adams. Another early form of microscope, Wilson Simple Scroll (1746), stamped on the cover of this book, and has thus become familiar to microscopists, was also made by Adams.

We now closely approach a period fertile in the improvement of the microscope, and in the discoveries made by its agency. The chief of those among the honoured names of the time we find Trembley, Ellis, Baker, Adams, Hill, Swammerdam, Lyonet, Needham, and a few others. Adams somewhat sarcastically observes "that every optician exercises his talents in improving (as he calls it) the microscope, in other words, in varying its construction and rendering it different in form from that sold by his neighbour; or at the best rendering it more complex and troublesome to manage." There were no doubt good reasons for these and other strictures upon inventors as well as makers of microscopes, even in the Adams' day. In the year 1787 the "Microscopical Essays" of his son were published, in which he described all the instruments in use up to that period.

Looking back, and taking a general survey of the work of nearly two centuries in the history of the microscope, it cannot be said that either in its optical or mechanical construction any great amount of progress was made. This in part may have arisen from the fact that no pressing need was felt for either delicate focussing or higher magnification. At all events, it was not until the application of achromatism to the instrument that new life was infused into its use, and a great impetus was given to its development, both optically and mechanically.

In the year 1823 a strong desire became manifest for improved forms of the instrument, in France by M. Selligue, by Frauenhofer in Munich, by Amici in Modena, by M. Chevalier in Paris, and by Dr. Goring, Mr. Pritchard, and Mr. Tully in London. The result was that in 1824 a new form of achromatic object-glass was constructed of nine-tenths of an inch focal length, composed of three lenses, and transmitting a pencil of eighteen degrees; and which, as regards accurate correction throughout the field, was for some years regarded as perfect.

Sir David Brewster was the first to suggest the great importance of introducing materials of a more highly refracting nature into the construction of lenses. He wrote: "There can be no essential improvement expected in the microscope unless from the discovery of some transparent substance which, like the diamond, combines a high refractive with a low dispersive power." Having experienced the greatest difficulty in getting a small diamond cut into a prism in London, he did not conceive it practicable to grind, polish, and form it into a lens.

Mr. Pritchard, however, was led to make the experiment, and on the 1st of December, 1824, "he had the pleasure of first looking through a diamond microscope." Dr. Goring also tried its performance on various objects, both as a single microscope and as an objective of a compound instrument, and satisfied himself of its superiority over other kinds of lenses. But here Mr. Pritchard's labours did not end. He subsequently found that the diamond used had many flaws in it, which led him to abandon the idea of finishing it. Having been prevented from resuming his operations on this refractory material for a time he made a third attempt, and met with another unexpected defect; he found that some lenses, unlike the first, gave a double or triple image instead of a single one, in consequence of some of their parts being either harder or softer than others. These defects were found to be due to polarisation. Mr. Pritchard having learned how to decide whether a diamond is fit for a magnifier or not, subsequently succeeded in making two planoconvex lenses of adamant; these proved to be perfect for microscopic purposes. "One of these, of one-twentieth of an inch in focal length, is now in the possession of his Grace the Duke of Buckingham; the other, of one-thirtieth of an inch focus, is in his own hands."

"In consequence of the high refracting power of a diamond lens over a glass lens, the former material may be at least one-third as thin as that of the latter, and if the focal length of both be equal, say, one-eightieth of an inch, the magnifying power of the diamond lens will be 2,133 diameters, whereas that of glass will be only 800." At a date (1812) before Brewster proposed diamond lenses he demonstrated a simple method of rendering both single and compound microscopes achromatic. "Starting," he says, "with the principle that all objects, however delicate, are best seen when immersed in fluid, he placed an object on a slip of glass, and put above a drop of oil, having a greater dispersive power than the single concave lens, which formed the object-glass of the microscope. The lens was then made to touch the fluid, so that the surface of the fluid was formed into a concave lens, and if the radius of the outward surface was such as to correct the dispersion, we should have a perfect achromatic microscope." Here we have the immersion system foreshadowed. Shortly after these experiments of Brewster's were in progress, Dr. Goring is said to have discovered that the structure of certain bodies could be readily seen in some microscopes and not in others. These bodies he named test objects. He then examined these tests with the achromatic combinations of the Tullys, and was led to the discovery that "the penetrating power of the microscope depends upon its angle of aperture."

"While these practical investigations were in progress," writes Andrew Ross, "the subject of achromatism engaged the attention of some of the most profound mathematicians in England, Sir John Herschel, and Professors Airy and Barlow. Mr. Coddington and others contributed largely to the theoretical examination of the subject; and although the results of their labours were not applicable to the microscope, they essentially promoted its improvement."

About this period (1812) Professor Amici, of Modena, was experimentally engaged in the improvement of the achromatic object-glass, and he invented a reflecting microscope superior to those of Newton, Baker, or Smith, made as early as 1738, and long ago abandoned. In 1815 Amici made further experiments, and introduced the immersion system; while Frauenhofer, of Munich, about the same time constructed object-glasses for the microscope of a single achromatic lens, in which the two glasses, although placed in juxtaposition, were not cemented together.

Dolland, it has been said, introduced achromatic lenses; but although he constructed many achromatic telescopes, he did not apply the same principle to microscopes, and those which he sold were only modifications of the compound microscope of Cuff.

Dr. Wollaston employed a new form of combination in a microscope constructed for his own use, and by which "he was able to see distinctly the finest markings upon the scales of the *Lepisma* and *Podura*, and upon those of the gnat's wing." His doublet is still employed, and to which I shall refer under "Simple Microscopes."

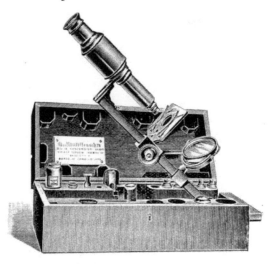

Fig. 3*a*.—Sir David Brewster's Microscope, of the early part of the century, recently presented to the British Museum.

CHAPTER I.

Elementary Optics.

Value of Inductive Science—Light: Its Propagation, Refraction, Reflection—Spherical and Chromatic Aberrations—Human Eye, formation of Images of External Objects in—Visual Angle increased—Abbe's Theory of Microscopic Vision.

The advances made in physics and mechanics during the 17th and 18th centuries fairly opened the way to the attainment of greater perfection in all optical instruments. This has been particularly exemplified with reference to the invention of the microscope, as briefly sketched out in the previous chapter. Indeed, in the first half of the present century the microscope can scarcely be said to have held a position of importance among the scientific instruments in frequent use. Since then, however, the zoologist and botanist by its aid have laid bare the intimate structure of plants and animals, and thereby have opened up a vast kingdom of minute forms of life previously undreamt of; and in connection with chemistry a new science has been founded, that of bacteriology.

For these reasons it will be of importance to the student of microscopy to begin at the beginning, and it will be my endeavour to introduce to his notice such facts in physical optics as are closely associated with the formation of images, and, so to speak, systematise such stepping stones for work hereafter to be accomplished. Elementary principles only will be adduced, and without attempting to involve my readers in intricate mathematical problems, and which for the most part are unnecessary for the attainment of the object in view. I therefore pass at once to the consideration of the propagation of light through certain bodies.

The microscope, whether simple or compound, depends for its magnifying power on the influence exerted by lenses in altering the course of the rays of light passing through them being REFRACTED. *Refraction* takes place in accordance with two well-known laws of optics. When a ray of light passes from one transparent medium to another it undergoes a change of direction at the surface of separation, so that its course in the second medium makes an angle with its course in the first. This change of direction is a resultant of refraction. The broken appearance presented by a stick partly immersed in water, and viewed in an oblique position, is an illustration of the law of refraction. Liquids have a greater refractive power than air or gases. As a rule, with some few exceptions, the denser of the two substances has the greater refractive power; hence it is customary in enumerating some of the laws of optics to speak of the denser medium and the rarer medium. The more correct designation would be the more refractive and the less refractive.[5]

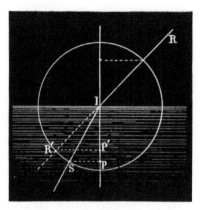

Fig. 4.—Law of Refraction.

Let R I (Fig. 4) be a ray incident at I on the surface of separation of two media, and let I S' be the course of the ray after refraction. Then the angles which R I and I S make with the normal are the *angle of incidence* and the *angle of refraction* respectively, and the first law of refraction is that these angles lie in the same plane, or the *plane of refraction* is the same as the *plane of incidence*. The law which connects the magnitudes of these angles, and which was discovered by Snell, a Dutch philosopher, can only be stated either by reference to a geometrical construction, or by using the language of trigonometry. Describe a circle about the point of incidence, I as a centre, and drop perpendiculars from the points where it cuts the rays on the normal. The law is that these perpendiculars, R' P', S' P, will have a constant ratio, or the sines *of the angles of incidence and refraction are in a constant ratio*; that is, so long as the media through which the ray first passes, and by which it is afterwards refracted, remain the same, and the light also of the same kind, then it is referred to as the law of sines.

Indices of Refraction.

The ratio of the sine of the angle of incidence to the sine of the angle of refraction, when a ray passes from one medium to another is termed the relative index of refraction. When a ray passes from vacuum into any medium, this ratio is always greater than unity, and is called the *absolute index of refraction*, or simply the index of refraction for the medium in question.

The absolute index of air is so small that it may be neglected in comparison with those of solids and liquids; but strictly speaking, the relative index for a ray passing from air into a given substance must be multiplied by the absolute index of the air, in order to obtain the true index of refraction.

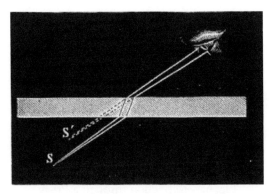

Fig. 5.—Vision through a Glass Plate.

Critical Angle.—It will be seen from the law of sines that, when the incident ray is in the less refractive of the two media, to every possible angle of incidence there is a corresponding angle of refraction. The angle referred to is termed the *critical angle*, and is readily computed if the relative index of refraction be given. When the media are air and water, this angle is about 48° 30'. For air and ordinary kinds of glass its value varies from 38° to 41°.

The phenomenon of total reflection may be observed in several familiar instances. For example, if a glass of water, with a spoon in it, is held above the level of the eye, the under side of the surface is seen to shine like a mirror, and the lower part of the spoon is seen reflected in it. Effects of the same kind are observed when a ray of sunlight passes into an aquarium—on the other hand rays falling normally on a uniform transparent plate of glass with parallel faces keep their course; but objects viewed obliquely through the same are displaced from their true position. Let S (Fig. 5) be a luminous point which sends light to an eye not directly opposite to it, on the other side of a parallel plate. The emergent rays which enter the eye are parallel to the incident rays; but as they have undergone lateral displacement, their point of concourse is changed from S to S', and this is accordingly the image of S. The rays in such a case which compose the pencil that enters the eye will not exactly meet in any one point; there will be two focal lines, just as in the case of spherical mirrors. The displacement produced, as seen in the figure referred to above, increases with the thickness of the plate, its index of refraction, and the obliquity of incidence. This furnishes one of the simplest means of measuring the index of refraction of a glass substance, and is thus employed in Pichot's refractometer ("Deschanel").

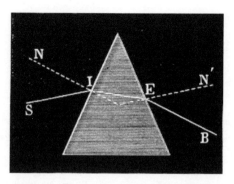

Fig. 6.—Refraction through a Prism.

Refraction through a Prism.—A prism is a portion of a refracting medium bounded by two plane surfaces, inclined at a definite angle to one another. The two plane surfaces are termed the *faces* of the prism, and their inclination to one another is the refracting angle of the prism. A prism preserves the property of bending rays of light from their original course by refraction. A cylinder may be regarded as the limit of a prism whose sides increase in number and diminish in size indefinitely: it may also be regarded as a pyramid whose apex is removed to an indefinite distance.

Let S I (Fig. 6) be an incident ray in the plane of the principal section of the prism. If the external medium be air, or other substance of less refractive power than the prism, the ray on entering the same will be bent nearer to the normal, taking such a course as I E, and on leaving the prism will be bent away from the normal, taking the course E B. The effect of these two refractions is, therefore, to turn the ray away from the edge (or refracting angle) of the prism. In practice, the prism is usually so placed that I E, the path of the ray through the prism, makes equal angles with the two faces at which refraction occurs. If the prism is turned very far from this position, the course of the ray may be altogether different from that represented in the figure; it may enter at one face, be internally reflected at another, and come out at the third.

It is evident, therefore, that the minimum number of sides, *i.e.*, the bounding faces, exclusive of the ends, which a prism can have is three. In this form, it constitutes a most valuable instrument of research in physical optics. A convex lens is practically merely a curved form of two prisms combined, their bases being brought into contact; on the other hand the concave lens is simply a reversal of the position of the apices brought into contact, as shown in Fig. 11. Both convex and concave lenses are therefore closely related to the prism.

Reflection.—The laws that govern the change of direction which a ray of light experiences when it strikes upon the surfaces of separation of two media and is thrown back into the same medium from which it approached is as follows:—When the reflecting surface is plain the direction of the reflected ray makes with the normal to the surface the same angle which the incident ray makes with the same normal; or, as it is usually expressed, the angles of reflection and incidence are equal. When the surfaces are curved the same law holds good. In all cases of reflection the energy of the ray is diminished, so that reflection must always be accompanied by absorption. The latter probably precedes the former. Most bodies are visible by light reflected from their surfaces, but before this takes place the light has undergone a modification, namely, that which imparts colour peculiar to the bodies viewed. When light impinges upon the surface of a denser medium part is reflected, part absorbed, and part refracted. But for a certain angle depending upon the refractive index of the refracting medium no refraction takes place. This angle is termed the angle of total reflection, since all the light which is not absorbed is wholly reflected.

Multiple images are produced by a transparent parallel plate of glass. If the glass be silvered at the back, as it usually is in the microscope-mirror, the second image is brighter than the first, but as the angle of incidence increases the first image gains upon the second; and if the luminous object be a lamp or candle, a number of images, one behind the other, will be visible to an eye properly placed in front. This is due to the fact that the reflecting power of a surface of glass increases with the angle of incidence.

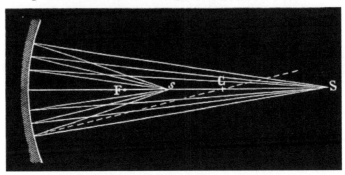

Fig. 7.—Conjugate Foci of Curved Surfaces.

Concave Surfaces.—Rays of light proceeding from any given point in front of a concave spherical mirror, are reflected so as to meet in another point, and the line joining the two points passes through the centre of the sphere. The relation between them is or should be mutual, hence they are termed *conjugate foci*. By a *focus* in general is meant a point in which a number of rays of light meet, and the rays which thus meet, taken collectively, are termed *a pencil*. Fig. 7 represents two pencils of rays whose foci, S s, are conjugate, so that, if either of them be regarded as an incident pencil, the other will be the corresponding reflected pencil. Each point, in fact, sends a pencil of rays which converge, after reflection, to the conjugate focus. *The principal focal distance is half the radius of curvature.* But it will not escape attention that concave mirrors have two reflecting surfaces, a front and a back. This, however, does not practically disturb its *virtual focus*, since the achromatic condenser when brought into use collects and concentrates the light received from the mirror upon an object for the purpose of rendering it more distinctly visible to the eye when viewing an object placed on the stage of the microscope. The images seen in a plane mirror are always virtual, and any spherical mirror, whether concave or convex, is nearly equivalent to a plane mirror when the distance of the object from its surface is small in comparison with the radius of curvature.

Lenses.

Forms of Lenses.—A lens is a portion of a refracting medium bounded by two surfaces which are portions of spheres, having a common axis, termed the *axis of the lens*. Lenses are distinguished by different names, according to the nature of their surfaces.

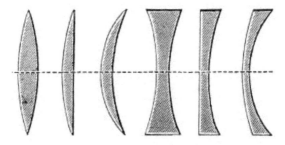

Fig. 8.—Converging and Diverging Lenses.

Lenses with sharp edges (thicker at the centre) are *convergent* or *positive* lenses. Lenses with blunt edges (thinner at the centre) are *divergent* or *negative* lenses. The first group comprises:—(1) The bi-convex lens; (2) the plano-convex lens; (3) the convergent meniscus. The second group:—(4) The concave lens; (5) the plano-concave lens; (6) the divergent meniscus (Fig. 8).

Principal Focus.—A lens is usually a solid of revolution, and the axis of revolution is termed the principal axis of the lens. When the surfaces are spherical it is the line joining the centre of curvature.

From the great importance of lenses, especially convex lenses, in practical optics, it will be necessary to explain their properties somewhat at length.

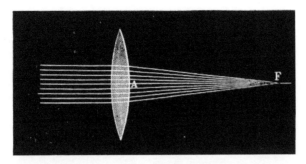

Fig. 9.—Principal Focus of a Convex Lens.

Principal Focus of Convex Lens.—When rays which were originally parallel to the principal axis pass through a convex lens (Fig. 9), the effect of the two refractions which they undergo, one on entering and the other on leaving the lens, is to make them all converge approximately to one point F, which is called the principal focus. The distance A F of the principal focus from the lens is called the principal focal distance, or more briefly and usually, the focal length of the lens. The radiant point and its image after refraction are known as the conjugate foci. In every lens the right line perpendicular to the two surfaces is the *axis* of the lens. This is indicated by the line drawn through the several lenses, as seen in the diagram (Fig. 8). The point where the axis cuts the surface of the lens is termed the *verte*.

Parallel rays falling on a *double-convex* lens are brought to a focus in the centre of its diameter; conversely, rays diverging from that point are rendered parallel. Hence the focus of a *double-convex* lens will be at just half the distance, or half the length, of the focus of a *plano-convex* lens having the same curvature on one side. The distance of the focus from the lens will depend as much on the degree of curvature as upon the refracting power (termed the index of refraction) of the glass of which it may be formed. A lens of crown-glass will have a longer focus than a similar one of flint-glass; since the latter has a greater refracting power than the former. For all ordinary practical purposes we may consider the *principal focus*—as the focus for parallel rays is termed— of a double-convex lens to be at the distance of its radius, that is, in its centre of curvature; and that of a plano-convex lens to be at the distance of twice its radius, that is, at the other end of the diameter of its sphere of curvature. The converse of all this occurs when divergent rays are made to fall on a convex lens. Rays already converging are brought together at a point nearer than the principal focus; whereas rays diverging from a point within the principal focus are rendered still more diverging, though in a diminished degree. Rays diverging from points more distant than the principal focus on either side, are brought to a focus beyond it: if the point of divergence be within the circle of curvature, the focus of convergence will be beyond it; and *vice-versâ*. The same principles apply equally to a *plano-convex lens*;

allowance being made for the double distance of its principal focus; and also to a lens whose surfaces have different curvatures; the principal focus of such a lens is found by multiplying the radius of one surface by the radius of the other, and dividing this product by half the sum of the radii.

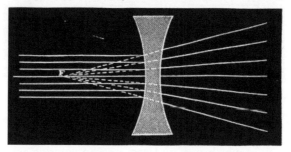

Fig. 10.—Principal Focus of Concave Lens.

In the case of a concave lens (Fig. 10), rays incident parallel to the principal axis diverge after passing through; and their directions, if produced backwards, would approximately meet in a point F; this is its *principal focus*. It is, however, only a virtual focus, inasmuch as the emergent rays do not actually pass through it, whereas the principal focus of a converging lens is real.

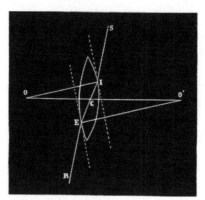

Fig. 11.—Principal Centre of Lens.

Optical Centre of a Lens.—*Secondary Axes.*—Let O and O' (Fig. 11) be the centres of the two spherical surfaces of a lens. Draw any two parallel radii, O I, O' E, to meet these surfaces, and let the joining line I E represent a ray passing through the lens. This ray makes equal angles with the normals at I and E, since these latter are parallel by construction; hence the incident and emergent rays S I, E R also make equal angles with the normals, and are therefore parallel. In fact, if tangent planes (indicated by the dotted lines in the figure) are drawn at I and E, the whole course of the ray S I E R will be the same as if it had passed through a plate bounded by these planes.

Let C be the point in which the line I E cuts the principal axis, and let R, R' denote the radii of the two spherical surfaces. Then from the similarity of the triangles O C I, O' C E, we have (O C)/(C O') = R'/R; which shows that the point C divides the line of centres O O' in a definite ratio depending only on the radii. Every ray whose direction on emergence is parallel to its direction before entering the lens, must pass through the point C in traversing the lens; and conversely, every ray which in its course through the lens traverses the point C, has parallel directions at incidence and emergence. The point C which possesses this remarkable property is called the *centre*, or *optical centre*, of the lens.

This diagram may also be taken to prove my former proposition, that the convex lens is practically a form of two prisms combined.

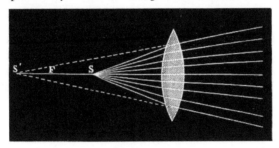

Fig. 12.—Conjugate Foci, one Real, the other Virtual.

Conjugate Foci, one Real, one Virtual.—When two foci are on the same side of the lens, one (the most distant of the two) must be virtual. For example, in Fig. 12, if S, S' are a pair of conjugate foci, one of them S being between the principal focus F and the lens, rays sent to the lens at a luminous point at S, will, after emergence, diverge as if from S'; and rays coming from the other side of the lens, if they converge to S' before incidence, will in reality be made to meet in S. As S moves towards the lens, S' moves in the same direction more rapidly; and they become coincident at the surface of the lens.

Formation of Real Images.—Let A B (Fig. 13) be an object in front of a lens, at a distance less than the principal focal length. It will have a real image on the other side of the lens. To determine the position of the image by construction, draw through any point A of the object a line parallel to the principal axis, meeting the lens in A'. The ray represented by this line will, after refraction, pass through the principal focus, F, and its intersection with the secondary axis, A O, determines the position of *a*, the focus conjugate to A. We can in like manner determine the position of *b*, the focus conjugate to B, another point of the object; and the joining line *a b* will then be the magnified image of the line A B. It is evident that if *a b* were the object, A B would be the image.

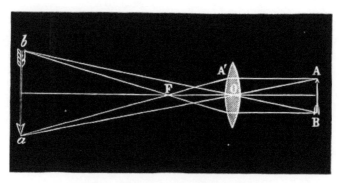

Fig. 13.—Real and Magnified Image.

The figures 12 and 13 represent the cases in which the distance of the object is respectively greater and less than twice the focal length of the lens.

The focal length of a lens is determined by the convexity of its surfaces and the refractive power of the material of which it is composed, being shortened either by an increase of refractive power, or diminution of the radii of curvature of the faces of the lens. The increase or decrease of spherical aberration is determined by the shape or curvature of the lens; it is less in the bi-convex than in other forms. When a lamp or other source of light is placed at the focus of the rays constituting that portion of its light which falls upon the lens, the light is so refracted as to become parallel. Should the source of light be brought nearer to the lens than the focus the refracted rays are still divergent, though not to the same extent; on the other hand, if the source be beyond the focus, the refracted rays are rendered convergent so as to meet at a point which is mathematically related to the distance of the luminous source from the focus. The former arrangement is that with which we are most familiar, since it is the ordinary magnifying glass.

Concave Lenses.

The refracting influence of a *concave* lens (Fig. 14) will be precisely the opposite of that of a convex. Rays which fall upon it in a parallel direction will be made to diverge as if from the principal focus, which is here called the *negative* focus. This will be, for a *plano-concave* lens, at the distance of the diameter of the sphere of curvature; and for a *double-concave*, in the centre of that sphere.

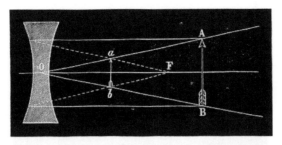

Fig. 14.—A Virtual Image formed by Concave Lens.

In Fig. 14 A B is the object and *a b* the image. Rays incident from A and B parallel to the principal axis will emerge as if they came from the principal focus F; hence, the points *a b* are determined by the intersections of the dotted lines in the figure with the secondary axis, O A, O B. An eye on the other side of the lens sees the image *a b*, which is always virtual, erect and diminished.

In the construction of the microscope, either simple or compound, the curvature of the lenses employed is usually spherical. Convergent lenses, with spherical curvatures, have the defect of not bringing all the rays of light which pass through them to one and the same focus. Each circle of rays from the axis of the lens to its circumference has a different focus, as shown in Fig. 15. The rays *a a*, which pass through the lens near its circumference, are seen to be *more refracted*, or come to a focus at a shorter distance behind it than the rays *b b*, which pass through near its centre or axis, and are *less refracted*. The consequence of this defect of lenses with spherical curvatures, which is called *spherical aberration*, is that a well-defined image or picture is not formed by them, for when the object is focussed, for the circumferential rays, the picture projected to the eye is rendered indistinct by a halo or confusion produced by the central rays falling in a circle of dissipation, before they have come to a focus. On the other hand, when placed in the focus of the central rays, the picture formed by them is rendered indistinct by the halo produced by the circumferential rays, which have already come to a focus and crossed, and now fall in a state of divergence, forming a circle of dissipation. The grosser defects of spherical aberration are corrected by cutting off the passage of the rays *a a*, through the circumferences of the lens, by means of a stop diaphragm, so that the central rays, *b b*, only are concerned in the formation of the image. This defect is reduced to a minimum, by using the meniscus form of lens, which is the segment of an ellipsoid instead of a sphere.

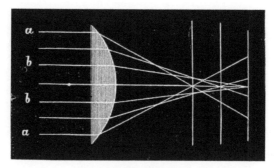

Fig. 15.—Spherical Aberration of Lens.

The ellipse and the hyperbola are forms of lenses in which the curvature diminishes from the central ray, or axis, to the circumference *b*; and mathematicians have shown that spherical aberration may be practically got rid of by employing lenses whose sections are ellipses or hyperbolas. The remarkable discovery of these forms of lenses is attributed to Descartes, who mathematically demonstrated the fact.

If *a l*, *a l'*, for example (Fig. 16) be part of an ellipse whose greater axis is to the distance between its foci *f f* as the index of refraction is to unity, then parallel rays *r l'*, *r'' l* incident upon the elliptical surface *l' a l*, will be refracted by the single action of that surface into lines which would meet exactly in the farther focus *f*, if there were no second surface intervening between *l a l'* and *f*. But as every useful lens must have two surfaces, we have only to describe a circle *l a' l'* round *f* as a centre, for the second surface of the lens *l' l*.

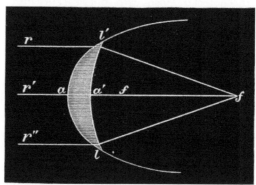

Fig. 16.—Converging Meniscus.

As all the rays refracted at the surface *l a l'* converge accurately to *f*, and as the circular surface *l a' l'* is perpendicular to every one of the refracted rays, all these rays will go on to *f* without suffering any refraction at the circular surface. Hence it should follow, that a meniscus whose convex surface is part of an ellipsoid, and whose concave surface is part of any spherical surface whose centre is in the farther focus, will have no appreciable spherical aberration, and will refract parallel rays incident on its convex surface to the farther focus.

Fig. 17.—Aplanatic Doublet.

The spherical form of lens is that most generally used in the construction of the microscope. If a true elliptical or hyperbolic curve could be ground, lenses would very nearly approach perfection, and spherical aberration would be considerably reduced. Even this defect can be further reduced in practice by observing a certain ratio between the radii of the anterior and posterior surfaces of lenses; thus the spherical aberration of a lens, the radius of one surface of which is six or seven times greater than that of the other, will be much reduced when its more convex surface is turned forward to receive parallel rays, than when its less convex surface is turned forwards. It should be borne in mind that in lenses having curvatures of the kind the object would only be correctly seen in focus at one point—the mathematical or geometrical axis of the lens.

Chromatic Aberration.—We have yet to deal with one of the most important of the phenomena of light, CHROMATIC ABERRATION, upon the correction of which, in convex lenses in particular, the perfection of the objective of the microscope so much depends. Chromatism arises from the unequal refrangibility and length of the different coloured rays of light that together go to make up white light; but which, when treated of in optics, is always associated with *achromatism*, so that a combination of prisms, or lenses, is said to be *achromatic* when the coloured rays arising from the dispersion of the pencil of light refracted through them are combined in due proportions as they are in perfectly white light.

A lens, however, of uniform material will not form a single white image, but a series of images of all colours of the spectrum, arranged at different distances, the violet being nearest, and the red the most remote, every other colour giving a blurred image; the superposition of these and the blending of the different elementary rays furnishing a complete explanation of the beautiful phenomenon of the rainbow. Sharpness of outline is rendered quite impossible in such a case, and this source of confusion is known as *chromatic aberration*.

In order to ascertain whether it is possible to remedy this evil by combining lenses of two different materials, Newton made some trials with a compound prism composed of glass and water (the latter containing a little sugar of lead), and he found it impossible by any arrangement of these two, or by other substances, to produce deviation of the transmitted light without separation into its component colours. If this ratio were the same for all substances, as Newton supposed, achromatism would be impossible; but, in fact, its value varies greatly, and is far greater for flint than for crown glass. If two prisms of these substances, of small refracting angles, be combined into one, with their edges turned in opposite directions, they will achromatise each other.

The chromatism of lenses may, however, be somewhat further reduced by stopping out the marginal rays, but as the most perfect correction possible is required when lenses are combined for microscopic uses, other means of correction are resorted to, as will be seen hereafter. I shall first proceed to show the deviations which rays of white light undergo in traversing a lens.

If parallel rays of light pass through a double-convex lens the violet rays, the most refrangible of them, will come to a focus at a point much nearer to the lens than the focus of the red rays, which are the least refrangible; and the intermediate rays of the spectrum will be focussed at points between the red and the violet. A screen held at either of these foci will show an image with prismatic fringes. The white light, A A" (Fig. 18), falling on the marginal portion of the lens is so far decomposed that the violet rays are brought to a focus at C, and crossing there, diverge again and pass on to F F', while the red rays, B B", do not come to a focus until they reach the point D, and cross the divergent violet rays, E E'. The foci of the intermediary rays of the spectrum (red, green, and blue) are intermediate between these extremes. The distance, C D, limiting the blue or violet, and the red is termed the longitudinal chromatic aberration of the lens. If the image be received upon a screen placed at C, violet will predominate and appear surrounded by a prismatic fringe, in which violet will predominate. If the screen be now shifted to D, the image will have a predominant red tint, surrounded by a series of coloured fringes in an inverted order to those seen in the former experiment. The line E E' joins the points of intersection between the violet and red rays, and this marks the mean focus, the point where the coloured rays will be least apparent.

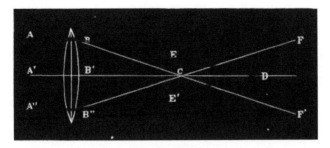

Fig. 18.—Chromatic Aberration of Lens.

In the early part of this century the optical correction of chromatic aberration was partially brought about by combining a convex lens of crown-glass with a concave lens of flint-glass, in the proportion of which these two kinds of glass respectively refract and disperse rays of light; so that the one medium may by equal and contrary dispersion neutralise the dispersion caused by the other, without at the same time wholly neutralising its refraction. It is a curious fact that the media found most available for the purpose should be a combination of crown and flint-glass, of *crown-glass* whose index of refraction is 1·519, and dispersive power 0·036, and of *flint-glass* whose index of refraction is 1·589, and dispersive power 0·0393. The focal length of the convex crown-glass lens must be 4⅓ inches, and that of the concave flint-glass lens 7⅔ inches, and the combined focal length 10 inches. The diagram (Fig. 19) shows how rays of light are brought to a focus, nearly free from colour. The small amount of residual colour in such a combination is termed the *secondary spectrum*; the violet ray F Y, crossing the axis of the lens at V, and going to the upper end P of the spectrum, the red ray F B going to the lower end T. But as the flint-glass lens *l l*, on the prism A *a* C, which receives the rays F V, F R, at the same points, is interposed, these rays will unite at *f*, and form a small circle of white light, the ray S F being now refracted without colour from its primitive direction S F Y into the direction F *f*. In like manner, the corresponding ray S F' will be refracted to *f*, and a white colourless image be the result.

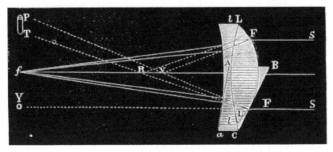

Fig. 19.—Correction of Chromatic Aberration.

The achromatic aplanatic objective constructed on the optical formula enunciated, did not meet all the difficulties experienced by the skilled microscopist, in obtaining resolution of the finest test objects, and whereby the intrinsic value of the objective (in his estimation) must stand or fall. There were other disturbing residuary elements besides those of the secondary spectrum, and which at a later period were met by the practical skill of the optician, who applied the screw-collar, and by means of which the back lens of the objective is made to approach the front lens, thus more accurately shortening the distance between the eye-piece, where the image is eventually formed, and the back lens of the objective.

In this diagram L L is a *convex* lens of *crown-glass*, and *l l* a *concave* one of *flint-glass*. A convex lens will refract a ray of light (S) falling at F on it exactly in the same manner as the prism A B C, whose faces touch the two surfaces of the lens at the points where the ray enters, and quits. The ray S F, thus refracted by the lens L L, or prism A B C, would have formed a spectrum (P T) on a screen or wall, had there been no other lens.

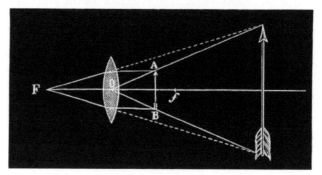

Fig. 20.—Virtual Image formed by Convex Lens.

Formation of Virtual Images.—The normal eye possesses a considerable power of adjusting itself to form a distinct image of objects placed at varying distances; the nearer, within a certain limit, the larger it appears, and the more distinctly the details are brought out. When brought within a distance of two or three inches, the images become blurred or quite indistinct, and when brought closer to the eye, cannot be seen at all, and it simply obstructs the light. Now the utility of a convex lens, when interposed between the object and the eye, consists in reducing the divergence of the rays forming the several pencils which issue from it, and send images to the retina in a state of moderate divergence, that is, as if they had issued from an object beyond the nearest point of distinct vision, and so that a more clearly defined image may reach the sensitive membrane of the eye. But, not only is the course of the several rays in each pencil altered as regards the rest, but the course of the pencils themselves is changed, so that they enter the eye under an angle corresponding with that under which they would have arrived from a larger object situated at a greater distance, and thus the picture formed by any object corresponds in all respects with one which would have been made by the same object increased in its dimensions and viewed at the smallest ordinary distance of distinct vision. For instance, let an object A B (Fig. 20) be placed between a convex lens and its principal focus. Then the foci conjugate to the points A B are virtual, and their positions can be found by construction from the consideration that rays through A, B, parallel to the principal axis, will be refracted to F, the principal focus on the other side. The refracted rays, if produced backwards, must meet the secondary axis O A, O B in the required points. An eye placed on the other side of the lens will accordingly see a virtual image erect, magnified, and at a greater distance from the lens than the object. This is the principle of the simple microscope.

The Human Eye.

To gain a clear insight into the mode in which a single lens serves to magnify objects, it will be necessary to revert to the phenomena of ordinary vision. An eye free from any defect has a considerable power of adjusting itself to very considerable distances. One of the special functions of the eye is bringing the rays of light, by a series of dioptric mechanisms, to a perfect focus on its nervous sensitive layer, the retina. The eye in this respect has been compared to a photographic camera. But this is not quite correct. The retina is destined simply to receive the images furnished by the dioptric apparatus, and has no influence upon the formation of these images. The luminous rays are refracted by the dioptric apparatus; the images would be formed quite as well—indeed, even better in certain cases—if the retina were not there. The dioptric apparatus and its action are absolutely independent of the retina.

The same laws with regard to the passage of the rays of light into the human eye hold good, as those already enunciated in the previous pages. As to change of direction when rays are passing obliquely from a medium of low density to that of a higher density, i.e., it changes its course, and is bent towards the perpendicular. On leaving the denser for the rarer medium it is bent once more from the perpendicular. Again, by means of a convex lens, the rays of light from one source will be refracted so as to meet at a point termed *the principal focus* of vision.

In the eye there are several surfaces separating the different media where refraction takes place. The refractive index of the aqueous humour and the tears poured out by the lachrymal gland is almost equal to that of the cornea. We may, therefore, speak of the refracting surfaces as three, viz.: Anterior surface of cornea, anterior surface of lens, and posterior surface of lens; and also of the refracting media as three—the aqueous humour, the lens, and vitreous humour. These several bodies are so adapted in the normal eye that parallel rays falling on the cornea are converged to a focus at the most sensitive spot (the *yellow spot*, or *fovea centralis*) in the retina, a point representing to the principal focus of the eye. A line drawn from this point through the centre of the cornea is called the optic axis of the eye-ball.

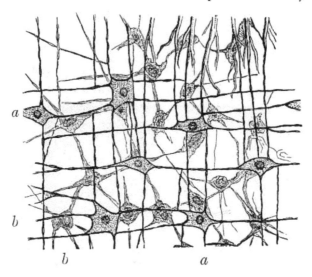

Fig. 21.—Nerve and Stellate Cell Layer of Cornea,[6] stained by chloride of gold; magnified 300 diameters. *a*, Nerve cells. *b*, Stellate cells.

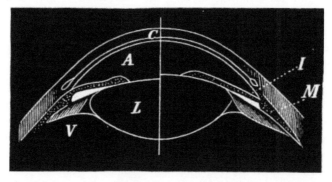

Fig. 22.—Anterior section of Eye, showing changed form of lens during the act of accommodation, a voluntary action in the eye. M, Ciliary muscle; I, Iris; L, Lens; V, Vitreous Humour; A, Aqueous Humour; C, Cornea and optic axis.

But as we are able to form a distinct image of near objects, and as we notice when we turn our gaze from far to near objects there is a distinct feeling of muscular effort in the eyes, there must be some means whereby the eye can readily adapt itself for focussing near and distant objects. In a photographic camera the focus can be readily altered, either by changing the lenses, employing a lens of greater or less curvature, or by altering the distance of the screen from the lens. The last method is obviously impossible in the rigid eye-ball, and therefore the act of focussing for near and distant objects is associated with a change in the curvature of the lens, a faculty of the eye termed *accommodation* (Fig. 22), a change chiefly accomplished by the ciliary (muscle) processes, which pull the lens forwards and inwards by virtual contracting power of the ciliary muscle, and by which its suspensory ligament is relaxed, and the front of the lens allowed to bulge forward. In every case, however, accommodation is associated with contraction of the iris, the special function of which is that of a limiting diaphragm (an iris-diaphragm), Fig. 23.

In an ordinary spherical bi-convex lens, as already pointed out, the rays of light passing through the periphery of the lens come to a focus at a nearer point than the rays passing through the central portion. In this way a certain amount of blurring of the image takes place, and which, in optical language, is termed *spherical aberration*. This defect of the eye is capable of correction in three possible ways, and which it may be well to repeat: 1. By making the refractive index of the lens higher at its centre than at its circumference; (2) By making the curvature of the lens less near the circumference than at the centre; (3) By stopping out the peripheral rays of light by a diaphragm. The two latter methods are those resorted to in most optical instruments.

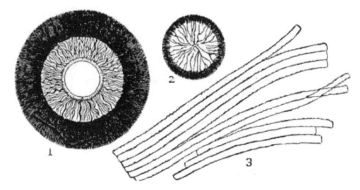

Fig. 23.—1. Equatorial section of Eyeball, showing Iris and Ciliary Processes, after washing away the pigment, × three diameters.

2. Nerves of the Cornea of Kitten's Eye, stained with iodine.

3. Fibres or Tubules of Lens, × 250, seen to be made up of superimposed crenated layers, and is therefore not homogeneous in structure, but made up of a number of extremely fine tubules, whose curvatures are nearly spherical.

In the human eye an attempt is made to apply all these methods, but the most important is the third, that of applying the diaphragm formed by the iris, a circular semi-muscular curtain lying just in front of the anterior surface of the lens. The iris is also furnished with a layer of pigmental cells which effectually stop out all peripheral rays of light that otherwise would pass into the eye, creating circles of diffusion of a disturbing nature to perfect vision. This delicate membrane, then, is kept in constant action by a two-fold nerve supply, derived from five or six sources, which it is unnecessary to describe at length. But the eye, with all its marvellous adaptations, has an obvious defect, that of secondary or uncorrected chromatic aberration.

Chromatic Aberration of the Eye.—White light, as previously explained, is composed of different wave lengths; and accordingly as these undulations are either longer or shorter, so do they produce on the eye the impression of different colours. We have seen how a pencil of white light may, by means of a prism, be decomposed into a multi-coloured band. In an ordinary magnifying reading-glass these coloured fringes are always seen around the margins. In practical optics chromatic aberration is partially corrected by employing two different kinds of glass in the construction of certain combined lenses. In the human eye chromatism cannot be corrected in this way; hence a blue light and a red light placed at the same distance from the eye appears to be unequally distant: the red light requiring greater accommodation in the eye than the blue, and this accordingly appears to be the nearer of the two.

This visual error may be experimentally shown and explained. There is a kind of glass which at first sight appears dark blue or violet, but which really contains a great deal of red. Take an ordinary microscope lamp, having a metal or opaque chimney, and drill a circular hole in it, about 3 mm. in diameter. This opening should be just at the height of the flame; cover it over with a piece of ground glass and a piece of the red-blue glass. Thus will be formed a luminous point whose light is composed of red and blue, *i.e.*, of colours far apart from each other in the spectrum.

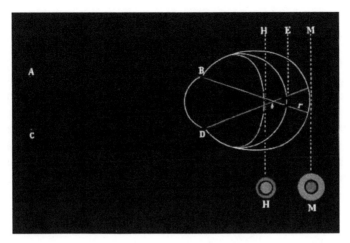

Fig. 24.—Chromatic Aberration of Eye, showing the wave differences of
the *blue and red rays of light (Landolt)*.

If rays coming from this point enter the eye, the blue rays (Fig. 24), being
more strongly reflected than the red, will come to a focus sooner than the
latter. The red rays, on the contrary, will be brought to a focus later than the
blue, while the latter, past their focus, are diverging. Let A B C D (Fig. 24)
be the section of a pencil of rays given off from a red-blue point sufficiently
distant so that these rays may be regarded as parallel. The focus of the blue
is at *b*, that of the red at *r*.

An eye is adapted to the distance of the luminous point when the circle of
diffusion, received upon the retina, is at its minimum. This is the case when
the sentient layer of the retina lies between the two foci E. In this case the
point will appear as a small circle, composed of the two colours, that is to
say—violet. If the retina be *in front* of this point, at the focus of the *blue* rays
for instance, the eye will perceive a *blue point surrounded by a red circle*, the latter
being formed by the periphery of the luminous cone of red rays, which are
focussed only after having passed the retina. The blue point will become a
circle of diffusion larger in proportion as the retina is nearer the dioptric
system, or as the focus for blue is farther behind it. But the blue circle will
always be surrounded by a red ring. If, on the contrary, the retina is *behind the
focus for red*, the blue cone will be greater in diameter than the red, and we shall
have a *red circle of diffusion*, larger in proportion as the retina is farther from the
focus, but always *surrounded by a blue ring* M. If the blue-red point is five
metres, or more, distant, the *emmetropic*[7] eye will evidently see it more
distinctly, *i.e.*, as a small *violet point*; the *hyperopic* eye, whose retina is situated
in front of the focus of its dioptric system, will see a *blue circle, surrounded by red*;
the *myopic* eye, whose retina is *behind* its focus, will see a *red circle, surrounded by*

blue. The size of these circles will be either larger or smaller when the principal focus of the eye is either in *front* of or *behind the retina.*[8]

The refractive surfaces of a perfectly formed eye are very like an ellipsoid of revolution with two axes, one of which, the major axis of the ellipse, is at the same time the optic axis and that of rotation; the other is perpendicular to it, and is equal in all meridians. Eyes, however, perfectly constructed are rarely met with. The curvature of the cornea is nearly always greater in one meridian than in another. Its surfaces then cannot be regarded as entirely belonging to an ellipsoid of revolution, since the solid figure, of which the former would constitute a part, has not only two axes, but three, and these unequal. This irregularity is not, however, always great enough to produce discomfort and it is therefore disregarded. But in other cases the difference of curvature in the different meridians of the eye attain to a higher degree, and vision falls far below the average.

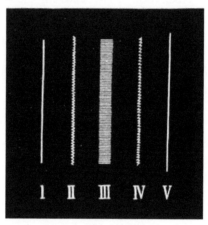

Fig. 25.—Lines as seen by the Astigmatic.

The refractive anomaly alluded to is termed *astigmatism* (from the Greek, α privative, στιγμα, a point—inability to see a point). The way in which objects appear to such a person will mainly result from the way in which he sees *a point.* Take, for example, the vertical to be the most, and the horizontal to be the least, refractive meridian: place a vertical line (Fig. 25, I) at a stated distance before the eye, and the line will appear elongated, owing to the diffusion image of each of the points composing it. It will also seem to be somewhat broadened, as at II. If the *vertical* meridian is adapted to the distance of the vertical, the line will appear very diffuse and broadened, as at III. All these little diffusion lines overlap each other, and give the line an elongated appearance. Hence a straight line is seen distinctly by an astigmatic eye only when the meridian to which it is perpendicular is perfectly adapted to its distance. A *vertical line* is seen distinctly when the *horizontal meridian* is adapted to its distance. It appears *indistinct* when its image is formed by the vertical meridian. The way in which an astigmatic person sees points and lines led to the discovery of this remarkable irregularity in the refraction of the eye. The late Astronomer Royal, Sir George Airy, suffered for some years until, indeed, he discovered how it could be corrected. This anomaly of curvature of the refractive surfaces of the eye is now known to prevail largely among the more civilised races of mankind. It is, then, of very great importance when using high powers of the microscope. In most persons the visual power of both eyes is rarely quite equal; on the other hand, the mind exerts an important influence, dominates, as it were, the eye in the interpretation of visual sensations and images. An example of this is presented in Wheatstone's pseudoscope, known to produce precisely the opposite effect of his stereoscope—conveys, in fact, the *converse of relief* produced by the latter and better known instrument.

Visual Judgment.—The apparent size of an object is determined by the magnitude of the image formed on the retina, and this is inversely proportional to the distance. Thus the size of an image on the retina of an object two inches long at a distance of a foot, is equal to the image of an object four inches long at a distance of two feet. An object can be seen if the visual angle subtended by it is not less than sixty seconds. This is equivalent to an image on the *fovea centralis* of the retina of about $4\ \mu^9$ across, and which corresponds to the diameter of a cone: so that while we have had under consideration the optical and physical conditions of human vision, we have likewise taken a lesson on the action of lenses used in the construction of the microscope.

The Theory of Microscopical Vision.

It has been said that no comparison can be instituted between microscopic vision and macroscopic; that the images formed by minute objects are not delineated microscopically under ordinary laws of diffraction, and that the results are dioptrical. This assertion, however, cannot be accepted unconditionally, as will be seen on more careful examination of the late Professor Abbe's masterly exposition of "The Microscopical Theory of Vision," and also his subsequent investigations on the estimation of aperture and the value of wide-angled immersion objectives, published in the "Journal of the Royal Microscopical Society."

The essential point in Abbe's theory of microscopical vision is that the images of minute objects in the microscope are not formed exclusively on the ordinary *dioptric* method (that is, in the same way in which they are formed in the camera or telescope), but that they are largely affected by the peculiar manner in which the minute construction of the object breaks up the incident rays, giving rise to *diffraction*.

The phenomena of diffraction in general may be observed experimentally by plates of glass ruled with fine lines. Fig. 26 shows the appearance presented by a single candle-flame seen through such a plate, an uncoloured image of the flame occupying the centre, flanked on either side by a row of coloured spectra of the flame, which become dimmer as they recede from the centre. A similar phenomenon may be produced by dust scattered over a glass plate, and by other objects whose structure contains very minute particles, or the meshes of very fine gauze wire, the rays suffering a characteristic change in passing through such objects; that change consisting in the breaking up of a parallel beam of light into a group of rays, diverging with wide angle and forming a regular series of maxima and minima of intensity of light, due to difference of phase of vibration.[10]

Fig. 26.

In the same way, in the microscope, the diffraction pencil originating from a beam incident upon, for instance, a diatom, appears as a fan of isolated rays, decreasing in intensity as they are further removed from the direction of the incident beam transmitted through the structure, the interference of the primary waves giving a number of successive maxima of light with dark interspaces.

When a diaphragm opening is interposed between the mirror, and a plate of ruled lines placed upon the stage such as Fig. 27, the appearance shown in Fig. 27a, will be observed at the back of the objective on removing the eye-piece and looking down the tube of the microscope. The centre circles are the images of the diaphragm opening produced by the direct rays, while those on the other side (always at right angles to the direction of the lines) are the diffraction images produced by the rays which are bent off from the incident pencil. In homogeneous light the central and lateral images agree in size and form, but in white light the diffraction images are radially drawn out, with the outer edges red and the inner blue (the reverse of the ordinary spectrum), forming, in fact, regular spectra the distance separating each of which varies inversely as the closeness of the lines, being for instance with the same objective twice as far apart when the lines are twice as close.

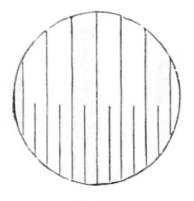

Fig. 27.

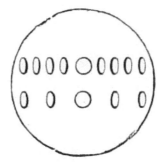

Fig. 27a.

The influence of these diffraction spectra may be demonstrated by some very striking experiments, which show that they are not by any means accidental phenomena, but are directly connected with the image which is seen by the eye.

The first experiment shows that with the central beam, or any one of the spectral beams alone, only the contour of the object is seen, the addition of at least one diffraction spectrum being essential to the visibility of the structure.

Fig. 28.

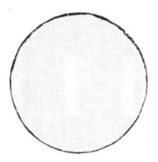

Fig. 28*a*.

When by a diaphragm placed at the back of the objective, as in Fig. 28, we cover up all the diffraction spectra of Fig. 27*a*, and allow only the central rays to reach the image, the object will appear to be wholly deprived of fine details, the outline alone will remain, and every delineation of minute structure will disappear, just as if the microscope had suddenly lost its optical power, as in Fig. 28*a*.

This experiment illustrates a case of the *obliteration* of structure by obstructing the passage of the diffraction spectra to the eye-piece. The next experiment shows how the appearance of fine structure may be *created* by manipulating the spectra.

Fig. 29.

Fig. 29*a*.

When a diaphragm such as that shown in Fig. 29 is placed at the back of the objective, so as to cut off each alternate one of the upper row of spectra in Fig. 27a, that row will obviously become identical with the lower one, and if the theory holds good, we should find the image of the upper lines identical with that of the lower. On replacing the eye-piece, we see that it is so, the upper set of lines are doubled in number, a new line appearing in the centre of the space between each of the old (upper) ones, and upper and lower set having become to all appearance identical, as seen in Fig. 29a.

Fig. 30.

Fig. 30a.

In the same way, if we stop off all but the outer spectra, as in Fig. 30, the lines are apparently again doubled, as seen in Fig. 30a.

A case of apparent creation of structure, similar in principle to the foregoing, though more striking, is afforded by a network of squares, as in Fig. 31, having sides *parallel* to this page, which gives the spectra shown in Fig. 31a, consisting of vertical rows for the horizontal lines and horizontal rows for the vertical ones. But it is readily seen that two diagonal rows of spectra exist at right angles to the diagonals of the squares, just as would arise from sets of lines in the direction of the diagonals, so that if the theory holds good we ought to find, on obstructing all the other spectra and allowing only the diagonal ones to pass to the eye-piece, that the vertical and horizontal lines have disappeared and are replaced by two new sets of lines at *right angles to the diagonals*.

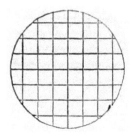

Fig. 31.

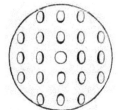

Fig. 31a.

Fig. 32.

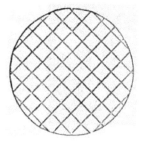

Fig. 32a.

On inserting the diaphragm, Fig. 32, and replacing the eye-piece, we find in the place of the old network the one shown in Fig. 32a, the squares being, however, smaller in the proportion of $1 : \sqrt{2}$, as they should be in accordance with the theory propounded.

An object such as *Pleurosigma angulatum*, which gives six diffraction spectra arranged as in Fig. 33, should, according to this theory, show markings in a hexagonal arrangement. For there will be one set of lines at right angles to *b*, *a*, *e*, another set at right angles to *c*, *a*, *f*, and a third at right angles to *g*, *a*, *d*. These three sets of lines will obviously produce the appearance shown in Fig. 33*a*.

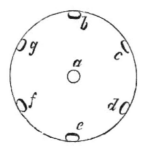

Fig. 33.

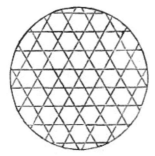

Fig. 33*a*.

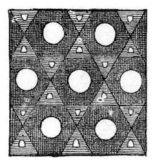

Fig. 34.

A great variety of appearances may be produced with the same arrangement of spectra. Any two adjacent spectra with the central beam (as *b*, *c*, *a*) will form equilateral triangles and give hexagonal markings. Or by stopping off all but *g*, *c*, *e* (or *b*, *d*, *f*), we again have the spectra in the form of equilateral triangles; but as they are now further apart, the sides of the triangles in the two cases being as $\sqrt{3} : 1$, the hexagons will be smaller and three times as numerous. Their sides will also be arranged at a different angle to those of the first set. The hexagons may be entirely obliterated by admitting only the spectra *g, c,* or *g, f,* or *b, f,* etc., when new lines will appear at right angles, or obliquely inclined, to the median line. By varying the combinations of the spectra, therefore, different figures of varying size and positions are produced, all of which cannot, of course, represent the true structure. Not only, however, may the appearance of particular structure be obliterated or created, but it may even be *predicted* before being seen under the microscope. If the position and relative intensity of the spectra in any particular case are given, the character of the resultant image, in some instances, may be worked out by mathematical calculations. A remarkable instance of such a prediction is to be found in the case recorded by Mr. Stephenson, where a mathematical student who had never seen a diatom, worked out the purely mathematical result of the interference of the six spectra *b-g* of Fig. 33 (identical with *P. angulatum*), giving the drawing copied in Fig. 34. The special feature was the small markings between the hexagons, which had not, before this time, been noticed on *P. angulatum*. On more closely scrutinizing a valve, stopping out the central beam and allowing the six spectra only to pass, the small markings were found actually to exist, though they were so faint they had previously escaped observation until the result of the mathematical deduction had shown that they *ought* to be seen.

These experiments seem to show that diffraction plays a very essential part in the formation of microscopical images, since dissimilar structures give identical images when the differences of their diffractive effect is removed, and conversely similar structures may give dissimilar images when their diffractive images are made dissimilar. Whilst a purely dioptric image answers point for point to the object on the stage, and enables a safe inference to be drawn as to the actual nature of that object, the visible indications of minute structure in a microscopical image are not always or necessarily conformable to the real nature of the object examined, so that nothing more can safely be inferred from the image as presented to the eye, than the presence in the object of such structural peculiarities as will produce the particular diffraction phenomena on which these images depend.

Further investigations and experiments led Abbe to discard so much of his theoretical conclusions relating to superimposed images having a distinct character as well as a different origin, and as to their capability of being separated and examined apart from each other. In a later paper he writes: "I no longer maintain in principle the distinction between the absorption image or direct dioptrical image and the diffraction image, nor do I hold that the microscopical image of an object consists of two superimposed images of different origin or a different mode of production. Thus it appears that both the absorption image and the diffraction image he held to be equally of diffraction origin; but while a lens of small aperture would give the former with facility, it would be powerless to reveal the latter, because of its limited capacity to gather in the strongly-deflected rays due to the excessively minute bodies the microscopical objective has to deal with."[11]

Abbe's theory of vision has been questioned by mathematicians, and since his death Lord Rayleigh went more deeply into the question of "the theory of the formation of optical images," with special reference to the microscope and telescope. He has shown that two lines cannot be fairly resolved unless their components subtend an angle exceeding that subtended by the wavelength of light at a distance equal to the aperture; also, that the measure of resolution is only possible with a square aperture, or one bounded by straight lines, parallel to the lines resolved.

Lord Rayleigh's Theory of the Formation of Optical Images, with Special Reference to the Microscope.[12]

Of the two methods adopted, that of Helmholtz's consists in tracing the image representative of a mathematical point in the object, the point being regarded as self-luminous; that of Abbe's the typical object was not, as we have seen, a luminous *point*, but a *grating* illuminated by plane waves of light. In the latter method, Lord Rayleigh argues that the complete representation of the object requires the co-operation of all the spectra which are focussed in the principal focal plane of the objective; when only a few are present the representation is imperfect, and wholly fails when there is only one. He then proceeds to show, by the aid of diagrams and mathematical formula, how the resolving power can be adduced.

On further criticism of the Abbe spectrum theory, he observes "that although the image ultimately formed may be considered to be due to the spectra focussed to a given point, the degree of conformity of the image to the object is another question. The consideration of the case of a very fine grating, which might afford no lateral spectra at all, shows the incorrectness of the usually accepted idea that if all the spectra are utilised the image will still be incomplete, so that the theory (originally promulgated by Abbe) requires a good deal of supplementing; while it is inapplicable when the incident light is not parallel, and when the object is, for example, a double point and not a grating. Even in the case of a grating, the spectrum theory is inapplicable, if the grating is self-luminous; for in this case no spectra can be formed since the radiations from the different elements of the grating have no permanent phase-relations." For these reasons Lord Rayleigh advises that the question should be reconsidered from the older point of view, according to which the typical object is a point and not a grating. Such treatment will show that the theory of resolving power is essentially the same for all instruments. The peculiarities of the microscope, arising from the divergence-angles not being limited to be small, and from the different character of the illumination, are theoretically only differences of detail. These investigations can be extended to gratings, and the results so obtained confirm for the most part the conclusions of the spectrum theory.

Furthermore, that the function of the condenser in microscopic practice in throwing upon the object the image of the lamp-flame is to cause the object to behave, at any rate in some degree, as if it were self-luminous, and thus to obviate the sharply-marked interference bands which arise when permanent and definite phase-relations are permitted to exist between the radiations which issue from various points of the object. This is capable of mathematical proof; and in the case where the illumination is such that each point of the row or of the grating radiates independently, the limit to resolution is seen to depend only on the width of the aperture, and thus to be the same for all forms of aperture as for those of the rectangular. That Abbe's theory of microscopic vision is fairly open to the criticisms passed on it by Lord Rayleigh must be taken for granted.

Definition of Aperture; Principles of Microscopic Vision.

It must be well within the last half-century that the achromatic objective-glass for the microscope was brought to perfection and its value became generally recognised. Prior to the discovery of the achromatic principle in the construction of lenses it was assumed that the formation of the microscopic image took place (as we have already seen) on ordinary dioptric principles. As the image is formed in the camera or telescope, so it was said to be in the microscope. This belief existed, it will be remembered, at a time when dry objectives only were in favour and the use of the term *angle of aperture* was misunderstood, when it was supposed that the different media with diffraction-indices were used; and the angle of the radiant pencil was believed not only to admit of a comparison of two apertures in the same medium, but likewise to admit of a standard of comparison when the media were entirely different in their refractive qualities.

It was during my tenure of office as secretary of the Royal Microscopical Society (1867 to 1873), that the aperture question, and also that of *numerical aperture*, came under discussion, both being met by the majority of the Fellows of the Society and practical opticians by a *non-possumus*.

Opticians alleged, that is, before the value of aperture became fully recognised (1860), that the achromatic objective had reached a stage of perfection, beyond which it was not possible to go; indeed, not only opticians, but physicists of high standing, as Professor Helmholtz, who made many important contributions to the theory of the microscope, and who, after duly weighing all the known physical laws on which the formation of images can be explained, emphatically stated that in his opinion "the limit of possible improvement of the microscope as an instrument of discovery had been very nearly reached." A quarter of a century ago I ventured to throw a doubt upon so questionable a statement. I determined, if possible, to submit the aperture question to an exhaustive examination. My views were accordingly submitted to two of the highest authorities in this country—Sir George Airy, the then Astronomer Royal, and Sir George Stokes, Professor of Physics at Cambridge University—both of whom agreed with me that the possible increase of aperture would be attended with great advantage to the objective, and open the way to an extension of power resolution in the microscope.[13] The discussion afterwards took a warm turn, as will be seen on reference to "The Monthly Microscopical Journals" of 1874, 1875 and 1876.

The confusion into which the aperture question at this period had lapsed was no doubt due to the fact that its opponents had not yet grasped the true meaning of the term *aperture*. It was believed to be synonymous with "angular aperture," much in use at the time. It will, however, appear quite unaccountable that even the older opticians should have confounded the latter with the former; and so entirely disregarded the fact that the angles of the pencil of light admitted by the objective cannot serve as a measure of its *aperture*, and that high refractive media can greatly reduce the value length of waves of light.

When the medium in which the objective works is the same as air, it is not that a comparison can be made by the angles of the radiant pencils only, but by their sines. For example, if two dry objectives admit pencils of 60° and 180°, their real apertures are not as 1 : 3, but as 1 : 2 only. Aperture in fact is computed by mathematicians by tracing the rays from the back focus through the system of lenses to the front focus, the front focus being the point at which the whole cone of rays converge as free as may be from aberration. If the front focus be in air, no pencil greater than 82°, "double the angle of total reflection," can *emerge* from the plane front of the lens; and, obviously, if no greater cone can emerge to a focus one way, neither can any greater cone enter the body of the lens from the radiant. This angle, then, of 82°, must be regarded as the limit for dry lenses or objectives.

This limit, it will be seen on more careful examination, is very nearly the maximum angle that can be computed for a lens to have a front focus in air. This can be proved by the consideration of the angle of the image of rays, as they are radiated from the object itself in balsam: for although this angle of image rays viewed as nascent from a self-luminous object capable of scattering rays in all directions, may be 180° in the substance of the balsam and cover-glass, of the 180° only 82° of the central portion will emerge into air—all rays beyond this limit are internally reflected at the cover-glass. This cone, then, of 82° becomes 180° in air, and a large part must necessarily be lost by reflection at the first incidence on the plane front of the lens. But with a formula permitting the use of a water medium between the front lens and the cover-glass, the aperture of the image rays may reach 126°—double the critical angle from glass to water; and with an oil medium, the aperture will be found to be limited only by the form of the front lens that can be constructed by the optician.

To sum up, then, the effect of the immersion system, greatly assists in the correction of aberration, gives increased magnification and angular aperture, increase of working distance between the objective and object, and renders admissible the use of the thicker glass-cover.

The aperture question would in all probability have remained unsolved many years longer (ten or twelve years elapsed after I brought the question under discussion before opticians gave way), but for the fortunate circumstance that the eminent mathematical and practical optician, Professor Abbe, of Jena, was about to visit London. This came off in the early part of the seventies, when the late Mr. John Mayall and myself had the good fortune to interview him. The subject discussed was naturally the increase of aperture and the theory of microscopical vision. He readily at our request undertook to re-investigate the question in all its bearings on the microscope. It is almost unnecessary to add that the conclusions he came to, and the results obtained, have proved of inestimable value to the microscopist and practical optician, and it may well seem necessary to explain somewhat at greater length the conclusions the learned Professor came to, and by the adoption of which the microscope has been placed on a more scientific basis than it had before attained to. Several papers were published *in extenso* in the "Journal of the Royal Microscopical Society," and I am greatly indebted to Mr. Frank Crisp, LL.D., for an excellent *resumé* of Abbe's Monograph.[14]

The essential step in the consideration of aperture is, as I have said, to understand clearly what is meant by the term. It will at once be recognised that its definition must necessarily refer to its primary meaning of *opening*, and must, in the case of an optical instrument, define its capacity for receiving rays from the object, and transmitting them to the image received at the eye-piece.

In the case of the telescope-objective, its capacity for receiving and transmitting rays is necessarily measured by the expression of its absolute diameter or "opening." No such absolute measure can be applied in the case of the microscope objective, the largest constructed lenses of which having by no means the largest apertures, being, in fact, the lower powers of the instrument, whose apertures are for the most part but small. The capacity of a microscope objective for receiving and transmitting rays is, however, as will be seen, estimated by its *relative* opening, that is, its opening in relation to its focal length. When this relative opening has been ascertained, it may be regarded as synonymous with that denoted in the telescope by *absolute* opening. That this is so will be better appreciated by the following consideration:—

In a single lens, the rays admitted within one meridional plane evidently increase as the diameter of the lens (all other circumstances remaining the same), and in the microscope we have, at the back of the lens, the same conditions to deal with as are in front in the case of the telescope; the larger or smaller number of emergent rays will therefore be measured by the clear diameter, and as no rays can emerge that have not first been admitted, this will give the measure of the admitted rays under similar circumstances.

If the lenses compared have different focal lengths but the same clear "openings," they will transmit the same number of rays to equal areas of an image at a definite distance, because they would admit the same number if an object were substituted for the image; that is, if the lens were used as a telescope-objective. But as the focal lengths are different, the amplification of the images is different also, and equal areas of these images correspond to different areas of the object from which the rays are collected. Therefore, the higher power lens with the same opening as the lower power, will admit a *greater* number of rays in all from the same object, because it admits the *same* number as the latter from a *smaller* portion of the object. Thus, if the focal lengths of two lenses are as 2 : 1, and the first amplifies N diameters, the second will amplify 2 N with the same distance of the image, so that the rays which are collected *to* a given field of 1 mm. diameter of the image are admitted *from* a field of $1/_N$ mm. in the first case, and of $1/_{2N}$ mm. in the second. As the "opening" of the objective is estimated by the diameter (and not by the area) the higher power lens admits *twice* as many rays as the lower power, because it admits the same number from a field of half the diameter, and, in general, the admission of rays by the same opening, but different powers, must be in the inverse ratio of the focal lengths.

In the case of the single lens, therefore, its aperture is determined by the ratio between the clear opening and the focal length. The same considerations apply to the case of a compound objective, substituting, however, for the clear opening of the single lens the diameter of the pencil at its emergence from the objective, that is, the clear utilised diameter of the back lens. All equally holds good whether the medium in which the objective is placed is the same in the case of the two objectives or different, as an alteration of the medium makes no difference in the power.

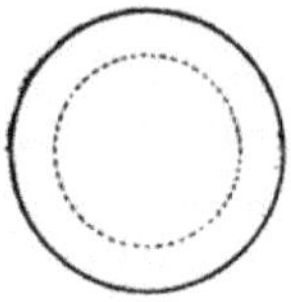

180° Oil Angle. (Numerical Aperture 1·52.)

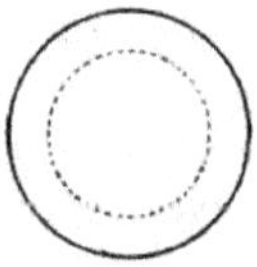

180° Water Angle. (Numerical Aperture 1·33.)

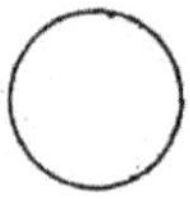

180° Air Angle. 96° Water Angle. 82° Oil Angle. (Numerical Aperture 1·00.)

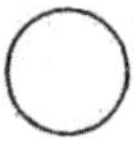

97° Air Angle. (Numerical Aperture ·75.)

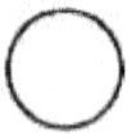

60° Air Angle. (Numerical Aperture ·50.)

Fig. 35.—Relative diameters of the (utilized) back lenses of various dry and immersion objectives of the same power (¼-in.) from an air angle of 60° to an oil angle of 180°.

Thus we arrive at a general proposition for all kinds of objectives: 1st, when the power is the same, the admission of rays (or aperture) varies with the diameter of the pencil at its emergence; 2nd, when the powers are different, the same aperture requires different openings in the ratio of the focal lengths, or conversely with the same opening the aperture is in inverse ratio to the focal lengths. We see, therefore, that just as in the telescope the absolute diameter of the object-glass defines its *aperture*, so in the microscope *the ratio between the utilised diameter of the back lens and the focal length* of the objective defines its aperture also, and this is clearly a definition of aperture in its primary and only legitimate meaning as "opening;" that is, the capacity of the objective for admitting rays from the object and transmitting them to the image.

If, by way of illustration, we compare a series of dry and oil-immersion objectives, and commencing with small air angles, progress up to 180° air angle, and then take an oil-immersion of 82° and progress again to 180° oil angle, the ratio of opening to power progresses also, and attains its maximum, not in the case of the air angle of 180° (when it is exactly equivalent to the oil angle of only 82°), but is greatest at the oil angle of 180°. If we assume the objectives to have the same power throughout we get rid of one of the factors of the ratio, and we have only to compare the diameters of the emergent beams, and can represent their relations by diagrams.

Fig. 35 illustrates five cases of different apertures of ¼-in. objectives, viz.: those of dry objectives of 60°, 97°, and 180° air angle, a water-immersion of 180° water angle, and an oil-immersion of 180° oil angle. The inner dotted circles in the two latter cases are of the same size as that corresponding to the 180° air angle.

A dry objective of the maximum air angle of 180° is only able to utilise a diameter of back lens equal to twice the focal length, while an immersion lens of even only 100° utilises a *larger* diameter, *i.e.*, it is able to transmit more rays from the object to the image than any dry objective is capable of transmitting. Whenever the angle of an immersion lens exceeds twice the critical angle for the immersion fluid, *i.e.*, 96° for water or 82° for oil, its aperture is in excess of that of a dry objective of 180°.

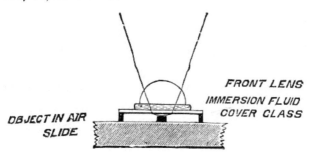

Fig. 36.

This excess will be *seen* if we take an oil-immersion objective of, say 122° balsam angle, illuminating it so that the whole field is filled with the incident rays, and use it first on an object not mounted in balsam, but dry. We then have a *dry objective* of nearly 180° angular aperture, for, as will be seen by reference to Fig. 36, the cover-glass is virtually the first surface of the objective, as the front lens, the immersion fluid, and the cover-glass are all approximately of the same index, and form, therefore, a front lens of extra thickness. When the object is close to the cover-glass the pencil radiating from it will be very nearly 180°, and the emergent pencil (observed by removing the eye-piece) will be seen to utilise as much of the back lens of the objective as is equal to twice the focal length, that is, the *inner* of the two circles at the head of Fig. 35.

If now balsam be run in beneath the cover-glass so that the angle of the pencil taken up by the objective is no longer 180°, but 122° only (that is, *smaller*), the diameter of the emergent pencil is *larger* than it was before, when the angle of the pencil was 180° in air, and will be approximately represented by the *outer* circle of Fig. 35. As the power remains the same in both cases, the larger diameter denotes the greater aperture of the immersion objective over a dry objective of even 180° angle, and the excess of aperture is made plainly visible.

Having settled the principle, it is still necessary, however, to find a proper *notation* for comparing apertures. The astronomer can compare the apertures of his various objectives by simply expressing them in inches, but this is obviously not available to the microscopist, who has to deal with the ratio of two varying quantities.

In consequence of a discovery made by Professor Abbe in 1873, that a general relation existed between the pencil admitted into the front of the objective and that emerging from the back of the objective, he was able to show that the ratio of the semi-diameter of the emergent pencil to the focal length of the objective could be expressed by the formula n Sin u, *i.e.*, by the sine of half the angle of aperture (u) multiplied by the refractive index of the medium (n) in front of the objective (n being $1 \cdot 0$ for air, $1 \cdot 33$ for water, and $1 \cdot 52$ for oil or balsam).

When, then, the values in any given cases of the expression n Sin u (which is known as the "numerical aperture") has been ascertained, the objectives are instantly compared as regards their aperture, and, moreover, as 180° in air is equal to $1 \cdot 0$ (since $n = 1 \cdot 0$ and the sine of half 180° $= 1 \cdot 0$) we see, with equal readiness, whether the aperture is smaller or larger than that corresponding to 180° in air. Thus, suppose we desire to compare the apertures of three objectives, one a dry objective, the second a water immersion, and the third an oil immersion; these would be compared on the angular aperture view as, say 74° air angle, 85° water angle, and 118° oil angle, so that a calculation must be worked out to arrive at the actual relation between them. Applying, however, the *numerical*[15] notation, which gives $\cdot 60$ for the dry objective, $\cdot 90$ for the water immersion, and $1 \cdot 30$ for the oil immersion, their relative apertures are immediately recognised, and it is seen, for instance, that the aperture of the water immersion is somewhat less than that of a dry objective of 180°, and that the aperture of the oil immersion exceeds that of the latter by 30%.

The advantage of immersion, in comparison with dry objectives, becomes at once apparent. Instead of consisting merely in a diminution of the loss of light by reflection or increased working distance, it is seen that a wide-angled immersion objective has a larger aperture than a dry objective of maximum angle, so that for any of the purposes for which aperture is essential an immersion must necessarily be preferred to a dry objective.

That pencils of identical angular extension but in different media are different physically, will cease to appear in any way paradoxical if we recall the simple optical fact that rays, which in air are spread out over the whole hemisphere, are in a medium of higher refractive index such as oil *compressed* into a cone of 82° round the perpendicular, *i.e.*, twice the critical angle. A cone exceeding twice the critical angle of the medium will therefore embrace a *surplus* of rays which do not exist even in the hemisphere when the object is in air.

The whole aperture question, notwithstanding the innumerable perplexities which heretofore surrounded it, is in reality completely solved by these two simple considerations: First, that "aperture" is to be applied in its ordinary meaning as representing the greater or less capacity of the objective for receiving and transmitting rays; and second, that when so applied the aperture of an objective is determined by the ratio between its opening and its focal length; the objective that utilises the larger back lens (or opening) relatively to its focal length having necessarily the larger aperture. It would hardly, therefore, serve any useful purpose if we were here to discuss the various erroneous ideas that gave rise to the contention that 180° in air must be the maximum aperture. Amongst these was the suggestion that the larger emergent beams of immersion objectives were due to the fact that the immersion fluid abolished the refractive action of the first plane surface which, in the case of air, prevented there being any pencil exceeding 82° within the glass. Also the very curious mistake which arose from the assumption that a hemisphere did not magnify an object at its centre because the rays passed through without refraction. A further erroneous view has, however, been so widespread that it seems to be desirable to devote a few lines to it, especially as it always appears at first sight to be both simple and conclusive.

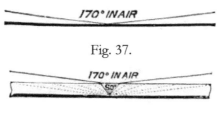

Fig. 37.

Fig. 37a.

If a dry objective is used upon an object in air, as in Fig. 37, the angle may approach 180°, but when the object is mounted in balsam, as in Fig. 37a, the angle at the object cannot exceed 82°, all rays outside that limit (shown by dotted lines) being reflected back at the cover-glass and not emerging into air. On using an immersion objective, however, the immersion fluid which replaces the air above the cover-glass allows the rays formerly reflected back to pass through to the objective, so that the angle at the object may again be nearly 180° as with the dry lens. The action of the immersion objective was, therefore, supposed to be simply that it repaired the loss in angle which was occasioned when the object was transferred from air to balsam, and merely restored the conditions existing in Fig. 37a with the dry objective on a dry object.

As the result of this erroneous supposition, it followed that an immersion objective could have no advantage over a dry objective, except in the case of the latter being used upon a balsam-mounted object, its aperture then being (as was supposed) "cut down." The error lies simply in overlooking the fact that the rays which are reflected back when the object is mounted in balsam Fig. 37a) are not rays which are found when the object is in air (Fig. 37), but are *additional and different* rays which do not exist in air, as they cannot be emitted in a substance of so low a refractive index.

Lastly, it should also be noted that it is numerical and not angular aperture which measures the quantity of light admitted to the objective by different pencils.

Fig. 38.

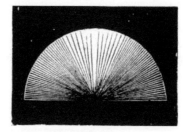

Fig. 38a.

First take the case of the medium being the same. The popular notion of a pencil of light may be illustrated by Fig. 38, which assumes that there is equal intensity of emission in all directions, so that the quantity of light contained in any given pencils may be compared by simply comparing the contents of the solid cones. The Bouguer-Lambert law, however, shows that the quantity of light emitted by any bright point varies with the obliquity of the direction of emission, being *greater* in a perpendicular than in an oblique direction. The rays are less intense in proportion as they are more inclined to the surface which emits them, so that a pencil is not correctly represented by Fig. 38, but by Fig. 38*a*, the density of the rays decreasing continuously from the vertical to the horizontal, and the squares of the sines of the semi-angles (*i.e.*, of the numerical aperture) constituting the true measure of the quantity of light contained in any solid pencil.

If, again, the media are of different refractive indices, as air (1·0), water (1·33), and oil (1·52), the total amount of light emitted over the whole 180° from radiant points in these media under a given illumination is not the same, but is *greater* in the case of the media of greater refractive indices in the ratio of the squares of those indices (*i.e.*, as 1·0, 1·77 and 2·25). The quantity of light in pencils of different angle and in different media must therefore be compared by squaring the product of the sines and the refractive indices, *i.e.* ($n \sin u^2$), for the square of the numerical aperture.

The fact is therefore made clear that the aperture of a dry objective of 180° does not represent, as was supposed, a maximum, but that aperture increases with the increase in the refractive index of the immersion fluid; and it should be borne in mind that this result has been arrived at in strict accordance with the ordinary propositions of geometrical optics, and without any reference to or deductions from the diffraction theory of Professor Abbe.

There still remains one other point for determination, namely, the proper function of aperture in respect to immersion objectives of large aperture. The explanation of the increased power of vision obtained by increase of aperture was, that by the greater obliquity of the rays to the object "shadow effects" were produced, a view which overlooked the fact, first, that the utilisation of increased aperture depends not only on the obliquity of the rays sent to the *object*, but also to the *axis of the microscope*; and exactly as there is no acoustic shadow produced by an obstacle, which is only a few multiples of the length of the sound waves, so there can be no shadow produced by minute objects, only a few multiples from the light waves, the latter then passing completely *round* the object. The Abbe diffraction theory, however, supplies the true explanation of this, and shows that the increased performance of immersion objectives of large aperture is directly connected (as might have been anticipated) with the larger "openings" in the proper sense of the term, which, as we have already explained, such objectives really possess. Furthermore, in order that the image exactly corresponds with the object, all diffracted rays must be gathered up by the objective. Should any be lost we shall have not an actual image of the object, but a spurious one. Now, if we have a coarse object, the diffracted rays are all comprised within a narrow cone round the direct beam, and an objective of small aperture will transmit them all. With a minute object, however, the diffracted rays are widely spread out, so that a small aperture can admit only a fractional part—to admit the whole or a very large part, and consequently to see the minute structure of the object, or to see it truly, a large aperture is necessary, and in this lies the value of *aperture* and of a *wide-angled immersion objective* for the observation of minute structures.

Numerical Aperture.

Measure of Apertures of Objectives. N.A.—Numerical aperture, as it is termed, is measured by the scale of measurement calculated by the late Professor Abbe, and which has since been generally recognised and adopted. He showed that even in lenses made for the same medium (as air) their comparative aperture as compared with their focus was not correctly measured by the angle of the rays grasped, but by the actual diameters of the pencil of rays transmitted, which depend, as already seen, more upon the back of the lens than the front. To get a geometric measure for comparison, he took the radii, or half diameters (whose relative proportions would be the same), and which geometrically are the sines of the semi-angle of the outermost rays grasped. Abbe further showed that if this sine of half the outside angle were multiplied by the refractive index of the medium used we should have a number which would give the comparative *aperture* of any lens, whatever the medium. This number, then, determines both the numerical aperture and the resolving power of the objective.

The following table of numerical apertures shows the respective angular pencils which they express in air, water and cedar oil, or glass.[16] The first column gives the numerical apertures from 0·20 to 1·33; the second, third, and fourth, the air, water and oil (or balsam) angles of aperture from 23° 4' air angle to 180° balsam angle. The theoretical resolving power in lines to the inch is shown in the sixth column; the line E of the spectrum being taken from about the middle of the green, the column giving "illuminating power" being of less importance; while in using that of penetrating power, it must be remembered that several data beside that of $1/a$ go to make up the total depth of vision with the microscope.

ABRIDGED NUMERICAL APERTURE TABLE.

(1)	Corresponding Angle (2 u) for	Limit of Resolving Power, in Lines to an Inch.	(8)	(9)

	(2)	(3)	(4)	(5)	(6)	(7)		
1·33	...	180° 0'	122° 6'	128,225	138,989	168,907	1·769	·752
1·32	...	165° 56'	120° 33'	127,261	137,944	167,637	1·742	·758
1·30	...	155° 38'	117° 35'	125,333	135,854	165,097	1·690	·769
1·28	...	148° 42'	114° 44'	123,405	133,764	162,557	1·638	·781
1·26	...	142° 39'	111° 59'	121,477	131,674	160,017	1·588	·794
1·24	...	137° 36'	109° 20'	119,548	129,584	157,477	1·538	·806
1·22	...	133° 4'	106° 45'	117,620	127,494	154,937	1·488	·820
1·20	...	128° 55'	104° 15'	115,692	125,404	152,397	1·440	·833
1·18	...	125° 3'	101° 50'	113,764	123,314	149,857	1·392	·847
1·16	...	121° 26'	99° 29'	111,835	121,224	147,317	1·346	·862
1·14	...	118° 0'	97° 11'	109,907	119,134	144,777	1·300	·877
1·12	...	114° 44'	94° 55'	107,979	117,044	142,237	1·254	·893
1·10	...	111° 36'	92° 43'	106,051	114,954	139,698	1·210	·909
1·08	...	108° 36'	90° 34'	104,123	112,864	137,158	1·166	·926
1·06	...	105° 42'	88° 27'	102,195	110,774	134,618	1·124	·943
1·04	...	102° 53'	86° 21'	100,266	108,684	132,078	1·082	·962

1·02	...	100° 10'	84° 18'	98,338	106,593	129,538	1·040	·980
1·00	180° 0'	97° 31'	82° 17'	96,410	104,503	126,998	1·000	1·000
0·98	157° 2'	94° 56'	80° 17'	94,482	102,413	124,458	·960	1·020
0·96	147° 29'	92° 24'	78° 20'	92,554	100,323	121,918	·922	1·042
0·94	140° 6'	89° 56'	76° 24'	90,625	98,223	119,378	·884	1·064
0·92	133° 51'	87° 32'	74° 30'	88,697	96,143	116,838	·846	1·087
0·90	128° 19'	85° 10'	72° 36'	86,769	94,053	114,298	·810	1·111
0·88	123° 17'	82° 51'	70° 44'	84,841	91,963	111,758	·774	1·136
0·86	118° 38'	80° 34'	68° 54'	82,913	89,873	109,218	·740	1·163
0·84	114° 17'	78° 20'	67° 6'	80,984	87,783	106,678	·706	1·190
0·82	110° 10'	76° 8'	65° 18'	79,056	85,693	104,138	·672	1·220
0·80	106° 16'	73° 58'	63° 31'	77,128	83,603	101,598	·640	1·250
0·78	102° 31'	71° 49'	61° 45'	75,200	81,513	99,058	·608	1·282
0·76	98° 56'	69° 42'	60° 0'	73,272	79,423	96,518	·578	1·316
0·74	95° 28'	67° 37'	58° 16'	71,343	77,333	93,979	·548	1·351
0·72	92° 6'	65° 32'	56° 32'	69,415	75,242	91,439	·518	1·389
0·70	88° 51'	63° 31'	54° 50'	67,487	73,152	88,899	·490	1·429

0·68	85° 41'	61° 30'	53° 9'	65,559	71,062	86,359	·462	1·471
0·66	82° 36'	59° 30'	51° 28'	63,631	68,972	83,819	·436	1·515
0·64	79° 36'	57° 31'	49° 48'	61,702	66,882	81,279	·410	1·562
0·62	76° 38'	55° 34'	48° 9'	59,774	64,792	78,739	·384	1·613
0·60	73° 44'	53° 38'	46° 30'	57,846	62,702	76,199	·360	1·667
0·58	70° 54'	51° 42'	44° 51'	55,918	60,612	73,659	·336	1·724
0·56	68° 6'	49° 48'	43° 14'	53,990	58,522	71,119	·314	1·786
0·54	65° 22'	47° 54'	41° 37'	52,061	56,432	68,579	·292	1·852
0·52	62° 40'	46° 2'	40° 0'	50,133	54,342	66,039	·270	1·923
0·50	60° 0'	44° 10'	38° 24'	48,205	52,252	63,499	·250	2·000
0·45	53° 30'	39° 33'	34° 27'	43,385	47,026	57,149	·203	2·222
0·40	47° 9'	35° 0'	30° 31'	38,564	41,801	50,799	·160	2·500
0·35	40° 58'	30° 30'	26° 38'	33,744	36,576	44,449	·123	2·857
0·30	34° 56'	26° 4'	22° 46'	28,923	31,351	38,099	·090	3·333
0·25	28° 58'	21° 40'	18° 56'	24,103	26,126	31,749	·063	4·000
0·20	23° 4'	17° 18'	15° 7'	19,282	20,901	25,400	·040	5·000

INDEX:

(1) Numerical Aperture. ($n \sin u = a$.)

(2) *Air* ($n = 1\cdot00$).

(3) *Water* ($n = 1\cdot33$).

(4) *Homogeneous Immersion* ($n = 1\cdot52$).

(5) White Light. ($\lambda = 0\cdot5269$ μ, Line E.)

(6) Monochromatic (Blue) Light.($\lambda = 0\cdot4861$ μ, Line F.)

(7) Photography. ($\lambda = 0\cdot4000$ μ, Near Line *hk*.)

(8) Illuminating Power (a^2.)

(9) Penetrating Power ($1/_a$.)

Abbe's Apertometer.

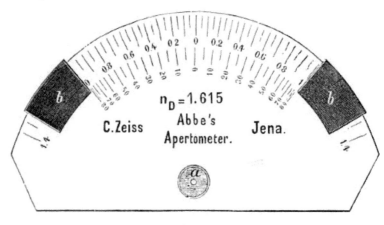

Fig. 39.—Abbe's Apertometer.

The apertometer is an auxiliary piece of apparatus invented by Abbe, for testing the fundamental properties of objectives and determining their numerical and angular apertures. This accessory of the microscope involves the same principles as that of Tolles, which the late Mr. J. Mayall and myself brought to the notice of the Royal Microscopical Society of London in 1876. Abbe's apertometer (Fig. 39) consists of a flat cylinder of glass, about three inches in diameter, and half an inch thick, with a large chord cut off, so that the portion left is somewhat more than a semicircle; the part where the segment is cut is bevelled from above downwards, to an angle of 45°, and it will be seen that there is a small disc with an aperture in it denoting the centre of the semicircle. To use this instrument the microscope is placed in a vertical position, and the apertometer is placed upon the stage with its circular part to the front and the chord to the back. Diffused light, either from the sun or lamp, is assumed to be in front and on both sides. Suppose the lens to be measured is a dry one-quarter inch; then with a one-inch eye-piece having a large field, the centre disc, with its aperture on the apertometer, is brought into focus. The eye-piece and the draw-tube are now removed, leaving the focal arrangement undisturbed, and a lens supplied with the apertometer is screwed into the end of the draw-tube. This lens, with the eye-piece in the draw-tube, forms a low-power compound microscope. This is now inserted into the body-tube, and the back lens of the objective whose aperture we desire to measure is brought into focus. In the image of the back lens will be seen stretched across, as it were, the image of the circular part of the apertometer. It will appear as a bright band, because the light which enters normally at the surface is reflected by the bevelled part of the chord in a vertical direction, so that in reality a fan of 180° in air is formed. There are two sliding screens seen on either side of the figure of the apertometer; they slide on the vertical circular portion of the instrument. The images of these screens can be seen in the image of the bright bands. *These screens should now be moved so that their edges just touch the periphery of the back lens.* They act, as it were, as a diaphragm to cut the fan and reduce it, so that its angle just equals the aperture of the objective and no more.

This angle is now determined by the arc of glass between the screens; thus we get an angle in *glass* the exact equivalent of the aperture of the objective. As the numerical apertures of these arcs are engraved on the apertometer, they can be read off by inspection. A difficulty is not infrequently experienced from the fact that it is not easy to determine the exact point at which the edge of the screen touches the periphery of the back lens, or rather the limit of the aperture. Zeiss, to meet this difficulty, made a change in the form of the apparatus—furnished a glass disc mounted on a metal plate, with a slot for the purpose of its more accurate adjustment.[17]

Stereoscopic Binocular Vision.

Professor Wheatstone's remarkable discovery of stereoscopic vision led, at no distant period, to the application of the principle to the microscope. It may therefore prove of interest to inquire how stereoscopic binocular vision is brought about. Indeed, the curious results obtained in the stereoscope cannot be well understood without a previous knowledge of the fundamental optical principles involved in this contrivance, whereby two slightly dissimilar pictures of any object become fused into one image, having the actual appearance of relief. The invention of the stereoscope by Sir Charles Wheatstone, F.R.S., 1838, and improved by Brewster, was characterised by Sir John Herschel as "one of the most curious discoveries, and beautiful for its simplicity, in the entire range of experimental optics," led to a more general appreciation of the value of the conjoint use of both eyes in conveying to the mind impressions of the relative form and position of an object, such as the use of either eye singly does not convey with anything like the same precision. When a near object having three dimensions is looked at, a different perspective representation is seen with each eye. Certain parts are seen by the right eye, the left being closed, that are invisible to the left eye, the right being closed, and the relative positions of the portions visible to each eye in succession differ. These two visual impressions are simultaneously perceived by both eyes, and combined in the brain into one image, producing the effect of perspective and relief. If truthful right-and-left monocular pictures of an object be so presented to the two eyes that the optic axes when directed to them shall converge at the same angle as when directed to the object itself, a solid image will be at once perceived. The perception of relief referred to is closely connected with the doubleness of vision which takes place when the images on corresponding portions of the two retina are not similar. But, if in place of looking at the solid object itself we look with the right and left eyes respectively at pictures of the object corresponding to those which would be formed by it on the retina of the two eyes if it were placed at a moderate distance in front of them, and these visual pictures brought into coincidence, the same conception of a solid form is generated in the mind just as if the object itself were there.

Professor Abbe, however, contended that the method by which dissimilar images are formed in the binocular microscope differs materially from that of ordinary stereoscopic vision, and that the pictures are united solely by the activity of the brain, not by the prisms which ordinarily give rise to sensations of *solidity*. This can be only partially true, as binocularity in the microscope is due to difference of projection exhibited by the different parallax displacement of the images, and also to the perception of depth imparted by the instrument.

Wheatstone was firmly convinced that his stereoscopic principle could be applied to the microscope, and he therefore applied first to Ross and then to Powell to assist him in its adaptation. But whether either of these opticians made any attempt to give effect to his wishes and suggestions is not known. In the year 1851 Professor Riddell, of America, succeeded in constructing a binocular microscope by employing two rectangular prisms behind the objective. M. Nachet also constructed a binocular with two body-tubes and a series of prisms. But neither Riddell's nor Nachet's instrument was ever brought into use; they were either too complicated or too costly.

It will be understood, however, that the binocular stereoscope combines two dissimilar pictures, while the binocular microscope simply enables the observer to look with both eyes at images which are essentially identical. Stereoscopic vision, to be effective, requires that the delineating pencil shall be equally separated, so that one portion of the admitted cone of light is conducted to one eye, and the other portion to the other eye.

Select any object lying in an inclined position, and place it in the centre of the field of view of the microscope; then, with a card held close to the object-glass, stop off alternately the right or left hand portion of the front lens: it will then appear that during each alternate change certain parts of the object will change their relative positions.

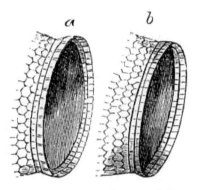

Fig. 40.—Portions of Eggs of Cimex.

To illustrate this, Fig. 40 *a*, *b* are enlarged drawings of a portion of the egg of the common bed-bug (*Cimex lecticularis*), the operculum which should cover the opening having been forced off at the time the young was hatched. The figures exactly represent the two positions that the inclined orifice will occupy when the right- and left-hand portions of the object-glass are stopped off. This object is viewed as an opaque object, and drawn under a two-thirds object-glass of about 28° aperture. If this experiment is repeated, by holding the card over the eye-piece, and stopping off alternately the right and left half of the ultimate emergent pencil, exactly the same changes and appearances will be observed in the object under view. The two different images just produced are such as are required for obtaining stereoscopic vision. It is therefore evident that if instead of bringing them confusedly together into one eye we can separate them so as to bring together *a*, *b* into the left and right eye, in the combined effect of the two projections we obtain at once all that is necessary to enable us to form a correct judgment of the solidity and distance of the several parts of the object.

Nearly all objectives from the one inch upwards of any considerable aperture give images of the object seen from a different point of view with the two opposite extremes of the margin of the cone of rays; the resulting effect is that there are a number of dissimilar perspectives of the object blended together at one and the same time on the retina. For this reason, if the object under view possesses bulk, a more accurate image will be obtained by reducing the aperture of the objective.

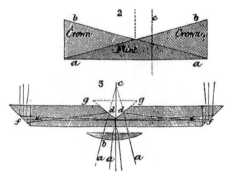

Fig. 41.

Diagram 3, Fig. 41, represents the method employed by Mr. Wenham for bringing the two eyes sufficiently close to each other to enable them both to see through the double eye-piece at the same moment. *a a a* are rays converging from the field lens of the eye-piece; after passing the eye-lens *b*, if not intercepted, they would come to a focus at *c*; but they are arrested by the inclined surfaces, *d d*, of two solid glass prisms. From the refraction of the under incident surface of the prisms, the focus of the eye-piece becomes elongated, and falls within the substance of the glass at *e*. The rays then diverge, and after being reflected by the second inclined surface *f*, emerge from the upper side of the prism, when their course is rendered still more divergent, as shown by the figure. The reflecting angle given to the prisms is 47½°, to accommodate which it is necessary to grind away the contact edges of the prisms, as represented, otherwise they prevent the extreme margins of the reflecting surfaces from coming into operation, which are seldom made quite perfect.

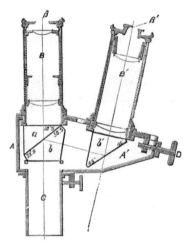

Fig. 42.—Professor Abbe's Stereoscopic Eye-pieces.

Fig. 42 represents a sectional view of Abbe's stereoscopic eye-pieces, which consist of three prisms of crown glass, *a*, *b* and *b'*, placed below the field-glass of the two eye-pieces; the tube *c* is slipped into the tube or body like an ordinary eye-piece. The two prisms *a* and *b* are united so as to form a thick plate with parallel sides, inclined to the axis at an angle of 38·5°. The cone of rays from the objective is thus divided into two parts, one being transmitted and the other reflected; that transmitted passing through *a b* and forming an image of the object in the axial eye-piece B. Adjustment for different distances between the eyes is effected by the screw placed to the right-hand side of the figure, which moves the eye-piece B', together with the prism *b'*, in a parallel direction. The tubes can also be drawn out, if greater separation is required. The special feature of this instrument is that on halving the cone of rays by turning the caps, an orthoscopic or pseudoscopic effect is produced. This double-eyed piece arrangement of Abbe's has not been at all brought into use in this country; this is partly owing to its original adaptation for use with the shorter Continental body-tube of 160 mm., and not for our 10-inch body.

The most perfect method of securing pleasing satisfactory stereoscopic vision of objects is that devised by Mr. Wenham. In his binocular microscope an equal division of the cone of rays, after passing through the objective is secured and again united in the eye-pieces, which act as one, so that each eye is furnished with an appropriate and simultaneous view of the object. The methods contrived by the earlier experimenters not only materially interfered with the definition of the objective and object, but also required expensive alterations and adaptations of the microscope, and sometimes separate stands for their employment. Mr. Wenham's invention, on the contrary, offers no such obstacle to its use, and the utility of the microscope as a *monocular* is in no way impaired either when using the higher powers.

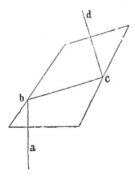

Fig. 43.

The most important improvement, then, effected by Wenham consists in the splitting up or dividing the pencil of rays proceeding from the objective by the interposition of a prism of the form shown in Fig. 43. This is placed in the body or tube of the microscope so as to interrupt only one-half (*a c*) of the pencil, the other half (*a b*) proceeding continuously to the field-glass, eye-piece, of the principal body. The interrupted half of the pencil on its entrance into the prism is subjected to very slight refraction, since its axial ray is perpendicular to the surface it meets. Within, the prism is subjected to two reflections at *b* and *c*, which send it forth again obliquely on the line *b* towards the eye-piece of the secondary body, to the left-hand side of the figure; and since at its emergence its axial ray is again perpendicular to the surface of the glass, it suffers no further refraction on passing out of the prism than on entering. By this arrangement, the image sent to the right eye is formed by rays which have passed through the left half of the objective; whilst the image sent to the left eye is formed by rays which have passed through the right half, and which have been subjective to two reflections within the prism, and passing through two surfaces of glass. The prism is held by the ends only on the sides of a small brass drawer, so that all the four polished surfaces are accessible, and should slide in so far that its edge may just reach the central line of the objective, and be drawn back against a stop, so as to clear the aperture of the same.

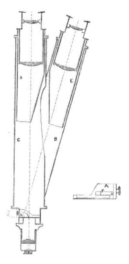

Fig. 44.—Sectional view of the Wenham Binocular.

The binocular, then (Fig. 44), consists of a small prism mounted in a brass box A, which slides into an opening immediately above the object-glass, and reflects one-half of the rays which form an image of the object, into an additional tube B, attached at an inclination to the ordinary body C. One half of the rays take the usual course with their performance unaltered; and the remainder, though reflected twice, show no loss of light or definition worthy of notice, if the prism be well made.

As the eyes of different persons are not the same distance apart, the first and most important point to observe in using the binocular is that each eye has a full and clear view of the object. This is easily tried by closing each eye alternately without moving the head, when it may be found that some adjustment is necessary by racking out the draw-tubes D, E, of the bodies by means of the small milled head near the eye-pieces; this will increase the distance of the centres; and, on the contrary, the tubes, when racked down, will suit those eyes that are nearer together.

If the prism be drawn back till stopped by the small milled head, the field of view in the inclined body is darkened, and the rays from the whole aperture of the object-glass pass into the main body as usual, neither the prism nor the additional body interfering in any way with the use of the instrument as a monocular microscope.

The prism can be withdrawn altogether for the purpose of being wiped: this should be done frequently, and very carefully, on all four surfaces, with a perfectly clean cambric or silk handkerchief or a piece of wash-leather; but no hard substance must be used. During this process the small piece of blackened cork fitted between the prism and the thick end of the brass box may be removed; but it must be carefully replaced in the same position, as it serves an important purpose in stopping out extraneous light.

As the binocular microscope gives a real and natural appearance to objects, this effect is considerably increased by employing those kinds of illumination to which the naked eye is accustomed. The most suitable are all the opaque methods where the light is thrown down upon the surface; but for those objects that are semi-transparent, as sections of bone or teeth, diatomaceæ, living aquatic animalcules, &c., the dark-field illumination by means of the parabolic reflector will give an equally good result.

For perfectly transparent illumination, it is much better to diffuse the light by placing under the object various substances, such as tissue-paper, ground glass, very thin porcelain, or a film of yellow bees' wax, run between two pieces of thin glass.

To ensure the full advantage and relief to both eyes in prolonged observations with high as well as low powers, and with objectives of large aperture, Mr. Wenham devised a compound prism for use with his binocular microscope, the body tubes of which are also made expressly to suit the prism, as extreme accuracy is necessary to bring them into proper position. The main prism somewhat resembles in form the ordinary Wenham prism. Over the first reflecting surface is placed a second smaller prism, the top plane of which is parallel with the base of the first, so that direct rays pass through without deviation, but at the two inclined surfaces of the prisms (nearly in contact) there is a partial reflection from each, which, combined, give as much light as in the direct tube. The reflected image from these two surfaces is directed up into the inclined tube as usual. A somewhat later improvement is that of Dr. Schroeder, the high power prism, by means of which the whole of the rays emanating from the objective pass through it, and the full aperture of any power is thereby effectively utilised. Furthermore, Messrs. Ross have also constructed a right- and left-hand pair of eye-pieces, which ensure greater perfection of the image. It was, in fact, noticed that the size of the image in the left-hand field glass slightly differed from that of the right when examined by the ordinary Huyghenian eye-pieces. To compensate for this difference, the left-hand eye-piece has been carefully calculated, and its focus is now so accurately adjusted that the position of each eye in observing is brought into one plane of the binocular. The pairs of the several series of eye-pieces A, B and C have also been altered, and the effect is to greatly improve the image and give increased comfort to the observer.

Dr. Carpenter, who warmly espoused the binocular, and constantly employed it in his work, very truly said of it: "The important advantages I find it to possess are in penetrating power, or focal depth, which is in every way superior to that of the monocular microscope, so that an object whose surface presents considerable inequalities is very much more distinctly seen with the former than with the latter."

This difference may in part be attributed to the practical modification in the angle of aperture of the objective, produced by the division of the cone of rays transmitted through the two halves, so that the picture or image received through each half of the objective of 60° is formed by rays diverging at an angle of only about 30°. He confesses, however, that this does not satisfactorily explain the fact that the binocular brings to the *mind's* eye the *solid* image of the object, and thus gives to the observer a good idea of its form and which could hardly be obtained by the monocular microscope. Carpenter cites in support of his views the wing of a little-known moth, *Zenzera Œsculi*, which has an undulating surface, whereon the scales are set at various angles instead of having the usual imbricated arrangement, a good object for demonstrating; the general inequality of surface and the obliquity of its scales, which are at once seen by the binocular with a completeness not obtained by the monocular instrument.

To one unaccustomed to work with the binocular the views expressed by Dr. Carpenter as to the extreme value of the instrument for ordinary work may appear somewhat exaggerated, but from my own experience, having long had in constant use a Ross-Zentmayer binocular, furnished with a special prism, constructed for working with a ⅛ dry objective or a ¹/₁₀ immersion, the perfection of picture obtained was in every case quite equal to that of the monocular microscope. The relief to the eyes can hardly be over-estimated; the slight inequality of the pencil rays may be regarded rather as a part of the welcome rest afforded when a prolonged examination is made; it certainly appears to me to equalise the slight physiological difference known to exist between the eyes of most people. If one image is seen a little clearer by the stronger eye, the weaker eye assists rather more the stereoscopic effect of the object under observation. The advantage gained by the binocular is perhaps more appreciated when opaque objects are under examination, as the eggs of insects, and the tongue of the blow-fly, specimens of mosses, lichens, parasites (vegetable and animal), whose planes and inequalities of surface require penetration, and which usually demand more time for their observation.

Fig. 45.—Swift-Stephenson's Erecting Binocular.

No variation or change of any kind proposed either in the form of the instrument or the prism has proved of sufficient value or importance to bring it into use, and therefore Wenham's instrument is scarcely likely to be superseded. It must be admitted that the improvement effected in the eye-piece form by Mr. Tolles, of Boston, U.S., is an exception to the rule laid down. It consists in mounting the prisms in a light material, vulcanite, made to fit into the monocular microscope body, thus taking the place of the ordinary eye-piece. The image transmitted by the objective is brought to a focus on the face of the first equilateral triangular prism by the intervention of an erector-eye-piece inserted beneath it. The second set of prisms have a rack and pinion movement to adjust them to any visual angle. The illumination of both fields in this eye-piece is nearly equal in brightness. Mr. Stephenson's erecting binocular (Fig. 45) has proved to be of some practical value. It has the advantage of being of equal use with high and low powers, and with little loss of definition. When used for dissecting purposes it gives an erect image of the object. It is equally useful as a working microscope, for arranging diatoms and botanical specimens of every kind. The sub-stage tube will receive a diaphragm or illuminating apparatus; the eye-pieces have a sliding adjustment for regulating the widths between eyes.

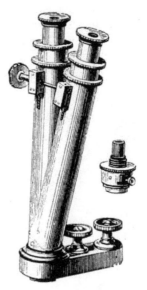

Fig. 46.—An early form of the Ross-Wenham Binocular; nose-piece and prism-holder detached.

CHAPTER II.

Simple and Compound Microscope.

Microscopes are known as simple and compound. The simple microscope may, for convenience, be divided into two classes; those used in the hand (hand magnifiers), and those provided with a stand (mounted, as it is termed) for supporting the object to be viewed, together with an adjustment for the magnifying power, and a mirror for reflecting the light through the object.

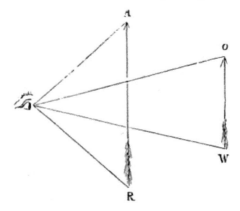

Fig. 47.—Visual Angle.

A *simple microscope*, mounted, is preferable to a single lens, being usually composed of two or more lenses separated by a small distance on a common axis; the increase of the size of an object being the angle it subtends to the eye of the observer, or the angle formed by the combination drawn from the axis of vision to the extremity of the object, as in Fig. 47. The lines drawn from the eye to a and r form an angle, which, when the distance is small, is nearly twice as large as the angle from the eye to o w, formed by lines drawn at twice the distance. This is called the angle of vision, or the visual angle. Now, the utility of a convex lens interposed between a near object and the eye consists in its reducing the divergence of the rays forming the several pencils issuing from it, so that they enter the eye in a state of moderate divergence, as if they were issuing from an object beyond the near point of distinct vision, and a well-defined image is thereby formed upon the retina. In the next Fig. (48), a double-convex lens illustrates the action of the *simple microscope*, the small arrow being the object brought under view, and the large arrow the magnified image. The rays having first passed through the lens are bent into nearly parallel lines, or pencils diverging from some point within the limits of distinct vision. Thus altered, the eye receives rays precisely as if they had emanated directly from a larger arrow placed about ten inches away from it. The difference between the real and the imaginary object represents the magnifying power of the lens. The object in this case is magnified nearly in the proportion the focal distance of the lens bears to the distance of the object when viewed by the unassisted eye; and this is due to the object being more distinctly viewed so much nearer to the eye than it otherwise could be without the lens.[18]

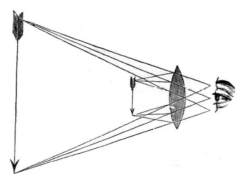

Fig. 48.—Virtual Image formed by Convex Lens.

It should be remembered that the shorter the focus and the nearer the eye the magnifying lens is placed the smaller will be the diameter of the sphere of which it forms a part, and unless its aperture be proportionally reduced, the distinctness of the image will be destroyed by the spherical and chromatic aberrations of its high curvature. Nevertheless, it was by the use of lenses so constructed that the older microscopists—of whom Leeuwenhoek was the more eminent—were enabled to do so much excellent work.

The various kinds of simple pocket lenses for the most part consist of a double-convex, or a plano-convex, or a combination of both, varying in focal length from a quarter of an inch to two inches. Sometimes they are set in pairs with a hole, a small diaphragm, cut in the piece of horn placed between them. These are extremely useful for carrying in the waistcoat pocket; to the anatomist and field botanist for examining various objects and preparations.

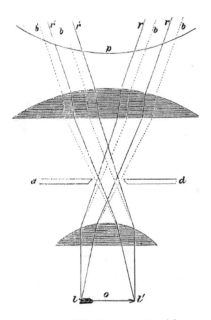

Fig. 49.—Wollaston's Doublet.

Perhaps the most important improvement effected in this form of the simple microscope was that ascribed to the celebrated Dr. Wollaston, who devised a doublet of two plano-convex lenses having their focal lengths, in the proportion of one to three, mounted with their convex side directed towards the eye of the observer, and the lens of shorter focal length next the object. The explanation given of the correction thus effected in Dr. Wollaston's doublet will be best understood on reference to the annexed diagram, *l l'*, in Fig. 49, being the object for a segment of the cornea of the eye, and *d d'* the stop or diaphragm. Now, it will be seen that each pencil of light proceeding from *l l'*, the object, is rendered excentrical by the limiting aperture or the diaphragm *d d*; consequently, they pass through the lenses on opposite sides of their common axis *o p*; thus each becomes affected by opposite errors, which to some extent balance and correct each other. To take the pencil *l*, for instance, as it enters the eye at *r b*; *r b* is bent to the right at the first lens, and to the left at the second; and as each bending alters the direction of the blue ray more than the red, and as the blue ray falls nearer the margin of the second lens, where the refraction is greater than that nearer the centre, and compensates to some extent for the greater focal length of the second lens, the blue rays will emerge very nearly parallel, and colourless to the eye. At the same time, its spherical aberration has been diminished, since the side of the pencil as it proceeds through one lens passes nearer the axis, and in the other nearer the margin.

This must be taken to apply to pencils farthest from the centre of the object. Central rays, it is obvious, would pass both lenses symmetrically, the same portions of rays occupying nearly the same relative places in both lenses. The blue ray would enter the second lens nearer its axis than the red; and being thus less refracted than the red by the second lens, some amount of compensation would take place, differing in principle, and inferior in degree, to that which is found in the excentrical pencils. In the intermediate spaces the corrections are still more imperfect and uncertain; and this explains the cause of aberrations which must of necessity exist even in the best-made doublet. It is, however, infinitely superior to a single lens, and will transmit a pencil of an angle of from 35° to 50°.

The next step towards improving the simple microscope was in relation to the eye-piece, and was effected by Holland. It consisted in substituting two lenses for the first in the doublet, and placing a stop between them and the third. The first bending of the pencils of light being effected by two lenses instead of one, produces less spherical and chromatic aberration, which are more nearly balanced or corrected at the second bending, and in the opposite direction, by the third lens.

Another form of simple lens was devised by Dr. Wollaston, the "Periscopic." This combination consists of two hemispherical lenses cemented together by their plane faces, with a stop between them to limit the aperture. A similar proposal, made by Sir David Brewster in 1820, is known as the Coddington lens,[19] shown at Fig. 50: this has a somewhat larger field, and is equally balanced in all directions, as is made evident, the pencils *a b* and *b a* passing through under precisely the same circumstances. Its spherical form has the further advantage of rendering the position in which it is held of comparatively little consequence. It is still used as a hand magnifier, although its definition is certainly not so good as that of a well-made doublet. It is usually set in a folding case, as represented in the figure, and so contrived as to be admirably adapted for the waistcoat-pocket. It is usually sold with the small *holder*, Fig. 50*a*, for holding and securing small objects during examination. Browning's Platyscopic Pocket Lens is a useful form of pocket lens for the botanist and mineralogist. Its focus is nearly three times longer than that of the Coddington, and allows of opaque objects being more easily examined; it has also a magnifying power of 15, 20, and 30 diameters.

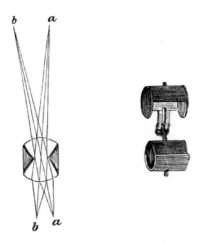

Fig. 50.—The Coddington Lens.

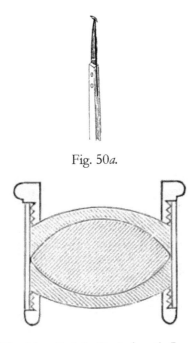

Fig. 50*a*.

Fig. 51.—Steinheil's Aplanatic Lens.

One of the best combinations of the hand or pocket form of lens is that known as *Steinheil's aplanatic lens* (Fig. 51); it consists of a bi-convex lens cemented between two concavo-convex lenses, giving a relatively long focal distance and a large flat field. The higher powers of this lens are much used for dissecting purposes. This handy magnifier appears to have suggested a later combination, the apochromatic of Zeiss. No hand lens can compare with Steinheil's "*loups*."

Fig. 52.—Simple Microscope.

When the magnifying power of a lens is considerable, or when its focal length is short, or it is wished to use it with greater precision and steadiness, it should be mounted on a short stand with a tubular stem, with rack-work focussing movement and mirror illumination. Fig. 52 represents a simple dissecting microscope, with a glass circular stage, 4½ inches in diameter, supported on three legs—a handy and useful form of instrument for many purposes.

The Compound Microscope.

The compound microscope differs from the simple, inasmuch as the image is formed by an object-glass, and further magnified by one or more lenses forming an eye-glass. For a microscope to be a compound one, its essential qualification is that it should have an object-glass or objective, and an eye-glass or eye-piece, so called because they are respectively near the object and the eye of the observer when the instrument is in use. The microscope consists of a tube or *body*, and a *stand*, an arrangement for carrying the *body*, combined with which is a *stage* for holding the object, and a *mirror* for its illumination. To the more modern instrument has been added a substage, to carry a condenser and other accessories.

The *body* of a microscope, which carries the system of magnifying lenses, must be placed at one particular distance from the object, termed the *focus*, in order that a clear image may be obtained. For the purpose of *focussing* two motions are supplied, the one for *coarse adjustment*, with lower powers; the other for higher powers, termed the *fine adjustment*. It is in this wise that the magnifying power of the compound microscope is turned to good account.

There are, however, limits to the use to which lenses can be put with advantage in the direction of magnifying the object, just as there are in varying the magnifying power of the eye-glass. Defects in either, although not first seen, that is, when the image is but moderately enlarged, are brought into prominence by greater amplification. In practice, therefore, it is found to be of advantage to vary the power by employing object-glasses of different values (foci). In whatever way increase of amplification is brought about, two things will always result from the change: the proportion of surface of the object of which an image can be formed must be diminished, and the amount of light spread over the image proportionally lessened.

In addition to the two lenses mentioned, it was found to be of considerable advantage to introduce a third lens between the object-glass and the image formed by it at eye-piece, the purport of which is to change the course of the rays (bend in the pencil) so that the image may not be found of too great a dimension for the whole to be brought within the circumference of the eye-glass. This, it will be readily seen, allows more of the object to be viewed at the same time by the *field-glass*, as the eye-piece of the microscope is termed.

Fig. 53.

Fig. 53 represents the body of an ordinary compound microscope with its triplet object-glasses; o is an object, above it is the triple achromatic object-glass, in connection with the eye-piece *e e*, *f f* the plano-convex lenses; *e e* being the eye-glass, and *f f* the field-glass, between which, at *b b*, the arrow represents the diaphragm. The course of the light is shown by three rays drawn from the centre, and three from each end of the object *o*; these rays, if not prevented by the lens *f f*, and the diaphragm *b b*, would form an image at *a a*; but here, as they meet with the lens *f f* in their passage, are converged by it at *b b*, the diaphragm at *b b* intercepting a portion of peripheral rays, permitting only those to pass that are necessary for the formation of the image, the further magnification of which is, however, here brought about by the eye-glass *e e*, precisely as if it were that of the original object under examination. It will be apparent, then, that the field-lens *f f* belongs in principle to the object-glass, or objective, taking a share in the image-forming rays, although this is taken to be a part of the eye-piece.

Evolution of the Modern Achromatic Microscope.

The great advances made in the optical arrangements of the modern microscope necessitated important changes and improvements in its several mechanical parts. Indeed, as the apertures of objectives became increased, and focal planes became correspondingly shallower, it was absolutely necessary to apply a more sensitive system of focussing than that for many years past commonly in use. The leading manufacturers at once grasped the situation, and in a short space of time the older model microscopes were discarded, and replaced by instruments better in workmanship and finish, and in every way more suitable for the student and the promotion of original scientific research.

From an early period English amateurs appear to have bestowed greater attention on the improvement of the microscope than those of any other country. Between 1820 and 1835 Tully, Pritchard, Dolland, James Smith, Andrew Ross, and Hugh Powell, encouraged by Wollaston, Brewster, Goring, Herschel, and Lister, worked out innumerable combinations of single and compound lenses to be employed as simple microscopes, explained in a previous chapter.

The theories propounded about this time for the improvement of lenses and the various combinations for amateurs were not of lasting value. Nevertheless, they were not wholly made in vain, as during the last twenty years they have indirectly borne good fruit, inasmuch as by working in another direction Professor Abbe was led to the discovery of new and better kinds of glass, by which the secondary spectrum has been so nearly eliminated, and the optical parts of the microscope so materially improved. In pursuing this subject I would not have it supposed that Continental opticians were either idle or supine. On the contrary, Oberhäuser, Fraunhofer, Chevalier, Nachet, Hartnach, and others took an active part in the work.

The compound microscope made for anatomists by the first-named optician about 1825 has not been entirely superseded. He was the first to make a rotating stage, to apply mechanism to focussing, and to introduce the system of direct push or pull of the condenser tube within the sub-stage socket. Nachet made other improvements on the Oberhäuser microscope by applying under the stage a tail-piece having a dove-tailed groove in which a slide carrying the sub-stage was moved by a stud-pin. More recently the lever movement was superseded by American opticians, who made other changes. Hartnach ultimately very much improved Oberhäuser's model, and this remains with us.

The English modern compound microscope, together with the achromatic objective, we owe to a mind teeming with scientific inventions, Joseph Jackson Lister, F.R.S., who in 1826 supplied Mr. Tully, a well-known London optician of that period, with original drawings for the important improvements in its mechanical details and accessory apparatus which followed so soon afterwards.

Among the many ingenious novelties enumerated in his published papers we find the graduated lengthening of the body-tube of the microscope; a stage-fitting for clamping and rotating the object; a subsidiary stage; a dark-well, and a large disc to incline and rotate opaque objects; a ground-glass light moderator; a live-box with bevelled flat-glass plate; an erector-eye-piece; an adapter for using Wollaston's camera lucida for microscopical drawing; and, above all, a combination of lenses to act as a condenser under the object (evidently the first approach to the present achromatic sub-stage condenser). The value of the erector-eye-piece for facilitating dissections under the microscope is not even yet sufficiently appreciated. Tully published a descriptive account of Lister's microscope, the first one of which he made, and acknowledged his indebtedness to "Mr. Lister's ingenuity and skill." Shortly afterwards Lister made known his discovery of the two aplanatic foci in a double achromatic object glass, and gave verbal directions to the three principal makers of microscopes in London, James Smith, Andrew Ross, and Hugh Powell, for the future construction of the achromatic objective, all of whom were intent on the improvement of their several models. To the latter the Society of Arts awarded, in 1832, a medal for his improved mechanical stage movements, on the "Turrell system," which Powell first constructed for Edmund Turrell. This stage was made to rotate completely on its optic axis by means of an obliquely-placed pinion acting on a bevelled rack on the inner face of the stage-ring supporting the mechanism. In 1834 Powell once more received a Society of Arts medal, "the Iris," for improvements in the application of a new form of fine adjustment.

About the same date (1835) Andrew Ross introduced the socket-carrier of the body-tube of the microscope on a strong stem, with rack bent in the middle, thus affording space for a larger stage. He likewise devised the hollow cross-bar, placed at right angles to the rack-stem, whereby he was enabled to use a new system of fine adjustment, consisting of a delicate screw with large milled head, acting by a point on the long arm of a lever, the short arm of which ends in a fork in contact with a stud placed on either side of a cylindrical sliding tube forming the nose-piece of the body-tube, and into which the objective is screwed. A spiral spring presses down the nose-piece, and against this the screw and lever act.

This appears to have been the first really sensitive focussing method applied to the nose-piece; it was, and probably is, one of the most delicate systems ever applied to the microscope. It has enjoyed a long period of popularity, and I believe it still survives in Powell and Lealand's instruments, which are very generally admitted to be of superior excellence for all purposes where extreme delicacy of focussing is an essential element.

The rival system of fine adjustment—the short lever and screw applied externally to the body-tube—known as the Lister-Jackson system, which appears to have been contrived to allow the body-tube to be supported more firmly on the limb or stem, has had its merits ably realised in the microscopes of Smith and Beck and their successors, but, except as modified by the successors of Andrew Ross (Schrœder's form), it is, I believe, admitted that it has been superseded by other modifications lately introduced into the Ross-Jackson instrument.

The year 1830 was, however, a propitious period in the history of the modern microscope, as in January of that year Mr. Lister published his epoch-making paper, "On the Improvement of the Achromatic Microscope." This appeared together with certain personal practical directions (for no man was ever more anxious to communicate his knowledge than Mr. Lister) to the before-mentioned opticians, which led up to changes lasting until 1840, when, by the efforts of this gentleman and his personal friends, "The Microscopical Society of London" came into existence. Among the more prominent members of the Society was Mr. George Jackson, a name still well known to microscopists, and who, jointly with Mr. Lister, gave us the Jackson-Lister form of microscope. This was forthwith accepted as a perfect model. Soon after Andrew Ross effected a further change in the instrument, shown in Fig. 54 in its complete form as left by this optician. It is here represented as having a bar movement, with a claw foot bolted to two uprights to carry the trunnions with the body and stage. This base, is insufficiently wide and extended to carry so large an instrument with its centre of gravity so high. The coarse adjustment bar also was rectangular, and the fine adjustment a lever, with the milled head in the middle of the bar, which involved a certain amount of tremor; withal it was an instrument of excellent workmanship, and its defects were not regarded as irremediable. Messrs. Ross, however, preferred to construct an entirely new model designed by Zentmayer, the "Ross-Jackson-Zentmayer," to which I shall refer presently. A later model, however, has to some extent taken its place, "the Histological and Bacteriological Microscope," Fig. 55.

Fig. 54.—An early Ross-Jackson Microscope.

My reference to the older form of instrument is chiefly with the view of directing attention to the sensitive focussing system, applied in the first instance to the nose-piece; now placed below the coarse adjustment. It certainly is a delicate form of fine adjustment. This model possesses other points of interest well worth preserving, which fully entitle it to occupy the prominent place given in the list of the house of Ross. In the Ross-Jackson "Histological and Bacteriological Microscope" much attention seems to have been given to eliminate certain weak points in the earlier Ross-Jackson model—defects still extant in stands of certain English and foreign makers— while retaining the more practical improvements of both constructions. Steadiness is secured by an extension of the tripod or claw-foot and the shorter and more solid uprights that sustain the whole weight of the instrument.

Fig. 55.—The Ross-Jackson Histological Microscope.

Fig. 56.—Powell and Lealand's Students' Microscope, with Amici prism arranged for oblique illumination, the Sub-stage and Condenser being detached.

The Ross-Jackson, then, survives, together with the original tripod stand of Hugh Powell's, upon which he expended all the resources of the practical optician, and applied the early principles involved in the Lister-Jackson instrument, but from different points of view. However, there is hardly a choice between one and the other in workmanship, both opticians having furnished microscopes of a typical class and very high order. The firm of Powell and Lealand have but one form of stand, from which they have never been tempted to deviate. It is supported on a true tripod base, forming a solid and substantial support to the body, which is of such a length as to give as nearly as possible the standard optical interval of 10 inches between the posterior principal focus of the objective and the anterior focus of the eye-piece; the variation in the optical tube length does not exceed a quarter of an inch with objectives of ½ inch and upwards. The arm on which the body is fixed is 5¾ inches long, which not only gives a clearance of 3½ inches from the optic axis, but also permits of the introduction of a long fine-adjustment lever.

Fig. 57.—Powell's larger No. 2 Instrument.

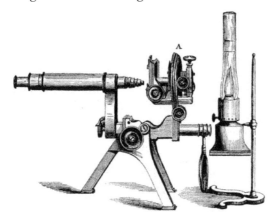

Fig. 58.—Powell and Lealand's Students' Microscope arranged for direct illumination. *A*. Secondary or Sub-stage racked up to bring the Achromatic Condenser close to the object.

The cross arm encloses the lever mechanism for the fine adjustment, as originally devised by Andrew Ross. This cross arm is longer than that used by Ross, and carries the body more forward, so as to provide radial space for the complete rotation of the stage and the optic axis, and at the same time the lever of the adjustment is lengthened, and delicacy of motion secured. The stage retains the mechanical movements invented by E. Turrell, and first applied by Hugh Powell. It also rotates completely by means of an obliquely placed pinion acting on a bevelled rack on the inner face of the stage-ring supporting the mechanism. Finders are engraved on the plates, and the main support of the stage-ring is graduated for angle measuring, a pointer on the ring marking the unit of motion in arc.

The *sub-stage* is carried by rack-work, and has rectangular centring movements, supporting an inner socket that can be rotated by rack and pinion, and which carries the several sub-stage accessories. A fine adjustment, by screw-cone and stud, is applied by means of an extra slide.

The *stage* is attached to the sheath of the stem by a special arrangement of screws, by which the rotation in the optic axis can be centred; sliding spring clips and a movable and a removable and adjustable angle-piece to hold the slides are applied on the upper surface. The body-tube is pivoted to move laterally on the top of the stem, and an adjustable steel stud beneath serves to stop the movement in the axis. Such is Powell's present instrument, and it represents the results of sixty years' steady devotion to secure perfection, and at the same time embody the best ideas of mechanical design by Andrew Ross.

A cheaper form of students' microscope is furnished by Powell and Lealand, with ¾-inch stage movement, coarse and fine adjustments to body, plane and concave mirrors, revolving diaphragm, two eye-pieces, and Lister's dark wells. These makers also adopt a gauge of tubing, the size being such that it will take in a binocular body, a Huyghenian 2 inch eye-piece having the largest field-glass possible. The tube of the sub-stage is the same size, so as to secure one gauge of tubing throughout. This allows of a Kellner or other eye-piece to be used as a condenser.

Ross's Microscopes.

Messrs. Ross have more recently introduced several changes and modifications in the Zentmayer stand, all tending to improve it, so that the Ross-Zentmayer model takes its place as a first-class microscope.

Messrs. Ross have lately manufactured other forms of microscopes; one especially designed for those commencing the study of bacteriology (Fig. 59). This instrument is one of the steadiest among those lately constructed for high-class work. The circular foot and short stout pillar support the whole instrument, and a substantial knee-joint sustains the full weight in the upright or inclined positions, while the centre of gravity is by no means disturbed, and absolute steadiness secured. The stage is of the horse-shoe form, which affords convenient space for the fingers to lift the slide up while the oil is placed in contact with the objective. The fine adjustment is extremely sensitive, working smoothly and direct; this is entirely covered, to prevent injury by dust. The micrometer screw works directly in the centre of its fittings, the milled head being divided to read to $\frac{1}{500}$ of an inch. The sub-stage is fitted with a new centring coarse and fine adjustment, so that when using high powers with the Abbe condenser accurate focus can be secured with the least amount of trouble.

Fig. 59.—Ross's "Bacteriological and Histological" Microscope.

The amount of activity shown during the last few years by opticians in the manufacture of new forms of microscopes renders it somewhat difficult to keep pace with improvements, some of which are novel. A further source of congratulation is that economy has all along been studied; so much so, that the instruments in question are within the reach of persons of moderate means. Messrs. Ross and Co. have taken a new departure in this respect, and their *"Eclipse" Microscope* is an entirely new form of stand with a ring foot. This microscope has been produced for the especial use of students, and can be purchased for a moderate sum. It will be seen at a glance (Fig. 60) how steady this form of stand must necessarily be, since the centre of gravity is secured in every direction and inclination. The body-tube carries eye-pieces, numbered, of the Continental size and optical tube-length (160 mm.), for which the object glasses are adjusted, and a draw-tube extending to eight inches.

Fig. 60.—Ross's Rigid Pattern "Eclipse" Microscope.

The fine adjustment is independent of set screws, and not subject to derangement. It is extremely sensitive and direct in action, and from its construction is equal in perfection of working to the best that can be made. Its fitting, by a new contrivance, is completely covered at all points, being thus preserved from disturbance or injury by dust.

The Eclipse is furnished with two eye-pieces, 1" and ¼" object glasses of highest excellence and large angular aperture, both adjusted to a double nose-piece, so that they focus in the same plane; and a swinging mirror and stage iris diaphragm.

In "Wenham's Radial" Microscope the chief aim has been directed towards providing a very considerable range of effects, both in altitude and azimuth. The leading principle followed throughout in the construction of this form of stand is that of facilitating the work of the microscopist and of obtaining the maximum range of oblique illumination in all directions. This is fairly well attained by causing all the movements of inclination and rotation to radiate from the object as a common centre. Thus it has been found possible to combine seven radial motions, so that when the instrument is inclined backwards, as in Fig. 61, or placed in the horizontal, as in Fig. 62 or rotated from in the brass plate, a pencil of light from a fixed source shall always reach the object and pass to the objective. The stage is made to rotate completely, and its rectangular motions are effected by milled heads acting entirely within the circumference. The sub-stage is mounted on the Zentmayer system, with two centring screws, by means of which the optic axis is secured. It is also provided with rectangular and rotating motions. The coarse adjustment is that of the Ross-Jackson form—a spiral pinion and diagonal rackwork, while the fine is on an entirely new principle designed by Dr. H. Schrœder.

Fig. 61.—Ross's Wenham Radial Microscope.

The "Ross-Zentmayer Microscope" is a thoroughly substantial and practical instrument, combining elegance of appearance with strength and firmness.

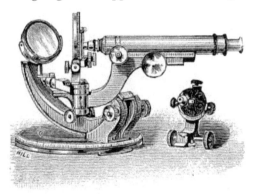

Fig. 62.—The Ross-Wenham Radial Microscope.

It is a true tripod model, consisting of a triangular base with two pillars rising from a cross-piece, which carries the trunnions. The slow movement is obtained by a second slide close behind the first; but to avoid the friction of rubbing surfaces, hardened steel rollers are inserted between them, which give a frictionless fine motion, amenable to the slightest touch of the milled-head screw situated conveniently at the back of the limb, through which a steel lever passes which actuates the slow motion slide. The body of the instrument is therefore not touched during the fine focussing, so that all lateral movement is avoided. The mechanical stage rotates axially, and the outer edge of the lower plate is divided into degrees, in order to register the angles; a simple mode of adjustment is provided for setting the centre of rotation exactly coincident with the focal point of the objective. As the plates of the stage have no screw or rackwork between them (these are placed externally), they are brought close together, thus affording the advantage of a thin substantial stage, and ensuring rigidity where most required; phosphor-bronze being used in its construction. The stage is attached to the limb by a conical stem, with a screw and clamp nut at the back, so that it can be easily removed for the substitution of a simple plate or other stage; by turning the stem in the socket the stage may be tilted sideways at any angle required. A feature in the Ross-Zentmayer stand is the swinging sub-stage and bar carrying the mirror, having its axis of rotation situated from an axial point in the plane of the object, which consequently receives the light without requiring alteration of focus in any position of the bar; by this means facilities are afforded for the resolution of objects requiring oblique light and for the development of their structure. Rays are thus obtained from any angle and indicated by the graduated circle round the top of the swing-bar, and many troublesome and expensive pieces of sub-stage apparatus dispensed with. The value of this arrangement was long ago recognised in Grubb's "Sector Stand," the movement of which was obtained in a far less efficient manner.

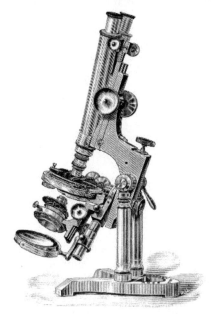

Fig. 63.—The Improved Ross-Zentmayer Model.

The base or foot of the Ross-Zentmayer instrument is made in one piece. Preference must be given to the double pillar support, as this is firmer, and allows the sub-stage to swing free while the microscope is in a vertical position, as in working with fluid preparations. The sub-stage is provided with screws for centring, and, when determined, secured by a clamping screw.

The sub-stage, with its apparatus in place, can be instantly removed, by being drawn out sideways, so as to use the mirror alone, which is a great convenience.

The mechanical movements of this instrument are perfect, and well adapted to their purpose.

Messrs. Ross have other typical forms of microscopes. Their *"New Industrial" Microscope*, for the use of farmers, horticulturists, textile and other trades, for the examination of produce and raw materials, is a surprisingly cheap one, and deserving of commendation. The great utility of microscopical research to purposes of advanced agriculture is fully recognised, and a less costly instrument than that usually supplied for more complex investigations was much needed. It is provided with a broad square stage for the purpose of receiving a glass dish to contain liquids or manifold objects, and which may be moved on the stage to bring the various particles under observation. A fitting beneath the stage carries a plate with diaphragm apertures for modifying the light, and as seeds, textile fibres, and other opaque objects form a large portion of those to be examined, this sub-stage plate has a space between the perforations which, when brought into position, provides a dark ground by preventing the passage of light from underneath. A condensing lens is, however, provided for the better lighting of opaque objects. Here we have a microscope which combines efficiency with stability, while its very simplification allows of a really good and effective instrument for the small sum of £3 3s.

Fig. 64.—Ross's "New Industrial" Microscope.

Messrs. Beck's Microscopes.

Messrs. Beck have adopted what may be termed a rival system of fine adjustment in their modern microscopes. The short lever and screw applied externally to the body tube is peculiar, I may say, to the Ross-Jackson system, and was originally devised to allow of the body tube being supported somewhat more firmly on the limb. This change had its merits fully realised in the early microscopes of Smith and Beck. To their successors, R. & J. Beck, the microscope owes much, and very many important improvements, while all their instruments and accessories are excellent examples of good workmanship and finish. In their *Pathological Microscope* we have a movement originally found in Tolles' microscopes: a vertical disc, by which the centre can be raised or depressed to correspond with the thickness of the slide. The stage can also be brought into an inverted position by rack and pinion. Their fine adjustment has been greatly improved, as we shall presently see, whereby it has been made more sensitive and delicate of adjustment. The general construction of their microscopes as a rule possess the following advantages: the stands are strong, firm, and yet not too light or too heavy, the instruments cannot alter from the position in which they are placed, as, unfortunately, will occasionally happen when joints work loose; in every position the heavier part of the stand maintains the centre of gravity.

Beck's *Pathological Microscope* (Fig. 65) is a nearly perfect instrument, furnished with a firm triangular foot, which ensures great steadiness in any position. It has a well adapted joint for placing the instrument at any angle of inclination;

coarse adjustment by spiral rack and pinion; fine adjustment by delicate lever and micrometer screw motion; rack and pinion focussing and screw centring sub-stage, made to carry all condensers and other sub-stage apparatus; mechanical stage with horizontal and vertical traversing motions. The stage is attached to the instrument by two screws and can therefore be removed at pleasure, leaving a large square flat glass stage for the culture-plate. It is likewise provided with finder divisions, and as it always fits on to the same place, any particular portion of the object can be recorded and found at any moment. The triple nose-piece is a convenient addition, and a very acceptable one to the student while diligently engaged in histological research.

Fig. 65.—Beck's Pathological Microscope, with square and removable stage.

Fig. 66.—Beck's Large "Continental Model" Microscope.

Beck's Large "Continental Model" Microscope is of superior finish. It is provided with a substantial horse-shoe foot, which gives support to the strong, well-balanced body, jointed for giving the microscope any angle of inclination. The body is provided with a draw-tube which can be racked down to the Continental measurement. It has a spiral rack and pinion coarse adjustment, and a fine adjustment of the most perfect workmanship, which will be described in detail presently. It has a large square stage with vulcanite top plate to receive culture preparations. The sub-stage is of the most approved form for centring, and carries an achromatic or Abbe condenser, iris diaphragm, &c. The double mirror can be swung out of place for direct illumination and micro-photography. Altogether, this instrument is in every way fitted for critical or class-room work.

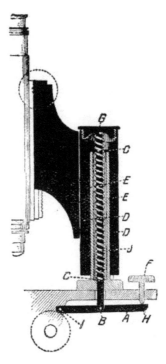

Fig. 67.—Beck's "New Fine Adjustment."

To return to the fine adjustment of this, as of other forms of Messrs. Beck's microscopes, the applied mechanism of which is believed to be one of the most sensitive and delicate character yet contrived. It is constructed as shown in the accompanying figure. The body of the instrument is supported upon the barrel D D; this barrel is accurately and smoothly fitted to the triangular core E E. At the top of barrel D D is screwed the cap G, to which is attached the rod C; this rod passes through the centre of the core E E and connects with the lever arm A at B. The action of the spring J, which is wrapped spirally around the rod C, raises the body of the microscope and holds the lever arm A tightly against the screw arm F. The slightest motion, therefore, of the screw F is communicated through the lever A and the rod C to the body of the microscope.

The great delicacy of this arrangement will be appreciated when it is noticed that the distance from I H is double the distance of I B, therefore any motion at B is only half that at H. This adjustment is one of the most delicate made for use with high powers.

Fig. 68.—Beck's National Binocular Microscope.

In the construction of Beck's Binocular National Microscope, the body is held in a sliding fitting in the limb, and is moved up or down by means of a rack and pinion motion. This constitutes the coarse focussing adjustment. The fine adjustment is effected by the milled head, which acts upon the body by means of a lever inside the limb. The upper circular surface of the stage is made of glass, and carries the object holder, which is provided with a ledge and spring to hold the object by means of the pressure of an ivory-tipped screw, so that it can be moved about readily and smoothly. The pressure of the screw is adjusted by the milled head, which permits of more or less pressure being made upon the edge of the object.

Fig. 69.—Beck's Star Microscope.

When the stage is required for other purposes the object holder can be unscrewed and removed. Beneath the stage there is a cylindrical fitting for the reception of a diaphragm, a polariser, or other apparatus. The mirror, besides swinging in a rotatory semi-circle, is made to slide up or down the stem. The microscope is supported by a firm pillar on a tripod base, and the body can be inclined at any angle convenient for working. A sub-stage can be added at any time for the reception of an achromatic condenser fitted with concentric screws—a necessity for more delicate microscopical research work.

Beck's Star Microscope is in every sense a students' or class-room instrument. It is firm and well made, with joint for inclination, large square stage, sliding coarse adjustment and fine adjustment by micrometer screw, draw-tube, iris diaphragm, double mirror on swinging crank arm, A or B eye-piece, a one-inch and quarter-inch objective, the magnifying power of which ranges from 38·5 to 183.

Fig. 70.—Beck's Binocular Dissecting Microscope.

An early binocular microscope for dissecting purposes was devised by the late Mr. R. Beck. (Fig. 70.) This took the form of a simple instrument built up on a square mahogany base A raised about four inches upon four brass supports B B, having a large circular stage plate made to revolve on a second plate, on which the object is placed and brought under the eye for dissection. On the left hand side is a milled head rack and pinion K, which acts upon a horizontal bar I for focussing the magnifying lens. Another bar, R, carries the prism P and a pair of eye-pieces arranged on the principle of M. Nachet's binocular microscope. Mr. Beck preferred to adopt Wenham's method of arranging these prisms; that is, by allowing half the cone of rays to proceed to one eye without interruption, while the other half is intercepted by the prisms and transmitted to the other eye. Beneath the stage is the ordinary mirror L. The condensing lens M is supported on a separate brass holder let into one of the supports of the stand. In practice, however, this arrangement was found inconvenient, and the microscope has therefore not been brought into general use.

Messrs. Watson's Microscopes.

Among London opticians, the various microscopes manufactured by Messrs. Watson, of Holborn, are of high finish and good workmanship. Those specially designed for the use of students possess merits of their own in their mechanical construction, and also embody a provision, as indeed do all their instruments, whether for students or more pretentious work, whereby wear and tear in their frictional parts can be compensated for by the user himself. This is effected in a simple but efficient manner. The fittings are sprung, and screws set just outside the dove-tails. The very slightest turn of the screws compresses the dove-tails, and a very large amount of wear can in this way be prevented.

I am glad to notice that Messrs. Watson have adopted certain standard sizes recommended some time ago by the Royal Microscopical Society for the diameters of eye-pieces. It would be a great advantage if the same standard became generally recognised and brought into use, since it is a matter of much importance to microscopists.

Watson's Edinburgh Students' Microscope (Fig. 71) is a thoroughly efficient one for all practical purposes, great care having been bestowed upon its smallest details, and it is not difficult to perceive the reason of its popularity among students. The tripod form of foot ensures great steadiness and firmness; the body carries the smaller 0·92 eye-piece, and with draw-tube closed is of the Continental length. The draw-tube is graduated to millimetres, and when fully extended the body measures 10 inches. The stage is provided with mechanical and rotary movements; the compound sub-stage with centring screws, rack and pinion to focus, and a means of lifting the condenser out of the optical axis when not required for use. Notwithstanding, none of the movements are at all cramped; a clear distance is maintained beneath the stage, affording plenty of room for manipulating the mirror. Both coarse and fine adjustments work with smoothness, the latter being on Watson's latest improved principle—one revolution of the milled head moves the body $\frac{1}{300}$ of an inch. The stage is of extra large size, to allow of the use of large culture-plates. No Continental stand of higher price compares with the Edinburgh microscope. Its height when placed in the vertical position is 11½ inches.

Fig. 71.—Watson's Edinburgh Students' Microscope.

Fig. 72.—Sub-stage of Edinburgh Students' Microscope. This view of underside of stage of students' instrument shows the mirror set at an angle for oblique illumination, and sub-stage turned aside.

The various sizes of oculars adopted by opticians and at present in vogue cause considerable confusion. A standard size is specially needed for students' and small microscopes. The standard long used by Continental manufacturers is 0·92 of an inch. The adoption of this size would place the eye-piece in the same position as that of the universal screw for the objective, formulated by the Royal Microscopical Society many years ago. The desirability of using standard sizes has been fully recognised by Messrs. Watson and they are now adapted to most of their microscopes. The English diameter, 1·35 of an inch, known as the "Ross" size, is retained in all their microscopes of large size.

Watson's Mechanical Draw-tube.

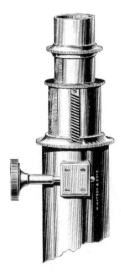

Fig. 73.—Watson's Mechanical Draw-tube (full-size).

An important feature in connection with the body-tube of Watson's Edinburgh Students' Microscope (as, indeed, in all their fully furnished instruments) is that they are provided with two draw-tubes; one moved by rack-work, the other sliding inside the body-tube. The advantage is, that the body can be made very short or extremely long, while sufficient latitude can be given to objectives corrected for either Continental or English tube-lengths, and to adjusting the same for thickness of cover-glass by variation of tube length. Should the cover-glass be thicker than that for which the objective is corrected, a shorter tube-length is necessary; if thinner, the body must be lengthened. This is effected by means of the rackwork draw-tube. The length of the body when closed is 142 millimetres (5⅝ inches), and when the two draw-tubes are extended, 305 millimetres (12 inches), being, therefore, shorter than the Continental and longer than the English tube lengths. Both draw-tubes are divided into millimetres, and on the rackwork draw-tube a double scale is engraved, reading continuously from the sliding draw-tube when fully drawn out, or giving the body length when the rackwork draw-tube alone is in use. The utility of this mechanical draw-tube is that it permits of quick manipulation with perfect results.

Fig. 74.—Watson's Histological Microscope. Stand "A."—Height, when placed vertically and tube pushed home, 9½ inches.

The inside top of the draw-tube is smaller than the remainder, the former making a fitting for the eye-piece about 1 inch long, permitting of the tube being blackened inside up to this fitting, thus minimising reflection. The end of the draw-tube has the universal screw for using the apertometer, &c.

Watson's Histological Microscope (Fig. 74) is a somewhat cheaper form of instrument, designed for the student; although of plainer construction it is quite as well made as the costlier model. It is provided with spiral rack and pinion coarse adjustment, and with this motion the greatest smoothness is preserved. There is no backlash, the teeth of the pinion never leaving the rack; so effective is it that a high power can be perfectly focussed by its means. It is also furnished with their universal pattern of fine adjustment. This can be had for £3 3s.

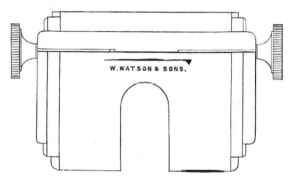

Fig. 75.—Watson's Semi-Mechanical Stage.

Messrs. Watson have among other accessories of value introduced in connection with their several microscopes a semi-mechanical stage, whereby they are enabled to reduce the cost of manufacture. Fig. 75 is an outline sketch of the same.

This stage is of the horse-shoe shape, with cut-out centre, constructed of ¼-inch brass plate, and measures over all 5¼ inches wide by 4 inches deep. Fitting on the edges of the main stage is a frame which is actuated vertically by means of a double rack and pinion from beneath, giving ¾-inch of movement, having controlling heads on either side of the stage; on the edges of this mechanical frame a sliding bar is fitted, consequently movement may be imparted either by rackwork or by hand. The mechanical movement, however is in one direction only; but as the bar carries the object, the worker can easily move the object out horizontally with the finger. The advantage of this stage is that the whole surface is perfectly flush, and the pinion heads are below its level, so that culture plates or continuous sections may be conveniently examined.

Fig. 76.—New Centring Underfitting for Microscope.

Another addition of considerable value is the centring underfitting for students' microscopes.

This fitting places in the hands of student workers a means of accurately centring the sub-stage condenser, at a low cost. It consists of the usual underfitting tube, having a flange at the top which is fitted in a box between two plates. The centring is effected by means of two screws, which press the flange against a spring, as in the ordinary sub-stage centring movement. The fitting can be adapted to any form of Messrs. Watson's and most other makers of students' microscopes.

Watson's Bacteriological Improved Van Heurck's Microscope (Fig. 77) is in every way a superior instrument, and it at once conveys a favourable impression to the practical worker. When set up for use its many convenient points—its excellence of workmanship and the precision of its movements—seem to imply its special adaptation for the bacteriological laboratory and for other high-class work where absolute reliance has to be placed in the results obtained. Every detail of the instrument is carried out in the best possible manner. The coarse adjustment is effected by means of a diagonal rack and spiral pinion, which ensures the smoothest possible motion; while the fine, the most important movement in the instrument, is made with an extra long lever, a specialty of Messrs. Watson's, and which imparts an extremely slow action: this is now one of the most delicate and reliable forms of fine adjustment. By its means the entire body is raised or lowered by means of a milled head fixed to a screw having a hardened steel point acting on a lever against a point attached to the body slide, in a dove-tailed fitting about 2½ inches long. Owing to the position of the controlling milled head on the limb, it can be worked with either hand. Another feature of importance is that, in using the fine adjustment the distance between the eye-piece and objective remains unaltered. All the frictional parts of the microscope have spring slots to the dove-tailed fittings, in which compensating screws are fitted. These are some few of the more important points, to which much thought and attention have been given. The body permits also of the use of objectives of any other optician, since its total length when the draw tubes are closed up is only 143 mm.; when extended, a total length of 320 mm. is available. By this means an ample margin is left for the correction for cover-glass thickness, whether the objective used be intended for the 160 mm. or 250 mm. tube length. The height of the microscope when placed in the vertical position is 13⅛ inches.

Fig. 77.—Watson's Improved "Van Heurck Bacteriological" Microscope.

The Stage.—A somewhat new design has been used in building this up so as to reduce vibration to a minimum. The bracket carrying the stage, instead of being screwed on to the front of the limb, as is usually done, is made in a solid casting, taking the sub-stage beneath, and passing into the joint at the top of the foot. The joint bolt goes through the whole (limb and stage bracket), rendering the limb stage and sub-stage as firm as if it were one piece; a point of considerable importance.

The mirrors, which are plain and concave, are mounted on a swing arm, so that they may be turned aside when direct illumination of the object is required. On the right hand side also there is a steel clamping bar for fixing the microscope at any angle of inclination. The tripod foot, which has superseded most other forms, is adopted. At the points of contact with the table the feet are provided with cork pads, which give increased firmness and prevent vibration to some extent.

The sub-stage is provided with a fine adjustment of similar design to that employed for the focussing of the objective. It has become needful to embody such a refinement, in order that sub-stage condensers of large aperture, such as are in constant use for critical high-power work, may be adjusted with the same facility and precision as the objective—they, in fact, require it if the best work is to be got out of them. No pains have been spared by Messrs. Watson to render it absolutely perfect.

Watson's Portable Microscope.—This instrument is similar in general detail to the Histological Microscope, but the foot, mirror stem, &c., are made to fold up in exceedingly compact form, and when set up for use the stand is perfectly rigid. Portable microscopes are, as a rule, but makeshifts. This, however, is a thoroughly sound, practical instrument and capable of best work with the highest power objectives, having good adjustments and universal size fittings throughout, so that the objectives and apparatus made for the larger instruments can be employed with it.

Fig. 78.—Watson's Portable Microscope. Height of instrument when placed vertically and racked down is 9⅜ inches.

Watson's Petrological Microscope (Fig. 79) is a modification of their Edinburgh Students' pattern, and designed specially for petrological and mineralogical work.

Fig. 79.—Students' Petrological Microscope.

A polariscope having prisms of large size is supplied with it, the analyser being fitted in the body, and the polariser in the under-stage fitting. The latter has a divided circle and a spring catch at every quarter circle. By removing the polariser and withdrawing the analyser, for which provision is made, the microscope can be used for purposes of ordinary research. A Klein's quartz plate is fitted beneath the analyser, also in the body of the microscope.

The stage, which has a glass surface, rotates concentrically, and has a divided circumferential edge reading by the verniers. The eye-piece has cross webs to the diaphragm, and when it is desired, an analyser, having a divided circle fitted with a calc-spar plate, can be used above the eye-piece, and condenser lenses attached to the polariser for stereoscopic purposes. All the fittings have the universal thread, and are interchangeable.

Fig. 80.—Swift's Histological and Physiological Microscope.

Messrs. Swift's Microscopes.

Messrs. Swift's Microscopes have a well-established reputation for quality and good workmanship, and therefore can in no way suffer by comparison when placed beside those of other opticians. One of the characteristics of Messrs. Swift's microscopes—and this runs through the whole series—is that they are all made to a *standard* gauge, so that the several parts of the instruments, as well as their accessories, are interchangeable; the cheaper forms, with those of the first quality and finish. Should the student, then, start with a No. 1 model, he can at any time build it up, as it were, with the accessories designed for a No. 3 or 4, that is, for an instrument of double the price he started with. The optical centre is preserved throughout the whole series of microscopes.

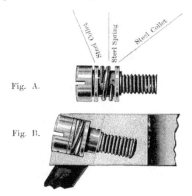

Fig. 81.—Swinging Leg Attachment of Swift & Son's Four-Legged Microscope Stand.

The tripod foot has, it appears, taken the place of some of their other forms of instruments, while their four-legged *tripod*, if it can be so designated, is a novelty of quite an unusual character.

The swing leg is attached to the framework of the tripod by the screw (Fig. A), which is provided with a powerful steel spiral spring, compressed between two steel collets when the screw is driven home, as shown in Fig. B.

The expansion of this spring will obviously take up and compensate automatically any wear and tear that is likely to occur between the bearing surfaces, and it is therefore impossible for the fitting to get loose.

Swift's Four-legged Microscope (Fig. 80) is one possessing great stability in whatever position it may be placed; the body being supported on a horse-shoe platform, from which its four legs spring, the two front legs being fixed, while the hind legs are pivoted to the platform. This arrangement of pivoting the hind legs enables the microscope to adapt itself to any uneven surface, thus keeping it always in a steady position, while it also reduces the danger of being upset by any lateral movement of an accidental nature. The feet are studded with corks, an additional aid to steadiness and fixity for microphotography. The length of the body from the ocular to the nose-piece is 6½ inches, and can be extended to 9 or 10 inches by means of the draw-tube, which has a millimetre graduation. The stage, which is of horse-shoe shape, is provided with spring clips, to which a movable mechanical stage can at any time be attached. The sub-stage partakes of two forms, one being an ordinary fitting, taking an ordinary condenser; the other, the regular rack and pinion achromatic condenser with centring adjustments. It has a diagonal rack and pinion coarse adjustment, the fine adjustment being made by micrometer screw of the finest character.

Fig. 82.—Swift's Spiral Rack and Pinion Coarse Adjustment.

Fig. 82 is intended to illustrate the advantage of the spiral rack and pinion which Messrs. Swift fit to their microscopes, in place of the ordinary conventional horizontal rack and pinion movement. The advantage will at once be seen, since there is more gearing contact between rack and pinion, thus ensuring durability and reducing loss of time or back lash to a minimum, with less wear and tear. The leaves of the pinion also roll into the teeth of the rack by degrees, ensuring a very much smoother action, which, if properly made and fitted, prevents the gearing of the two being felt by the hand whilst focussing.

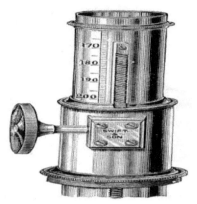

Fig. 83.—Graduated Supplementary Draw-Tube.

Fig. 83 is a supplementary draw-tube with rack and pinion movement, which can be adapted to any of Swift's microscopes in place of the ordinary draw-tube, the size of the thread being of the same diameter, so as to render all draw-tubes, as well as other parts of these instruments, interchangeable. The draw-tube being divided into millimetres can be extended from 160 to 250 millimetres. One advantage of this arrangement is that the correct adjustment of any objective with each eye-piece is easily found and recorded for future observations with the same combination.

Messrs. Swift's Three-legged Tripod Microscope (Fig. 86). In most respects the description already given of the four-legged instrument is applicable to this stand. Although of an apparently different form, it can be built up, as already explained, into one of a higher class. It is suitable in every way for histological investigations. The horse-shoe platform in this, as in the preceding stand, is extremely serviceable, as it allows the pillar of the instrument to rest firmly upon it, thus rendering the stand very rigid.

Swift's Bacteriological Microscope (Fig. 84), designed by Professor Wright, of the Army Medical School, Netley, a sufficient warranty of its excellency and perfect adaptation for bacteriological high-class work. One of the advantages connected with this microscope is the facility with which it can be adapted for either high or low power investigation, without the necessity of adding or detaching any part. The objectives, arranged on a triple nose-piece, are approximately in focus when revolved into position for immediate use, thus effecting a saving of time in changing the objective. Moreover, the nose-piece carrying the objectives is of new construction, and fitted in such a way that the entry of dust is rendered impossible.

Fig. 84.—Swift's Army Bacteriological Microscope.

Fig. 85. Under-Stage of same.

The Abbe condenser, fitted with an iris diaphragm, is mounted on an eccentric arm, so that it can readily be thrown out of the axis of the microscope when not required, without having to re-arrange the focus when again brought into position. The condenser must be turned aside when plate cultivations and preparations of unstained bacteria are being looked over for selection of colonies for mounting, in which case an arm carrying a quadrant with three apertures is brought into position in place of the condenser, the apertures being severally centred by a spring catch and used with oblique light. This arrangement, shown in Fig. 85, is seen from the under surface of the stage. The stage is sufficiently large, so that when Petrie plates are being examined at the extreme edges there is little fear of their overbalancing.

Fig. 86.—Swift's Histological Students' Microscope.

The fine adjustment is the Swift's Patent Campbell Differential Screw, which offers great facilities for delicate focussing with the highest power objectives. The stand is of the most substantial and rigid form, and thus ensures the microscope from vibration.

The under-stage of microscope (Fig. 85) is seen to be of the most approved form.

Fig. 87.—Swift's Advanced Students' Microscope.

Swift's Advanced Students' Microscope.—In this microscope (Fig. 87) we have a superior instrument for the use of the advanced student, which may be described as of high mechanical excellence, well suited for every requirement of work. The stand is the well-known tripod form of their Challenger Microscope, and admits of the instrument being placed at any angle of inclination; the body is short enough to work with objectives of Continental makers, and is provided with a draw-tube, to elongate it to the standard of 10 inches, with a diameter of $1\frac{3}{16}$ inch to take the same eye-pieces as the larger stands. The coarse adjustment is by spiral rack and pinion; the fine, by a carefully made differential screw motion for delicate focussing. The stage is of the horse-shoe pattern, to which a mechanical stage can at any time be adapted, as well as an achromatic condenser to the sub-stage seen beneath. Here the student will find the foundation for a superior instrument.

Messrs. Baker's Microscopes.

Of Messrs. Baker's larger stands, the Improved "Nelson Model," No. 2 (Fig. 88) stand is selected in preference to their more elaborate No. 1, and their simpler form, No. 3, as a high-class instrument, and one well suited for fine critical work; the former being somewhat better, only from having extra adjustments; the latter possessing no superior advantage over the "Advanced Students'" Microscope. This microscope is mounted on a solid tripod foot, which insures stability, whether placed in a vertical, horizontal, or inclined position; the front toes are slotted, so that they may be clamped to the base plate of a photo-micrographic apparatus, first introduced for photo-micrographic work, and will also be found convenient in ordinary work; as the fine adjustment milled head is placed at the bottom of the pillar, instead of at the top, the more usual place. For photo-micrographic work the advantage is that the strain of the pulley in such apparatus actuates the fine adjustment, and is less liable to cause vibration of the instrument. The advantage when the instrument is used for ordinary work lies in the fact that the weight of the hand is rested on the top of the tripod, thus admitting of steadier movement of the milled head. The fine adjustment is obtained by a "Campbell" differential screw, each revolution of which is equal to $\frac{1}{200}$ m.m. The draw-tubes being graduated in m.m., allow of either short or long tube objectives being used, closing up to 150 m.m. and extending to 280 m.m., the rack and pinion adjustment to the lower tube affording a ready means of correction for cover-glass thicknesses. The eye-piece gauge, as will be seen from its dimensions, is of large size, being the same as that adopted by Zeiss for his long tube compensating oculars; smaller eye-pieces can, however, be adapted at any time.

Fig. 88.—Baker's Improved "Nelson Model" Microscope. Dimensions.—
Height when in vertical position and body racked down, 11"; Height of stage,
$4\frac{1}{8}$"; Height of optic axis when in horizontal position, $8\frac{1}{2}$"; Spread of tripod
foot, 8 × $8\frac{1}{2}$"; Diameter of mirrors, $2\frac{3}{8}$"; Internal diameter of draw-tube,
$1\frac{3}{10}$".

The mechanical rotating stage is divided on brass to $\frac{1}{100}$ inch, with clamping
bars and stop, by which a specimen can always be brought back to a certain
position for registration. The sub-stage has rack-work focussing adjustment,
and centring screws; a fine adjustment is added, if desired. On the whole, the
instrument is suitable for special critical work, and is equally well suited for
photo-micrography.

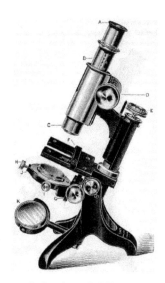

Fig. 89.—Baker's Advanced Students' Microscope. Dimensions.—Height when in vertical position and body racked down, 11¼"; Height of stage, 4¾"; Width of stage, 4"; Height of optic axis when in horizontal position, 6½"; Spread of foot, 6" × 6"; Diameter of mirrors, 1¾"; Internal diameter of draw-tube, ¹¹⁄₁₂".

Explanatory lettering of instrument: A, Huyghenian eye-piece; B, draw-tube graduated in millimetres; C, nose-piece; D, coarse adjustment; E, fine adjustment with millimetre screw; F, horse-shoe sliding stage, graduated with sliding bar in vertical and horizontal directions *for use as finder*; G, sub-stage rack and pinion screw; H and I, centring screws to sub-stage; J, carrier for condenser; K, mirror with movable arm supported on solid tripod foot.

The points of difference between this stand and the No. 1 model are that in the latter the fine adjustment carries the body only, and not the rack adjustment; the limb carrying both the body and the sub-stage is in one piece, giving, if possible, still greater rigidity; the rotation of the mechanical stage, which is divided on silver, is complete, and can be actuated by hand or rack work; it has a clamping screw and fine adjustment to sub-stage.

Baker's Advanced Students' Microscope (Fig. 89) may be described as a typical instrument, equally suitable for histological work and that of the advanced student. The intention of the maker in simplifying the adjustments and reducing the instrument in size, was to furnish a well-finished portable instrument at a moderate cost. This object has not been attained by supplying adjustments of second-rate quality, but by reducing their number to a minimum.

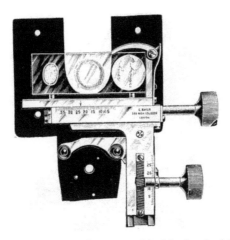

Fig. 90.—The Mayall Removable Mechanical Stage.

The tripod foot of the "Nelson Model" is replaced by a claw foot, which is in effect a tripod, as it rests on three points; it has not the same wide spread, but this, far from being a disadvantage, renders the instrument more portable. It has rack and pinion coarse and Campbell differential screw fine adjustments, draw-tube graduated in m.m., extending to 180 m.m., eye-piece gauge the same as the Continental size, large square open stage to afford the greater freedom of manipulation; sliding bar with graduations on bar and stage, which suffice for registering any given field under a low power; holes are also drilled in the stage ready to receive an attachable mechanical stage should it be thought advisable to add one at a later date. The sub-stage is of the universal size with rack-work focussing, adjustment, and centring screws.

Fig. 91.—Baker's Model Histological Microscope. Dimensions.—Height when in vertical position and body racked down, 10½"; Height of stage, 4"; Width of stage, 3½"; Height of optic axis when in horizontal position, 5¼"; Spread of foot, 5¼"; Diameter of mirrors, 1⅝"; Internal diameter of draw-tube, $^{11}/_{12}$".

Messrs. Baker have recently introduced a similar instrument with swing-out sub-stage and adjustments for compensating for wear and tear of rack. The stage is also somewhat larger from back to front.

These stands are very suitable for bacteriological research, and for amateurs wishing to obtain a stand which will carry all the apparatus they are likely to need, without going to the expense of the larger models, no better instrument could be desired.

Their "Removable Mechanical Stage" (Fig. 90) is a modification of the pattern designed by the late Mr. J. Mayall. The vertical movement is by rack and pinion, giving a range of 1⅛ inch. The horizontal motion of 1½ inch is accomplished by means of a quick-acting screw. The object is pressed tightly to the stage of the microscope by means of three points, and the whole of the mechanical part is firmly clamped by two thumb screws which can be readily removed. The stage is made to carry slides of any size less than 1¾ inch wide.

Baker's Histological Microscope (Fig. 91) is of a different type to the preceding, and is intended to represent one of medium power, affording magnification of about × 400 as a maximum. It is supplied with a diaphragm beneath the stage, without other illuminating apparatus than that of the mirror. But if the adjustments of such a stand are good, there is no reason why some form of sub-stage condenser should not be added, to make the instrument somewhat more serviceable. There is, however, a rather too limited space beneath the stage of an instrument of this kind to admit of a sub-stage condenser, consequently it cannot be said to be suitable for critical work. For all ordinary students' work this microscope is certainly available.

Fig. 92.—Rousselet's Tank Microscope.

The stand of the Model Histological Microscope has the same form of foot as the more advanced student's stand. It is somewhat lighter, and more portable, a matter of consideration in a student's microscope, which often has to be carried to and from a class-room. It is provided with rack and pinion coarse adjustment, and a Campbell differential screw fine adjustment, draw-tube, and diaphragm; the diaphragm carrier being of the universal size, so that it can be replaced by an Abbe condenser at any time. With the additions suggested, this instrument can be made equal to those of a higher standard.

Rousselet's Tank Microscope (Fig. 92), for rapidly looking over pond water and weeds, consists of a jointed arm moving parallel to the side of the tank to carry an aplanatic lens; the arm is focussed by means of rack and pinion fixed to the upright of a mahogany stand, upon which the tank can be placed, or it can be clamped directly to the tank by means of a screw. This handy form of pond microscope is made by Messrs. Baker.

Pillischer's Microscopes.

Mr. Pillischer (New Bond Street) is favourably known for the excellency of his instruments. He has lately brought out several microscopes of an improved form. His larger model, the "New International," consists of a solid, well-built, firm tripod stand of the Ross-Jackson pattern, which appears to be quite in the ascendant among London opticians; rack and pinion coarse adjustment, and a superior micrometer fine adjustment; sub-stage with centring screws and rack and pinion focussing adjustment; a new form of sliding pin-hole diaphragm and iris diaphragm; B and C eye-pieces; $\frac{5}{8}$ and $\frac{1}{7}$ objectives; Abbe condenser, N.A. $1\cdot20$; in every respect a perfect model, neatly packed in a mahogany case, for a very moderate sum. Mr. Pillischer's No. 2 (Fig. 93) "International" Microscope, being the *Army pattern* as well as the *student's*, is well adapted for clinical work. A firm tripod stand supports two dark bronze uprights, with rack and pinion coarse adjustment, e, and fine adjustment, d, the stage, i, is wide and suitable for clinical work, and large enough for dissecting upon. The whole instrument is well made; the coarse adjustment is so good that the one-eighth inch can be focussed with ease, and without using the fine adjustment.

For a few shillings extra, a mechanical stage can be added, consisting of levers, having an action similar to the movements of a parallel ruler, which is so easy of adjustment that it can be worked under the eighth-inch objective with the hands—an advantage in a clinical microscope.

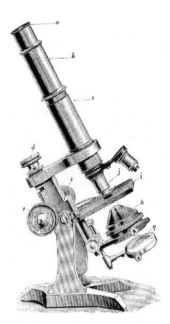

Fig. 93.—Pillischer's "International" Microscope.

The following reference letters serve to explain the general construction of the microscope (Fig. 93):—*a*, the eye-piece; *b*, the draw-tube; *c*, the sliding-tube; *d*, micrometer or fine adjustment; *e e*, the coarse adjustment; *g*, the mirror arm and mirror; *h*, sub-stage carrying Abbe condenser; *i*, the stage with spring-clips; *j*, objectives screwed into place and double nose-piece.

The "Kosmos" is Pillischer's cheaper model. The stand of this somewhat novel and original microscope is framed entirely of brass and gun-metal. The fine adjustment is very sensitive and perfectly steady, admitting of the highest immersion objectives being used. The optical parts are constructed upon principles consistent with the latest improvements. It has a claw-foot stand with a semi-circular arm, which carries the body, with sliding-tube coarse adjustment, and micrometer screw fine adjustment, with a large square stage diaphragm and mirror. The instrument is neatly packed in a mahogany box, together with the A or B eye-piece, 1-inch and ⅕-inch objectives of good defining and penetrating power, magnifying from 30 to 380 diameters, in mahogany cabinet, for the moderate sum of £5.

Pillischer's Binocular Microscope (Fig. 94) is constructed on a plan somewhat intermediate between that of Beck's and Ross's well-known patterns, and in point of finish is equal to any student's microscope in use. The semi-circular form given to the arm carrying the body increases the strength and solidity of the instrument, although it is doubtful whether it adds to its steadiness when placed in the horizontal position. The straight body rests for a great part of its length upon a parallel bar of solid brass ploughed into which is a groove for the reception of the rack attached to the body, the groove being of such a form that the rack is held firmly while the pinion glides smoothly through it. A steady, uniform motion is thus obtained, which almost renders the fine adjustment unnecessary. The binocular bodies are inclined at a smaller angle to one another than in most instruments; nevertheless, the range of motion given to the eye-pieces by the rack and pinion enables those whose eyes are widely separated to use the instrument with comfort. The prism is so well set that it illuminates both fields with equal intensity. The stage is provided with rectangular traversing movements to the extent of an inch and a quarter in each direction. The milled heads which effect these are placed on the same axis, instead of side by side, one of them—the vertical one—being repeated on the left of the stage, so that the movements may be communicated either by the right hand alone or by both hands acting in concert. The stage-plate has the ordinary vertical and rotatory motions, but to a much greater extent than usual; and the platform which carries the object is provided with a spring clip to secure the object when the stage is placed in the vertical position. A new form of sub-stage with centring screws is made to carry the Abbe achromatic condenser, diaphragm, polarising and other apparatus.

Fig. 94.—Pillischer's Binocular Microscope.

Continental Microscopes.

Continental Microscopes.—The better known among continental opticians are Zeiss, Leitz, Seibert, Reichert and Hartnack. All seem to have vied with each other in the attainment of perfection in the manufacture of the most useful forms of microscopes. The late Carl Zeiss did more for the modern microscope than either of the opticians referred to above. I therefore take a medium typical model of his from a long series of highly-finished instruments for my illustration. Zeiss's successors have of late endeavoured to perfect the mechanical details of their instruments in three or four directions, i.e., fundamental features of the stand, stage arrangements, means of focussing, and illumination.

The Stand.—The general form of the stand still partakes too much of the original sameness of type introduced by Oberhäuser, and modified and improved by Hartnack; the "Babuchin" stand being still in favour with some few makers. The greater firmness and steadiness of Zeiss's stand (Fig. 95) is secured by the horse-shoe form of foot, which, for the most part, is massive and well adapted to carry the stout uprights, which support a well-balanced, substantial body-tube and a graduated draw-tube, circular stage with a vulcanite disc, 4 inches in diameter; a sub-stage with centring arrangement for Abbe's illuminating apparatus, and iris diaphragm and other diaphragms for use when the condenser is thrown aside. The mirror is full-sized, plane and concave. The coarse adjustment is regulated by a rack and pillion movement so perfect that objectives of medium power can be focussed by it alone. The fine adjustment is made by micrometer screw, the force exercised by which is transferred to the movable body by a single contact between two hardened steel surfaces. This ensures extremely delicate and uniform motion of the body which carries the tube.

The divisions in the milled head of the screw furnish a means for the registration of the vertical movements of the tube. In the latest stands, each division corresponds to an elevation or depression of the tube in the direction of the optic axis of 0·01 mm. By this means measurements of thicknesses may be made with a considerable degree of accuracy, the upper and lower surfaces of the object being successively focussed, and the amount read off on the milled-head, by the fixed index. In doing this, care must be taken to make both adjustments by a rotation of the screw in the same direction. The thickness of an object in air is then equal to the difference between the two readings. By this means the thickness of any other substance may be measured—that, for instance, of the cover-glass of the object.

Fig. 95.—Zeiss's Medium Stand Microscope.

The medium tube-length of the microscope is 160 mm. from the attachment of the objective to the eye-piece end. The draw-tube admits of the length being increased or diminished, and this may be read off by means of the millimetre scale engraved on the tube. My description of this model also applies to the higher class microscopes, which will be found in every way well finished and adapted to biological and scientific research.

Fig. 96.—E. Leitz's Medium-sized Microscope.

E. Leitz's of Wetzlar Microscopes.—This optician publishes a series of twelve high-class forms of instruments. By preference, the horse-shoe form of stand

(Fig. 96) is adopted in the whole of this maker's models, the body being supported on a hinge joint and clamped over, and fitted with a circular revolving centred mechanical stage, attached to the ordinary stage by means of a set pin, which fixes the stage in position. By removing the screw, the stage can be detached; in this way, the stage serves for searching over large surfaces and registering the results.

Fig. 97.—Leitz's Dissecting Microscope.

The coarse adjustment is made by rack and pinion, and the fine adjustment by micrometer screw, the head of which is provided with a scale reading $\frac{1}{100}$ mm. The draw-tube is also cut and ruled to millimetre scale. The sub-stage has rack and pinion movement, and is arranged for the Abbe condenser and iris diaphragm. This is attached to the upper stage by means of a set pin, which fixes and retains it in position after perfect centring. By removing the pin, the sub-stage can be either detached or swung aside by pressing a button. In short, this microscope is in all respects well furnished and fitted with the requisite complex mechanism necessitated by modern high-class technicological work.

Leitz's students' microscope, with sliding body, micrometer screw fine adjustment, concave mirror, two eye-pieces and two objectives, ¾ inch and ⅛ inch, in mahogany case, costs £3 10s. Leitz's dissecting microscope, with a heavy foot and rests, is fitted with two aplanatic lenses, magnifying × 10, × 20 diameters.

Reichert and Seibert adhere to the same model as that of Zeiss, and therefore require only a brief notice. Their microscopes are characterised by substantial workmanship, suitable construction, and exact centring. The coarse adjustment is obtained in the usual way by rack and pinion, the fine by micrometer screws, which work easily, and are protected against wear and tear by having their working surfaces hardened. The stands of the better class instruments have micrometer screws graduated, and draw-tubes cut to millimetre scale. Their mechanical stages and sub-stages and accessories are in every way well finished; stage forceps, tests, and an assortment of cover glasses and slides being added. Their first-class microscopes are sent out in mahogany boxes.

On going through the continental makers' catalogues, it will be noticed that their well-equipped microscopes are rather more costly than that of their English *confreres*. It is understood Messrs. Baker and Watson are the constituted agents for these opticians.

Nachet's Microscope, a new form of which was first seen at the Antwerp Exhibition 1892, is very solidly built, and has all the qualities necessary for histological work. The stage rotates about the optic axis, and carries a movable slide holder. The coarse adjustment is by rack and pinion movement, the fine by the new system of micrometer screw (described in the journal of the Royal Microscopical Society of 1886), with divided head indicating the $\frac{1}{400}$ part of a mm. The plane and convex mirror is mounted on a jointed arm. The draw-tube is divided into millimetres. The illuminating system, consisting of a wide-angled Abbe condenser (N.A. 1·40) with iris diaphragm, is raised or lowered by rack and pinion screws. The iris diaphragm, being mounted on a wheel, is worked by a tangent screw, which by a very slight movement causes the aperture of the diaphragm to pass from the centre to the periphery of the condenser. Altogether the arrangement of the sub-stage is novel, and the instrument is extremely well arranged and adapted to modern requirements.

Nachet and Hartnack, of Paris, hold an almost equal rank as makers of first-class microscopes, and in point of excellence of workmanship fairy rival those of our English makers.

Fig. 98.—Nachet's Class Demonstrating Microscope.

There are very many other London and Continental makers of microscopes besides those especially mentioned, who have well-sustained reputations as opticians, and who, from want of space, I have been obliged to pass over. Messrs. Newton's Students' Microscope must be mentioned with respect. It is a good and useful instrument, has a firm stand with a reversible (rotatory) body movement, which seems to ensure steadiness when brought into the horizontal position for micro-photographic purposes. There are other opticians whose microscopes have stood the test of time—Messrs. Collins, Crouch, &c. It may, however, be taken as a well-established fact that those opticians known to manufacture the more highly-finished models also produce the more serviceable forms of students' class-room, and other microscopes.

The Bacteriological Microscope.

The microscope required for bacteriological studies should be perfect in all its parts. With regard to the choice of an instrument, it is very much a matter of price, since the most perfect is usually the most costly; I shall therefore proceed to give a typical example of the instrument in use in a bacteriological laboratory. The microscope should possess the following qualifications, all of which are absolutely necessary for the study of such minute objects as bacteria and other micro-organisms.

"The typical bacteriological microscope should be well equipped with objectives of sufficiently high magnifying power, and with a special form of illuminating apparatus; while the mechanical arrangements for focussing should act with the greatest smoothness and precision; the stage, also, should be wide enough to admit of the examination of plate cultivations."

We will consider these several points and recommendations *seriatim*, commencing with the stand.

Messrs. Watson & Sons' Van Heurck model stand so well answers the several conditions laid down by an experienced teacher of bacteriology, that I have no hesitation in presenting it to my readers as a typical instrument, one in every way worthy of the high praise it has already received from those who have worked with it, and whose judgment may be relied upon in every way. The microscope is fully described among Messrs. Watson's instruments, page 108.

The Stand.—A good firm stand is undoubtedly of the first importance for all high-class work. The steadiness of the instrument and its entire freedom from vibration depends largely upon the form of the stand. I am glad to find Dr. Crookshank in accord with me as to the Ross-Jackson model, one which, in my opinion, has not been entirely superseded by models of a more recent date. Indeed, the latest improvement effected in the Ross-Jackson form, in which attention has been given to the spreading-out of the feet, has converted it into as solid and firm a stand as Powell's; it is equally free from vibration when placed in the horizontal position.

There are, however, four different forms of stands—the tripod; the plate with double columns; the single column ending in a plate or a bent claw; and the horse shoe. The tripod stand, with cork feet, is by far the steadiest form of model. The single upright pillar support should unquestionably be condemned, as it admits of considerable vibration, and is most inconvenient for laboratory work. The heavy horse-shoe form is compact and firm, and the weight of it can hardly be considered an objection.

The Tubular Body is from eight to ten inches in length, to which is added a draw-tube with an engraved millimetre scale. By extending the draw-tube greater magnification is obtained, but since this is at the cost of definition it should hardly ever be employed in the examination of bacteria. *A Triple Nose-piece* is doubtless a convenience, saving time which is otherwise spent in replacing objectives of different magnifying powers; there is also less risk of injuring them. *Focus* should be obtained by means of a rack and pinion coarse adjustment, together with the most approved kind of fine adjustment. The sliding tube cannot be recommended, as the motion may be stiff, encouraging the use of force, which in turn may result in the objective being brought violently into contact with the specimen, thus doing injury to the lens or damage to the preparation; or it may get too loose and readily slip out of focus.

The Stage should be flat and rigid, either rectangular or circular, so long as it is sufficiently large to accommodate plate cultivation. A removable mechanical stage is of great advantage for working with high powers, as a motile bacterium can be constantly kept in view, while one hand is engaged in working the fine adjustment; it may also be employed as a finder, if engraved with a longitudinal and vertical scale, and provided with a stop. The mechanical stage must be removable, so that the stage proper may be free from any attachments when required for the examination of cultures.

Diaphragms.—The plan of using a series of separate discs of different sizes should be avoided, as they are easily lost, and bacteriological investigations may have to be made under conditions in which it is difficult to replace them. A better plan is a revolving plate with apertures of different sizes, but the most convenient form is the *iris diaphragm*.

The Sub-stage Condenser is as necessary in biological work as in the objective— in fact, the condenser and the objective should be considered as forming one piece of optical apparatus; the microscope must be regarded as incomplete without it.

It is by the *sub-stage condenser* that the rays of light are concentrated at one point, or on one particular bacterium; for the best definition it is essential that there should be mechanical arrangements for accurately centring and focussing the condenser. All this will be explained and enlarged upon under "Practical Optics."

In the historical review presented to my readers on the evolution of the modern microscope, I have for the most part relied upon my long and close association, extending over a period of upwards of half a century, with microscopy. I need hardly say I could have very much extended my remarks with pleasure and profit had space permitted, and thereby much increased the number of names of manufacturers, who have well-established reputations for the quality of their work, and whose instruments, more or less complete in design, realise the wants of students and of that large class of present-day workers engaged in microscopical pursuits to whom economy of outlay is almost a first consideration. No valid reason, however, can be assigned for splitting up, as some writers do, the several forms of microscopes into some six different classes, which implies inferiority in mechanical details or finish, whereas the difference wholly consists in luxurious appliances to save time, and in accessories for special work or original research. Before bringing these remarks to a close, it is my wish to direct the student's attention to one or two points of importance in connection with the use of the instrument, viz.: variations in body-lengths of microscopes, especially between those of English and of Continental manufacture. The *optical-standard* measurement adopted in this country for the body-tube-length is 10 inches; and for its *mechanical*, 8¾ inches. That of Continental opticians is, optical-tube-length 7·08 inches, or 180 mm.; the mechanical, 6·3 inches = to 168 mm.

Professor Abbe constructed an apochromatic immersion objective especially for the English optical tube-length of 10·6 inches (= to 270 m.m.), and mechanical tube-length somewhat less in measurement. This may be taken to mean a slight increase in the standard value of the tube, and therefore the addition of the rack-and-pinion to the draw-tube, now generally made a part of the microscope, is certainly of some practical value. This difference, however, when working with the English body-tube of 10 inches, may be discarded; it is, in fact, only where the shorter Continental body is in use, that so small a difference of tube-length exercises a disturbing effect over adjustment. Moreover, an object placed on the stage of the shorter body microscope will not be seen with the same distinctness by the draughtsman should he wish to make use of the *camera lucida*.

The *optical* tube-length of the body is measured from the back lens of the objective to the front lens or principal focus of the eye-piece; the *mechanical* tube-length from the end of nose-piece of objective to the top lens of the eye-piece.

The Hartnach Students' Model Microscope.

CHAPTER III.

Applied Optics:—Eye-pieces; Achromatic Objectives; Condensers.

It is almost unnecessary to say that the eye-piece forms a most important part of applied optics in the microscope. It is an optical combination designed to bring the pencil of rays from the objective to assist in the formation of a real or virtual image before it arrives at the eye of the observer. Greater attention has been given of late years to the improvement of the eye-piece, since flatness of field much depends upon it. Opticians have therefore sought to make it both achromatic and compensatory.

There are several forms of eye-pieces in use, some of which partake of a special character, and these will receive attention in their proper places. It is, however, customary among English opticians to denote the value of their several eye-pieces by Roman capitals, A, B, C, D, and E. Continental opticians, on the other hand, have a preference for numerals, 1, 2, 3, 4, 5 and 6, or more, and by which they are recognised.

The eye-piece in more general use is that known as the *Huyghenian* (Fig. 99); this came into use upwards of two centuries ago. It was constructed by Christian Huyghens, a Dutch philosopher and eminent man of science, secretary to William III.

It was made for the eye-piece of a telescope he constructed with his own hands, and it has been in constant use as the eye-piece of the microscope for nearly two centuries. It consists of two plano-convex lenses, with their plane surfaces turned towards the eye, and divided at a distance equal to half the sum of their focal lengths—in other words, at half the sum of the focal length of the eye-glass and of the distance from the field-glass at which an image from the object glass would be formed, a stop, or diaphragm, being placed between the two lenses for the reason about to be explained. Huyghens himself appears to have been quite unaware of the value of an eye-piece so cleverly constructed.

Fig. 99.—Huyghenian Eye-piece A, the dotted lines show position of lenses.

It was reserved for Boscovich to point out that, by this important arrangement, he had corrected a portion of the chromatic aberration incidental to the earlier form of eye-pieces. Let Fig. 100 represent the Huyghenian eye-piece of a microscope, ff being the field-glass, and $e\ e$ the eye-glass, and $l\ m\ n$ the two extreme rays of each of the three pencils emanating from the centre and ends of the object, of which, but for the field-glass, a series of coloured images would be formed from $r\ r$ to $b\ b$; those near $r\ r$ being red, those near $b\ b$ blue, and the intermediate ones green, yellow, and so on, corresponding with the colours of the prismatic Spectrum.

The effect described, that of projecting the blue image beyond the red, over-correcting the object-glass as to colour, is purposely produced; it is also seen that the images $b\ b$ and $r\ r$ are curved in the wrong direction to be seen distinctly by the convex eye-lens; this then is a further defect of the compound microscope made up of two lenses. But the field-glass, at the same time that it bends the rays and converges them to foci at $b'\ b'$ and $r'\ r'$, also reverses the curvature of the images as here shown, giving them the form best adapted for distinct vision by the eye-glass $e\ e$. The field-glass has at the same time brought the blue and red images closer together, so that they produce an almost colourless image to the eye. The chromatic aberration of lenses has been clearly explained in a previous chapter. But let it be supposed that the object-glass had not been over-corrected, that it had been perfectly achromatic; the rays would then have appeared coloured as soon as they had passed the field-glass; the blue rays of the central pencil, for example, would converge at b'', and the red rays at r'', which is just the reverse of what is required of the eye-lens; for as its blue focus is also shorter than its red, it would require that the blue image should be at r'', and the red at b''. This effect is due to over-correction of the object-glass, which removes the blue foci $b\,b$ as much beyond the red foci $r\,r$ as the sum of the distances between the red and the blue foci of the field-lens and eye-lens; so that the separation $b\,r$ is exactly taken up in passing through those two lenses, and the several colours coincide, so far as focal distance is concerned, as the rays pass the eye-lens. So that while they coincide as to distance, they differ in another respect—the blue image is rendered smaller than the red by the greater refractive power of the field-glass upon the former. In tracing the pencil l, for instance, it will be noticed that, after passing the field-glass, two sets of lines are drawn, one whole and one dotted, the former representing the red, and the latter the blue rays. This accidental effect in the Huyghenian eye-piece was pointed out by Boscovich. The separation into colours of the field-glass is like the over-correction of the object-glass—and opens the way to its complete correction. If the differently-coloured rays were kept together till they reached the eye-glass, they would still be coloured, and present coloured images to the eye. The separating effected by the field-glass causes the blue rays to fall so much nearer the centre of the eye-glass, where, owing to its spherical figure, the refractive power is less than at the margin, so that spherical error of the eye-lens may be said to constitute a nearly equal balance to the chromatic dispersion of the field-lens, and the blue and red rays l' and l'' emerge nearly parallel, presenting a fairly good definition of a single point to the eye. The same may be said of the intermediate colours of the other pencils. The eye-glass thus constructed not only brings together the images $b'\,b'$, $r'\,r'$, but it likewise has the most important effect of rendering them flatter, and assisting in the correction of chromatic and spherical aberration.

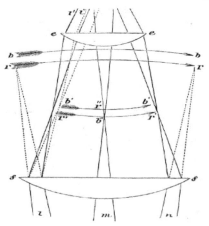

Fig. 100.—Huyghenian Eye-piece.

Fig. 101.—Ramsden's Eye-piece.

The later form of the Huyghenian eye-piece is that of the late Sir George Airy, the field-glass of which is a meniscus with the convex side turned towards the objective, and the eye-lens a crossed convex with its flatter side towards the eye. Another negative eye-piece is that known as the *Kellner*, or orthoscopic eye-piece. It consists of a bi-convex field-glass and an achromatic doublet eye-lens. This magnifies ten times, but it in no way compares with the Huyghenian in value. Neither does it afford the same flatness of field.

The *Ramsden*, or positive eye-piece, is chiefly employed as a micrometer eye-piece for the measurement of the values of magnified images. The construction of this eye-piece is shown in Fig. 101, a divided scale being cut on a strip of glass in $\frac{1}{100}$ths of an inch, every fifth of which is cut longer than the rest to facilitate the reading of the markings, and at the same time that of the image of the object, both being distinctly seen together, as in the accompanying reduced micro-photograph of blood corpuscles, Fig. 102.

The value of such measurements in reference to the real object, when once obtained; is constant for the same objective. It becomes apparent, then, that the value of the divisions seen in the eye-piece micrometer must be found with all the objectives used, and carefully tabulated.

It was Mr. Lister who first proposed to place on the stage of the microscope a divided scale of a certain value. Viewing the scale as a microscopic object, he observed how many of the divisions on the scale attached to the eye-piece corresponded with one or more of a magnified image. If, for instance, ten of those in the eye-piece correspond with one of those in the image, and if the divisions are known to be equal, then the image is ten times larger than the object, and the dimensions of the object ten times less than that indicated by the micrometer. If the divisions on the micrometer and on the magnified scale are not equal, it becomes a mere rule-of-three sum; but in general this trouble is taken by the maker of the instrument, who furnishes a table showing the value of each division of the micrometer for every object-glass with which it will be employed.

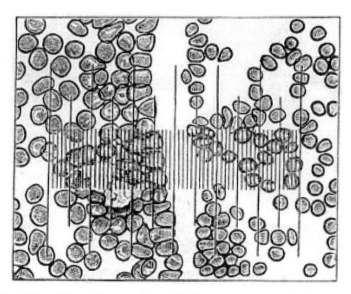

Fig. 102.—Blood Corpuscles and Micrometer, magnified 1·3500.

Mr. Jackson's simple and cheap micrometer is represented in Fig. 103. It consists of a slip of glass placed in the focus of the eye-glass, with the divisions sufficiently fine to have the value of the ten-thousandth part of an inch with the quarter-inch object-glass, and the twenty-thousandth with the eighth; at the same time the half, or even the quarter of a division may be estimated, thus affording the means of attaining considerable accuracy, and may be used to supersede the more complicated and expensive screw-micrometer, being handier to use, and not liable to derangement in inexperienced hands.

The positive eye-piece affords the best view of the micrometer, the negative of the object. The former is quite free from distortion, even to the edges of the field; but the object is slightly coloured. The latter is free from colour, and is slightly distorted at the edges. In the centre of the field, however, to the extent of half its diameter, there is no perceptible distortion, and the clearness of the definition gives a precision to the measurement which is very satisfactory.

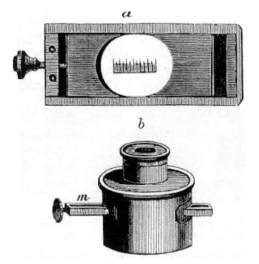

Fig. 103.—Jackson's Eye-piece Micrometer.

Short bold lines are ruled on a piece of glass, *a*, Fig. 103, to facilitate counting, the fifth is drawn longer, and the tenth still longer, as in the common rule. Very fine levigated plumbago is rubbed into the lines to render them visible; they are then covered with a piece of thin glass, cemented by Canada balsam, to prevent the plumbago from being wiped out. The slip of glass thus prepared is secured in a thin brass frame, so that it may slide freely into its place.

Slips are cut in the negative eye-piece on each side, so that the brass frame may be pressed across the field in the focus of the eye-glass, as at *m*; the cell of which should have a longer screw than usual, to admit of adjustment for different eyes. The brass frame is retained in its place by a spring within the tube of the eye-piece; and in using it the object is brought to the centre of the field by the stage movements; the coincidence between one side of it and one of the long lines is made with great accuracy by means of the small screw acting upon the slip of glass. The divisions are then read off as easily as the inches and tenths on a common rule. The operation, indeed, is nothing more than the laying of a rule across the body to be measured; and it matters not whether the object be transparent or opaque, mounted or unmounted, if its edges can be distinctly seen, its diameter can be taken.

Previously, however, to using the micrometer, the value of its divisions should be ascertained with each object-glass; the method of doing this is as follows:—

Place a slip of ruled glass on the stage; and having turned the eye-piece so that the lines on the two glasses are parallel, read off the number of divisions in the eye-piece which cover one on the stage. Repeat this process with different portions of the stage-micrometer, and if there be a difference, take the mean. Suppose the hundredth of an inch on the stage requires eighteen divisions in the eye-piece to cover it; it is plain that an inch would require eighteen hundred, and an object which occupied nine of these divisions would measure the two-hundredth of an inch. Take the instance supposed, and let the microscope be furnished with a draw-tube, marked on the side with inches and tenths. By drawing this out a short distance, the image of the stage micrometer will be expanded until one division is covered by twenty in the eye-piece. These will then have the value of two-thousandths of an inch, and the object which before measured nine will then measure ten; which, divided by 2,000, gives the decimal fraction ·005.

Enter in a table the length to which the tube is drawn out, and the number of divisions on the eye-piece micrometer equivalent to an inch on the stage; and any measurements afterwards taken with the same micrometer and object-glass may, by a short process of mental arithmetic, be reduced to the decimal parts of an inch, if not actually observed in them.

In ascertaining the value of the micrometer with a deep objective, if the hundredth of an inch on the stage occupies too much of the field, then the two-hundredth or five-hundredth should be used and the number of the divisions corresponding to that quantity be multiplied by two hundred or five hundred, as the case may be.

The micrometer should not be fitted into too deep an eye-piece, as it is essential to preserve good definition. A middle-power Kellner or Huyghenian is frequently employed; at all events, use the eye-piece of lower power rather than impair the image.

The eye-lens above the micrometer should not be of shorter focus than three-quarters of an inch, even with high-power objectives.

The Ramsden Eye-piece.—The cobweb micrometer is the most efficient piece of apparatus yet brought into use for measuring the magnified image. It is made by stretching across the field of the eye-piece two extremely fine parallel wires or cobwebs, one or both of which can be separated by the action of a micrometer screw, the trap head of which is divided into a hundred or more equal parts, which successively pass by an index as the milled head is turned, shown in Fig. 104. A portion of the field of view is cut off at right angles to the filaments by a scale formed of a thin plate of brass having notches at its edges, the distances between which correspond to the threads of the screw, every fifth notch (as in the previous case) being made deeper than the rest, to make the work of enumeration easier. The number of entire divisions on the scale shows then how many complete turns of the screw have been made in the separation of the wires, while the number of index points on the milled head shows the value to the fraction of a turn, that may have been made in addition. A screw with one hundred threads to the inch is that usually employed; this gives to each division in the scale in the eye-piece the value of $\frac{1}{100}$th of an inch. The edge of the milled head is also divided into the same number of parts.

Micrometer scale to drop into Eye-piece.

Fig. 104.—Ramsden Screw Micrometer Eye-piece.

In Watson's Ramsden screw micrometer, Fig. 104, the micrometer scale (seen detached) is ruled on a circular piece of glass, and this, by unscrewing the top, is dropped into its place, and one of the wires, both being fixed, is set a little to the side of the field, the teeth of the screw being cut to $\frac{1}{100}$ths, and the drum giving the fractional space between the teeth to $\frac{1}{100}$ths, so that the $\frac{1}{10000}$th of an inch can be read off. This micrometer eye-piece is constructed entirely of aluminium, a decided advantage, being so much lighter than brass to handle.

In the screw micrometer of other makers, other modifications are found. An iris diaphragm being placed below the web to suit the power of the eye-piece employed, a guiding line at right angles to the web is sometimes added. Care should be taken to see that when the movable web coincides exactly with the fixed web, the indicator on the graduated head stands at zero.

The Compensating Eye-piece.—The very important improvements effected in the construction of the objective naturally led up to an equally useful change for the better in the eye-piece.

All objectives of wide aperture, from the curvature of their hemispherical front lenses, show a certain amount of colour defect in the extra-axial portion of the field, even if perfectly achromatic in the centre. Whether an image be directly projected by the objective, or whether it be examined with an aplanatic eye-piece, colour fringes may be detected, possibly in an increasing degree towards the periphery. This residual chromatic aberration has at length been very nearly eliminated by the aid of the compensating eye-piece.

The construction of compensating eye-pieces is somewhat remarkable, since they have an equivalent error in an opposite direction—that is, the image formed by the red rays is greater than that corresponding to the blue rays; consequently, eye-pieces so constructed serve to compensate for the unequal magnification produced by different coloured rays, and images appear free from colour up to the margin of the field.

Zeiss's compensating eye-pieces are so arranged that the lower focal points of each series lie in the same plane when inserted in the body-tube of the microscope; no alteration of focus is therefore required on changing one eye-piece for another. This of itself is not only an advantage but also a saving of time, while the distance between the upper focal point of the objective and the lower one of the eye-piece, which is the determining element of magnification, remains constant.

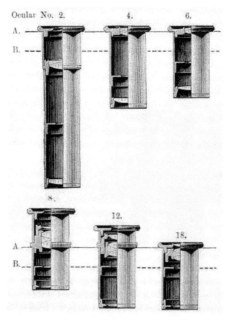

Fig. 105.—A sectional view of Zeiss's Compensating series of Eye-pieces, ½ the full size.

A.—Plane of the upper edge of the tube.

B.—Lower focal plane of eye-pieces, with their lenses *in situ*.

The ordinary working eye-pieces, Huyghenian and others, commencing with a magnification of four diameters, are so constructed that they can be conveniently used, as we are accustomed to use them in England, with high powers, Zeiss's Nos. 12 and 18 compensating eye-pieces being adapted for use with his lower power apochromatic lenses of 16 and 8 mm. The numbering of the eye-pieces is carried out on the plan originally proposed by Professor Abbe—that is, the number denotes how many times an eye-piece, when employed with a given tube-length, increases the initial magnifying power of the objective, and at the same time furnishes figures for their rational enumeration. It is on this basis that the German compensating eye-pieces have been arranged in series, and in agreement with their magnifying power and distinctive numberings of 2, 4, 6, 8, 12, 18. Of these several eye-pieces, 12 is found to be the most useful. The magnification obtained by combining a compensating eye-piece with any apochromatic objective is found by multiplying its number by the initial magnification of the objective, as given in the following proof:—An objective of 3·0 mm. focus, for example, gives in itself a magnification of 83·3 (calculated, for the conventional distance of vision, 250 mm.); eye-piece 12 therefore gives with this objective a magnification of $12 \times 83\cdot3 = 1000$ diameters. The classification, however, of these eye-pieces, as furnished by Abbe, is dependent upon increase in the total magnifying power of the microscope obtained by means of the eye-piece as compared with that given by the objective alone. The numbering, then, denotes how many times an eye-piece increases the magnifying power of the objective when used with a given body-tube; the proper measure of the eye-piece magnification; and, at the same time, the figures for rational enumeration.

Fig. 106.—B and C Achromatic Eye-pieces.

Compensating eye-pieces have been introduced for the correction of certain errors in high-power objectives—those made with hemispherical fronts. All such lenses, whether apochromatic or not, are greatly improved by the compensating eye-piece, but the dry objective and the lower powers are certainly deteriorated. The lower power compensating eye-pieces are Huyghenian, the higher are combinations, with no field-lens, and therefore in working act as a single or positive eye-piece. This is of importance to those who work with low powers—the older forms of objectives.

Messrs. Watson and Swift have adopted a new formula for their series of *achromatic eye-pieces*, whereby their magnification and flatness of field are improved. These also bear a constant ratio to the initial power of their objectives.

The compensating eye-pieces of these makers are constructed on the same principle as those of Zeiss's for the correction of errors of colour in the marginal portion of the field, and consequently are in every way as effective as those of Continental manufacture. Figs. 106, 107, and 108 show in dotted outline the form and position of the several lenses combined in these eye-pieces.

Projection Eye-pieces are chiefly used in micro-photography, and for screen demonstrations. The cap of this eye-piece is provided with a spiral adjustment for focussing, the diaphragm being placed in front of the eye-lens, an essential arrangement for obtaining an accurate focus. The ring seen below the cap, Fig. 108, is graduated so that the rotation for distance of screen may be carefully recorded.

Fig. 107.—The Compensating Eye-piece.

Fig. 108.—Projection Eye-piece.

Schmidt's goniometer positive eye-piece, for measuring the angles of crystals, is so arranged as to be easily rotated within a large and accurately graduated circle. In the focus of the eye-piece a single cobweb is drawn across, and to the upper part is attached a vernier. The crystals being placed in the field of the microscope, care being taken that they lie *perfectly flat*, the vernier is brought to zero, and then the whole apparatus turned until the line is parallel with one face of the crystal; the frame-work bearing the cobweb, with the vernier, is now rotated until the cobweb becomes parallel with the next face of the crystal, and the number of degrees which it has traversed may then be accurately read off.

Goniometer.—If a higher degree of precision is required, then, the double-refracting goniometer invented by the late Dr. Leeson must be substituted. With this goniometer (Fig. 109) the angles of crystals, whether microscopic or otherwise, can be measured. It has removed the earlier difficulties incident to similar instruments formerly in use. Among other advantages, it is capable of measuring opaque and even imperfect crystals, beside microscopic crystals and those in the interior of other transparent media. It is equally applicable to the largest crystals, and will measure angles without removing the crystal from a specimen, provided only the whole is placed on a suitable adjusting stage. The value of the goniometer depends on the application of a doubly refracting prism, either of Iceland spar or of quartz, cut of such a thickness as will partially separate the two images of the angle it is proposed to measure.

Dr. Leeson strongly insisted on the importance of the microscope in the examination of the planes of crystals subjected to measurement, as obliquity in many cases arises from not only conchoidal fractures, but also from imperfect laminæ elevating one portion of a plane, and yet allowing a very tolerable reflection when measured by the double refracting goniometer.

Fig. 109.—Leeson's Goniometer.

Microscopes for crystallographic and petrological research are now specially constructed for measuring the angles of crystals.

Erector eye-pieces and erecting prisms are employed for the purpose of causing the image presented to the eye to correspond with that of the object. They are also helpful in making minute dissections of structure; the loss of light, however, by sending it through two additional surfaces is a drawback, and impairs the sharpness of the image. Nachet designed an extremely ingenious arrangement whereby the inverted image became erect; he adapted a simple rectangular prism to the eye-piece. The obliquity which a prism gives to the visual rays when the microscope is used in the erect position, as for dissecting, is an advantage, as it brings the image to the eye at an angle very nearly corresponding to that of the inclined position in which the microscope is ordinarily used.

The Achromatic Objective.

Fig. 110.—Pan-aplanatic Achromatic Objectives.

The Achromatic Objective, of all the optical and mechanical adjuncts to the microscope, is in every way the most necessary, as well as the most important. The ideal of perfection aimed at by the optician is a combination of lenses that shall produce a perfect image—that is, one absolutely perfect in definition and almost free from colour. The method resorted to for the elimination of spherical and chromatic aberration in the lens has been fully explained in a former chapter. It will now be my endeavour to show the progressive stages of achromatism and evolution of the microscope throughout the present century.

It is almost as difficult to assign the date of the earliest application of achromatism to the microscope as to that of the inception and many modifications of the instrument in past ages; indeed, the question of priority in every step taken in its improvement has been the subject of controversy.

Among the earlier workers in the first decade of this century will be found the name of Bernardo Marzoni, who was curator of the Physical Laboratory of the Lyceum of Brescia. He, an amateur optician, it has come to light, in 1808 constructed an achromatic objective, and exhibited it at Milan in 1811, when he obtained the award of a silver medal for its merits, under the authority of the "Institute Reale delli Scienzo." Through the good offices of the late Mr. John Mayall one of Marzoni's objectives, which had been carefully preserved, was presented to the Royal Microscopical Society of London in 1890.[20] This objective is a cemented combination, with the plane side of the flint-lens presented to the object. This was an improvement of a practical kind, and of which Chevalier subsequently availed himself. In 1823 Selligue, a French optician, is credited with having first suggested the plan of combining two, three, or four plano-convex achromatic doublets of similar foci, one above the other, to increase the power and the aperture of the microscope. Fresnel, who reported upon this invention, preferred on the whole Adam's arrangement, because it gave a larger field. Selligue subsequently improved his objective by placing a small diaphragm between the mirror and the object.

In this country, Tully was induced by Dr. Goring to work at the achromatic objective, and his first efforts were attended with a success quite equal to that of Chevalier's. Lister on examining these lenses said:—"The French optician knows nothing of the value of aperture, but he has shown us that fine performance is not confined to triple objectives." Amici, the amateur optician of Modena, visited this country in 1827 and brought his achromatic microscope and objectives, which were seen to give increase of aperture by combining doublets with triplets. The most lasting improvement in the achromatic objective was that of Joseph Jackson Lister, F.R.S., the father of Lord Lister, and one of the founders of the Royal Microscopical Society of London.

Lister's discoveries at this period (1829) in the history of the optics of the microscope were of greater importance than they have been represented to be. That he was an enthusiast is manifest, for, being unable to find an optician to carry out his formula for grinding lenses, he at once set to work to grind his own, and in a short time was able to make a lens which was said to be the best of the day.

Lister, in a paper contributed to the proceedings of the Royal Society the same year, pointed out how the aberrations of one doublet could be neutralised by a second. He further demonstrated that the flint lens should be a plano-concave joined by a permanent cement to the convex crown-glass. The first condition, he states, "obviates the risk of error in centring the two curves, and the second diminishes by one half the loss of light from reflection, which is very great at the numerous surfaces of every combination." These two conditions then—that the flint lens shall be plano-concave, and that it shall be joined by some cement (Canada balsam) to the convex—may be taken as the basis for the microscopic objective, provided they can be reconciled with the correction of spherical and chromatic aberration of a large pencil.

Andrew Ross was not slow to perceive the value of Lister's suggestions and in 1831 he had constructed an object-glass on the lines laid down by Lister, Fig. 112; *a a'* representing the anterior pair, *m* the middle, and *p* the posterior, the three sets combined forming the achromatic objective, consisting of three pairs of lenses, a double-convex crown-glass, and a plano-concave of flint.

Fig. 111.—Lister's double-convex crown and plano-concave flint cemented combination.

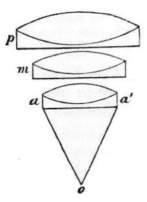

Fig. 112.—Andrew Ross's ¼-inch Objective.

Lister proposed other combinations, and himself made an object-glass consisting of a meniscus pair with a triple middle, and a back plano-convex doublet. This had a working distance of ·11 and proved to be so great a success that other opticians—Hugh Powell, 1834; James Smith, 1839—made objectives after the same formula.

The publication of Lister's data proved of value in another direction: it stimulated opticians to apply themselves to the further improvement of the achromatic objective. Andrew Ross was one of the more earnest workers in giving effect to Lister's principles and a short time afterwards found that a triple combination, with the lenses separated by short intervals, gave better results. In the accompanying diagram the changes made in the combination of the objective from 1831, and extending over a period of about twenty years from this date, are shown.

Each objective, from the ½-inch to the ¹⁄₁₂-inch, is seen to be built up of at least six or eight different fronts, the back combinations being a triplet formed of two double-convex lenses of crown glass with an intermediary double concave lens of flint-glass.

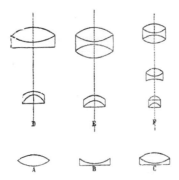

Fig. 113.—Combinations of Early Dry Objectives.

- 143 -

A, Double-convex lens; *B*, Plano-concave; *C*, Bi-convex and plano-concave united; shown in their various combinations, as at *D*, form the 3-in., 2-in. or 1½-in.; at *E*, 1-in. and ⅔-in.; and at *F*, the ½-in., ⁴⁄₁₀-in., ¼-in. and ¹⁄₂₅-in. objectives.

Combination *D* was for many years known as the Norfolk Objective.

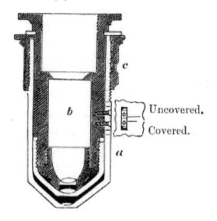

Fig. 114.—Lister's CorrectionCollar, (in section).

No sooner had Ross constructed ¼-inch achromatic objectives on Lister's formula than he discovered an error which had hitherto escaped attention, viz., that the thinnest cover-glass of an object produced a considerable amount of refractive disturbance. A marked difference was observed in the image when viewed with or without a cover-glass. This difficulty was first met by the addition of a draw-tube to the microscope body. But as this also impaired the image, Lister overcame the difficulty by mounting the front lens of the objective in a separate tube made to fit over a second tube carrying the two pairs of lenses. This arrangement led up to his invention of the *screw-collar adjustment*, the mechanism for applying which is shown in Fig. 114. The anterior lens *a* at the end of the tube is enclosed in a brass-piece *b* containing the combination; the tube *a*, holding the lens nearest the object, is then made to move up or down the cylinder *b*, thus varying the distance, according to the thickness of the glass covering the object, by turning the screw ring *c*, thus causing the one tube to slide over the other, and clamping them together when properly adjusted. An aperture is made in the tube *a*, within which is seen a mark engraved on the cylinder, on the edge of which are two marks, a longer and a shorter, engraved upon the tube. When the mark on the cylinder coincides with the longer mark on the tube, the adjustment is made for an uncovered object; and when the coincidence is with the shorter mark, the proper distance is obtained to balance the aberrations produced by a cover-glass the hundredth of an inch thick; such glass covers are now supplied. The adjustment should be tested experimentally by moving the milled edge which separates or closes the combinations, and at the same time using the fine adjusting screw of the microscope. The difficulty associated with the cover-glass of old has, by the introduction of the homogeneous immersion system, been very nearly eliminated. There still remains, however, a disturbing amount of residual colour aberration in the achromatic dry objective, and for the correction of which Zeiss proposed mounting the several lenses on a method somewhat different to that so long in use in this country. Fig. 115 shows an objective in which the screw-collar ring *b b* is made to adjust the exact distance between the two back lenses placed at *a a*. The value of the screw-collar is not questioned. It is difficult to obtain at all times cover-glasses of a perfectly uniform thickness; they will vary, and therefore perfect definition must be obtained, as heretofore, by adjusting for each separate preparation while the object is under examination.

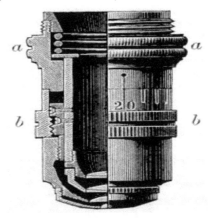

Fig. 115.—The Continental Screw-collar Adjustment.

As early as 1842 the excellence of Andrew Ross's achromatic objectives were acknowledged, and his formula for their construction was generally followed. No doubt many of these early objectives of his manufacture are still regarded as treasures. I possess a ½-inch and a ¼-inch, which I believe to be comparable with any achromatic objectives of the same apertures of the present day. These I have always found most serviceable for histological work.

In 1850 Mr. Wenham produced an achromatic objective of considerable achromatic value. This consisted of a single hemispherical front combination, shown in the accompanying enlarged diagram, Fig. 116. Wenham's formula seems to have been generally adopted by Continental opticians, who sold these lenses at a reduction of price. In Paris, Prazmowski and Hartnack—I have had one of Hartnack's earliest immersions in use for many years—brought this form of objective to greater perfection, and in 1867 Powell and Lealand adopted the single front combination system in their early water-immersion objective, whereby the focal distance was said to be "practically a constant quantity, while reduction of aperture by making the front lens thinner ensures a much greater working distance without affecting the aberrations, since the first refraction takes place at the posterior or curved surface of the front lens, the removal of any portion of thickness at the anterior or plane surface simply cuts off zones of peripheral rays without altering the distance—any space being filled by the homogeneous immersion fluid, or by an extra thickness of cover-glass."[21]

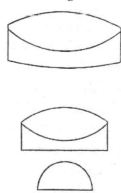

Fig. 116.—A Single Front Combination formulated by Wenham for Messrs. Ross (enlarged).

Great improvements were brought about by R. B. Tolles, of Boston, 1874, in the objective, as well as in the optical and mechanical parts of the microscope, most of which, however, must be ascribed to the criticisms and suggestions of amateur workers skilled in the exhibition of test-objects—the late Dr. Woodward of Washington, for example, whose series of photographs of the more difficult frustules of diatoms have rarely been surpassed. Such results were due to improvements made in the optical part of the microscope at his suggestion. He came to the conclusion, arrived at about the same time by mathematical scientists, that increase of power in the microscope was only possible in two directions, the qualitative and the quantitative.

It was now that microscopists turned to the late Professor Abbe for assistance in perfecting the objective in the dioptric direction. This, he pointed out, must be looked for in further improvements in the art of glass-making.

A series of experiments ultimately brought to light a mineral substance, *Fluorite*, which, when combined in the proper proportion, one part to two of German crown and flint glass, was found to have the qualities looked for, and to possess different relations of a dispersive and refractive power. From Professor Abbe's researches, begun in 1876, we have had the aperture of the objective greatly enlarged, and the homogeneous system brought into general use.

Previous to this date the best made objective merely approximated to colour correction. Undoubtedly the chief object to be obtained was the removal or diminution of the secondary colour aberration. This, together with other residual errors Abbe pointed out in 1880, led to the improvement of the optical quality of the glass used in the manufacture of all optical instruments, the chief difficulties being surmounted in the Jena glass factory, whereby a complete revolution was effected in the microscopic objective. The apochromatic glasses of Zeiss, Powell, Beck, Ross, Watson, Swift, and other makers, in which the secondary spectrum has been totally eliminated, or only a negligible tertiary spectrum remains—that is to say, the objectives of these makers—are now corrected for three spectrum rays, and not two, as in the older objectives; and only those who look forward for making further discoveries in the intimate structure of bacilli or for resolving the finest diatom markings can be said to fully appreciate the importance and value of the investigations of the late Professor Abbe, and which have, so to speak, entirely changed old empirical views as to the value of high aperture, and demonstrated that high amplification, unless associated by proportionally high aperture, necessarily produces untrue images of minute structures. It was he also who introduced a practically perfect system of estimating apertures, known as the "numerical aperture notation," by which not only can an accurate comparison be made of the relative apertures of any series of objectives, whether dry or immersion, but their resolving power under the various conditions of the kind of light employed. Their penetrating power and their illuminating power can now be estimated with mathematical exactness.

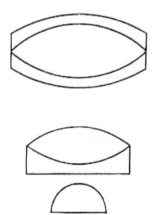

Fig. 117.—Diagram of an Apochromatic Combination.

The practical advantages, then, secured by the adoption of the homogeneous system were, on the whole, greater than any before made or believed to be possible, and when taken into account in connection with the improvement of the eye-piece (also due to Abbe), almost perfect achromatism and homogeneity between objective, object, and eye-piece is secured, together with a sharp definition of the image over the whole visual field. These, with an increase of working distance between the object and the objective, and other important results, have been placed within the reach of the microscopist by men of science, and the outcome is the general adoption of the homogeneous system, termed by Carl Zeiss, a fellow-worker with Abbe, the[22] apochromatic system of constructing objectives.

Relative Merits of the English and German Objectives.

As to the relative merits of German-made objectives, no superiority can be claimed for them over those made by English opticians.

The Continental form of the $\frac{1}{12}$-inch oil-immersion objective, shown in Fig. 118, on the scale of 6 to 1, consists of four systems of lenses, namely, the front, a deep hemispherical crown lens of high refractive index; the second front of the system, an achromatic lens of such a form that it gathers the light from the hemispherical front; the middle lens, a single meniscus; and the back an achromatised lens, the second front of the back being connected in such a way as to compensate for the spherical and chromatic aberrations of the front lens.

The first homogeneous immersion objective which came under my observation was manufactured in the well-known Jena workshop of Carl Zeiss, December, 1877. This had a very considerable increase of *numerical aperture*, upwards of 50 per cent.; a clear gain, as an oil angle of even 110° proved to be of greater value than an angle of 180° in air, while the resolving power of the objective was increased in like proportion. There does not at present appear to be a bar to the construction of objectives of yet higher power, with increase of aperture. The available course open in this direction is the further discovery of another vitreous material and a suitable immersion fluid with an index of $1 \cdot 8$ or $1 \cdot 9$, and glass with a corresponding index, so as to ensure homogeneity of the combination. Zeiss asserts that in the more difficult departments of microscopical research the apochromatic lenses will supplant the older objectives, yet there are many problems in microscopy awaiting solution which do not demand the highest attainable degree of perfection in the objective, and in the majority of cases the older achromatic objective is all that is needful, provided it is good of its kind. The achromatic objectives and eye-pieces of the older type have still an advantage, as, owing to their simpler construction, really good lenses of the class required can be purchased at considerably lower prices than the objectives of the new series.

These, from being more complicated in construction, involve a greater amount of skilled manual labour.

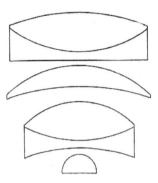

Fig. 118.—The Continental $\frac{1}{12}$-in. Oil-immersion Combination (enlarged diagram).

The German glasses of to-day afford satisfactory evidence both of skill and workmanship displayed in their production. Their cost is greater, then, for the reason given, as will be seen on reference to Continental catalogues. The dry series of objectives cost somewhat less, a $\frac{1}{2}$-inch (numerical aperture 0·30) can be had for £1 10s., and a $\frac{1}{6}$-inch (numerical aperture 0·65) for £2. On the other hand, the apochromatic series rapidly increase in price as the numerical aperture approaches the limit of numerical aperture 0·40. The best of Zeiss's series are the 12 mm. ($\frac{1}{2}$-inch) and the 3 mm. ($\frac{1}{8}$-inch), numerical aperture 1·4, both of which possess the optical capacity assigned to them. These objectives are undoubtedly the finest to be met with in the workshop of any optician. Achromatic objectives of Continental manufacture have been as much improved as those of English make by the introduction of the newer varieties of glass, as already explained, while a new nomenclature has sprung up in consequence. We now have semi-apochromatic and parachromatic. The German opticians have followed Zeiss's lead, since almost the same series of objectives are given in the catalogues of Leitz, Reichert, and Seibert, while the quality of both dry and immersion objectives is found to be much the same. The low price of Reichert's immersion objectives should be noted, as their performance is quite perfect. A $\frac{1}{12}$-inch (numerical aperture 1·30) of Leitz's, with which I have worked at *bacteria*, has given me much satisfaction; supplied by Watson and Baker at £5. A $\frac{1}{12}$-inch dry objective by the same maker (numerical aperture 0·87) costs £3, and a water immersion $\frac{1}{12}$-inch (numerical aperture 1·10) £3 5s. Leitz reminds me that it requires a good lens of from six to seven hundred magnifying power for the examination of bacteria. For this reason he has constructed a new form of lens, a $\frac{1}{10}$-inch oil-immersion of 2·5 mm. focus, for the purpose of adding to the resources of bacteriology. This lens necessarily has a lower magnification than his former $\frac{1}{12}$-inch oil-lens, but as it is less costly to manufacture it is sold at a smaller price. The before-mentioned $\frac{1}{12}$-inch, with a No. 3 compensating eye-piece, gives a magnification of over seven hundred or eight hundred diameters. To secure the best results in using the higher powers of Leitz's, from No. 5 upwards, a cover-glass of 0·17 mm. in thickness should be used, and care taken to make the length of the draw-tube equal to 170 mm. This length of tube should be adhered to in the use of this optician's oil-immersion lenses. If the microscope be provided with a nose-piece, the draw-tube should be drawn out to 160 mm.; in its absence it should be set at 170 mm., a deviation of 10 mm. or more from the correct tube-length deteriorates from the value of Leitz's oil-immersion objectives as of other opticians. It is suggested that the German apochromatic combination of three cemented lenses is that adopted by Steinheil long before, in the construction of his well-known hand-magnifier (see page 77, Fig. 51). Zeiss's 3 mm. objective has a triple front, balanced by two triple backs—in all nine lenses—a somewhat amplified diagram of which is represented in Fig. 118. The formula for this combination was furnished by Tolles, of Boston, America, and it at once secured increase of aperture (the value of this optician's many contributions to microscopy has since his death been generally acknowledged). The metrical equivalent focus assigned by Zeiss to his series of dry achromatic objectives is given in somewhat ambiguous terms, which tend to confuse rather than classify them; for instance, two lenses of the same aperture—24 mm. and 16 mm.—corresponding to the English 1-inch and $\frac{2}{3}$-inch, each have assigned to them an aperture of 0·30; a 12 mm. and 8 mm., corresponding to the English $\frac{1}{2}$-inch and $\frac{1}{3}$-inch, have an aperture of 0·65; while a 6 mm. = $\frac{1}{4}$-inch, and a 4 mm. = $\frac{1}{4}$-inch and $\frac{1}{6}$-inch, have each an aperture of 0·95.

Nachet exhibited at the Antwerp Exhibition a fine $\frac{1}{10}$-inch oil-immersion, which was highly praised by the jurors.

It is necessary, to make the fact perfectly clear, that dry and immersion lenses having the same angular aperture have also a similar defining power. The pencil of rays, however, differs in intensity and density as the rays emerging from the cover-glass of the object into air are very considerably deflected, and the cone suffers a corresponding loss of brightness. On this important point, then, I believe it will prove of value to interpolate a clear and full exposition of the change brought about by the cover-glass.

It is not difficult, then, to perceive the importance of Amici's discovery as to the value of a drop of water inserted between the object and the objective, and it now seems somewhat surprising it should have been so long neglected by opticians, since it is at once seen to diminish the reflection which takes place in the incidence of oblique light. The film of water not only gives increased aperture, but also greater cleanness and sharpness to the image. The film, then, as already shown, collects the straying away of peripheral rays of light, and sends them on to the eye-piece, and greatly assists in rendering the image more perfect, and materially aids in the removal of residuary secondary aberrations; while with air, or dry objectives, a certain amount of aberration takes place, sufficient to affect the pencils on their passage from the radiant to the medium of the front lens, adding a considerable ratio to the total spherical aberration with the objective, which, in the case of wide angles, increases disproportionately from the axis outwards. This can only be corrected by a rough method of balancing; that is, by introducing an excess of opposite aberration in the posterior lens. An uncorrected residuum, rapidly increasing with larger apertures, is then left, and this appears in the image amplified by the total power of the objective, so that with a non-homogeneous medium there is a maximum angular aperture which cannot be surpassed without undergoing a perceptible loss of definition, provided working distance is required. If we abolish the anterior aberration for all colours, by an immersion fluid which is equal to cover-glass in refractive and dispersive power, the difficulty is at once overcome. If, for instance, we have an objective of 140° in glass (= 1·25 N.A.) and water as the immersion fluid, the aberration in front would affect a pencil of 140°. Substituting a homogeneous medium, the same pencil, contracted to the equivalent angle in that medium of 112°, will be admitted to the front lens without any aberration, and may be made to emerge from the curved surface also without any disturbing aberration, but contracted to an angle varying from 70° to 90°. The first considerable spherical aberration of the pencil then occurs at the anterior surface of the *second* lens, where the maximum obliquity of the rays is already considerably diminished.

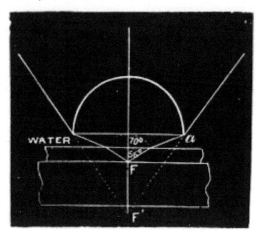

Fig. 119.

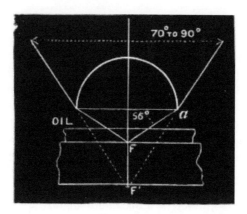

Fig. 119*a*.

Figs. 119 and 119*a* will doubtless make this clearer. If the objective of 140° works with water (Fig. 119), there would be a cone of rays extending up to 70° on both sides of the axis, *and this large cone would be submitted to spherical aberration at the front surface a.* But with homogeneous immersion Fig. 119*a*) the whole cone of 112° is admitted to the front lens without any aberration, there being no refraction at the plane surface; and as the spherical surface of the front lens is without notable spherical aberration, the incident pencil is brought from the focus F to the conjugate focus F', and contracted to an angle of divergence of 70°-90° *without having undergone any spherical aberration at all.*

The problem of correcting a very wide-angled objective has thus been reduced by the homogeneous oil-immersion system, both in theory and practice.[23]

Abbe's Test-plate.

Abbe designed the test-plate (Fig. 120) for testing the spherical and chromatic aberrations of objectives, and estimating the thickness of cover-glasses corresponding to the most perfect correction: six glasses, having the exact thickness marked on each, 0·09 to 0·24 mm., cemented in succession on a slip, their lower surface silvered and engraved with parallel lines, the contours of which form the test. These being coarsely ruled are easily resolved by the lowest powers; yet, from the extreme thinness of the silver, they form also a delicate test for objectives of the highest power and widest aperture. The test-plate in its original size is seen in Fig. 120, with one of the circles enlarged.

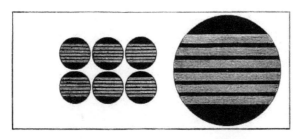

Fig. 120.—Abbe's Test-plate for estimating thickness of glass-covers.

To examine an objective of large aperture, the discs must be focussed in succession, observing in each case the quality of the image in the centre of the field, and the variation produced by using, alternately, central and very oblique illumination.

When the objective is perfectly corrected for spherical aberration, the outlines of the lines in the centre of the field will be perfectly sharp by oblique illumination, and without any nebulous doubling or indistinctness of the edges. If, after exactly adjusting the objective for oblique light, central illumination is used, no alteration of the focus should be necessary to show the outlines with equal sharpness.

If an objective fulfils these conditions with any one of the discs, it is free from spherical aberration when used with cover-glasses of that thickness. On the other hand, if every disc shows nebulous doubling, or an indistinct appearance of the edges of the line with oblique illumination, or, if the objective requires a different focal adjustment to get equal sharpness with central as with oblique light, the spherical correction of the objective is more or less imperfect.

Nebulous doubling with oblique illumination indicates over-correction of the marginal zone; indistinctness of the edges without marked nebulosity indicates under-correction of the zone; an alteration of the focus for oblique and central illumination points to an absence of concurrent action of the separate zones, which may be due to either an average under or over correction, or to irregularity in the convergence of the rays.

Fig. 121.—Zeiss's Cover-glass Gauge.

COVER-GLASS GAUGE.

Zeiss has gone a step further to lay the microscopist's ghost of the cover-glass. He invented a measurer (Fig. 121) whereby the precise determination of thickness of glass-covers can be obtained. This measurement is effected by a clip projecting from a circular box; the reading is given by an indicator moving over a divided circle on the lid of the box. The divisions seen cut round the circumference show $\frac{1}{100}$ths of a millimeter. This ingenious gauge measures upwards of 5 mm.

This necessary and important digression has led me away from the consideration of the achromatic objective, and to which I shall now return.

English Immersion and Dry Objectives.

The homogeneous immersion system met with its earliest as well as its staunchest advocates among English opticians. Among its more energetic supporters were Messrs. Powell and Lealand, who were the first to construct a $\frac{1}{8}$-inch immersion objective on a formula of their own, and which was found to resolve test-objects not before capable of resolution by their dry objectives. This encouraged them to make a $\frac{1}{16}$-inch, acquired by Dr. Woodward for the Army Medical Department, Washington, and subsequently a $\frac{1}{25}$-inch; neither of which surpassed their $\frac{1}{8}$-inch in aperture, and a new formula was tried in the construction of their first oil-immersion objective. This had a duplex front, and two double backs; but even this did not quite accomplish what was expected of it, and another change was subsequently made; the anterior front combination became greater than a hemisphere—a balloon-lens. This at once gave an increase of aperture to a $\frac{1}{12}$-inch objective of 1·43 numerical aperture. After some few more trials a more important change of the formula took place. The front lens was made of flint-glass, and the combination took the form represented in diagram (Fig. 122). This, on an enlarged scale, represents Powell's $\frac{1}{12}$-inch numerical aperture 1·50. It is a homogeneous apochromatic immersion of high quality and very flat field. It will be noticed that in this combination the four curves of the lenses are very deep compared with those of other opticians.

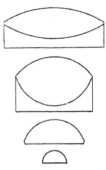

Fig. 122.—Powell and Lealand's ¹⁄₁₂-in. Oil-immersion Objective, drawn on a scale of 6-1.

Messrs. Ross have made many important improvements and changes in the construction of their several series of achromatic objectives; the calculations and formulæ for which were made exclusively for them by Dr. Schrœder. The list is too long to quote, but most of these lenses are of a high-class character, and work with admirable precision. Among the best of their objectives, I can commend a 1-inch of 30° and two oil-immersions, a ¹⁄₈-inch of 1·20 and a ¹⁄₁₂-inch of 1·25 numerical aperture, each of which bear the highest oculars equally well; a good test, as I have always maintained, of excellence. Their ¹⁄₁₀-inch has a somewhat larger aperture, and therefore shows a fine image of the podura scale. The finish of Ross's several series of objectives fully maintains the high character and reputation of this old-established firm of opticians.

Messrs. R. and J. Beck have bestowed great attention upon the improvement of their dry-objective series, much in demand for histological work, especially among the students of city hospitals, who usually commence their pathological work with the cheaper forms of objectives. In that case an inch objective of about 25° air angle, a ½-inch of not less than 40°, and a ¼-inch or ¹⁄₅-inch magnifying from 50 to 250 diameters, is quite sufficient for most of their work. For bacteriological research, Messrs. Beck supply a ¹⁄₆-inch immersion taken from a series, having a high aperture and a better finish at a moderate price. Their ¹⁄₁₀-inch immersion has in my hands proved a serviceable power for bacteriological research; it requires a good sub-stage illuminating achromatic condenser to obtain the best results.

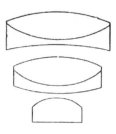

Fig. 123.—⅙-in. English Combination, largely used.

Messrs. Watson and Sons have much enhanced their reputation by the marked improvement lately brought about in the manufacture of their whole series of objectives. This probably is chiefly due to the introduction of the *Jena* glass into their manufacture, and which has enabled them to give increase of aperture to one series in particular, that of the para-chromatic, all of which in consequence are of very high quality. It is difficult to particularise their several objectives, the whole having special features in proportion to their magnifying powers, while much care seems to have been bestowed on them for the elimination of residual colour. A ⅛-inch with correction collar is comprised of a single deep and rather thick front lens, plano-concave flint, and double convex-crown for the middle and triple combination for the back, the latter consisting of two crown lenses cemented to a dense flint (Fig. 124) drawn to scale of 5-1, with lined portions intended to represent the flint, and white the crown glass lenses of the combination. The initial magnification of this objective is 83 diameters, and the numerical aperture ·94. This superior objective can be had for the small sum of £2. Another remarkably useful and cheap objective, their 1-inch numerical aperture 0·21, consists of two achromatic systems forming the front and back with the separation between them of about half an inch, and may also be especially recommended for students' work.

In the accompanying diagram the lenses are drawn on too large a scale, and therefore the distance between the two combinations should be much greater.

Among the more useful of Watson's series, the 1-inch, the ½-inch, and the ⅙-inch, together with the ⅛-inch dry-objective, and a ⅑-inch, will be found the most serviceable.

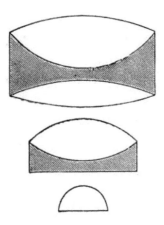

Fig. 124.—Watson's ⅛-in. Objective Para-chromatic Combination, scale
5-1.

Fig. 125.—Watson's 1-in. Achromatic Combination.

Messrs. Baker have their own series of objectives, most of which are so very nearly allied to those of the continental opticians; and what has been said of Zeiss's and Leitz's objectives may be taken to apply also to Baker's, who have an established reputation for their histological series, all of which are well suited for students' and class-room work.

Messrs. Swift and Son have a new series of objectives, semi-apochromatic and pan-aplanatic, most of which are excellent in quality and show increased flatness of field together with that of achromatism; the index of refraction in each series having been correctly determined together with exact radial focal distance, thus affording more available aperture. I may select for special commendation their ¹⁄₁₂-inch £5 5s. homogeneous immersion objective, which is in every way suitable for bacteriological work; its definition is very good, as is seen in a micro-photograph of podura scale, given further on. Their dry ⅙-inch can be had for £1 16s.—a marvel of cheapness. Of their general series the most useful for histological work are the ½-inch, the ⅓-inch at £1 12s., and their ⅕-inch of numerical aperture 0·87 at £3.

Mr. Pillischer, of Bond Street, has manufactured many excellent objectives. A fine homogeneous oil-immersion ¹⁄₁₂-inch numerical aperture 1·25 is worthy of special notice; it will be found suitable for bacteriological work; it has fine definition with a considerable amount of penetration.

A more intelligent idea of the magnifying power of the objective combined with the eye-piece will be gained by consulting the table given below; precision in this respect has long been a desideratum with microscopists.

Magnifying Powers of Eye-Pieces and Objectives.

A TYPICAL AND INITIAL SELECTION OF POWERS OF EYE-PIECES CALCULATED FOR THE 10-INCH TUBE-LENGTH.

HUYGHENIAN EYE-PIECES.

NAME	A	B	C	D	E	F	
OF MAKER.	0 or No. 1	2	3	4	5	6	
Baker	6	8	12	15	—	—	Diameters.
Beck, R. & J.	4	8	15	20	25	not made.	"
Leitz	5	6	7	8	10	12	"
Powell & Lealand	5	7·5	10	20	40	"	"
Reichert	2·5	3·5	4	5	6·5	"	" 24
Ross	3	8	12½	20	25	40	" 25
Swift & Son	6	9	12	15	18	21	"
Watson & Sons	4	6	8	10	12	15	"
Zeiss	3	4	5·5	7	9	not made.	"

COMPENSATING EYE-PIECES FOR USE WITH APOCHROMATIC OBJECTIVES.

Zeiss   2   4   8   12   18   27   Diameters.

This may be taken as a typical set, further treated of among Eye-pieces.

INITIAL POWERS OF OBJECTIVES CALCULATED FOR THE 10-INCH TUBE-LENGTH.

This is ascertained by dividing the distance of distinct vision 10 inches by the focus of the objective, thus—

Focus-inches	4	3	2	1½	1	⅔	½	4/10	¼	⅕	⅙	⅛	1/12	
Initial magnifying power	2·5	3·3	5	7·5	10	15	20	25	40	50	60	80	120	diameters.

A reference to the above table will at once show that the nomenclature of objectives expresses at once the initial magnifying powers, but as makers have great difficulty in so calculating their formulæ so as to obtain the *exact* power, these figures must be taken as approximate. Thus a ¼-inch, which should magnify 40 diameters if true to its description, might actually magnify a little more or less.

The magnifying powers of Zeiss's and other apochromatic objectives can be ascertained by dividing the focal length of the objective in millimeters into 250 mm. (the distance of distinct vision), thus

Focus millimetres	24	16	12	4	3	2	1·5	
Initial magnifying power	10·5	15·5	21	63	83	125	167	diameters.

The total magnification, when any eye-piece is working in conjunction with an objective, is ascertained by multiplying the initial power of the objective by that of the eye-piece.

The above calculations are all for a 10-inch tube-length. Should, however, a shorter or longer length of body be employed, the magnification can at once be ascertained by a proportion sum. If the magnification be 180 with 10-inch tube-length, what would it be with a 6-inch body—10 : 6 :: 180 = 108 diameters.

Abbe designed three different forms of eye-pieces: 1, the searcher eye-piece; 2, the working eye-piece; and 3, the projecting eye-piece. The *Searcher* is a negative form of low power. The working is both negative and positive, the positive form of which is constructed on a newer principle; while the projection is chiefly intended for microphotography, its field being small and its definition superlatively sharp. These are severally explained among eye-pieces.

High-Power Objectives.

Points of Importance for securing the best results with High-power Objectives.—Always give to the body-tube of the microscope the length for which the objective is corrected, 0·160 mm. for the short continental tube, and 0·250 mm. for the English tube (10-inch). Employ both dry and immersion objectives mounted for correction, commencing with a numerical aperture of 0·75 (that is about 100° in air). If the graduation is not given in thickness of cover-glass apply to the maker to correct this omission.

With the homogeneous oil-immersion objective it is highly necessary to utilise all marginal pencils of light, to optically unite the upper lens of the condenser with the preparation as well as the front lens of the objective by means of a liquid having the same index of refraction or at least equal to that of the immersion. *Cedar Oil* has been generally adopted for the purpose mentioned, the better way of using which is as follows: place a drop on the centre of the front objective, or on the top of the cover-glass, and then lower the objective by means of the coarse adjustment until it comes in contact with the oil, and carefully bring into focus by the fine adjustment. If the slide is held between the finger and thumb of one hand and moved from side to side, while the other hand is working the fine adjustment, there can be no danger of injuring either the objective or the specimen. Before putting the microscope away, take a fine camel-hair brush dipped in ether, alcohol, or methylated spirit, and carefully remove the oil from the objective and the glass cover of the object; a soft chamois leather or cambric pocket handkerchief will dry it off, or a piece of fine white blotting paper answers equally well. Should the lens come accidentally into contact with the Canada balsam, it must be very carefully removed either by ether or alcohol. The former is by far the safest, as alcohol, if not very carefully used, quickly dissolves out the balsam and loosens the cover-glass of the object.

Achromatic Condensers.

The Achromatic Condenser can no longer be classed among the *accessories* of the microscope, since it is an absolutely indispensable part of its optical arrangements. Its value, then, cannot be overrated, and the corrections of the lenses which enter into the construction of the condenser should be made as perfect as they can be made—in fact, as nearly approaching that of the objective as it is possible to make them. It may therefore be of interest to know something of the rise and progress of the achromatic condenser. In my first chapter I have noticed the earlier attempts made by Dr. Wollaston, whose experiments led him to fit to the underside of the stage of his microscope a short tube, in which a plano-convex lens of about three-quarters of an inch focal length was made to slide up and down (afterwards moved up and down by two knobs); to improve definition he placed a stop between the mirror and the lens. The stop was found to act better when placed between the lens and the object. From this improvement Dr. Wollaston enunciated that "the intensity of illumination will depend upon the diameter of the illuminating lens and the proportion of the image to the perforation, and may be regulated according to the wish of the observer."

Dujardin in France and Tully in England were at work in the same direction. The former a year or two later on contrived an instrument, which he termed an *eclairage*, to remedy the defects of Wollaston's, and for illuminating objects with achromatic light. This was submitted for approval to Sir David Brewster, who, when the use of the achromatic condenser was first broached, used these encouraging words:—"I have no hesitation in saying that the apparatus for illumination requires to be as perfect as the apparatus for vision, and on this account I would recommend that the illuminating lens should be perfectly free from chromatic and spherical aberration, and that the greatest care be taken to exclude all extraneous light both from the object and eye of the observer." This far-seeing observer in optical science has borne good fruit, and the outcome of his views is seen in the great development and improvement of the achromatic condenser. In 1839 Andrew Ross made his first useful form of condenser, and gave rules for the illumination of objects in an article written for the "Penny Cyclopædia." These, epitomised, read as follows: 1. That the illuminating cone should equal the aperture of the objective, and no more. 2. With daylight, a white cloud being in focus, the object has to be placed nearly at the apex of the cone. The object is seen better sometimes above and sometimes below the apex of the cone. 3. With lamplight a bull's-eye lens is to be used, to parallelise the rays, so that they may be similar to those coming from the white cloud. It has been seen that Mr. Lister foreshadowed the sub-stage condenser.

The early form of Ross's condenser consists of two small brass tubes made to slide one in the other. To the outer one is attached a flat brass plate which slides underneath the stage of the microscope, and by means of a screw the adjustment of the axis of the illuminator is effected. The upper portion of the apparatus carries the achromatic combination, which by a rack and pinion movement is brought nearer to, or removed further from the object on the stage. The several parts of the illuminator unscrew, so that the lenses may be used either combined for high powers, or separated for low powers.

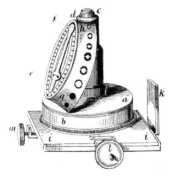

Fig. 126.—Original form of Gillett's Achromatic Condenser.

Messrs. Smith & Beck greatly improved upon Ross's condenser by adding another achromatic lens to the combination, three being employed when used with high-power objectives and two or even one with the lower, the adjustment and focussing being made by rack and pinion arrangement beneath the stage. Some further changes for the better were made in the condenser by Powell, and in 1850 an amateur microscopist, Mr. Gillett, fully grasping the value of controlling the cone of rays passing into the microscope, devised a new form of condenser, in connection with which a revolving series of diaphragms of different values were made to pass between the achromatic lenses and the source of light.

Andrew Ross constructed the first condenser on Gillett's principle, and this proved to be one of the most successful pieces of apparatus contrived. *Gillett's Condenser* consists of an achromatic lens *c*, about equal to an object-glass of one quarter of an inch focal length, with an aperture of 80°. This lens is screwed into the top of a brass tube, and intersecting which, at an angle of about 25°, is a circular rotating brass plate *a b*, provided with a conical diaphragm, having a series of circular apertures of different sizes *h g*, each of which in succession, as the diaphragm is rotated, proportionally limits the light transmitted through the illuminating lens. The circular plate in which the conical diaphragm is fixed is provided with a spring and catch *e f*, the latter indicating when an aperture is central with the illuminating lens, also the number of the aperture as marked on the graduated circular plate. Three of these apertures have central discs for circularly oblique illumination, allowing only the passage of a hollow cone of light to illuminate the object. The illuminator above described is placed in the secondary stage *i i*, which is situated below the general stage of the microscope, and consists of a cylindrical tube having a rotatory motion, also a rectangular adjustment, which is effected by means of two screws *l m*, one in front, and the other on the left side of its frame. This tube receives and supports all the various illuminating and polarising apparatus, and other auxiliaries.

Directions for using Gillett's Condenser.—In the adjustment of the compound body of the microscope for using with Gillett's illuminator, one or two important points should be observed—first, centricity; and secondly, the fittest compensation of the light to be employed. With regard to the first, place the illuminator in the cylindrical tube, and press upwards the sliding bar *k* in its place, until checked by the stop; move the microscope body either vertically or inclined for convenient use; and, with the rack and pinion which regulates the sliding bar, bring the illuminating lens to a level with the upper surface of the object-stage; then move the arm which holds the microscope body to the right, until it meets the stop, whereby its central position is attained; adjust the reflecting mirror so as to throw light up the illuminator, and place upon the mirror a piece of clean white paper to obtain a uniform disc of light. Then put on the low eye-piece, and a low power (the half-inch), as more convenient for the mere adjustment of the instrument; place a transparent object on the stage, adjust the microscope-tube, until vision is obtained of the object; then remove the object, and take off the cap of the eye-piece, and in its place fix on the eye-glass called the "centring eye-glass,"[26] which will be found greatly to facilitate the adjustment now under consideration, namely, the centring of the compound body of the microscope with the illuminating apparatus of whatever description. The centring-glass, being thus affixed to the top of the eye-piece, is adjusted by its sliding-tube (without disturbing the microscope-tube) until the images of the diaphragms in the object-glass and centring lens are distinctly seen. The illuminator should now be moved by means of the left-hand screw on the secondary stage while looking through the microscope, to enable the observer to recognize the diaphragm belonging to the illuminator, and by means of the two adjusting screws to place this diaphragm central with the others: thus the first condition, that of centricity, will be accomplished. Remove the white paper from the mirror, and also the centring-glass, and replace the cap on the eye-piece, also the object on the stage, of which distinct vision should then be obtained by the rack and pinion, or fine screw adjustment, should it have become deranged.

Fig. 127.—The Ross Improved Achromatic Condenser, with diaphragm stops.

The re-publication of the original directions is given with the view of showing what a clear conception Gillett had of the value of his invention. The careful directions given for centring must be regarded with interest, although nearly superseded by the centring screw arrangement in connection with the sub-stage. The best results, he goes on to say, will be secured by using the plain mirror and focussing the window-bar on the object, while a white-cloud illuminator will afford as much light as may be required. It is a mistake to suppose that direct light is more critical than indirect. As a rule, the student is given to over-illuminate the object. These questions will, however, be discussed further on.

Very many modifications of Gillett's condenser have, since 1850, become known to microscopists. Ross's present improved form (Fig. 127) is made to drop into the sub-stage of the microscope, and when adjusted, is an extremely efficient instrument. The optical part is similar to a $\frac{4}{10}$-inch objective. It has two sets of revolving diaphragms, with apertures and stops for showing surface markings in a perfect manner.

Abbe's Condenser.

The essential feature of this condenser is its short focus, which collects the light reflected by the mirror, so as to form a cone of rays of very large aperture, having its focus in the plane of the object.

Fig. 128.—The Iris Diaphragm, and carrier for Stops.

The full aperture of the illuminating cone should only be used when finely granular and deeply stained particles (protoplasm, bacteria, &c.) are being examined with objectives of large aperture. In all cases the cone must be suitably reduced, either by an iris, or other form of diaphragm (*central illumination*). By placing the diaphragm excentrically, by means of rack-work attached to the carrier, the central rays are excluded and a certain extra-axial portion of the illuminating pencil falls upon the object (*oblique illumination*). When the diaphragm is thus excentrically placed, this oblique pencil can be directed from all sides by rotating the carrier round the optic axis. The central stop diaphragm shuts off all the axial and transmits only the marginal rays, thus producing *dark-ground illumination*. The iris diaphragm (Fig. 128) is so shaped that the edge of its smallest opening closely approximates the object-slide on the stage.

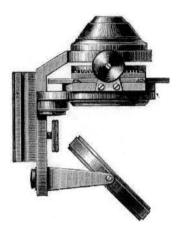

Fig. 129.—The Abbe Condenser, detached from the Sub-stage of the Microscope.

The Abbe condenser is the most popular form in use, for all purposes. Owing to the large aperture of the cone of light which it projects, it can be employed with the highest powers; by removing the top lens it can also be used with low powers. Dark ground illumination may be obtained with it up to a ¼-inch objective.

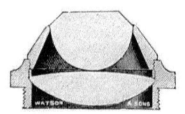

Fig. 130.—Optical Arrangement of Abbe Illuminator, 1·2 N.A.

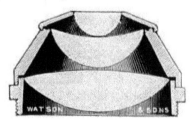

Fig. 131.—Optical Arrangement of Abbe Illuminator, 1·4 N.A.

The condenser is made in two forms of 1·2 and 1·4 numerical aperture by Messrs. Watson. The lenses are mounted in aluminium. Fig. 130 is in more general use, but by workers with high powers Fig. 131 is preferred, as it ensures the most oblique illumination with objectives of largest aperture. It is preferred for photo-micrographic purposes.

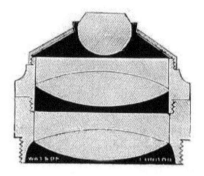

Fig. 132.—The Optical Arrangement of Watson's Achromatic
Condenser.

Watson's Achromatic Condenser (Fig. 132), 1·0 numerical aperture, shown in
section, although originally designed for use with the micro-spectroscope, is
equally efficient for ordinary purposes. This condenser transmits a larger
aplanatic cone of light than Abbe's. It may therefore be employed with higher
power objectives, and by removing the top lens it is just as useful a condenser
for lower powers. Being constructed with lenses of an unusually large size, it
is well adapted for use with the micro-spectroscope. It is certainly one of the
best all-round condensers in use. The new Schott glass enters into the
construction of the lenses, and these are mounted in aluminium.

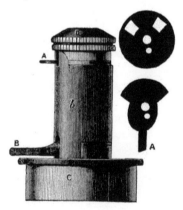

Fig. 133.—Powell's Achromatic Condenser.

Many microscopists consider on the whole that Powell's sub-stage
apochromatic condenser with collar correction (Fig. 133) surpasses that of
Abbe. The mechanical arrangement of Powell's is very simple: the correction
collar is similar to that of an ordinary objective, it has a steeper spiral slot and
only half a revolution of movement; a long arc is fixed to the collar so that it
may conveniently be reached by the finger. It is so constructed as to turn
easily and smoothly at the slightest touch. The collar moves only the back

lens of the combination, leaving the mount rigid. The diaphragms are regulated by A and B.

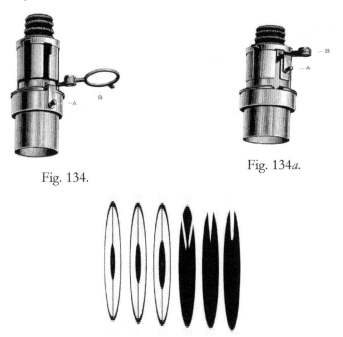

Fig. 134.

Fig. 134*a*.

Fig. 134*b*.—Powell's Apochromatic Oil Immersion Condenser, N.A. 1·40.

The object of the correctional movement is to increase the maximum aplanatic aperture of the condenser by separating the lenses. If the back of a wide-angled objective be examined when an object is illuminated by the full aperture of the condenser, the edge of the flame being in focus, it will be noticed that the illuminated portion of the back lens will be oval and pointed instead of circular. Also that when the condenser is racked up, although the external shape of the illuminated portion becomes more circular, two dark patches will appear on either side of the centre, showing the operation of the spherical aberration of the condenser. If under these circumstances the lenses are separated by means of the collar adjustment, the black spots will be closed up, and a circular and evenly-illuminated disc of illumination of a larger size will result. The wheel of diaphragms, or a series of graduated diaphragm discs to drop into a holder, is intended for critical work; the diaphragm can always be recorded, and the identical illuminating cone reproduced.

Hence we have a simple method of graduating apertures between any two contiguous diaphragms; if, for example, we place the lever to the left, so that the lens may be separated as far as possible, and use a No. 6 diaphragm, and if, on examining the object, it is thought that the illuminating cone is not large enough, and if when No. 7 is turned on it is found too much, we can go back to No. 6, and by turning the lever 60° towards the right, closing the lenses and increasing the power a little, we shall obtain an aperture somewhere between Nos. 6 and 7 diaphragm. Thus we can by means of the correction collar graduate the aperture with the facility as with an iris, and we can record any particular aperture with a degree of accuracy foreign to the iris. It must be admitted, however, that the cone of light transmitted by the condenser is a very small one.

Powell also supplies an apochromatic oil-immersion condenser, numerical aperture 1·40, but without collar correction; Fig. 134 shows the sliding tube lowered by arm A and cell B withdrawn for changing stops, which can be done without altering the focus of the condenser. Fig. 134a shows the cell B closed and raised by arm A close to the back lens of optical combination. In Fig. 134b six of the principal stops are shown. Powell's dry apochromatic condenser, of nearly 0·9 aplanatic cone, is also very good; but the high price of all is a bar to their more general use. The speciality of these is the conversion of axis light into condensed oblique incident light by the refraction of the condenser.

Messrs. R. & J. Beck have various forms of achromatic condensers, some of which partake of a somewhat elaborate arrangement; others are simple and inexpensive, to suit the students' microscope; as when the light of the concave mirror proves insufficient for any object requiring intense transmitted light, an achromatic condenser must be adapted to even the students' form of microscope. The latest form of condenser (Fig. 135) is fitted with revolving stops and iris diaphragm, and other appliances for obtaining satisfactory results.

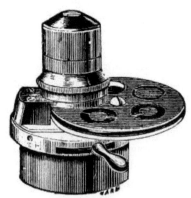

Fig. 135.—Beck's newer form of Achromatic Condenser.

Beck's Compound Illuminating Apparatus (Fig. 136).—It is useful in working with the microscope to be enabled to rapidly change the illumination, and for this reason this compound form of condenser has been constructed. It consists of an upper portion A, a wide-angle condenser, the aperture of which can be reduced at will by an iris diaphragm, moved by the lever B. This can be used for all other purposes. Below this diaphragm is a plate C, which can be swung back out of position at will, as shown in outline. Into a cell in this plate the stops D can be dropped, and the condenser can be used for dark field illumination, or for high powers as an oblique illuminator. A large-size polarising prism E, fastens to the plate C, and can be removed when not required. In this way any of the various modes of illumination may be separately or conjointly obtained.

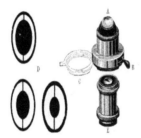

Fig. 136.—Beck's Compound Condenser.

Fig. 137.—Beck's Spherical Achromatic Condenser.

Their condenser (Fig. 137) has a large aperture, and facilities for rotating the series of diaphragms. It is available for either dry or immersion objectives up to 1·3 numerical aperture on diatoms, and wet or dry histological objects. The spherical form of the front is worked by a milled-head that rotates a series of lenses and diaphragms. It also avoids the inconvenience of having the connecting fluid drawn away by capillary attraction, as would be the case if mounted on a flat surface. It is also less in the way of the sub-stage movements.

Fig. 138.—Watson's Parachromatic Condenser.

The Parachromatic Condenser of Messrs. Watson (Fig. 138) was made to meet a demand for a condenser giving a large solid cone of illumination free from colour. The optical part of this condenser consists of a full hemispherical front lens, and the middle and back combinations of such forms as to produce the necessary corrections. The Jena phosphate crown and silicate flints are used in its manufacture, and to these are due its special qualities. The total aperture of the condenser is $1\cdot0$, and it yields an aplanatic aperture of $\cdot90$ numerical aperture. The magnifying power is $\frac{2}{7}$ths of an inch. From this it will be seen that it is especially suitable for use with high-power objectives.

It can also be employed without the front lens, when the magnifying power is $\frac{4}{10}$ths of an inch, and the numerical aperture $\cdot35$. It is mounted in an exceedingly convenient manner, the iris diaphragm being fitted in such a way as to be absolutely central with the optical system.

The arc through which the handle controlling the iris travels is divided, and indicates the aperture at which the condenser may be working at any time. An important feature in this condenser is that it is almost wholly free from colour. As a rule condensers of the same form are found difficult to work with, because of the small diameter of the field or back lens. This difficulty has been successfully overcome by increasing the size of this lens, and the whole of which is fully utilised.

Most London opticians have their own especial form of achromatic condenser, designed for and fitted to their several stands and objectives, varying from a small price to the more expensively-fitted accessories.

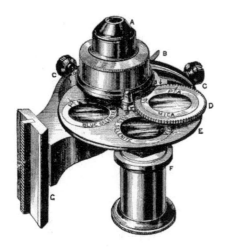

Fig. 139.—Swift's Illuminating Polarising Apparatus.

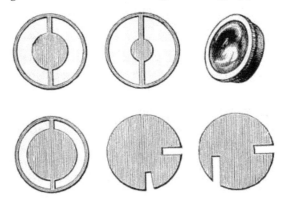

Fig. 139a.—Swift's Diaphragms and Central Stops.

Messrs. Swift's illuminating apparatus (Fig. 139) is conveniently supplied with numerous useful appliances. The optical combination A is computed to be used as an effective spot lens from a 3-inch objective up to a sixth. C C are two small milled heads by means of which the optical combination A is centred to the axis of the objective. The revolving diaphragm E has four apertures for the purpose of receiving central stops, oblique light discs, and selenite films. D is a frame carrying two revolving cells, into one of which a mica film is placed, which can be revolved with ease over either of the selenites below, whereby changes of colour can be obtained in experimenting with polarised light. The darts and P A's indicate the position of the positive axis of the mica and selenite films, and by this means results can be recorded, etc. Either of the revolving cells can be thrown into the centre of the condenser, and there stopped by means of a spring catch; when so arranged the mica film, &c., may be revolved in its place by turning the cell D, as both cells are geared together with fine racked teeth. F is a polarising prism mounted on an eccentric arm, rendered central when in use, or thrown out, as seen, when out of use. G is the rack dove-tail slide for indicating and focussing the condenser on the object. The advantages associated with this condenser consist in having the polarising prism, selenite films, dark-ground, and oblique light stops, so that they may be brought close under the optical combination.

Fig. 140.—Baker's Nelson Achromatic Condenser.

Baker's Nelson Condenser, shown in Fig. 140, is intended for use with their medium instruments. It has, however, many pieces of apparatus essential to those of a higher class. It is applicable, indeed, to all instruments having sufficient depth beneath the stage to receive it. It comprises an achromatic combination of 90° aperture, available with all powers up to ⅛-inch tinted glass for neutralising the yellow rays of artificial light, focussing adjustment, dark-ground illuminator, large diaphragm with rotating tube to carry oblique light stops, small wheel of apertures, polarising prism with two selenite films, clear aperture, and oblique light-shutter for low powers.

Baker's Students' Condenser (Fig. 141) is designed to take the place of Abbe's, and costs much less. It transmits a larger aplanatic cone of light, and can be used either with high or low powers by removing the front lens. It is equally useful for photo-micrographic work.

Mr. J. Mayall's semi-cylinder or prism for oblique illumination (Fig. 142) is a convenient form, as it permits of the semi-cylinder being tilted and placed excentrically; in this manner, without immersion contact, and by suitable adjustment, a dry object can be viewed with any colour of monochromatic light. If placed in immersion contact with the slide, the utmost obliquity of incident light can be obtained. Objects in fluid may be placed on the plane-surface of the semi-cylinder, and illuminated by ordinary transmitted light, or rendered "self-luminous" in a dark field, as with the hemispherical illuminator or Wenham's immersion paraboloid. A concave mirror with a double arm is quite sufficient to direct the illuminating pencil. This semi-cylinder was originally made by Tolles, of Boston, for measuring apertures, but, at Mr. Mayall's suggestion, Messrs. Ross mounted it as an illuminator.

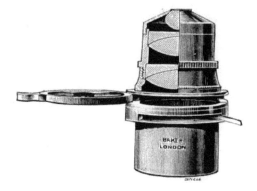

Fig. 141.—Optical Arrangement of Baker's Abbe Condenser.

The spiral slot should be fixed close beneath the larger lens of the condenser, and when properly arranged will be found a convenient mode of obtaining oblique light.

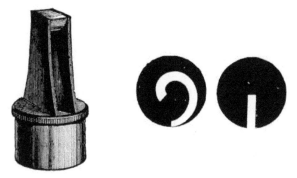

Fig. 142.—Mayall's Semi-Cylinder Illuminator and Spiral Diaphragms.

The Webster-Collins Universal Condenser (Fig. 143) is so well known that it scarcely calls for any lengthy description. It is an inexpensive form of condenser, designed in the first instance for use with the students' microscope. It is fitted into the sub-stage; has an iris diaphragm as well as a series of revolving diaphragms moved by a milled head screw arrangement.

Iris Diaphragm removed

Fig. 143.—The Webster-Collins Universal Condenser.

Oblique Illumination.

Wenham's Parabolic Condenser.—Mr. Wenham's many useful additions to the microscope and its accessories demand especial notice. When mention is made of the various immersion condensers (illuminators, as he preferred to call them), his original right-angled prism, his truncated hemispherical lens, his immersion paraboloid, and his reflex illuminator, in which rays beyond the angle of total reflexion are utilised by reflex action from cover-glass on to the surface of the object, every one of these well-devised inventions will always be spoken of in terms of praise. All in their turn conferred a great service upon the microscope, and enabled the student to clear up difficulties that stood in the way of developing structure when achromatic lenses and dry-objectives were considered perfect. The superior illumination of the object was wholly due to, and effected by, *reflected* rays from the object to the aperture of the objective, and obviously, reflex action could only take place with dry-objectives. This reflex action must be regarded as Mr. Wenham's special discovery. It must be observed, however, that it is not the same as the more modern achromatic appliances used for throwing *direct* rays upon the object, and which proved the existence of apertures capable of direct transmission up to 27° measured in the body of the front lens.

Fig. 144.—Wenham's Parabolic Reflector.

The most practical of Mr. Wenham's inventions is probably the hemispherical lens, since adopted by Messrs. Ross in connection with their excellent Zentmayer stand, and which has proved eminently serviceable. But the fact is that devices of the kind for obtaining direct oblique light require a thin stage, and therefore most of those who possess the earlier-made microscope stand would doubtless hail the appearance of any appliance which will convert axial light into oblique light; as by so doing the possessors of such instruments, in which the stage is generally of considerable thickness, would enjoy the pleasure of seeing the best resolution it is possible to get with their dry-objectives.[27]

Wenham's Parabolic Reflector.—This will be better understood by reference to Fig. 145, which represents it in section A B C, and shows that the rays of light r r' r'', entering perpendicularly at its surface C, and then reflected by its parabolic surface A B to a focus at F, can form no part of the largest pencil of light admitted by the object-glass and represented by G F H; but an object placed at F will interrupt the rays and be strongly illuminated. A stop at S prevents any light from passing through direct from the mirror.

In the microscope the *parabolic reflector* fits into the cylindrical fitting under the stage, and the adjustment of its focus upon the object is made by giving it a spiral motion when fitted in—that is, carefully pushing it up or down at the same time that it is turned round by the milled edge B B. It must then be focussed by the rack and pinion motion. As the rays of light must be parallel when they enter it, a *flat mirror*, which in this case should be added to the instrument, is generally used; daylight will then require only direct reflection, but the rays from an artificial source will have to be made parallel by placing a side condenser between the light and the mirror, about 1¾ inch from the former and 4½ inches from the latter. Nearly the whole surface of the mirror should be equally illuminated; this may be tested by temporarily placing upon it a card or piece of white paper. Parallel rays can also be obtained from the concave mirror, if the light is placed about 2½ inches from it. Dark-ground illumination is not suitable for very transparent objects—that is, unless there is a considerable difference in their index of refraction, or they are pervaded by air-cells.

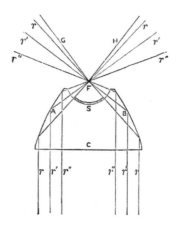

Fig. 145.—Parabolic Reflector.

One very remarkable example of this may be seen in the tracheal system of insects. If any of the transparent larvæ of the various kinds of gnat be mounted in gelatine and glycerine jelly, slightly warmed but not enough to kill the insect outright, about the third day the fluids circulating in the body will be absorbed and replaced by air. Illuminated by the parabolic condenser, and viewed with a binocular microscope, and a low power, the gnat-larva becomes a superb object. The body of the insect is but faintly visible, and in its place is displayed a marvellous tracheal skeleton, with the tubes standing out in perspective, shining brilliantly, like a structure of burnished silver. Unfortunately, such objects are not permanent, for when the whole of the water dries up, the tracheal tubes either collapse or become refilled with fluid.

As to the blackness of field, and luminosity of the object, this depends upon excess of light from the paraboloid received beyond the angle of aperture of the object-glass. It is found in practice that more and more of the inner annulus of rays from the paraboloid has to be stopped off, until at last, with high-angled objectives, it is scarcely possible to obtain a black field.

The light, on the whole, most suitable for this method of illumination is lamp, the rays of which should in all cases be rendered more parallel by means of a large plano-convex lens, or condenser.

Fig. 146.—Wenham's Hemispherical Lens.

Wenham's Immersion Condenser.—Mr. Wenham, in the year 1856, described various forms of oblique illuminators, one of which was an immersion; a simple right-angled prism, connected by a fluid medium of oil of cloves. This, however, was abandoned for a nearly hemispherical lens connected with the slide, and although an improvement, did not touch the point of excellence Mr. Wenham was looking for. Ultimately he adopted a semi-circular disc of glass of the exact form and size represented in the drawing, Fig. 146, having a quarter-inch radius, with a well-polished rounded edge, the sides being grasped by a simple kind of open clip attached to the sub-stage, the fluid medium used for connecting the upper surface with the slide being either water, glycerine, or oil; an increase of oblique illumination being obtained by swinging the ordinary mirror sideways. By means of an illuminator of the kind difficult objects mounted in balsam are resolved. This simple piece of glass collects and concentrates light in a marvellous manner, and is by no means a bad substitute for some of the more costly forms of achromatic condenser. It can be used either in fluid contact with the slide, or dry, as an ordinary condenser.

Mr. Wenham subsequently contrived a small truncated glass paraboloid, for use in fluid contact with the slide; water, glycerine, oil, or other substance being employed as a contact medium. The rays of light in this illuminator, being internally reflected from a convex surface of glass, impinge obliquely on the under surface of the slide, and are transmitted by the fluid uniting medium, and internally reflected from the upper surface of the cover-glass to the objective. To use the reflex illuminator efficiently it must be racked up to a level with the stage. The centre of rotation is then set true by a dot on the fitting, seen with a low power, a drop of water is then placed on the top, and upon this the slide is laid. Minute objects *on the slide* must be found either by the aid of a low power, by their greater brilliancy, or by rotating the illuminator; the effect on the podura scale is superb, the whole scale appearing dotted with bright blue spots in a zig-zag direction. Objects for this illuminator should be especially selected and mounted.

Fig. 147.—The Amici Prism.

The Amici Prism, originally designed for oblique illumination, consists of a flattened triangular glass prism, the two narrower sides of which are slightly convex, while the third or broadest side forms the reflecting surface. When properly used, it is capable of transmitting a very oblique pencil of light. The prism is either mounted, as in Fig. 147, for slipping into the fitting of the sub-stage, or on an independent stand, as arranged for Powell's microscope, page 85, Fig. 56.

Method of Employing the Achromatic Condenser to the Greatest Advantage.

Its Illumination.—Good daylight is the best for general work. The microscope should be placed near a window with a northern aspect. Direct sunlight should never be utilised; the best light is that reflected from a white cloud. A good paraffin lamp is the most serviceable artificial source of light, and it is quite under control. As an illuminant more often brought into requisition in the smoky atmosphere of towns, the paraffin lamp is on the whole the handiest and the most useful. If gas-light can be brought into use as suggested for micro-photography, with the incandescent mantle, it will be found to be the purest and best form of artificial illumination for the microscope. Among paraffin lamps those constructed by Baker and Swift are all that can be desired.[28]

Sectional view of the Optical Arrangement of the Aplanatic Bull's-eye Lens, fitted in gymbal on the front of the lamp.

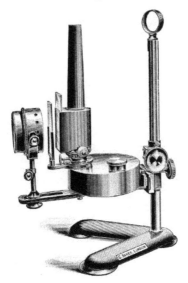

Fig. 148.—Baker's Microscope Lamp.

As the chimneys of these lamps are made of metal, and blackened, no reflected light disturbs the eye. Care must be taken to have the wick evenly trimmed; the metal chimney has a glazed front, giving exit to the rays of light, the flat of the flame being used with low powers, and the image of the flame being reflected by a plane mirror to give equal illumination of the whole field. In working with high powers, the lamp is turned with the flame edge-wise, and at the same time the mirror must be dispensed with. By working, as it is termed, directly on the edge of the flame, the illumination is greatly increased, and a band of light can be concentrated on any part of the preparation it is desired to make a careful study of.

To obtain the best results, time and care must be given to the illumination of the object. The lamp and microscope having been placed in position, a low power is first used and the smallest diaphragm. On looking through the microscope it will probably be observed that the image of the diaphragm is not in the centre of the field; by moving the centring screw of the condenser this may be adjusted. The low power is then replaced by a high power, the largest diaphragm used, and the bacteria or diatom brought into focus. The diaphragm must now be replaced by one of medium size, and by racking the condenser up and down, a point will be arrived at when the image of the edge of the flame appears as an intensely bright band of light. If this is not exactly in the centre of the field the centring screw of the condenser must again be adjusted. With regard to the use of diaphragms, various sizes should be tried while focussing with the fine adjustment, at the same time using the correction colour; in this way we obtain the sharpest possible image. When the condenser has been accurately centred, it will still be necessary to focus it for each individual specimen, so as to correct for difference in the thickness of slides and the layers of mounting medium. Correction for different thickness of cover-glasses must be made by the aid of the collar adjustment in the following way: a high-power eye-piece is substituted for the ordinary eye-piece, and the faults in the image will thereby be intensified. By moving the collar completely round, first in one direction and then in the other, while carefully observing the effect of the image, it will be seen to become obviously worse whichever way the collar is turned. The collar must then be turned through gradually diminishing distances until an intermediate point is reached at which the best image results with the high-power eye-piece, and on replacing this by the low-power eye-piece the sharpest possible image will be obtained.

Effect of the Sub-stage Condenser.—The sub-stage condenser gives the most powerful illumination when it has been racked up until it almost touches the specimen. It produces a cone of rays of very short focus, and the apex of the cone should correspond with the particular bacterium or group of bacterias under observation. The effect of the condenser without a diaphragm is to obliterate what Koch has termed a *structure picture*. If the component parts of a tissue section were colourless and of the same refractive power as the medium in which the section is mounted, nothing would be visible under the microscope. As, however, the cells and their nuclei and the tissues do not differ in this respect, the rays which pass through them are diffracted, and an image of lines and shadows is developed. If in such a tissue there were minute coloured objects, and if it were possible to mount the tissue in a medium of exactly the same refractive power, the tissue being then invisible, the detection of the coloured objects would be much facilitated. This is exactly what is required in dealing with bacteria which has been stained with aniline dyes, and the desired result can be obtained by the use of the sub-stage condenser.

If we use the full aperture of the condenser the greatly converged rays play on the component parts of the tissue, light enters from all sides, the shadows disappear, and the structure picture is lost. If now a diaphragm is inserted, so that we are practically only dealing with parallel rays, the structure picture reappears. As the diaphragm is gradually increased in size the structure picture gradually becomes less and less distinct, while the colour picture, the image of the stained bacteria, becomes more and more intense. When, therefore, bacteria in the living condition and unstained tissues are examined, a diaphragm must be used, and when the attention is to be concentrated upon the stained bacteria in a section or in a cover-glass preparation the diaphragm must be removed and the field flooded with light—(Crookshank).

The wide-angle condenser, it will be understood, consists of a combination of lenses, which concentrate all the light entering them to a small point, and the condenser must be so accurately focussed that this brilliant cone of light, when it emerges from the upper lens of the condenser, falls upon the object from all directions, forming a wide-angle cone of light, at the apex of which the object must be placed (see Fig. 149). That is to say, the object is illuminated by a cone of rays passing through it in all directions.

Fig. 149.—Front Lens of Condenser.

There are, however, objects which require a fully illuminated field, when the lamp should be turned round and the Herschel lens condenser (shown in section, Fig. 148) should be used to collect the light and throw it upon the mirror. For moderate powers, as a four-tenth or one-fifth, the condenser should be used a little below the focus to give an even illumination over the whole field. Moreover, as to the use of the condenser for defining general objects, it must be borne in mind that to show different kinds of structure different apertures in the iris diaphragm are necessary, and that whereas some objects show their structure better with a large angle of light cut down in intensity by the use of blue glass, others show better with a small pencil of direct rays. For the resolution of diatoms it is often necessary to use oblique light only, and for this purpose diaphragms with central patches are used, the iris diaphragm being opened to its full extent. An annular ring of oblique light emerges from the condenser upon the object, and it is in this manner also that dark-ground illumination is obtained with moderate and low powers.

THE DIAPHRAGM.

Fig. 150.—The Diaphragm.

The early form of diaphragm in use was that shown in Fig. 150.

Fig. 151.—Shutter Diaphragm.

It consists simply of a circular brass plate with a series of circular openings of different sizes, arranged to revolve upon another plate by a central pin or axis, the last being also provided with an opening as large as the largest in the diaphragm-plate, and corresponding in situation to the axis of the microscope body. The holes in the diaphragm-plate are centred and retained in place by a bent spring in the second plate, which rubs against the edge of the diaphragm-plate and catches in a notch. The blank space shuts off the light from the mirror when condensed light is about to be used. It is usually made to fit in under the stage of the microscope. This has been almost superseded by the iris diaphragm, originally designed by Wales, of America. It was made by this optician for his working students' microscope. An early form of the iris diaphragm is seen in Fig. 151. By pressing upon the lever handle at the side the aperture gradually closes up, and without for a moment losing sight of the object under examination.

The Mirror.

The mode in which an object is illuminated is, in the words of the late Andrew Ross, "second only in importance to the excellence of the glass through which it is seen." To ensure good illumination the mirror should be in direct co-ordination with the objective and eye-piece; it must be regarded as a part of the same system, and tending by a combined series of acts to a perfect result. Illumination of the object is recognised as of three kinds or qualities—reflected, transmitted, and refracted light. For the illumination of transparent objects, transmitted light is brought into use; for opaque objects, reflected light is needed.

The mirror should be about 2½ or 3 inches in diameter, and it must not be fixed, but made to slide up and down the stem under the stage, so that the rays of light emanating from it may be brought to a focus. The utility of the mirror is so obvious that it is occasionally passed over in silence by writers. To myself it appears to be an important accessory of the microscope, and I shall therefore proceed to combine theory with practice in what I have to say with regard to the mirror.

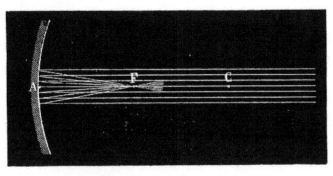

Fig. 152.—Principal Focus of Mirror.

The microscope mirror should be the segment of a true sphere, and its centre that of a true curvature. If the mirror has a true circular boundary, the central point on line A (Fig. 152) of the reflecting surface, is the pole of the same. The line A C is known as its principal axis, and any other straight line through C, which meets the mirror, is its secondary axis. When the incident axis is perfectly parallel to the principal axis, the reflected rays converge to a point F, its principal focus. So much for the theory of the mirror. Now we come to its practical use.

Simple as the mirror of the microscope may appear to be, if the curve of the surface is not perfect, it will yield a secondary reflection or double pencil of rays. The plane mirror will occasionally be found to emit more than one reflection of the lamp-flame; this we find may be corrected by rotating the mirror in its cell. Many years ago I proposed to meet a difficulty of the kind by arranging a rectangular prism on a separate stand, shown in Fig. 153, consisting of a prism A B, mounted in gimbal C, D, and E, secured to a brass tube G, fitted to the stem, and thus made to take the place of the mirror.

The direct method of employing the mirror, that more generally resorted to, is by reflecting rays from the concave surface; the plane surface is preferred when the condenser is used. Whichever is employed, it should not be forgotten that the *optic axis* must be preserved throughout, and so brought to the centre of the open tube of the microscope. Another method is to interpose a bull's-eye lens, and in this way supply the mirror with a beam of parallel rays of light. The plane side of the bull's-eye lens should be turned towards the lamp, so that lamp, bull's-eye, sub-stage condenser, and objective, are brought into an exact line, the bull's-eye being set at right-angles to the line. A piece of thin white paper held across the bottom of the sub-stage will serve to show whether the rays of light are fairly parallel. The next care is to focus the object on the stage, and then the sub-stage condenser on the slide; further correction should be made by means of the centring screws of the sub-stage, or by moving the bull's-eye lens or lamp slightly, thus perfecting the arrangements for working with parallel rays of light.

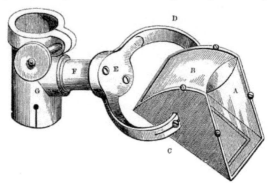

Fig. 153.—Rectangular Prism.

Accessories of the Microscope.

The accessories and appliances of the microscope have become so very numerous, that any attempt to describe them and explain the uses to which they are put would demand more space than I find myself in a position to bestow upon them. I must therefore confine my remarks to those accessories in more general use.

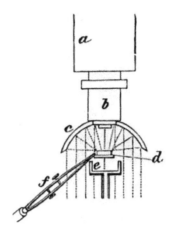

Fig. 154.—The Lieberkühn.

Having described the method of employing transmitted light, I have a few words to add with regard to the illumination of opaque objects by reflected light. A very early and efficient form of opaque illumination is the well-known *Lieberkühn*. This has not been entirely surpassed by more recent inventions. The concave speculum termed a Lieberkühn, so named after its celebrated inventor, directly reflects down upon the object the light received either from the mirror or bull's-eye lens. It consists of a silver cap, which slides over the objective (Fig. 154), *a* indicating the lower part of the compound body, and *b* the objective over which slides the Lieberkühn, *c*; the rays of light are collected to a focus upon the object at *d*. The object may either be mounted on a slip of glass, or held by the stage-forceps, *f*; if very small, or transparent, it may be gummed to the dark well, *e*, or mounted on a Beck's opaque disc-revolver.

Fig. 155.—Stage Forceps, for holding objects while under examination.

Fig. 156.—Beck's Disc-holder.

This holder will be found useful for the examination of opaque or other objects that cannot be conveniently held by the stage forceps, the specimen being temporarily attached to it by gum or gold size. The holder is intended to rotate, so that every portion of the object can be brought into view. In this way it will be found useful in the study of insects, foraminifera, &c.

With the Lieberkühn, however, the illumination of opaque objects must be more or less one-sided, and therefore, the silver side-reflector has superseded it for general use (Fig. 157). To ensure a more perfect illumination of the object, the bull's-eye lens should also be used. Mr. Sorby devised a reflector to fit over the objective. It consists of a semi-circular cap; is, in short, a modification of the parabolic reflector. The light from the mirror can, by slightly varying its inclination, be brought into use with this reflector.

The silver side-reflector is usually made with a ball-and-socket joint, so that it can be turned in any direction. It is secured to the stage of the microscope by the pin, which drops into a hole purposely drilled to receive it, and facility given for turning up and down, or in any position. If daylight is used the microscope should be placed in such a position that the light from a white cloud falls upon the speculum, but the light of the lamp is far more manageable for use with the reflector.

Fig. 157.—Silver Side-reflector.

The Lieberkühn is only intended to be used with low powers—a 2-inch, ½-inch and a ⅔-inch. Such objects as the elytra of the diamond and other beetles are well suited for examination.

Fig. 158.—Sorby's Modification of the Parabolic Reflector.

While experimenting with a parabolic reflector (Fig. 158), Mr. Sorby saw the value of examining objects under every kind of illumination. As on viewing specimens of iron and steel with this reflector he found that, from the great obliquity of the illumination obtained, the more brilliantly polished parts of the specimen reflected the light beyond the aperture of the objective, and these could not be distinguished from those parts which absorbed light, he thereupon proceeded to place a small flat mirror in front of the objective, and cover half its aperture, and at the same time stop off by means of a semi-cylindrical tube the light from the parabolic reflector. This arrangement produced the reverse appearance of that first employed, and it proved to be a useful aid in determining structure.

The Bull's-eye Condensing Lens.

This accessory is brought into constant use for the purpose of converging rays from a lamp or mirror; or, for reducing the diverging rays of the lamp to parallelism with the parabolic illuminator, or silver side-reflector. The form in use is a plano-convex lens of about three or four inches in focal length (Fig. 159). It is usually mounted on a brass stand, so that it may be placed and turned in any direction, and at any height. When used by daylight, its plane side should be turned towards the object, and the same position maintained when used for converging the rays of light from the lamp; but when used with the side-reflector the plane side must be towards the lamp. Much attention has been paid to this very necessary accessory, the bull's-eye lens. A doublet has been brought into use which has increased the value of the bull's-eye condenser in bacteriological research, and in micro-photography generally.

Fig. 159.—Bull's-eye Lens.

"During a recent investigation of the spherical aberration in doublets, it was believed to be impossible to construct a doublet of the form known as 'Herschel's doublet' free from aberration, although these doublets figure in many books on optics. In a condenser made by Baker the aberration is reduced to a minimum, 27 per cent. less than Sir John Herschel's. This doublet, it appears, differs from Herschel's both in the ratio of the radii of the meniscus, and also in the ratio of the foci of the two lenses; indeed, the only point of similarity is in the first lens, which is crossed. To test this, project the image of the flat lamp-flame on a piece of white card with a plano-convex lens (the field-lens of the Huyghenian eye-piece), use first the convex side and then the plane side towards the card, the lamp being placed about 6 feet from the lens. Focus the lamp-flame as sharply as possible, and a circular halo of misty light will be seen to surround the lamp-flame; but when the plane side of the lens is made to face the card this halo of misty light will be seen to be greatly reduced, and the brightness of the image of the flame proportionately increased. If the lens, then, were strictly aplanatic there should be no misty halo, all the light being concentrated in the image of the lamp-flame, and the image of maximum brightness. In short, the diameter of the halo or misty light is the measure of the spherical aberration. If the condenser referred to above, having the form of minimum aberration for two planes, be compared in the same manner with an ordinary single bull's-eye of the same focus, the diameter of the misty halo will be found reduced to a radius of about $\frac{1}{5}$-inch, but, with this new condenser there is a further reduction, so that the radius of the misty halo measures only $\frac{1}{20}$-inch. These experiments are instructive, because the brightness, or the mistiness of the microscopical image is an associated phenomenon."[29]

A sectional view of the optical arrangement of Baker's aplanatic bull's-eye doublet is shown, together with lamp, in Fig. 148.

The Microscope Lamp.—The introduction of paraffin into household use has somewhat modified our views with regard to the most suitable artificial source of illumination. Good paraffin burns with a whiter and purer flame than colza oil, and consequently is less liable to fatigue the eyes. The first cost of the lamp is trifling; for a moderate sum a handy form of lamp can be had, mounted on an adjustable sliding ring stand, and with a porcelain, metal or paper shade, to protect the eyes from scattered rays of light. All opticians supply accepted forms of lamps.

To give the increased effect of whiteness to the light ("white cloud illumination" as it is termed), take a piece of tissue paper, dip it into a hot bath of spermaceti, and, when nearly cold, cut out a circular piece and secure it over the largest opening in the diaphragm plate. This will be found to materially moderate and soften the light.

Fig. 160.—Beck's Complete Lamp.

Beck's Complete Lamp is constructed especially for delicate microscopical work. It has a burner giving a flat flame; this can be rotated to enable the edge or the flat of the flame to be used; likewise a metal chimney with two apertures, in which 3 × 1 glass slips slide; either white or coloured glasses may be used. A Herschel aplanatic condenser is carried on a swinging arm, which rotates around the lamp flame as a centre, and can be clamped in any position. The whole lamp has a raising and lowering motion, with a spring clamp to hold it in any position. The lamp is so designed that at its lowest position the flame is only three inches from the table. Here the microscopist is furnished with a lamp which will accomplish all he may require with regard to illumination.

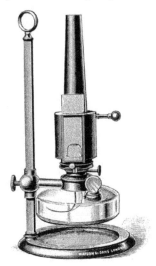

Fig. 161.—Watson's Microscope Lamp.

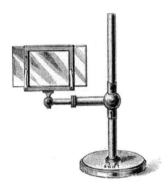

Fig. 162.—Glass Holder for carrying Coloured Glasses.

Watson's lamp (Fig. 161) has a metal chimney, and is somewhat simpler in structure than those already referred to. For the student, the simpler and cheaper form will answer every purpose. A glass holder for carrying various tinted slips of coloured glass to act as a screen or modifier of the light is much employed, and assists in determining fine structures (Fig. 162).

Nose-pieces and Objective Changers.

A convenient appendage to the microscope is the rotating nose-piece, invented by Mr. Charles Brooke, F.R.S., and intended to carry two or more objectives, whereby a saving of time is effected, and the trouble of repeatedly screwing and unscrewing is avoided. In the application of the nose-piece attention should be given to centring. Messrs. Baker's objective changer is intended to facilitate the placing and replacing the nose-piece in position. This adaptation consists of a milled head, acting on three jaws, having a universal screw thread, a decided improvement on the screw. Zeiss has adopted a tube-sliding objective changer with centring adjustments. Messrs. Watson met the difficulty of centring by making the nose-piece a part of the body-tube of their microscopes (Fig. 163). This, when adapted to the shorter body of the students' microscope, fully compensates for want of length.

Fig. 163.—Watson's Centring Nose-piece of Microscope.

Their triple nose-piece is constructed with much care, and when in use is found very effective. It is manufactured of that very light metal aluminium, and which minimises the strain produced by the heavier brass nose-piece.

Finders.—The finder affords a necessary and useful means of registering the position of any particular object, so that it may be readily found again at any subsequent period. In the work of examination the finder will save time when making a special research, extending over a considerable surface.

Fig. 164.—Triple Nose-pieces.

That the finder has been of use may be surmised from the number invented and figured in the "Journal of the Royal Microscopical Society." By far the most useful form is that of graduating the plates of the mechanical stage, dividing a certain portion into 100 parts. Powell and Lealand have adopted this system in their No. 1 stands, while Baker and Watson have added a graduated scale on silver to $\frac{1}{100}$th mm. as a finder, and also a stage micrometer in $\frac{1}{10}$th and $\frac{1}{100}$th of a millimetre, together with a Maltwood finder for lodging the position of any desired portion of a specimen under examination.

The *Maltwood* finder (Fig. 165) can be used with any microscope, and without a mechanical stage. This useful finder continues to occupy a permanent place among the accessories of the microscope. It consists of a glass slide, 3 × 1¼ inches, on which is photographed a scale occupying a square inch; this is divided by horizontal and vertical lines into 2,500 squares, each of which contains two numbers marking its "latitude," or place in the vertical series, and its "longitude," or place in the horizontal series. The scale is in each instance an exact distance from the bottom and left-hand end of the glass slide; and the slide, when in use, should rest upon the ledge of the stage of the microscope, and be made to abut against a stop, a simple pin, about an inch and a half from the centre of the stage.

Fig. 165.—Maltwood's Finder.

Dr. Pantacsek's finder appears to have some advantage over Maltwood's, but it cannot be used with the same facility, and therefore will not displace an old favourite. *The Amyot* finder I have long had in use; it is efficient and inexpensive—can indeed, if misplaced or lost, be replaced by the aid of the square and compasses.

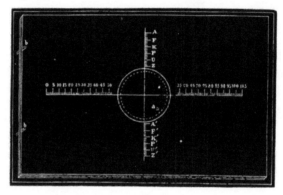

Fig. 166.—Amyot's Object Finder.

The Okeden finder consists of two graduated scales, one *vertical*, attached to the fixed stage-plate, the other *horizontal*, attached to an arm carried by the intermediate plate; the first of these scales enables the worker to "set" the vertically-sliding plate to any determinate position in relation to the fixed plate, while the second gives the power of setting the horizontally-sliding plate by that of the intermediate.

Micrometers.—It is of the utmost importance to have a means of measuring with accuracy the objects, or part of objects, under observation. The most efficient piece of apparatus for the purpose is the micrometer eye-piece, the earlier form of which, Jackson's, has been described under the heading *Eye-pieces* (p. 144). In the case of micrometers, as in that of most other accessories, every optician has his own adaptation and method of employing the same.

For the measurement of bacteria, a stage micrometer should be used with a camera lucida. The stage micrometer consists of a slip of thin glass ruled with a scale consisting of tenths and hundredths of a millimetre. The image is projected on to a piece of paper placed on the table, and the drawing made, and the object to be measured can be readily compared with the scale.

Fig. 167.—The Ramsden Micrometer Eye-piece.

In the Ramsden micrometer eye-piece, as previously explained, two fine wires are stretched across the field of an eye-piece, one of which can be moved by a micrometer screw. In the field there is also a scale with teeth, and the interval between them corresponds to that of the threads of the screw.

The circumference of the brass head is usually divided into one hundred parts, and a screw with one hundred threads to the inch is used. The bacterium to be measured is brought into a position in which an edge appears to be in contact with the fixed wire, and the micrometer screw is turned until the travelling wire appears to be in contact with the other edge. The scale in the field and scale on the milled head, together, give the number of complete turns of the screw and the value of a fraction of a turn in separating the wires.

In the micrometer eye-piece constructed by Zeiss, the eye-piece with a glass plate with crossed lines is carried across the field by means of a micrometer screw. Each division on the edge of a drum corresponds to ·01 mm. Complete revolutions of the drum are counted by means of a figured scale in the visual field.

In the micrometer used with Zeiss's *apochromatic* objectives and compensating eye-pieces the divisions are so computed, that, with a tube-length of 160 mm., the value of one interval represents, with each objective, just as many micra (·0001 mm.) as there are millimetres in its focal length. A value of tables is therefore not required for these eye-pieces, since the focus of the lenses indicates their micrometer values within 5 per cent.

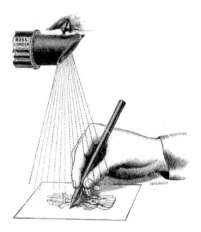

Fig. 168.—The Wollaston Camera Lucida.

The *Camera Lucida* will prove an extremely useful adjunct to the micrometer, and a large number of contrivances have been devised for its employment. There are those which project the image on to the surface of a sheet of paper provided for the drawing, and those which project the pencil and paper into the field of the microscope. The former method is that usually adopted. To draw an object, with either a Wollaston camera lucida or a neutral tint reflector, such as that of Beale's, both of which are made to slide on and take the place of the cap of the eye-piece, as shown in Fig. 168, with its flat side uppermost, the whole instrument must be raised until the edge of the prism is exactly 10 inches from a piece of paper placed upon the table; with the latter the instrument retains its vertical position, and the image of the object is thrown on the paper placed in front of the stand. The light must be so regulated that no more than is really necessary is upon the object, whilst a full light should be thrown upon the paper. Only one eye is to be used; and if one half of the pupil be directed over the edge of the prism, the object will appear upon the paper, and can be traced on it by a pencil, the point of which will also be seen. Should any blueness be visible in the field, the prism is pushed too far on, and should be drawn back till the colour disappears.

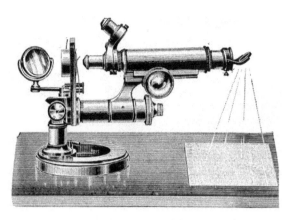

Fig. 169.—Microscope in position for drawing.

Fig. 170.—Beale's Neutral Tint Reflector.

The position in which the microscope must be placed is shown in the accompanying illustration (Fig. 169).

Beale's neutral tint reflector (Fig. 170) is much in use, and its advantages are utility, simplicity, and inexpensiveness.

Fig. 171.—The Abbe Model Camera Lucida.

The Abbe model of camera lucida has been brought into use because the projected image can be better illuminated, and is consequently so much brighter. This form is now made in aluminium by Messrs. Watson & Sons. In place of the image being traced by projection on paper, the reverse is the case, both the paper and pencil are projected into the field of view. The mirror reflects the paper on to the silvered surface of a prism placed over the eye-lens of the eye-piece of the microscope, and it is thereby conveyed to the eye. There is a central opening in the silvering through which microscopic vision is obtained. It is fitted in a new manner by means of a cloth-lined adapter, fitting over the outside of the microscope tube; this saves all trouble in centring and ensures concentricity. Where the instrument has capped eye-pieces, the camera lucida must be adapted to the eye-piece, the cap being removed. The apparatus can be disconnected from the fitting adapter by means of a sliding pin, and readily replaced, or can be lifted over out of the way, as shown in the drawing. Being made almost entirely in aluminium it is very much lighter than other forms of apparatus, and does not cause vibration. It can be used with the microscope *at any angle*, the only necessity being that the paper on which the sketch is made should be kept at the same angle as the instrument.

Micro-Photography.

Micro-photography or photo-micrography, as it is indifferently termed, has, to a very considerable extent, superseded the use of the camera lucida for the delineation of images seen under the microscope. I may claim to be among the first workers with the microscope (1841) to prove beyond a doubt that the camera could be made to render invaluable aid to the microscopist, whereby a great saving of time might be effected, and a drawing obtained with greater accuracy than that of the pencil of the draughtsman.

It was about 1864-5 that Dr. Woodward's earlier micro-photographs were first seen in London. His skill in the manipulation of the microscope had been long known. His first series of photographs of test diatoms created, I remember, quite a sensation; they have probably never been surpassed. These were taken by sun-light, magnesium, and electric-light. I was the recipient of a series taken at a later date (1870), and which, bound in quarto volume, are almost as perfect in definition as any of a later date taken by oil-immersion objectives.

The objectives used by Dr. Woodward, throughout, were a $\frac{1}{8}$-inch of Wales's (new series), and a $\frac{1}{16}$-inch immersion, of Powell & Lealand's, especially produced for work with the camera. The magnification varied from 800 to 3,000 diameters, a frustule of *Grammatophora Marina* magnified 2,500, and a scale of podura, marked 3,000 in my collection, are equal in definition to those taken by a high-angle $\frac{1}{12}$-inch oil-immersion. Pathological specimens taken with lower powers are equally instructive, a section of epithelial cancer showing both nuclei and cells with distinctness.

Dr. Maddox in 1864 was also experimentally engaged in the improvement of the processes of photography for the purpose of promoting the work of microscopists. His labours were attended with great success. To him we are indebted for the gelatine dry-plate process, which gave a remarkable impetus to photography in general. Dr. Maddox has, for a period extending over forty years, diligently and successfully cultivated and promoted micro-photography. Among other workers to whom we are indebted for improvements in micro-photography I may mention Wenham, Draper, Shadbolt, Highley, Koch, Sternberg, Pringle, Leitz, and Pfeiffer.

Dr. Koch justly claims the credit of having extended the application of micro-photography to the delineation of bacteria. A series of instructive micro-photographs were published by him in 1877.

The importance of the camera has become more manifest as the work of the bacteriologist has progressed. Koch strongly advocated micro-photography on the ground that illustrations, especially of bacteria, should be as true to nature as possible. Dr. Edgar Crookshank holds the same opinion, and in support of his views we have numerous illustrations of the bacteria given in his valuable "Text-book of Bacteriology." But he does not disguise the truth that there are difficulties to be encountered, the first of which is owing to the fact that the smallest and most interesting bacteria can only be made visible in animal tissues by *staining*. This drawback has been very nearly overcome by the use of eosin-collodion. With this medium, and by shutting off portions of the spectrum by coloured glasses, Koch succeeded in obtaining photographs of bacteria, which were stained with blue and red aniline dyes. This method, however, introduced a disturbing element of another kind. Owing to the longer exposure required, the results were wanting in definition, attributable, it was thought, to vibrations of the apparatus produced by passing traffic, or by assistants moving about over the floor of the laboratory.

Koch nevertheless showed, at the great meeting of the International Medical Association in London, 1881, a series of micro-photographs of bacteria and tissue sections, which were the admiration of all who saw them. To meet a difficulty occasioned by the aniline dyes, Koch recommended that the preparations should be stained brown; other experimenters found that preparations stained either yellow or yellowish-brown gave good photographic representations; but it is by no means an easy matter to find a good differential stain of bacteria in the tissues, as even Bismarck brown is not entirely successful. Other bacteriologists have encountered similar difficulties at the outset. Hauser succeeded in showing the value of micro-photography in the production of pictures of *impression* preparations and colonies of bacteria in nutrient-gelatine. But to give the general effect, as well as faithfully reproduce the minute details in these preparations of bacteria by the aid of the pencil, would in most cases create insurmountable difficulties, except in the hand of the most accomplished draughtsman. Hauser employed Gerlach's apparatus, and Schleusser's dry-plates, and obtained his illumination by means of a small incandescent lamp, which gave a strong white light. The preparations so photographed were for the most part stained brown, and mounted in the ordinary way in Canada balsam.

In 1884, Van Ermengen succeeded in photographing preparations of comma-bacilli stained with fuchsine and methyl violet. These pictures afforded the first practical illustration of the value of iso-chromatic plates in micro-photography, and their introduction marks a distinct era in the progress of micro-photography. The iso-chromatic, or more properly the ortho-chromatic, dry-plate process was introduced because in photography blue or violet comes out almost or quite white, while other colours, yellow and red, are represented by a sombre shade or even by black. This is due to the want of equality of strength between the luminous and the actinic or chemical rays of light. In other words, the violet and blue rays are more chemically active than any other portion of the spectrum. It was found, then, that if plates were coloured yellow with turmeric, the blue and violet rays were intercepted, and their actinism proportionately reduced.

"In 1881, the so-called iso-chromatic plates were introduced. The emulsion of bromide of silver and gelatine was stained with eosin, and it was claimed that colours could be represented with their relative intensity; chlorophyll and other stains have also been tried, and by such methods the ordinary gelatine dry-plates can be so treated that they will reproduce various colours, according to their relative light intensity, and thus be rendered *iso-*, or what is now known as ortho-chromatic."

Apparatus and Material.

Apparatus and Material used in micro-photography have, from time to time, been greatly varied by different workers, some preferring to use the microscope in the vertical position with the camera superimposed or fitted on the eye-piece of the microscope tube; others, again, prefer that both the microscope and the camera should be arrayed horizontally. In another form the ordinary microscope is dispensed with and the objective stage and mirror are adapted to the front of the camera, together with a suitable arrangement for holding the object. Lastly, the camera is lain aside, and an operating-room rendered impervious to light, takes its place, and the image is projected and focussed upon a ground glass screen held in its place by a separate support. This method has been made practical since the introduction into microscopy by Zeiss of the *projection* eye-piece. It is well known that micro-photographs can be produced by employing these projection eye-pieces, as well as for screen illustrations in the lecture-room.

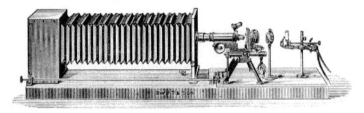

Fig. 172.—Swift's Horizontal Apparatus.

With regard to the position of the microscope and camera, the horizontal affords greater stability than the vertical, and is on this account to be preferred. The simplest apparatus consists of a camera fixed upon a base board, four or five feet in length, upon which the microscope can be clamped, and which also carries the lamp and bull's-eye lens (Fig. 172). This arrangement I have found economical and useful. No more elaborate arrangement is actually necessary. Sunlight is no doubt the best, but a good paraffin lamp is a handy and available illuminant.

With the former, and rapid plates, a short exposure of three or four seconds, even when high powers are used, is found sufficient; whereas, with the paraffin lamp it will vary from three to ten minutes.

Walmsley gives the following table for exposures with the lamp:—

1½-inch	objective	3 to 45	seconds.
⅔-inch	"	7 to 90	"
4/10-inch	"	½ to 3	minutes.
⅕-inch	"	2 to 7	"
1/10-inch	"	4 to 10	"

For micro-photography the following practical rules must be observed. The sub-stage condenser may be dispensed with when low powers are used, as well as the mirror, and the lamp so placed that the image of the flat of the flame appears accurately adjusted in the centre of the field of the microscope. The bull's-eye lens is so interposed, that the image of the flame disappears, and the whole field becomes equally illuminated with high powers; the sub-stage achromatic condenser must be used, and a greater intensity of illumination is obtained by placing the lamp-flame edgeways. It is advisable to begin the practice of micro-photography with low powers, and a trial experiment should be made with some well-known object as the blow-fly's tongue.

Dr. Crookshank is of opinion that, in the case of micro-organisms when their biological characters are studied under low powers of the microscope, photographs are preferable, because they give a more faithful representation of the object. A micro-organism, even under the highest powers of the microscope, is so minute an object, that to represent it in a drawing requires a very delicate touch, and it is only too easy to make a *picture* which gives an erroneous impression to those who have not seen the original. Photography enables the scientific worker to record rapid changes, and it is quite possible as the art advances we may find the film more sensitive than the human retina, and that it will bring out details in bacteria which would be otherwise unrecognised. The result, therefore, of experience is that in research laboratories it will come into more general use as a faithful and graphic method. I cannot better bring these observations to a close than by giving a quotation from Dr. Piersoll's practical method of obtaining micro-photographs.

The three essential conditions to ensure success in micro-photography are:— (1) Satisfactory apparatus; (2) good illumination; (3) suitable preparations. With high amplifications (1,000 diameters and over), the conditions are greatly changed by the approach to the limit both of the shortness of the focus of the objective and of the length of the camera which can be advantageously used; for the first experience leads to the adoption of the $\frac{1}{12}$-inch, for the second four feet is the limit, since a given high amplification, say 2,000 diameters, can be more satisfactorily and more conveniently obtained with a superior $\frac{1}{12}$-inch connection with suitable optical means to increase the initial magnifying power of the objective, than with an unaided $\frac{1}{25}$-inch lens, and the plate removed to a greater distance. Until quite recently the various amplifiers offered the best means of increasing the power of an objective, but the introduction of the *projection-oculars* of Zeiss is an accessory piece of apparatus, far superior to any older device. These projection-oculars resemble ordinary microscopical oculars or eye-pieces only in general form and name, being optically a projection-objective in connection with a collecting lens. The new oil-immersion apochromatic lenses, in combination with these projection-oculars, form undoubtedly the more efficient equipment for high-power work; it is as true for high-power photography as for microscopical observation in general, that the best results are obtained with fine and necessarily expensive, optical appliances. If for the satisfactory study of the intimate structure of a cell, or of a micro-organism, the most improved immersion lenses are necessary, it is to be expected that, for the successful photography of the same, tools at least as good are needed. Sunlight certainly affords the most satisfactory illumination whereby good micro-photographs can be obtained, as well as for recording microscopical images. That by good lamp-light fair impressions of objects under extreme magnification can be secured is encouraging, but the negatives produced by such illumination seldom, if ever, possess the characteristics of a really good sunlight negative, where the sharpest details are combined with an exquisite softness and harmony of half-tones.

If the mirror of the microscope be of good size, it will only be necessary to make an arm on which to support the removed mirror outside some southerly exposed window, since it is desirable to have a greater distance between the mirror and the stage than would be possible were the mirror attached in its usual place. Where the microscope mirror is too small to be satisfactorily used, a rectangular wood-framed looking-glass is readily mounted, with the aid of a few strips of wood, so as to turn about both axes.

The rays from the plane side of the mirror should pass through a condensing lens (of 8-10-inch focus, if possible), so placed that they are brought to a focus before reaching the plane of the object. The exact position of the condensing lens is a matter of experience; usually, however, the most favourable illumination is obtained at that point where the field is brilliantly and *uniformly* illuminated, just before the rays form the image source of light; the nearer the focus the less disturbance from diffraction rings. Ordinary objectives will require the employment of monochromatic light—produced either by a deep blue solution of ammonia-sulphate of copper, or by the green glass screen—since the optical and actinic foci do not usually perfectly coincide. Powers up to the ¾-inch will require no further condenser; with the ¼ or ⅙-inch objectives, the low power (1 or ¾-inch) serves with advantage as an achromatic condenser, when attached to the sub-stage. The Abbe condenser, although so important for fine microscopical investigation, is not adapted to photography unless a very wide cone of light is desired, which, for the majority of preparations, is some advantage; a low-power objective, used as a condenser, is found to be more satisfactory than the Abbe with a small diaphragm.[30]

The greatest delicacy in manipulation is necessary, as in working with a 1/12-inch objective a turn too much of the fine adjustment will cause the image to vanish. With fine preparations of bacteria it is not easy to trace the image, and hence the advantage of commencing with a well-marked object, as that of the fly's tongue. The development and fixation of the image must be proceeded with as in the ordinary photographic process. In the text-books of photography full accounts of failures will be found, their causes and prevention. Numerous papers and suggestions for micro-photographic work will also be found scattered throughout the "Journal of the Royal Microscopical Society."

The *Projection Eye-piece* has become an essential part of micro-photography, and it is so arranged that it may be employed with advantage with objectives of either the apochromatic or ordinary series for photographic purposes, projecting an exquisitely sharp image of the object on the plate. A diaphragm between the lenses limits the field, and a sharp image of it should appear on the screen when the eye-piece is adjusted. The adjustment may be effected by revolving the eye-piece cap in a spiral slot, so that the eye or top lens is either brought closer or removed farther away from the diaphragm, as may be required, and divisions and a reader are usually provided for registering positions. Such eye-pieces are made to fit any size microscope body.

Initial magnifying powers:—

English length of tube	10-in.	3 and 6.
Continental " "	6-in.	2 and 4.

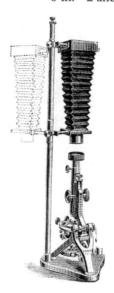

Fig. 173.—Baker's Pringle Vertical Micro-photographic Apparatus.

The microscope and camera (Fig. 173) are here seen to be part of the same instrument. The bellows of the camera have an extension varying from 6 in. to 30 in. The board on which the microscope and limelight jet are fixed is made to turn out of the line of the camera to facilitate adjusting the instrument and radiant, either limelight, electric light or paraffin lamp; when this is done the board carrying the same is turned back to a stop which brings the microscope into a central position with the focussing screen. An adjustment is supplied at the side of the camera, geared to the slow movement, for finely focussing the object upon the screen. A light-excluding connection is fitted to the front of the camera and microscope; immediately behind this, in the bellows, is an exposing shutter which is manipulated by means of a small milled head. Two focussing screens are usually supplied, one grey, and one patent plate, together with a double dark slide.

Mr. Andrew Pringle's vertical micro-photographic apparatus is an excellent form; it consists of a heavy base and brass support, carrying a quarter-plate camera, grey and plain glass focussing screen, double dark back, camera extending to 24 inches, and turning aside as shown in Fig 173. It is light-tight in all its connections.

To secure uniform results in micro-photography, only thin preparations, which lie as nearly as possible in one plane, can be relied upon for good and perfect negatives.

Fig. 174.—Ross's Arc Lamp.

An electric arc lamp specially designed for micro-photographic work, wherever the electric current is available, is that known as "the Ross-Hepworth projection arc lamp." The advantage gained by this form of lamp is not only on account of the ease with which it may be employed, but also on account of its superior power and quality. It is of primary importance that the lamp employed to convert the electricity into light should be of a good and reliable pattern. It is not essential that it should be automatic in its working—many experienced micro-photographers preferring a simple hand-feed lamp to the one of a more complicated kind, being so much less difficult to keep in order. A good hand-feed microscope-lamp has the advantage of greater simplicity and portability.

The argand gas-light arranged for me many years ago for micro-photography may be employed with advantage. It is clean, and always ready for use when brought down to the table attached by a piece of india-rubber tubing. The incandescent form of burner enhances its value, since the light is thereby rendered whiter. The arrangement is shown in the diagrammatic drawing, Fig. 175.

Over the argand burner B, is a pale-blue glass chimney, resting on a wire gauze, stage A; this secures a uniform current of air. The colour of the flame may be still more influenced by a disc of neutral tint, or other coloured glass, inserted into the circular opening at E, in a half-cylinder of metal, G, used to cut off all extraneous light; can be rotated on the stage by the ivory nob at H, a metallic reflector I, attached to the standard rod, on being brought parallel to F serves to concentrate the light and send it on to the bull's-eye, and through it to the mirror, or directly to the photo-microscopic camera.

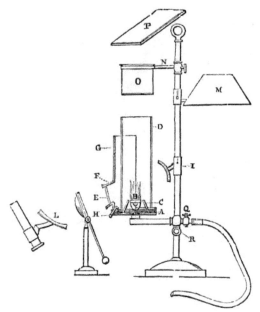

Fig. 175.—Table Incandescent Gas-lamp.

By removing the shield G, and bringing the shade M over the burner, it is at once converted into a useful microscopical lamp, for all ordinary purposes. The screw R clamps the lamp-flame at any height, while the support N carries a water-bath O, or a plate P, both of which will be found useful in preparing and mounting objects.

A special incandescent gas-lamp is made by Messrs. R. & J. Beck.

Polarisation of Light.

Common light moves in two planes at right angles to each other, while polarised light moves in one plane only. Common light may be turned into polarised light either by transmission or reflection; in the first instance, one of the planes of common light is got rid of by reflection; in the other, by absorption. Huyghens was one of the first physicists to notice that a ray of light has not the same properties in every part of its circumference, and he compared it to a magnet or a collection of magnets; and supposed that the minute particles of which it was said to be composed had different poles, which, when acted on in certain ways, arranged themselves in particular positions; and thence the term *polarisation*, a term having neither reference to cause nor effect. It is to Malus, however, who, in 1808, discovered polarisation by reflection, that we are indebted for the series of splendid phenomena which have since that period been developed; phenomena of such surpassing beauty as to exceed most ordinary objects presented to the eye under the microscope.

Certainly no more misleading name could well have been found to describe the causation, in one particular direction, of small displacements in the medium, through which the light waves are made to pass.

The effect of "polarising" light is simply to alter the directions of the vibrations of light, and allow of certain waves to pass which are vibrating in one direction only, vertical, horizontal, or oblique, as the case may be. The most efficient agent discovered for the polarisation of light is that of Iceland spar, cut and mounted as a "Nicol" prism.

By cutting crystals of Iceland spar into two parts, at a particular angle, and cementing them together again in the reverse way, Nicol succeeded in showing that one of the two polarising pencils could be totally deflected to one side, while the other is directly transmitted through the Nicol prism, and thereby the beam of light becomes at once "polarised" in one plane only. No apparent difference can be seen in the prism on holding it up to the light, except it be in a very slight loss of brightness; but if another similarly heated crystal be held before, and made to revolve around, a quarter of the circle just where the two cross each other, total darkness results. This phenomenon alternately recurs at every quadrature of the circle. A pair of Nicol prisms, when appropriately mounted, constitute "a polarising apparatus" for the microscope, one being fitted into the sub-stage, and the other either immediately above the objective or eye-piece, where it can be easily rotated, the object to be examined being placed on the stage of the microscope, that is, between the polarising and analysing prisms.

POLARISCOPE OBJECTS.

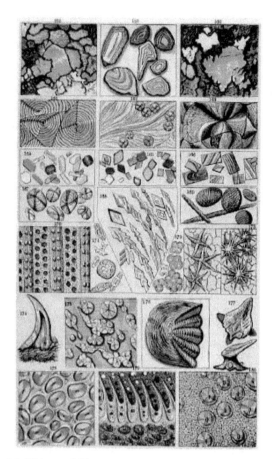

Tuffen West, del. Edmund Evans.

PLATE VIII.

The significance of polarised light centres in the fact that it affords a wider insight into the structure of crystals, minerals, and a number of other substances, and which could not otherwise be obtained without its aid. Its usefulness is multifold, as even glass itself, when not properly annealed, exhibits points of fracture, by a display of Newton's rings. The knowledge thus acquired is turned to account by glass manufacturers.

Double refraction.—When an incident ray of light is refracted into a crystal of any other than the cubic system, or into compressed or *unannealed glass*, it gives rise to two refracted rays which take different paths; this phenomenon is termed *double refraction.* Attention was called to this in 1670, by Bartolin, who first observed it in Iceland spar; and the laws for this substance were accurately determined by Huyghens.

Iceland spar or calc spar is a form of crystallized carbonate of lime. It is composed of fifty-six parts of lime and forty-four parts of carbonic acid, and is usually found in rhombohedral forms of crystallization.

To observe the phenomenon of double refraction, a rhomb of Iceland spar may be laid on a page of a printed book, when all the letters seen through it will appear double; the depth of the blackness of the letters is seen to be considerably less than that of the originals, except where the two images overlap.

In order to state the laws of the phenomena with precision, it is necessary to attend to the crystalline form of Iceland spar, which has equal obtuse angles. If a line be drawn through one of these corners, making equal angles with the three edges which meet there, it, or any line parallel to it, is called the *axis* of the crystal; the axis being, properly speaking, not a definite *line* but a definite *direction*.

The angles of the crystals are the same in all specimens. If the crystal is of such proportions that these three edges spoken of are equal, as in the smaller crystal (Fig. 176), the axis is the direction of one of its diagonals, as represented.

Any plane containing (or parallel to) the axis is called the *principal plane* of the crystal.

In the next diagram, Fig. 177, the line appears double, as *a b* and *c d*, or the dot, as *e* and *f*. Or allow a ray of light, *g h*, to fall thus on the crystal, it will in its passage through be separated into two rays, *h f*, *h e*; and on coming to the opposite surface of the crystal, will pass out at *e f* in the direction of *i k*, parallel to *g h*. The plane *l m n o* is designated the principal section of the crystal, and the line drawn from the solid angle *l* to the angle *o* is where the axis of the crystal will be found; this is its optic axis. Now when a ray of light passes along this axis, it is undivided, and there is only one image; but in all other directions there are two images.

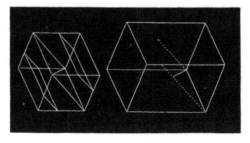

Fig. 176.—Axis of Crystals of Iceland Spar.

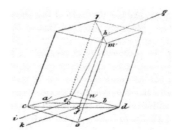

Fig. 177.—A Rhomb showing the passage of Rays of Light.

Mr. Nicol, of Edinburgh first succeeded in making a rhomb of Iceland spar into a *single-image prism*. His method of splitting up the crystal into two equal parts was as follows:—

A rhomb of Iceland spar of one-fourth of an inch in length, and about four-eighths of an inch in breadth and thickness, is divided into two equal portions in a plane, passing through the acute lateral angle, and nearly touching the obtuse side angle. The sectional plane of each of these halves must be carefully polished, and the two portions cemented firmly together with Canada balsam, so as to form a rhomb similar to that before division; by this management the ordinary and extraordinary rays are so separated that only one is transmitted: the cause of this great divergence of the rays is considered to be owing to the action of the Canada balsam, the refractive index of which (1·549) is that between the ordinary (1·6543) and the extraordinary (1·4833) refraction of calcareous spar, and which will change the direction of both rays in an opposite manner before they enter the posterior half of the combination. The direction of rays passing through such a prism is indicated by the arrow, Fig. 178.

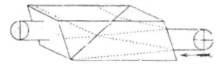

Fig. 178.

Polarised light cannot be distinguished from common light, as already said, by the naked eye; and for all experimental purposes in polarisation, two pieces of apparatus must be employed, one to produce polarisation, and the other to show or an analyse it. The former is called the *polariser*, the latter the *analyser*, and every apparatus that serves for one of these purposes will also serve for the other.

Fig. 179.—Polariser.

Fig. 179a.—Analyser.

Polarising Apparatus for Students' Microscope.

In all cases there are two positions, differing by 180°, which give a minimum of light, and the two positions intermediate between these give a maximum of light. The extent of the changes thus observed is a measure of the completeness of the polarisation of light.

The two prisms mounted as shown in Figs. 179 and 179a constitute the apparatus adapted to the microscope. The polariser slips into place below the stage, and the analyser, with the prism fixed in a tube, is screwed in above the objective.

The definition is considered by some experimenters as somewhat better if the analyser be used above the eye-piece, and is certainly more easily rotated.

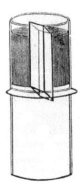

Fig. 180.—Prism mounted as an Eye-piece.

Method of employing the Polarising Prism (Fig. 179).—After having adapted it to slide into a groove on the under-surface of the stage, where it is secured and kept in place by the small milled-head screw, the other prism Fig. 179*a*) is screwed on above the object-glass, and thus passes directly into the body of the microscope. The light from the mirror having been reflected through them the axes of the two prisms must be made to coincide; this is done by regulating the milled-head screw until, by revolving the *polarising* prism, the field of view is entirely darkened twice during its revolution. If very minute salts or crystals are submitted for examination then it will be found preferable to place the analyser above the eye-piece, as in Fig. 180. Thus the *polariscope* is seen to consist of two parts; one for *polarising*, the other for *analysing* or testing the light. There is no essential difference between the two parts, except what convenience or economy may lead us to adopt; and either part, therefore, may be used as polariser or analyser; but whichever is used as the polariser, the other becomes the analyser.

Fig. 181.—More Modern Polariser and Analyser.

Opticians have their own methods of adapting the polariser and analyser to their several microscopes. Watson's special form of apparatus is represented in Fig. 181, the polariser being adapted to the sub-stage, and the analyser to screw into the objective.

Tourmaline.—A semi-transparent mineral, of a neutral or bluish tint, called tourmaline, when cut into thin slices (about $\frac{1}{20}$-inch thick) with their faces parallel to their axes exhibit the same phenomena as the Nicol prism. The only objection to which is that the transmitted polarised beam is more or less coloured. The tourmaline to be preferred stops the most light when its axis is at right-angles to that of the polariser, and yet admits the most when in the same plane. Make choice of a tourmaline as perfect as possible; size is of less importance when intended for use with the microscope.

Transmission of rays through tourmaline is only one of several ways in which light can be polarised. When a beam of light is reflected from a polished surface of glass, wood, ivory, leather, or any other non-metallic substance, at an angle of 50° to 60° with the normal, it is more or less polarised, and in like manner a reflector composed of any of these substances may be employed as an analyser. In so using it, it should be rotated about an axis parallel to the incident rays which are to be tested, and the observation consists in noting whether this rotation produces changes in the amount of reflected light.

For every reflected substance there is a particular angle of incidence, which gives a maximum of polarisation in reflected light. It is called the *polarising angle* for the substance, and its tangent is always equal to the index of refraction of the substance; or, what amounts to the same thing, it is that particular angle of incidence which is the complement of the angle of refraction, so that the refracted rays are at right angles. This important law was discovered experimentally by Sir David Brewster.

Tourmaline, like Iceland spar, is a negative uniaxial crystal; and its use as a polariser depends on the property which it possesses of absorbing the ordinary much more rapidly than the extraordinary ray, so that a thickness which is tolerably transparent to the latter is almost completely opaque to the former. Its pale cobalt blue colour enhances the beauty of certain crystal and mineral substances, but like Iceland spar, the paler and more perfect crystals are becoming scarce.

Selenite is another mineral of value in polarisation experiments. It is a native crystalline hydrated sulphate of lime. A beautiful fibrous variety called *satin-gypsum* is found in Derbyshire. The form of the crystal most frequently met with is that of an oblique rectangular prism, with ten rhomboidal faces, two of which are much larger than the rest. It is usually split up into thin laminæ parallel to their lateral faces; each film should have a thickness of from one-twentieth to one-sixtieth of an inch. In the two rectangular directions these films allow perpendicular rays of polarised light to traverse them unchanged, termed their *neutral axes*. In two other directions, however, which form respectively angles of 45° with the neutral axes, these films have the property of double refraction, a direction known as the *depolarising axis*.

Fig. 182.—Darker's Selenite Films and Stage.

The thickness of the film of selenite determines the particular tint. If, therefore, we use a film of irregular thickness, different colours are presented by the different thicknesses. These facts admit of very curious and beautiful illustration, when used under the object placed on the stage of the microscope. The films employed should be mounted between two glasses for protection. Some persons employ a large film, mounted in this way between the plates of glass, with a raised edge, to act as a stage for supporting the object, it is then called the "selenite stage." The best film for the microscope is that which gives blue, and its complementary colour yellow. The late Mr. Darker constructed a selenite stage for the purpose (Fig. 182). With this a mixture of colours will be brought about, by superimposing three films, one on the other. By slight variations in their positions, produced by means of an endless-screw motion, all the colours of the spectrum can be shown. When objects are thus exhibited, it should be borne in mind that all negative tints, as they are termed, are diminished, and all positive tints increased; the effect of which is to mask the true character of the phenomena.

For a certain thickness of selenite the ellipse will become a circle, and we have thus what is called *circularly-polarised* light, which is characterised by the property that rotation of the analyser produces no change of intensity. Circularly-polarised light is not, however, identical with ordinary light; for the interposition of an additional thickness of selenite converts it into elliptically (or in a particular case into plane) polarised light.

It is necessary, for the exhibition of colour in our experiments, that the plate of selenite should be very thin, otherwise the retardation of one component vibration as compared with the other will be greater by several complete periods for violet than for red, so that the ellipses will be identical for several different colours, and the total non-suppressed light will be sensibly white in all positions of the analyser.

Two thick plates may, however, be so combined as to produce the effect of one thin plate. For example, two selenite plates of nearly equal thickness may be laid one upon the other, so that the direction of greatest elasticity in the one shall be parallel to that of least elasticity in the other. The resultant effect in this case will be that due to the difference of their thicknesses. Two plates so laid are said to be *crossed*.

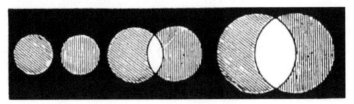

Fig. 183.—*Red* is represented by perpendicular lines; *Green* by oblique.

The following experiments will well serve to illustrate some of the more striking phenomena of double refraction, and will also be a useful introduction to its practical application. Take a plate of brass (Fig. 183) three inches by one, perforated with a series of holes from about one-sixteenth to one-fourth of an inch in diameter; the size of the smallest should be in accordance with the power of the objective, and the separating power of the double refraction.

Experiment 1.—Place the brass plate so that the smallest hole shall be in the centre of the stage of the microscope; employ a low power (1½ or 2 inches) objective, and adjust the focus as for the ordinary microscopic object; place the double image prism over the eye-piece, and two distinct images will be seen; by revolving the prism, the images will describe a circle, the circumference of which will cut the centre of the field of view; one of which is the ordinary, the other the extraordinary ray. By moving the slide from left to right the larger orifices will appear in the field, the images seen will not be completely separated, but will overlap, as represented in the figure.

Experiment 2.—Insert the Nicol's prism into its place under the stage, still retaining the double image prism over the eye-piece; then, by examining the object, there will appear in some positions two images, in others only one image; it will be seen, that at 90° this ray will be cut off, and that which was first observed will become visible; at 180°, or one-half the circle, an alternate change will take place; at 270°, another change; and at 360°, the completion of the circle, the first image will reappear.

Before proceeding to make the next experiment, the position of the Nicol's prism should be adjusted, and its angles brought parallel with the square of the stage. The true relative position of the selenite should also be determined by noticing the natural flaws in the film, which should run parallel with each other, and be adjusted at an angle of about 46° with the square bars of the stage.

Experiment 3.—If we now take the plate of selenite thus prepared, and place it under the piece of brass on the stage, we shall see, instead of the alternate black and white images, two coloured images composed of the constituents of white light, which will alternately change by revolving the eye-piece at every quarter of the circle; then, by passing along the brass, the images will overlap; and at the point at which they do so, white light will be produced. If, by accident, the prism be placed at an angle of 45° from the square part of the stage, no particular colour will be perceived, and it will then illustrate the phenomena of the neutral axis of the selenite, because when placed in the relative position no depolarisation takes place. The phenomena of polarised light may be further illustrated by the addition of a second double image prism, and a film of selenite adapted between the two. The systems of coloured rings in crystals cut perpendicularly to the principal axis of the crystal are best seen by employing the lowest object-glass.

Biaxial Crystals.—To show perfectly the beautiful series of *rings and brushes* which biaxial crystals exhibit, it becomes necessary to convert the microscope, for the time being, into (so to speak) a wide-angled telescope.

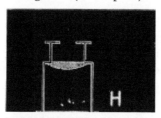

Huyghenian Eye-piece.

Inner draw-tube.

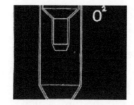

Objective in draw-tube.

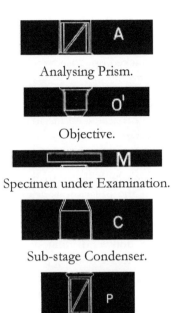

Analysing Prism.

Objective.

Specimen under Examination.

Sub-stage Condenser.

Polarising Prism, fixed in sub-stage below.

Fig. 184.—Diagrammatic arrangement of the Polarising Microscope.

In Sub-stage: P, polarising prism; C, sub-stage condenser on stage; M, mineral or crystal. On nose-piece: O[1], objective, $\frac{4}{10}$-inch; A, analysing prism.

In Draw-tube: O[2], 2 or 3 inch Objective; H, Huyghenian eye-piece.

For the purpose, screw on a low-power objective to the end of the draw-tube (Fig. 184).[31] As the light requires to be passed through the crystals at a considerable angle, a wide-angled condenser should be employed, but it need not be achromatic. The objective most suitable is a $\frac{4}{10}$-inch, of ·64 numerical aperture, but a $\frac{1}{4}$-inch of ·71 numerical aperture, or a $\frac{1}{3}$-inch of ·65 numerical aperture, will answer the purpose equally well. As the whole of the back lens of the objective should be visible through the analysing Nicol prism, the back lens of the objective must not be too large; thus a $\frac{1}{2}$-inch of ·65 numerical aperture will not be so effective. The analysing prism may be placed either where it is in the drawing, below the stage, or above the eye-piece. It works equally well above the objective, the position it ordinarily occupies in the microscope.

For the draw-tube a 2-inch objective and a B Huyghenian eye-piece answers very well. Before screwing the objective on to the end of the draw-tube centre the light in the usual manner, the Nicol's being turned so as to give a light field, then screw the objective on to the end of the aperture, and put the crystal on the stage, rack down the body so that the objective on the nose-piece nearly touches the crystal, then focus with the draw-tube only. The sub-stage condenser should be racked up close to the underside of the crystal.

Opticians, however, have more recently furnished a special form of microscope (*The Petrological Microscope*, Fig. 79, p. 112), for the use of those students who may desire to prosecute so fascinating a study, and determine the optic axial angles of crystals.

Fuess[32] lately introduced a new form of microscope for polarising and viewing biaxial crystals, which he believes to be needed, as in the ordinary microscope the opening of the polariser is scarcely a third of that of the condenser; moreover, it is not absolutely necessary that the polariser and analyser should be Nicol's prisms. This fact was discovered by myself many years ago. Fuess utilises a bundle of thin glass plates, as in the older Nuremberg polariscope. The frame holding plates can be readily adjusted at the proper polarising angle, the analyser being the ordinary small Nicol, screwed above the objective. The illuminator is an Abbe's triple condenser, of numerical aperture $1 \cdot 40$, which can be adjusted in the ordinary way. The front lens of this should have a diameter of $11 \cdot 12$ mm. and the lower lens of 30 mm. This increase in the condenser fully compensates for the loss of light by the bundle of glass plates, and also enables thick sections of crystals to be examined in convergent polarised light. The ocular used should have a large field; the A Huyghenian answers best. A suggestion to return to the original Nuremberg polariser is very opportune, as *Iceland spar is becoming scarce.*

Mr. A. Mickel accidentally discovered that an opalescent mirror can be converted into an excellent and inexpensive substitute for the Nicol-prism polariser.

Rotation of Plane of Polarisation.

When a plate of quartz (rock-crystal), even of considerable thickness, cut perpendicular to the axis, is interposed between the polariser and analyser, colour is exhibited, the tints changing as the analyser is rotated; and similar effects of colour are produced by employing, instead of quartz, a solution of sugar enclosed in a tube with plain glass ends.

The action thus exerted by quartz and sugar is called *rotation of the plane of polarisation*, a name which sufficiently expresses the observed phenomena. In the case of ordinary quartz, and solutions of sugar-candy, it is necessary to rotate the analyser in the direction of watch-hands as seen by the observer, and the rotation of the plane of polarisation is said to be *right-handed*. In the case of what is called *left-handed* quartz, and of solutions of non-crystallisable sugar, the rotation of the plane of polarisation is in the opposite direction, and the observer must rotate the analyser against watch-hands.

Quartz belongs to the uniaxial system of crystals, and accordingly exhibits one series of rings only, and no perfect central black cross.

On revolving the tourmaline the colour gradually changes, and passes through all the colours of the spectrum. It can be cut to exhibit either right-handed polarisation or left-handed polarisation and also to exhibit straight lines.

Calc Spar.—A uniaxial crystal showing only one system of rings, and a black cross, changing into a white cross on revolving the tourmaline.

Topaz.—A biaxial crystal exhibiting only one system of rings with one fringe, owing to the wide separation of the axes. The fringe and colours change on revolving the tourmaline.

Borax.—A biaxial crystal; the colours are seen to be more intense than in topaz, but the rings not so complete—only one set of rings can be seen, owing to their wide separation.

Rochelle Salt.—A biaxial crystal; the colours are more widely spread out than the former, and only one set of rings seen at the same time.

Carbonate of Lead.—A biaxial crystal; axes not so far separated, and both systems of rings are more widely spread than those of potassium nitrate.

Aragonite.—A biaxial crystal; axes widely separated, but both systems of rings seen at the same time. A fine crystal for displaying the biaxial system.

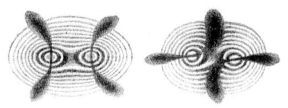

Fig. 185.—Crystal of Potassium Nitrate.

It was long believed that all crystals had only one axis of double refraction; but Brewster found that the greater number of crystals which occur in the mineral kingdom have *two axes* of double refraction, or rather axes around which double refraction takes place; in the axes themselves there is no double refraction.

Potassium nitrate crystallises in six-sided prisms with angles of about 120°. It has two axes of double refraction. These axes are each inclined about 2½° to the axes of the prism, and 5° to each other. If, therefore, a small piece be split off a prism of potassium nitrate with a knife driven by a sharp blow of a hammer, and the two surfaces polished perpendicular to the axes of the prism, so as to leave the thickness of the sixth or eighth of an inch, and then a ray of polarised light be transmitted along the axes of the prism, the double system of rings will be clearly visible.

When the line connecting the two axes of the crystal is inclined 45° to the plane of primitive polarisation, a cross is seen on revolving the potassium nitrate; it gradually assumes the form of two hyperbolic curves, as in Fig. 185. But if the tourmaline be again revolved through half a quadrant, the black cross will be replaced by white spaces, as in the second figure. These systems of rings have, generally speaking, the same colours as those of thin plates, or as those of a system of rings revolving around one axis. The orders of the colours commence at the centres of each system; but at a certain distance, which corresponds to the sixth ring, the rings, instead of returning and encircling each pole, encircle the two poles as an ellipse does its two foci. If the thickness of the plate of *nitre* be diminished or increased, the rings are diminished or increased according to the thickness of the crystal.

Small specimens of various salts may be crystallised and mounted in Canada balsam for viewing under the stage of the microscope; by arresting crystallisation at certain stages, a greater variety of forms and colours will be obtained: we may enumerate salicine, asparagine, acetate of copper, phospho-borate of soda, sugar, carbonate of lime, potassium chlorate, oxalic acid, and all the oxalates found in urine, with the other salts from the same fluid, a few of which are shown in Plate VIII.

The late Dr. Herapath described a salt of quinine, remarkable for its polarising properties. The crystals of this salt, when examined by reflected light, have a brilliant emerald-green colour, with almost a metallic lustre; they appear like portions of the elytræ of the cantharides beetle, and are also very similar to murexide in appearance. When examined by transmitted light, they scarcely possess any colour, there is only a slightly olive-green tinge; but if two crystals, crossing at right-angles, be examined, the spot where they intersect appears perfectly black, even if the crystals are not more than one five-hundredth of an inch in thickness. If the light be in the slightest degree polarised—as by reflection from a cloud, or by the blue sky, or from the glass surface of the mirror of the microscope placed at the polarising angle 65° 45'—these little prisms and films assume complementary colours: one appears green, and the other pink, and the part at which they cross is chocolate or deep chestnut-brown, instead of black. Dr. Herapath succeeded in making artificial tourmalines large enough to surmount the eye-piece of the microscope; so that all experiments with those crystals upon polarised light may be made without the tourmaline or Nicol's prism. The finest rosette crystals are made as follows:—To a moderately strong solution of *Cinchonidine* add a drop or two of Herapath's test-fluid.[33] A few drops of this is placed on the centre of a glass slide, and put aside until the first crystals are observed to be formed near the margin. The slide should now be placed upon the stage of the microscope, and the progress of formation of the crystals closely watched. When these are seen to be large enough, and it is deemed necessary to stop their further development, the slide must be quickly transferred to the palm of the hand, the warmth of which will be found sufficient to stop further crystallisation. These crystals attract moisture, deliquesce, and should therefore be kept in a perfectly dry place.

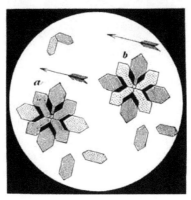

Fig. 186.—In this figure heraldic lines are adopted to denote colour. The dotted parts indicate *yellow*, the straight lines *red*, the horizontal lines *blue*, and the diagonal, or oblique lines, *green*. The arrows show the plane of the tourmaline, *a*, blue stage; *b*, red stage of selenite employed.

To render these crystals evident, it merely remains to bring the glass-slide upon the field of the microscope, with the selenite stage and single tourmaline, or Nicol's prism, beneath it; instantly the crystals assume the two complementary colours of the stage: red and green, supposing that the pink stage is employed; or blue and yellow, provided the blue selenite is made use of. All those crystals at right angles to the plane of the tourmaline produce that tint which an analysing-plate of tourmaline would produce when at right angles to the polarising-plate; whilst those at 90° to these educe the complementary tint, as the analysing-plate would also have done if revolved through an arc of 90°.

This test is a delicate one for quinine (Fig. 186, *a* and *b*); not only do these peculiar crystals act in the way just related, but they may be easily proved to possess the optical properties of that remarkable salt, the sulphate of iodo-quinine.

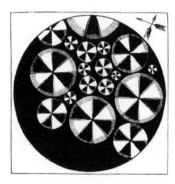

Fig. 187.—Polarised Crystals of Quinidine.

To test for quinidine, it is merely necessary to allow a drop of acid solution to evaporate to dryness upon the slide, and to examine the crystalline mass by two tourmalines, crossed at right angles, and without the stage. Immediately little circular discs of white, with a well-defined black cross, start into existence, should quinidine be present even in very minute traces. These crystals are represented in Fig. 187.

If the selenite stage be employed in the examination of this object, one of the most gorgeous appearances in the whole domain of the polarising microscope is displayed: the black cross disappears, and is replaced by one consisting of two colours, and divided into a cross having a red and green fringe, whilst the four intermediate sectors are a gorgeous orange-yellow. These appearances alter on the revolution of the analysing-plate of tourmaline; when the blue stage is employed, the cross assumes a blue or yellow tint, varying according to the position of the analysing plate. These phenomena are analogous to those exhibited by certain circular crystals of boracic acid, and to circular discs of salicine (prepared by fusion), the difference being that the salts of quinidine have more intense depolarising powers than either of the other substances; the mode of preparation, however, excludes these from consideration. Quinine prepared in the same manner as quinidine has a very different mode of crystallisation; but it occasionally presents circular corneous plates, also exhibiting the black cross and white sectors, but not with one-tenth part of the brilliancy, which of course enables us readily to discriminate the two.

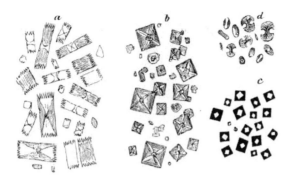

Fig. 188.—Urinary Salts, seen under Polarised Light.

a, Uric acid; *b*, Oxalate of lime, octahedral crystals of; *c*, Oxalate of lime allowed to dry, forming a black cube; *d*, Oxalate of lime as it occasionally appears, termed the dumb-bell crystal.

Urinary salts are more readily seen under polarised light than by white light. Ice doubly refracts, while water singly refracts. Ice takes the rhomboidic form; and snow in its crystalline forms may be regarded as the skeleton crystals of this system (Fig. 189). A sheet of clear ice, of about one inch thick, and slowly formed in still weather, shows circular rings with a cross by polarised light.

Fig. 189.—Snow Crystals.

Fig. 190.—Potato Starch, under Polarised Light.

It is probable that the conditions of snow formation are more complex than might be imagined, familiar as we are with the conditions relating to the crystallisation of water on the earth's surface. A great variety of animal, vegetable, and other substances possess a doubly refracting or depolarising structure, as: a quill cut and laid out flat on glass; the cornea of a sheep's eye; skin, hair, a thin section of a finger-nail; sections of bone, teeth, horn, silk, cotton, whalebone; stems of plants containing silica or flint; barley, wheat, &c. The larger-grained starches form splendid objects; *tous-les-mois*, the largest, may be taken as a type of all others. This presents a black cross, the arms of which meet at the hilum (Fig. 190). On rotating the analyser, the black cross disappears, and at 90° is replaced by a white cross; another, but much fainter, black cross is seen between the arms of the white cross, no colour being perceptible. But if a thin plate of selenite be interposed between the starch-grains and the polariser, a series of delicate colours appear, all of which change on revolving the analyser, becoming complementary at every quadrant of the circle. West and East India arrow-root, sago, tapioca, and many other starch-grains, present a similar appearance; but in proportion as the grains are smaller, so are their markings and colourings less distinct.

Molecular Rotation.

For the purpose of studying the various interesting phenomena of molecular rotation, a few necessary pieces of apparatus must be added to the microscope. First, an ordinary iron three-armed retort stand, to the lower arm of which must be attached either a polarising prism or a bundle of glass plates inclined at the polarising angle; in the upper an analysing prism. The fluid to be examined should be contained in a narrow glass tube about eight inches in height, and this must be attached to the middle arm. If the prisms be crossed before inserting a fluid possessing rotatory power, the light passing through the analyser will be coloured. If a solution of sugar be employed, and the light which passes through the second prism is seen to be red, but on rotating the analyser towards the right the colour changes to yellow, and passes through green to violet, it may be concluded that the rotation is right-handed. If, on the contrary, the analyser requires to be turned towards the left hand, we conclude that the polarisation is left-handed. These phenomena are wholly distinct from those accompanying the action of doubly refracting substances upon plane polarised light. It is not easy to explain in a limited space the course to be followed in ascertaining the amount of rotation produced by different substances. Monochromatic light should be used. If we are about to examine a sugar solution with the prisms crossed, the index attached to the analyser must first be made to point to zero. The sugar is then introduced, when it will be necessary to rotate the analyser 23° to the right, in order that the light may be extinguished. This is the amount of rotation for that particular fluid at a given density and that height of column. As the arc varies with increase or decrease of density and height of the fluid, it is needful to reduce it to a unit of height and density. The following formula is that given by Biot:—P = quantity of matter in a unit of solution; d = sp. gr.; l = length of column; a = arc of rotation; m = molecular rotation.

Then $m = a/(l\,p\,d)$.

The application of the polarising apparatus to the microscope is of much value in determining minute structure. It may also be defined as an instrument of analysis; a test of difference in density between any two or more parts of the same substance. All structures, therefore, belonging either to the animal, vegetable, or mineral kingdom, in which the power of unequal or double refraction is suspected to be present, are those that should especially be re-investigated by polarised light. Some of the most delicate of the elementary tissues of animal structure, the ultimate fibrillæ of muscles, &c., are amongst the most interesting subjects that might be studied with advantage under this method of investigation. The chemist may perform the most dexterous analysis; the crystallographer may examine crystals by the nicest determination of their forms and cleavage; the anatomist or botanist may use the dissecting knife and microscope with the most exquisite skill; but there are still structures in the mineral, vegetable, and animal kingdoms which will defy all such modes of examination, and will yield only to the magical analysis of polarised light.

Formation and Polarisation of Crystals.

The inorganic kingdom will afford to the microscopist a never-ending number of objects of unsurpassed beauty and interest. The phenomena of crystallisation in its varied combinations can be made a useful and instructive occupation. Although ignorant of the means whereby the great majority of minerals and crystals have been formed in the vast laboratory of Nature, we can, nevertheless, imitate in a small degree Nature's handiworks by crystallising out a large number of substances, and watch their numerous transformations in the smallest appreciable quantities, when aided by the microscope.

Among natural crystals we look for the material for the formation of our lenses, while the varieties of granites present us with the earliest crystallised condition of the earth's crust as it cooled down, the structure of which is beautifully exhibited under polarised light. In Plate VIII. various crystalline and other bodies are displayed. In No. 158 is a section of new red sandstone; 159 of quartz; and 160 of granite. Special reference is made to others in the following list of salts and other substances which form a beautiful series of objects for study under polarised light:—

SALTS.

Alum.
Asparagine.
Aspartic Acid. Plate VIII. No. 168.
Bitartrate of Ammonia.
Boracic Acid.
Borax. No. 164.
Carbonate of Lime.
" Soda.
Chlorate of Potash.
Chloride of Barium.
" Cobalt.
" Copper and Ammonia.
" Sodium.
Cholesterine.
Chromate of Potash.
Cinchonine.
Cinchonidine.
Citric Acid.
Hippuric Acid.
Iodide of Mercury.
" Potassium.
" Quinine.
Iodo-disulphate of Quinine.
Kreatine. No. 166.
Murexide.
Nitrate of Bismuth.
" Barytes.
" Brucine.
" Copper.
" Potash.
" Strontian.
" Uranium.
Oxalate of Ammonia.

" Chromium.
" Chromium and Potash.
" Lime.
" Soda.
Indurated Sandstone, Howth.
Indurated Sandstone, Bromsgrove.
Gibraltar Rock.
Granite, various localities. No. 160.
Hornblend Schist.
Labrador Spar.
Norway Rock.
Quartz Rock, various. No. 159.
" in Bog Iron Ore.
Quartzite, Mont Blanc.
Sandstone. No. 158.
Satin Spar.
Selenites, various colours.
Tin Ore, with Tourmalin.
Oxalic Acid.
Oxalurate of Ammonia.
Permanganate of Potash.
Phosphate of Lead and Soda.
Platino-cyanide of Magnesia.
Plumose Quinidine.
Prussiate of Potash, red and yellow.
Quinidine.
Santonine.
Salicine.
Salignine. No. 162.
Sulphate of Cadmium.
" Copper. No. 161.
" Copper and Potash.
" Iron. No. 163.
" Iron and Cobalt. No. 165.
" Magnesia.
" Nickel and Potash.
" Soda.
" Zinc.
Sugar.
Tartaric Acid.
Thionurate of Ammonia.
Triple Phosphate.
Urate of Ammonia.

" Soda.
Urea, and most urinary deposits.
Uric Acid.

MINERALS.

Agates, various.
Asbestiform Serpentine.
Avanturine.
Carbonate of Lime.
Carrara Marble.

ANIMAL STRUCTURES.

Cat's Tongue. No. 174.
Grayling Scale. No. 176.
Holothuria, Spicules of. Nos. 171-2.
Prawn Shell. No. 175.

VEGETABLE CRYSTALLINE SUBSTANCES.

CUTICLE of Leaf of Correa Cardinalis.
"   "   Deutzia scabra. No. 173.
"   "   Elæagnus.
"   "   Onosma taurica.
Equisetum. No. 170.
Fibro cells from orchid. No. 169.
" Oncidium bicallosum.
Scalariform Vessels from Fern.
Scyllium Caniculum. No. 177.
SILICIOUS CUTICLES, various.
Starches, various. No. 167.

The formation of artificial crystal may be readily effected, and the process watched, under the microscope, by simply placing a drop of saturated solution of any salt upon a previously warmed slip of glass.

Interesting results will be obtained by combining two or more chemical salts in the following manner. To a nearly saturated solution of the sulphate of copper and sulphate of magnesia add a drop on the glass-slide, and dry quickly. To effect this, heat the slide so as to fuse the salts in its water of crystallisation, and there remains an amorphous film on the hot glass. Put the slide aside and allow it to cool slowly; it will gradually absorb a certain amount of moisture from the air, and begin to throw out crystals. If now placed under the microscope, numerous points will be seen to start out here and there. The starting points may be produced at pleasure by touching the film with a fine needle point, so as to admit of a slight amount of moisture being absorbed by the mass of salt. Development is at once suspended by applying gentle heat; cover the specimen with balsam and thin glass. The balsam should completely cover the edges of the thin glass circle, otherwise moisture will probably insinuate itself, and destroy the form of the crystals.

Mr. Thomas succeeded in crystallising "the salts of the magnetic metals" at very high temperatures, with very curious results. In Plate VIII. are seen crystals of sulphate of iron and cobalt, No. 163; and of nickel and potash, No. 165, obtained in the following manner:—Add to a concentrated solution of iron a small quantity of sugar, to prevent oxidation. Put a drop of the solution on a glass slide, and drive out the water of crystallisation as quickly as possible by the aid of a spirit lamp; then with a Bunsen's burner bring the plate to a high temperature. Immediately a remarkable change is seen to take place in the form of the crystal, and if properly managed the "foliation" represented in the plate will be fairly exhibited. The slide must not be allowed to cool down too rapidly or the crystals will probably absorb moisture from the atmosphere, and in so doing the crystals alter their forms. Immerse them in balsam, and cover in the usual way before quite cold.

Sublimation of Alkaloids.—The late Dr. Guy, F.R.S., directed the attention of microscopists to the fact that the crystalline shape of bodies belonging to the inorganic world might be of service in medical jurisprudence. Subsequently, Dr. A. Helwig, of Mayence, investigated this subject, and found the plan applicable not only to inorganic but also to organic substances, and especially to poisonous alkaloids. By using a white porcelain saucer Dr. Guy was able to watch the process of crystallisation more minutely, and to regulate it more exactly. He was, in fact, able to obtain characteristic crusts composed of crystals of strychnine weighing not more than $\frac{1}{3000}$th or $\frac{1}{5000}$th of a grain. Morphia affords equally characteristic results. For the examination of these, Dr. Guy recommended the use of a binocular microscope with an inch object-glass. But it is not to crystalline forms alone that one need trust; the whole behaviour of a substance as it melts and is converted into vapour is eminently characteristic, and when once deposited on the microscopical slide, under the object-glass, the application of re-agents may give still more satisfactory results. The re-agents, however, which are here to be applied are not of the kind ordinarily employed. Colour-tests under the microscope are, comparatively speaking, useless; those that give rise to peculiar crystalline forms are rather to be sought after. For instance, the crystals produced by the action of carbozotic acid on morphia are by themselves almost perfectly characteristic. These experiments should not, however, be undertaken for medico-legal purposes by one unskilled in their conduct, for the effects of the reagents themselves might be mistaken by the uninitiated for the result of their action on the substance under examination. For the special method of procedure, see Dr. W. Guy, "On the Sublimation of the Alkaloids."[34]

The Micro-spectroscope.

Spectrum analysis has, from its first introduction by Kirschoff in 1859, maintained its fascination over men of science throughout the civilised world. Microscopists, astronomers, and chemists have assigned to the spectroscope a highly important position amongst scientific instruments of research. At quite an early period of its history it appeared to ourselves to promise an extension of the work of the microscope in pathology and microscopy, and second only to that of astronomy and chemistry. The chief hindrances to the use of the spectroscope were, in the early days, of a twofold nature; a widespread, but quite erroneous view of the serious difficulties of employing the instrument, and the want of a first aid to its use.

So valuable a means of research has this process of analysis proved to be, that the discoveries made by the spectroscope appear marvellous. The spectroscope was first made known as a refined instrument for the analysis of light by two Germans, a physicist and a chemist, Kirschoff and Bunsen. In 1860, the latter succeeded in detecting and separating two new alkaline bodies from all other bodies from the waters obtained from the Durkeim springs, less than $0 \cdot 0002$ part of a milligramme of which can be detected by spectrum analysis. It is to the labours of Huggins, Norman Lockyer and others that we are indebted for the wonderful discoveries made in astronomy; and chiefly so to Brewster, Herschel, and Talbot, for showing that certain metals give off light of a high degree of refrangibility; that distinct bands are situated at a distance beyond the last visible violet ray ten times as great as the length of the whole visible spectrum from red to violet.

With regard to the discoveries made in connection with physiological research, we are indebted to F. Hoppe, who in 1862 first described the absorption bands of human blood. His results were confirmed by the investigations of Professor Sir George Gabriel Stokes, who, by adding certain reducing agents to the blood, found that he could change scarlet blood into purple—"purple cruorine"—and in this way the place occupied by the absorption band in the spectrum could be made to change. He reduced the hæmoglobin by robbing the blood of its oxygen. Thus, by Stokes' and other methods, we have since arrived at extremely valuable results, and the explanation of the difference in colour between arterial and venous blood; and it has also enabled us to show wherein the breathing power of the red corpuscles resides, and further explains phenomena which before his investigations were inexplicable.

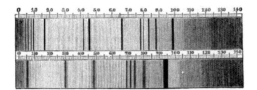

Fig. 191.—Fräunhofer's Spectrum Lines.

The spectroscope seems likely to be of almost as great use in medicine as it has already proved to be in solar and terrestrial chemistry, if we may form an opinion from the large amount of literature which has appeared on the subject. The inception of this magical instrument arose on the instance of a discovery made by Dr. Wollaston in 1802, who, on making a slit in the shutter of his room, instead of a round hole, the spectrum of sunlight, instead of being composed of a number of coloured discs, was now a band of pure colours, each colour being free from admixture with the next to it. Moreover, he found that this colour band was not continuous, as Newton described it, but interrupted here and there by *fine black lines*.

In 1814, Fräunhofer,[35] a German optician, discovered these lines quite independently, and mapped out 576 of them, calling the more prominent of them A, B, C, D, E, F, G, H, which lines he used as marks of comparison. He also found that the distances of these lines from each other may vary according to the nature of the substance composing the prism; thus, their relative distances are not the same in prisms of flint-glass, crown-glass, and bisulphide of carbon, but they always occupy the same position relatively to the colours of the spectrum. Kirschoff and Angström had mapped out in 1880 no less a number than 2,000 Fräunhofer lines, a portion of which are correctly shown in the accompanying chart (Fig. 191).

In 1830, Simms, a London optician, made an improvement in the construction of the spectroscope by placing a lens in front of the prism, so arranged that the slit was in the focus of the lens. This lens turns the light, after it has passed through the slit, into a cylindrical beam before entering the prism. Another lens, also introduced by him, receives the circular beam emerging from the prism, and compels it to throw an image of the slit, which may be magnified at pleasure for each ray. The lens between the prism and the slit is termed the *collimating* lens. Thus the following are the essential parts of a chemical spectroscope:—(1) a slit, the edges of which are two knife-edges of steel very truly ground, and exactly parallel to each other, and in a direction parallel to the refracting edge of the prism, to admit a pencil of rays. (2) A collimating lens; a convex lens with the slit at its principal focus, which renders the rays parallel before entering the prism. (3) A prism of dense glass, in which the rays are refracted and dispersed. (4) An observing telescope constructed like an astronomical refractor of small size, and placed so that the rays shall traverse it after emerging from the prism. Such are the essentials of a one-prism chemical spectroscope.

The form of instrument in use with the microscope is the *"direct vision"* spectroscope, consisting of two prisms of flint-glass, placed between three of crown-glass cemented together by Canada balsam; the spectrum being viewed directly by the eye. The earliest constructed form of micro-spectroscope is shown in Fig. 192, the Browning-Huggins.

It was, however, Mr. Sorby who suggested that the prism should be made of dense flint-glass and of such a form that it could be used in two different positions, and that in one it should give twice the dispersion that it would in the other, but that the angle made by the incident and emergent rays should be the same in both positions.

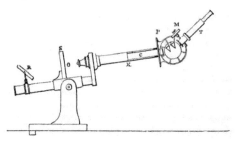

Fig. 192.—The Browning-Huggins Micro-spectroscope.

Fig. 193.

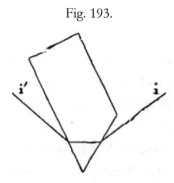

Fig. 193*a*.

Figs. 193 and 193*a* represent prisms of the kind arranged to use in two different positions, i and i' being the same angle as I and I'.

For most absorption-bands, particularly if faint, the prism should be used in the first position, in which it gives the least dispersion; when greater dispersion is required, so as to separate some particular lines more widely, or to show the spectra of the metals, or Fräunhofer's lines in the solar spectrum, then the prism must be used as in Fig. 193*a*. This answers well for liquids or transparent objects, but it is, of course, not applicable to opaque objects.

To combine both purposes, some form of direct vision-prisms that may be applied to the body of the microscope is required. Fig. 194 represents an arrangement of direct vision-prisms, invented by Herschel. The line R R' shows the path of a ray of light through the prisms, where it would be seen that the emergent ray R' is parallel and coincident with the incident ray R.

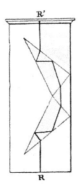

Fig. 194.

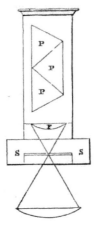

Fig. 194*a*.

Another very compact combination is shown in Fig. 194a. Any number of these prisms (P P P) may be used, according to the amount of dispersion required. They are mounted in a similar way to a Nicol's prism, and are applied directly over the eye-piece of the microscope. The slit S S is placed in the focus of the first glass (F) if a negative, or below the second glass if a positive eye-piece be employed. One edge of the slit is movable, and, in using the instrument, the slit is first opened wide, so that a clear view of the object is obtained. The part of the object of which the spectrum is to be examined is then made to coincide with the fixed edge of the slit, and the movable edge is screwed up, until a brilliant coloured spectrum is produced. The absorption-bands will then be readily found by slightly altering the focus. This contrivance answers perfectly for opaque objects, without any preparation; and, when desirable, the same prism can be placed below the stage, and a micrometer used in the eye-piece of the microscope, thus avoiding a multiplicity of apparatus.

Fig. 195.—The Sorby-Browning Micro-spectroscopic Eye-piece.

A later and better form of instrument is the Sorby-Browning eye-piece (Fig. 195), shown in section (Fig. 196) ready for inserting into the body-tube of the microscope, the prism of which is contained in a small tube, removable at pleasure. Below the prism is an achromatic eye-piece, having an adjustable slit between the two lenses, the upper lens being furnished with a screw motion to focus the slit. A side slit, capable of adjustment, admits, when required, a second beam of light from any object whose spectrum it is desired to compare with that of the object placed on the stage of the microscope. This second beam of light strikes against a very small prism, suitably placed inside the apparatus, and is reflected up through the compound prism, forming a spectrum in the same field with that obtained from the object on the stage.

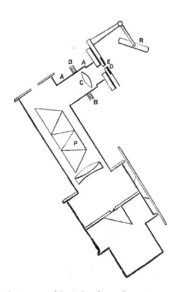

Fig. 196.—Sectional view of bright-line Spectroscope; the letters also apply to the standard spectrum scale (Fig. 198).

A is a brass tube, carrying the compound direct vision prism; B, a milled head, with screw motion to adjust the focus of the achromatic eye lens C, seen in the sectional view as a triple combination of prisms. Another screw at right angles to C, which from its position cannot be well shown in the figure, regulates the slit horizontally. This screw has a larger head, and when once recognised cannot be mistaken for the other. D D is a clip and ledge for holding a small tube, so that the spectrum given by its contents may be compared with one from an object on the stage. E is a round hole for a square-headed screw, opening and shutting a slit, admitting the quantity of light required to form the second spectrum. A light entering the round hole near E strikes against the right-angled prism, which is placed inside the apparatus, and is reflected up through the slit belonging to the compound prism. If any incandescent object be placed in a suitable position with reference to the round hole, its spectrum will be obtained. F shows the position of the field lens of the eye-piece. The tube is made to fit the microscope to which the instrument is applied. To use this instrument insert F as an eye-piece in the microscope tube, taking care that the slit at the top of the eye-piece is in the same direction as the slit below the prism. Screw on to the microscope the object-glass required, and place the object whose spectrum is to be viewed on the stage. Illuminate with the stage mirror if it be transparent; with mirror, Lieberkühn, and dark well, by side reflector, or bull's-eye condenser if opaque. Remove A, and open the slit by means of the milled-head, not shown in figure, but which is at right angles to D D. When the slit is sufficiently open the rest of the apparatus acts as an ordinary eye-piece, and any object can be focussed in the usual way. Having focussed the object, replace A, and gradually close the slit till a good spectrum is obtained. The spectrum will be much improved by throwing the object a little out of focus.

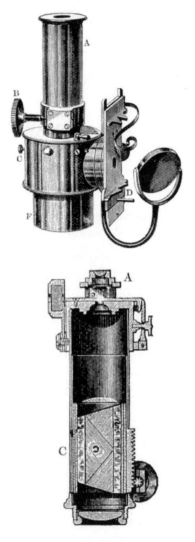

Sectional View.

Figs. 197 and 197*a*.—The Beck-Sorby Micro-spectroscope Eye-piece, drawn on a scale of one half size.

Every part of the spectrum differs a little from adjacent parts in refrangibility, and delicate bands or lines can only be brought out by accurately focussing that particular part of the spectrum. This can be done by the milled-head B.

Disappointment will occur in any attempt at delicate investigation if the directions given be not carefully followed out.

Opposite E a small mirror is attached. It is like the mirror below the stage of a microscope, and is mounted in a similar manner. By means of this mirror light may be reflected into the eye-piece, and in this way two spectra may be procured from one lamp.

Method of using the Micro-Spectroscope.

A beginner with the micro-spectroscope should first make himself fully acquainted with the spectroscope by holding it up to the sky and noting the effects of opening and regulating the slit, by rotating the screw C, Figs. 195 and 197. The lines will be well seen on closing down the opening. This screw diminishes the length of the slit, when the spectrum is seen as a narrow ribbon of prismatic colours. The screw E regulates the admission of light through the aperture above D. The better objects with which to commence the study of the absorption bands are, aniline dye, much diluted, madder, permanganate of potash, and blood. As each colour varies in refrangibility, the focus must be adjusted by the screw E. When it is desired to view the spectrum of a very minute object, the prisms should be removed by withdrawing the tube containing them, the slit set open, and the object brought into the centre of the field; the vertical and horizontal slits must then be partially closed up, and the prisms replaced, when a suitable objective is employed to examine the spectrum. For ordinary observations a magnifying power of an inch and a half or two inches will be suitable, but for small quantities of material a higher power must be employed, when a single blood corpuscle can be made to show its characteristic absorption band. After having obtained the best image of any object on stage, throw it slightly out of focus, and substitute the micro-spectroscopic eye-piece for the Huyghenian. Opaque objects should be examined by reflected light, by means of the bull's-eye condenser, or side reflector. Mr. Sorby uses a binocular microscope, which enables him to regulate the focussing and throwing out of focus of the object.

In examining crystals or other small objects, a small cardboard diaphragm should be placed beneath them; and when examining the spectra of liquids in cells, slip a small cap with a perforation of $\frac{1}{10}$-inch in diameter over the tube containing the $\frac{1}{2}$-inch or 2-inch objective. Substances which give absorption bands or lines in the red are best seen by artificial light, while those which show bands in the violet are better seen by daylight. By following rules of the kind we are less likely to mix the bands of the absorption spectrum with the Fräunhofer lines. For example, if the edge of a band happens to coincide with a Fräunhofer line, the observer is apt to imagine that the band is better defined and more abruptly shaded on one side than it really is.

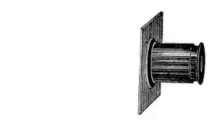

Standard Spectrum Scale.

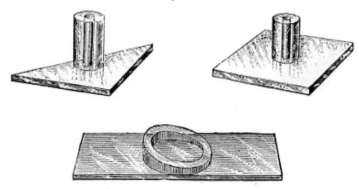

Cells for use with Spectroscope.

Fig. 198.

Cells and Tubes.—These are either supplied ready-made by the optician, or can be formed out of small pieces of barometer tubing, with the edges ground down and cemented on ordinary glass slips. In Fig. 198 is seen the several kinds of cells and tubes usually employed, while the little flat tubes commonly in use as bouquet holders will be found of use, with the side stage reflecting spectrum as comparison tubes; being of different diameters they allow of two or more depths of colour in the fluid intended for examination.

In the case of many other fluids the sloping form of cell (Fig. 198) will be useful, as different shades of fluids can be examined without removal from the stage of the microscope. The deeper cells are cut from a piece of barometer tubing of about half to an inch long, one end being cemented to a piece of flatted glass, and the other covered over temporarily or permanently with a thin piece of glass on the top, held in its place by capillary attraction, thus admitting of the tube being turned upside down.

Re-agents required.—A diluted solution of ammonia, citric acid, double tartrate of potash and soda (the last being used to prevent the precipitation of oxide of iron), and the double sulphate of the protoxide of iron and ammonia (employed to deoxidise blood, etc.). In some special cases, dilute hydrochloric acid, purified boric acid, and sulphate of soda are required.

The character of stains of blood varies with age and with the nature of the substance with which it happens to be combined. This is important to remember in connection with *Jurisprudence*, when the micro-spectroscope is brought into use for the detection of blood stains. The spectrum used in important cases of the kind should have a compound prism, with enough, but not too great dispersive power, otherwise the bands become, as it were, diluted, and less distinct.

If the blood stain is quite recent, the colouring matter will be hæmoglobin only. This easily dissolves out in water, and when sufficiently diluted gives the spectrum of oxy-hæmoglobin, which on the addition of ammonia, together with a small quantity of the double tartrate, a small piece of ferrous salt, and stirring carefully without the admission of air, changes the spectrum of reduced hæmoglobin. When stirred again, so as to expose the solution as much as possible to air, the two bands reappear; on gradually adding citric acid in small quantities the colour begins to change, and the bands are seen to gradually fade away; if there should have been much blood present, a band appears in the red; the further addition of ammonia makes all clear again, but does not restore the original bands, because the hæmoglobin has been permanently changed into hæmatin. This reaction alone distinguishes blood from most other colouring matters, since other substances after being changed by acids are restored by alkalies to their original state. There are many other curious facts connected with the spectroscopic analysis of blood, which are fully explained and illustrated by Dr. Maemunn in his book on "The Use of the Spectroscope in Medicine," and also in Dr. Thudicum's[36] reports and charts, which are the most complete. Sir George Stokes, F.R.S., was one of the first to show the essential value of the spectral phenomena of hematine, and who proved, after Hoppe had first drawn attention to the fact, that this colouring matter is capable of existing in two states of oxidation, and that a very different spectrum is produced according as the substance, which he termed *cruorine*, is in a more or less oxidised condition. The chart appended to his paper[37] affords an imperfect representation of the changes seen in the spectrum.

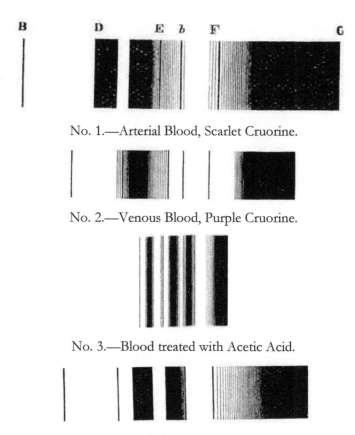

No. 1.—Arterial Blood, Scarlet Cruorine.

No. 2.—Venous Blood, Purple Cruorine.

No. 3.—Blood treated with Acetic Acid.

No. 4.—Solution of Hæmatin.

Fig. 199.—Sir George Stokes' Chart of the Absorption Bands of Blood.

Proto-sulphate of iron, or proto-chloride of tin, causes the reduction of the colouring-matter, but, on exposure to air, oxygen is absorbed, and the solution again exhibits the spectrum characteristic of the more oxidised state. The different substances obtained from blood colouring-matter produce different bands. Thus, *hæmatin* gives rise to a band in the red spectrum D; *hæmato-globulin* produces two bands, the second twice the breadth of the first in the yellow portion of the spectrum between the lines D and E, No. 1. The absorption-bands differ according to the strength of the solution employed, and the medium in which the blood-salt is dissolved; but an exceedingly minute proportion dissolved in water is sufficient to bring out very distinct bands. B represents the red end of the spectrum and G the green as it approaches the violet end.

Mapping the Spectra.—In the sectional view given of the micro-spectroscope (Fig. 196), the internal construction of the instrument is shown, and the arrangement made for throwing a bright point on to the surface of the upper prism is clearly seen. The mapping out is accomplished by means of a photographic scale fixed as a standard spectrum (Fig. 198), in the position of A A, illuminated by the small mirror at R, and focussed by a small lens at C, so that on looking into the instrument one can see the spectrum accurately divided into one hundred equal parts, and scale readings can be made at once; the only precaution needed is to be sure the D (or the sodium line, if D cannot be got) always stands at the same number on the scale. To map absorption spectra on this scale we have to lay down a line, as many millimetres long as there are divisions in the scale, and mark the position of the bands on this line. Mr. Browning supplies scales printed off ready for use. But the mapping out of spectra, as Mr. Sorby pointed out, requires some consideration; since the number of divisions depends on the thickness of the interference-plate, it becomes necessary to decide what number should be adopted. Ten it was thought would be most suitable; but, on trial, it appeared to be too few for practical work. Twenty is too many, since it then becomes extremely difficult to count them. Twelve is as many as can well be counted; it is a number easily remembered, is sufficiently accurate, and has other practical advantages. With twelve divisions the sodium-line 0 comes very accurately at $3\frac{1}{2}$; thus, by adjusting the plate so that a bright sodium-light is brought into the centre of the band, when the Nicol's prisms are also crossed accurately at $3\frac{1}{2}$, parallelism is secured, together with a wider field of observation. The general character of the scale will be best understood from the following figure, in which the bands are numbered, and given below the principal Fräunhofer lines. The centre of the bands is black, and they are shaded off gradually at each side, so that the shaded part is about equal to the intermediate bright spaces. Taking, then, the centres of the black bands as 1, 2, 3, &c., the centres of the spaces are $1\frac{1}{2}$, $2\frac{1}{2}$, $3\frac{1}{2}$, &c., the lower edges of each $\frac{3}{4}$, $1\frac{3}{4}$, &c., and the upper $1\frac{1}{4}$, $2\frac{1}{4}$, &c., we can easily divide these quarters into eighths by the eye: and this is as near as is required in the subject before us, and corresponds as nearly as possible to $\frac{1}{100}$th part of the whole spectrum, visible under ordinary circumstances by gaslight and daylight. Absorption-bands at the red end are best seen by lamp-light, and those at the blue end by daylight.

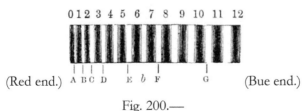

(Red end.) A B C D E b F G (Bue end.)

Fig. 200.—

On this scale the position of some of the principal lines of the solar spectrum is about as follows:—

A   ¾   B   1½   C   2⅜   D   3½

E   5¹¹⁄₁₆   b   6³⁄₁₆   F   7½   G   10⅝

At first plates of selenite, which are easily prepared, were used, because they can be split to nearly the requisite thickness with parallel faces; but their depolarising power varied much with temperature. Even the ordinary atmospheric changes alter the position of the bands. However, quartz cut parallel to the principal axis of the crystal is but slightly affected, and is not open to the same objection; but this is prepared with some difficulty. The sides should be perfectly parallel, the thickness about ·043-inch, and gradually polished down with rouge until the sodium-line is seen in its proper place. This must be done with care, since a difference of $\frac{1}{10000}$-inch in thickness would make it almost worthless.

The two Nicol's prisms and the intervening plate are mounted in a tube, and attached to a piece of brass in such a manner that the centre of the aperture exactly corresponds to the centre of any of the cells used in the experiments, and must be made to correspond with equal care, so that any of them, or this apparatus in particular, may be placed on the stage and in proper position without further adjustment, whereby both time and trouble are saved.

Absorption Spectrum of Chromule.

In 1869 I published in the Journal of the Royal Microscopical Society[38] a paper on results obtained by the spectrum analysis of the colouring-matter of plants and flowers, some of which were of considerable interest in many respects. My examinations extended to several hundred different specimens, from which I was led to conclude that the chromule of flowers is, for the most part, due to the chemical action of the actinic rays of light over the protoplasm of the plant, more so than to that of soil. But as certain roots of plants, as those of the alkanet, yield their colouring-matter to oil, and in a much smaller degree to spirit or water, it follows then that conclusions of any kind can only be drawn after a long and careful study of the question. Some of the results obtained were, however, of some interest at the time, that, for example, seen in three different solutions of the chlorophyll of *Cinchona succirubra*, one of three solutions in alcohol, scarcely coloured, having in fact only a faint tinge of green colour, and the spectrum of which much astonished me at the time. It gave four well-marked absorption-bands; one deep sharp line *in the red*; another, rather narrower, in the orange, coincident with D, or the sodium-line; one in the green, about *b*, coincident with the Thallium green band; and a fourth on the blue line F, nearly as broad as that in the red. The ethereal solution gave different results. It showed only three bands of absorption, nearly the same as in the last case (though all of them fainter); but the fourth in the blue was not apparent, the whole of that end of the spectrum being absorbed a little beyond the green line *b*. This solution was *deep emerald-green*, and even dilution did not alter the phenomena. The *acid* alcoholic solution was as deeply green as the last, but gave only the sharp broad absorption-band in the red, and two very faint ghostly bands in the position described above of the D and *b* lines respectively.

Further additional researches on the chlorophyll of plants furnished curious results, the chlorophyll being dissolved out by alcohol, digested for some hours, and without heat; some plants being fresh, and others dried. Five classes of phenomena exhibited themselves, but *all* agreed in having the red absorption-band broad, sharp, and well defined, some having this one band only, the Lilac being of this type.

There are two classes in which two absorption-bands occur. One has the red and the orange bands, of which the Fuchsia, Guelder-rose, and Tansy are examples; another, in which the red and the green bands are alone co-existent. Ivy is the type of the class, and it is immaterial whether we take last year's leaves or those of the early spring; the results are the same.

The fourth class consists of the two former spectra superposed. Three lines occur, the red, the orange, and the green bands, at C, D, and *b*, as before. This is by far the largest class, and I have thirty or forty examples of it. *Œnothera biennis*, Laurestinus, &c., are types with the ethereal solution of the leaves of Red Bark.

The fifth class consists of those having properties similar to the alcoholic solution of Red Bark described. But I only found eight of these, and not all equal in colour power, namely: Berberry, Sloe, Tea, Hyoscyamus, Digitalis, Senna, and Red Bark. The results obtained appeared at the time to be well worth following up to a more practical conclusion than that arrived at. It should be noted that in the preparation of vegetable colouring matters for the micro-spectroscope, care must be taken to employ only a small quantity of spirits of wine to filter the solution, and evaporate it at once to dryness at a very gentle heat, otherwise if we attempt to keep the colouring matters in a fluid state they quickly decompose. It is necessary also to employ various re-agents in developing characteristic spectra. The most valuable re-agent is sulphite of soda. This admits of the division of colours into groups.

It is better to use a dilute alcoholic solution for the extraction of colour from plants, and to observe the spectrum in a column of about three-quarters of an inch in height. By this means it is quite possible to ascertain that the spectrum of chlorophyll presents seven distinct absorption bands.

For further information on this interesting subject I must refer the reader to Mr. Sorby's paper "On a Definite Method of Qualitative Analysis of

Vegetable and Animal Colouring Matter by means of the Spectrum Microscope," "Proc. Roy. Soc.," No. 92, 1867.

CHAPTER IV.

Practical Microscopy: Manipulation, and Mode of Using the Microscope.

In this chapter it will be my aim to discuss the best practical methods of employing the microscope and its appliances to the greatest advantage. First, the student should select a quiet room for working in, with, if possible, a northern aspect, free from all tremor occasioned by passing vehicles. The table selected for use should be firm, and provided with drawers, in which his several appliances can be kept ready to hand. The microscope must be placed at such an inclination as will enable him to work in comfort, and without putting strain on the muscles of the neck or fatiguing the eyes. The next important point is that of light. Daylight, in some respects, is an advantage; this should come from a white cloud on a bright day, but as a rule more satisfactory results will be obtained by using a well-made lamp, as this can be controlled with ease, and used at a proper height and distance from the microscope. To have a good form of lamp is as much to be desired for the student as for those engaged in the more advanced work of microscopy.

Whatever the source of light we must on no account over-illuminate. The object having been placed on the stage of the microscope, the body should be racked down to within a quarter or half an inch of the specimen, and then, while looking through the eye-piece, should be slowly withdrawn until a sharp image comes into view. The fine adjustment may now be used for the more delicate focussing of the several parts of the field.

Accurate adjustment of focus is required when using a ¼-inch objective; details of the object, as striæ, being brought into view when a stronger light is thrown obliquely upon them from the mirror. If a 1-inch objective is used the light often proves to be in excess of what is required, and this must be regulated by the aid of the diaphragm.

The iris diaphragm, made to drop into the under-stage, is more generally employed, as when racked up to the object it affords every necessary graduation of illumination.

Fig. 201.—Bull's-eye Lens.

To illuminate opaque objects the light should be thrown upon them from above by the bull's-eye lens (Fig. 201). The focus of such a lens and the lamp placed at four inches from it, is about three inches for daylight, or two inches for artificial light. A large object may be placed upon the stage of the microscope at once, but smaller objects are either laid on a glass slide or held in the stage forceps.

When illuminating objects from above all light from the mirror, or that which might enter the objective from below the stage, should be carefully excluded. *Dark-field illumination* is a means of seeing a transparent object as an opaque one. The principle, however, is that all the light shall be thrown from below the object, but so obliquely that it cannot enter the object-glass unless interrupted by the object; this is best accomplished by *Wenham's Parabola.*

Glass of any kind requires occasional cleaning; a piece of soft washed chamois leather should be used for this purpose. The fronts of the objectives may be carefully wiped, but not *unscrewed* or tampered with; a short thick-set camel's hair brush may be passed down to the back lens, and all dust removed without doing any harm. If the objective is an *immersion*, carefully remove the fluid from the front lens, as even distilled water will leave a stain behind. For removing oil see special directions given at page 171.

When cleaning the *eye-pieces*, which should be done occasionally, the cells containing the glasses must be unscrewed and replaced one at a time, so that they may not be made to change places.

Any dirt upon the *eye-pieces* may be detected by turning them round whilst looking through the instrument; but if the *object-glasses* are not clean, or are injured, it will, for the most part, only be seen by the object appearing misty.

The *object-glasses*, when in use but not on the microscope, should be stood upon the table with the screw downwards, to prevent dust getting into the lenses, and they should always be put into their brass cases when done with.

A large bell-glass shade will be found the most useful cover for keeping dust from the instrument when not in use.

When looking through the eye-piece be sure to place the eye in close proximation to the cap, otherwise the whole field will not be perfectly visible; it should appear as an equally well-illuminated circular disc. If the eyelashes are reflected from the eye-glass, the observer is looking upon the eye-piece, and not through it.

The Mirror.—The working focal distance of the mirror is that which brings the images of the window-bars sharply out upon the object resting upon the stage. In other words, the focus of the mirror is that which brings parallel rays to a correct focus on the object-glass. If employing artificial light, then the flame of the lamp should be distinguishable; a slight change in the inclination of the mirror will throw the image of the lamp-flame out of the field.

The strongest light is reflected from the concave side of the mirror, that from the flat side is more diffuse and less intense. Oblique light can be obtained by turning the mirror on one side and then adjusting it so as to illuminate the field from that position. All the necessary mechanism of the microscope is easily and quickly learned. The object-glasses or objectives are, as previously explained, designated according to the focal distance of a single lens of the same magnifying power. Thus a 2-inch objective is understood to be a combination which has the magnifying power of a single lens whose focal point is two inches from the object, and so on with reference to other powers. By the aid of different eye-pieces an extensive range of magnifying power can be obtained; for example, the 2-inch objective with a deep eye-piece will give the same amplification as the quarter objective with the ordinary eye-piece. Indeed, for certain observations, the combination of a wide-angled low-power objective, with a deep eye-piece, or *compensating eye-piece*, is considered to have an advantage.

It has been already explained that two objectives, one of much greater power than the other, but both having only the same numerical aperture, will show only the same amount of *detail*; the higher power on a larger scale. That is, supposing with a $\frac{1}{4}$-inch objective of $1 \cdot 0$ numerical aperture certain structure is resolved, then a $\frac{1}{8}$-inch substituted with exactly the same numerical aperture, but with double the magnification, no more *resolving power* will be found in the latter objective than in the former. For this reason a doubt has been expressed as to whether high-power objectives—especially the more expensive oil-immersions, made to transmit large pencils of light through their larger apertures—are so well adapted for ordinary research as the best series of dry achromatic objectives, or even, in some instances, the medium aperture lenses; undoubtedly, for histological (physiological and pathological) work, the latter will be found to meet the students' requirements quite as well as the former.

The student or amateur will do well to commence with moderate or medium powers, a 2-inch, a 1-inch, a ½-inch, a ⁴⁄₁₀-inch, or ¼-inch. These, together with the A and B eye-pieces, will give a range of magnification from 30 to 250 diameters.

Penetration in the objective is a quality for consideration, as the adjustment of high powers is a work of delicacy, and in some cases their penetration is impaired by the arrangement made to obtain finer definition. The value, however, of penetration in an objective is always considered to be of more or less importance. It is a quality whereby, under certain conditions, a more perfect insight into structure is obtained. As a rule, the objective having the largest working distance possesses the better penetration. Theoretically, the penetration of an objective decreases as the square of the angular aperture increases. For this reason the medical student will be justified in choosing the objectives I have named, since these will be better adapted to his work and pursuits. The penetration of the objective is a relative quality assessed at a different value by workers whose aims are widely different. But for the observation of living organisms, the cyclosis within the cell of the closterium or valisneria, for instance, preference will undoubtedly be in favour of the objective with good penetration.

Resolving Power.—This is a quality highly prized by the bacteriologist. In the case of the high-angled apochromatic oil-immersion, with its compensating eye-piece, its resolution is found to be of very considerable advantage, because of its capacity to receive and recombine all the diffraction spectra that lie beyond the range of the older achromatic objective, with its smaller angular aperture. The actual loss of resolving power consequent upon the contraction of aperture from 180° to 128½° is ten per cent., if not more. Resolution depends, then, upon the quality and quantity of the light admitted, the power of collecting the greatest number of rays, and the perfection of centring. In other words, upon the co-ordination of the illuminating system of the microscope—mirror, achromatic condenser, objective and eye-piece. If diatoms are employed as test-objects, it should not be forgotten that there are great differences, even in the same species, in the distances their lines are apart. For this reason ruled lines of known value, as Nobert's lines, are to be preferred. The following example will suffice to show the value of a dry ⅛-inch objective of 120° in defining the rulings of a 19-band plate, which is equivalent to the ¹⁄₆₇₀₀₀th of an inch. This objective, with careful illumination, showed them all; but when cut down by a diaphragm to 110°, the eighteenth line was not separable; further cut down to 100° the seventeenth was the limit, to 80° the fourteenth, and to 60° the tenth was barely reached.

Flatness of Field.—This quality in the objective has, by the introduction of the immersion system, lost much of the importance formerly attached to it. Some writers assume it to be an "optical impossibility." The compensating eye-piece has had the effect of contracting the visual field, consequently the peripheral imperfections of the objective are of a less disturbing character. It has, however, not been made perfectly clear whether the highest perfection of the two primary qualities of a good objective, *defining power and resolving power*, can be always obtained in one and the same combination of lenses.

Doubtless, *defining* power can be more satisfactorily determined by the examination of a suitable object, and the perfection of the image obtained; to assist in securing which, a solid axial cone of light equal to about three-fourths of the aperture of the objective must be employed.

To sum up, then, "the focal power of all objectives depends in their perfect *definition*, a property on which their converging power depends, and in turn their magnifying action is dependent; again, focal power is the curvature imprinted by the lens on a plane wave, and is reciprocal of the true focal length. It is appropriately expressed in terms of the proper unit of focal curvature, the *dioptric*; a unit of curvature."[39]

Fig. 202.—Seiler's Test Slide.

It may be taken as an axiom with microscopists that "neither the penetrating power nor the high-power defining objective is alone sufficient for every kind of work. The larger the details of ultimate structure, the narrower the aperture—and the converse; the minuter the dimensions of elementary structure, the wider must be the aperture of the objective." Every worker with the microscope must have satisfied himself of the truth of this statement, when engaged in the study of the movements of living organisms, or defining the intimate structure of the minuter diatoms, or of the podura scale.

Test for Illumination.—Dr. C. Seiler recommends the human blood corpuscle as the best test of good illumination. He prepares the object in the following manner: Take for the purpose a clean glass slide of the ordinary kind, and place near its extreme edge a drop of fresh blood drawn by pricking the finger with a needle. Then take another slide of the same size, with ground edges, and bring one end in contact with the drop of blood, as shown in Fig. 202, at an angle of 45°; then draw it evenly and quickly across the underslide, and the result will be to spread out the corpuscles evenly throughout. Blood discs being lenticular bodies, with depressed centres, act like so many little glass-lenses, and show diffraction rings if the light is not properly adjusted.[40]

Errors of Interpretation.—To be in a position to draw an accurate conclusion of the nature and properties of the object under examination is a matter of great importance to the microscopist. The viewing of objects by transmitted light is of quite an exceptional character, rather calculated to mislead the judgment as well as the eye. It requires, therefore, an unusual amount of care to avoid falling into errors of interpretation. Among test objects the precise nature of the structural elements of the Diatomaceæ have given rise to great divergence of opinion. Then, again, the minute scales of the podura Springtails, one of the Collembola, and their congeners *Lepisma saccharina*, the structure of which is equally debatable. Mr. R. Beck, in an instructive paper published in the "Transactions of the Royal Microscopical Society," says that the scales of the Lepisma can be made to put on an appearance which bears little resemblance to their actual structure.

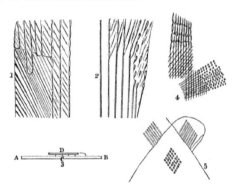

Fig. 203.—Portions of Scales of Lepisma.

In the more abundant kind of scales the prominent markings appear as a series of double lines. These run parallel and at considerable intervals from end to end of the scale, whilst other lines, generally much fainter, radiate from the quill, and take the same direction as the outline of the scale when near the fixed or quill end; but there is, in addition, an interrupted appearance at the sides of the scale, which is very different from the mere union, or "cross-hatchings," of the two sets of lines (Fig. 203, Nos. 1 and 2, the upper portions).

The scales themselves are formed of some truly transparent substance, for water instantly and almost entirely obliterates their markings, but they reappear unaltered as the moisture leaves them; therefore the fact of their being visible at all, under any circumstances, is due to the refraction of light by superficial irregularities, and the following experiment establishes this fact, whilst it determines at the same time the structure of each side of the scale, which it is otherwise impossible to do from the appearance of the markings in their unaltered state:—

"Remove some of the scales by pressing a clean and dry slide against the body of the insect, and cover them with a piece of thin glass, which may be prevented from moving by a little gum at each corner. No. 3 may then be taken as an exaggerated section of the various parts. A B is the glass slide, with a scale, C, closely adherent to it, and D the thin glass-cover. If a very small drop of water be placed at the edge of the thin glass, it will run under by capillary attraction; but when it reaches the scale, C, it will run first between it and the glass slide, A B, because the attraction there will be greater, and consequently the markings on that side of the scale which is in contact with the slide will be obliterated, while those on the other side will, for some time at least, remain unaltered: when such is the case, the strongly marked vertical lines disappear, and the radiating ones become continuous. (*See* No. 1, the lower left-hand portion.) To try the same experiment with the other, or inner surface of the scales, it is only requisite to transfer them, by pressing the first piece of glass, by which they were taken from the insect, upon another piece, and then the same process as before may be repeated with the scales that have adhered to the second slide, the radiating lines will now disappear, and the vertical ones become continuous. (*See* No. 2, left portion.) These results, therefore, show that the interrupted appearance is produced by two sets of uninterrupted lines on different surfaces, the lines in each instance being caused by corrugations or folds on the external surfaces of the scales. Nos. 1 and 2 are parts of a camera lucida drawing of a scale which happened to have opposite surfaces obliterated in different parts. No. 4 shows parts of a small scale in a dry and natural state; at the upper part the interrupted appearance is not much unlike that seen at the sides of the larger scales; but lower down, where lines of equal strength cross nearly at right angles, the lines are entirely lost in a series of dots, and exactly the same appearance is shown in No. 5 to be produced by the two scales at a part where they overlie each other, although each one separately shows only parallel vertical lines."

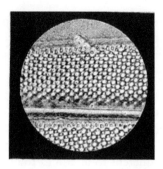

Fig. 204.—Outer Membrane of Upper Plane of Red Beads thrown by each alternate hole of grating; on lowering the focus white interspaces turn into blue beads.

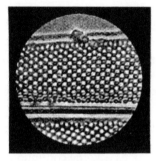

Fig. 204a.—Outer Membrane of Lower Plane of Beads thrown from remaining holes of grating; on raising the focus white interspaces turn into red beads.

Objective used, Zeiss's apochromatic $\frac{1}{12}$-inch oil-immersion, numerical aperture 1·40, magnifying power 1,750 diameters.

A well-known skilled observer of test objects[41] says: "Practically the resolving power of our achromatic objectives on lined objects reached their maximum in the late Dr. Woodward's hands. *Amphipleura pellucida* was then, as now, the finest known regular structure of the diatoms. There appeared then nothing more to be gained in resolution when one of the apochromatic $\frac{1}{12}$-inch objectives of Zeiss, with its entire absence of colour, passed into my hands, and I soon became convinced that it possessed the power of separating the different layers of structure in the valve, beyond the grasp of the dry-objective. The result of this increase of power enabled me to split up, as it were, the one plate of silex forming the valve of *Pleurosigma formosum* into three layers, and which had never before appeared to be possible; proving, in fact, that magnification without corresponding aperture is of little or no account."

"The intimate structure of these test objects," says Mr. Smith, "is built up on one plan, each being composed of two or more layers, (1) a valve with two layers, as in *Pleurosigma balticum*; (2) two layers with a grating and secondary markings placed diagonally, as in *Pleurosigma formosum*; (3) with two layers of a net-like structure, as in *Pleurosigma angulatum*, the fineness of the striæ or gratings of which measure the $\frac{1}{50000}$th of an inch. Five other diatoms afford evidence of this compound structure. The presence of beads or hemispheres in one of the focal planes, and depressions or pits in another, are emphasised in the micro-photograph itself; reduced portions of the valve are represented in Figs. 204 and 204*a*."

A portion of a diatom valve, *Pleurosigma angulatum*, micro-photographed on a higher scale of magnification, 4,500 diameters, is given further on.

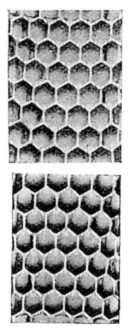

Fig. 205.—Sections of an old-fashioned Glass Tumbler, from photographs by the late Mr. R. Beck.

Errors of interpretation arise either from the small cones of illumination afforded by the dry-objective, or the oblique illumination formerly resorted to for the resolution of these difficult test objects, and several of the lights and shadows resulting from the refractive power of the object itself. But the most common error is that produced by the reversal of the lights and shadows resulting from the refractive powers of the object itself. To make this clear, I reproduce two reduced photographs of a small section of an old-fashioned glass tumbler, covered externally with numerous hemispheres, illuminated by transmitted light (Fig. 205).

This illustration well emphasises the difficulty there is in determining structure under precisely similar conditions to those we are accustomed to of examining valves of diatoms under the microscope. If these photographs be held in front of a strong light, they at once convey different impressions to the mind, the hemispheres appearing depressions in the one, and raised beads in the other. Both are prints from the same negative, but in mounting are reversed; and therefore the apparent dissimilarity is due to a slight inequality of illumination, which the mind accepts as light and shade.

Very similar appearances to those described will result if a thin plate of glass were studded with minute, equal, and equi-distant plano-convex lenses, the foci of which would very nearly lie in the same plane. If the focal surface, or plane of vision, of the objective be made to coincide with this plane, a series of bright points will result, from the excess of light falling on each lens. If the plane of vision be next made to coincide with the surfaces of the lenses, these points would appear dark, in consequence of the rays being refracted towards points *now* out of focus. Lastly, if the plane of vision be made to coincide with the plane *beneath* the lenses that contain their several foci, so that each lens may be, as it were, combined with the object-glass, then a second series of bright points will result from the accumulation of the rays transmitted at those points. Moreover, as all rays capable of entering the objective are concerned in the formation of the second series of bright focal points, the first series being formed by the rays of a cone of light only, it is evident that the circle of least confusion must be much less, and therefore the bright points better defined in the first than in the last series.

There are no set of objects which have given rise to more discussion as to their precise character than the scales of the podura (*Lepidocyrtus cervicollis*), to the intimate structure of which Mr. Smith turned his attention, and succeeded, I am inclined to think, in his attempt to settle the structure of these very minute scales, and which heretofore have been described as "notes of exclamation." By the aid of the same power as that employed in the examination of the *pleurosigma formosum*, the old conventional markings have disappeared, and well-defined "*featherlets*" have taken their place. By careful focussing up and down, a series of whitish pin-like bodies is to be seen, with an intervening secondary structure. A micro-photograph of a portion of a scale taken by Mr. Smith shows that these pin-like bodies are inserted in a fold of the basement membrane, which, in his opinion, furnish unmistakable evidence of the fact that these projecting bodies are real, and must no longer be looked upon as mere *ghosts*. Quite recently, a micro-photograph of a portion of a podura scale was placed in my hands, taken by Mr. J. W. Gifford with a Swift's $\frac{1}{12}$-inch apochromatic objective, of numerical aperture 1·40, and a deep eye-piece, having a combined magnifying power of 3,827 diameters. Fig. 206 shows a portion of the photograph which, it will be admitted, supports Mr. Smith's view of the structure of the podura scale.

Fig. 206.—Podura Scale, taken with a ¹⁄₁₂ Swift's Immersion × 3,827.

Many other errors of interpretation are not unknown to the experienced operator with the microscope, arising, for the most part, from an influence exerted by peculiarities in the internal structure of certain objects; for example, that offered by the human hair, and which, when viewed by transmitted light, presents the appearance of a flattened-out band, with a darkish centre, due to the refractive influence of the rays of light transmitted through the hair. That it is a solid or tubular structure is proved by making a transverse section of the hair-shaft, when it is seen filled up by medullary matter, the centre being somewhat darker than the outer part. It is, in fact, a spiral outgrowth of the epithelial scales, overlapping each other, imparting a striated appearance to the surface. A cylindrical thread of glass in balsam appears as a flattened, band-like streak, of little brilliancy. Another instance of fallacy arising from diversity in the refractive power of the internal parts of an object is furnished by the mistakes formerly made with regard to the true character of the *lacunæ* and *canaliculi* of bone structure. These were long supposed to be solid corpuscles, with radiating opaque filaments proceeding from a dense centre; on the contrary, they are minute chambers, with diverging passages—excavations in the solid osseous structure. That such is the case is shown by the effects of Canada balsam, which infiltrates the osseous substance.

Air bubbles are a perplexing source of trouble. The better way of becoming accustomed to deceptive appearances of the kind is to compare the aspect of globules of oil in water with bubbles of air in water, or Canada balsam.

The molecular movements of finely divided particles, seen in nearly all cases when certain objects are first suspended in water, or other fluids, are a frequent cause of embarrassment to beginners. If a minute portion of indigo or carmine be rubbed up with a little water, and a drop placed on a glass slide under the microscope, it will at once exhibit a peculiar *perpetual motion* appearance. This movement was first observed in the granular particles seen among pollen grains of plants, known as *fovilla*, and which are set free when the pollen is crushed. Important vital endowments were formerly attributed to these particles, but Dr. Robert Brown showed that such granules were common enough both in organic and inorganic substances, and were in no way "indicative of life."[42]

Professor Jevons succeeded in throwing light on these curious movements. He showed that they were not due to evaporation, as some observers contended, as they continue when all possibility of evaporation is cut off, when the fluid is surrounded by a layer of oil, and enclosed in an air-tight case: but as Professor Jevons pointed out, these movements are greatly affected by the admixture of various substances with water, being increased by a small quantity of gum, and checked by a drop of sulphuric acid, or a few grains of some saline substance, which increases the conducting power of water for electricity. The Brownian movement, now termed *pedesis*, much depends upon the size of the particles, their specific gravity, and the nature of the liquid in which they are immersed.

The correct conclusions to be drawn by the microscopist regarding the nature of an object will necessarily depend upon previous experience in microscopic observations, a knowledge of the class of bodies brought under observation, and the skill of the observer in the use of the instrument—that is, in securing the best focus possible with any objective brought into use. I am indebted to Messrs. Beck for the following series of illustrations, showing the effect of under and over correction of the objective.

DIRECTIONS FOR FINDING THE BEST FOCUS.

The method of finding and determining when the screw-collar adjustment of the high-power objective has arrived at a point of perfect definition and magnification is as follows:—

Select any dark speck of dust, or an opaque portion of the object, and carefully focus this small particle by working the screw of the fine adjustment, move the screw up and down until you are satisfied the image is the sharpest and blackest that can be obtained, then once more test the focus a little above and a little below while closely scrutinising the effect on the image. It will now be seen that whereas in focussing on one side of the best focus the object disappears in a fog, by focussing on the other side it remains in view for a longer period, but alters its appearance; it is now no longer a black dot, but a bright dot of light surrounded by a black margin. The effects being thus dissimilar on different sides of the best focus, show that the objective is not perfectly adjusted for the cover-glass in use.

The next step is to find out whether the bright image is above or below the best focus, as on this depends the direction in which the adjustment-collar should be turned. To determine this it is only necessary to ascertain which way the slow-motion milled head of the microscope turns when moving the objective upwards.

In the case under consideration, the bright image will be *above* the best focus, which shows that the cover-glass in use is *thicker* than that for which the objective is adjusted, consequently the adjustment-collar must be moved in the opposite direction.

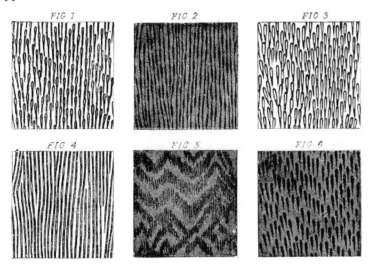

Fig. 207.—Podura Scale Test.

If the collar be turned too far in the opposite direction, it will be found that the bright image is *below* the best focus, and the cover-glass is then *thinner* than that for which the objective is adjusted. The collar must then be turned back again *until the effect on each side of the best focus is exactly similar.* This effect in the case of a circular speck of dust will be that the object disappears equally rapidly on either side, and does not instantly vanish into fog, on either side presenting the bright spot appearance, though not in so marked a degree on either side. When the object is in perfect adjustment the expansion of the outline is exactly the same, both within and without the focus.

A different indication, however, is afforded by such test-objects as the finer diatoms, and the podura scale, in which we have to do with a set of distinct dots and other markings. If the dots have a tendency to run into lines when the object is *without* the focus, the glasses should be brought closer together;

on the contrary, if the lines appear when the object is *within* the focal point, the glasses should be farther separated.

The adjustment of the objective by the screw-collar in the case of the podura scale should be carried out in the way described, when the following effects will be observed to take place, usually in the order of their arrangement.

Fig. 1 shows the appearance of a podura scale when the adjustment of the object-glass is correct, and Fig. 2 shows the effect produced on each side of the exact focus. Fig. 3 shows the way in which the markings individually divide when all the adjustments are correct, and when the focus is altered the least possible amount only each way.

Figs. 4 and 5 show the two appearances on one and the other side of the best focus when the adjustment is incorrect, Fig. 6 showing the appearance of the same at its best focus.

The scales are magnified 1,300 diameters, and each square measures ·001 of an inch.

This method, however, of finding the best focus of an objective can scarcely be accomplished without a sub-stage condenser. It may therefore be of service to the student, and to those who are not disposed to purchase expensive forms of condensers, to know that either an inch or an inch and a half objective, or convex-lens mounted on a simple wooden ring with a flange, can be arranged to slip in the place of the diaphragm under the stage. This kind of condenser will prove to be of considerable value with a ½-inch, a 4/10-inch, and a ¼-inch; while a still more excellent achromatic condenser can be made out of a Steinheil's *aplanatic-loup* arranged to drop into the central fitting of the sub-stage. As without a condenser of some kind it is hardly possible to enter upon any course of histological or scientific research.[43]

Working Accessories.

Troughs—Live-cages—Compressors.

A glass plate with a ledge, and some pieces of *thin glass*, although applicable for many purposes, are specially designed for objects in fluid. Thus a drop of fluid containing the object sought for is placed upon the slide and covered by a piece of thin glass; or, the object being put upon the glass slide and the thin glass over it, the fluid is applied near one side, and runs under by capillary attraction.

Fig. 208.—Varley's Live-box.

Troughs and Live-box.—These are made of various materials, glass, vulcanite, brass, &c., expressly for examining infusoria and live animals. They should be so constructed as to admit of the use of a medium power, a ½-inch at least, under the microscope. They should also admit of being easily cleaned and repaired when broken; matters rarely thought of by those who construct them. An early devised *live-box* (Varley's, Fig. 208) consists of two circular pieces of brass tubing, one sliding over the other carrying a disc of glass and fitting over another glass with bevelled edges to prevent the fluid flowing away.

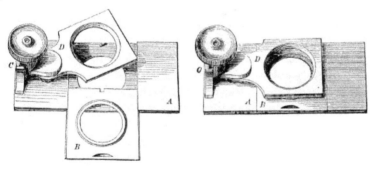

Fig. 209.—Ross's Compressorium.

The Compressorium is used for similar purposes. By a graduated pressure the fluid is *thinned out* and a higher power can be employed for the examination of the object. Ross's early compressorium consists of a plate of brass about three inches long, having in its centre a circle of glass like the bottom of the live-box. This piece of glass is set in a frame, *B*, which slides in and out so that it can be removed for the convenience of preparing any object upon it— under water if desirable. The upper movable part, *D*, is attached to a screw-motion at *C*; and at one end of the brass plate, *A*, which forms the bed of the instrument, is an upright piece of brass grooved so as to receive a vertical plate, to which a downward motion is given by a single fine screw, surrounded by a spiral spring, which elevates the plate as soon as the screw-pressure is removed.

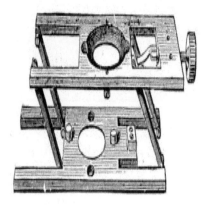

Fig. 210.—Beck's Parallel-plate Compressor.

Beck's Parallel-plate Compressor (Fig. 210) affords a more exact means of regulating the pressure, and can be used for a variety of purposes. It is also easily cleaned.

Fig. 211.—Rousselet's Compressorium.

Rousselet's Compressorium (Fig. 211) is a very effective form for general use. It is so arranged that the student has perfect control over the pressure to which the specimen should be subjected. The cover-glass is large in comparison with that beneath; being bevelled causes evaporation to go on very slowly while the pressure between the two glass surfaces is kept perfectly parallel.

Botterill's Live-trough (Fig. 212) consists of two brass plates screwed together by binding screws, and holding between them two plates of thin glass, which are maintained at a proper distance by inserting a semicircular flat disc of india-rubber.

Fig. 212.—Botterill's Live-trough.

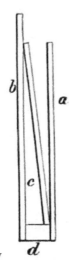

Fig. 213.—Glass Trough.

Glass troughs for chara and polypes (a sectional view of one shown at Fig. 213) are made of three pieces of glass, the bottom being a thick strip, and the front (*a*) of thinner glass than the back (*b*); the whole is cemented together with Jeffery's marine-glue. The method adopted for confining objects near the front glass varies according to circumstances. The most convenient is to place in the trough a piece of glass wide enough to stand across diagonally, as at *c*; then, if the object be heavier than water, it will sink until stopped by the glass plate. At other times, when used to view chara, the diagonal plate may be made to press it close to the front by means of a wedge of glass or cork. When using the trough the microscope should be placed in a nearly horizontal position.

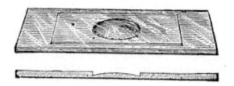

Fig. 214.—Weber's Slip with Convex Cell for use as a Live-trough.

Fig. 215.—Current-slide Live-cell.

Cells for viewing living objects, and watching their movements, take many forms, usually determined by the makers for the purposes they are required to serve. The smaller glass troughs (Figs. 216, 216a) are made for examining the small infusoria, rotifers, &c., some of which take special forms, as the double or divided trough (Fig. 217) intended for viewing the circulation of the blood in the tail of a small fish, and at the same time keep up a supply of water and air.

Fig. 216.

Fig. 216a.

The Frog-plate consists of a strip of plate-glass, or wood, pierced with holes on either side, through which tapes are passed to secure the frog in its place. At the extreme end is a shallow glass trough, made to hold a sufficient quantity of water to keep the web of the foot moist while under examination. In this way a continuous view of the circulation of the blood of the animal is obtained.

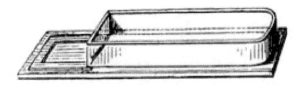

Fig. 217.

Growing Cells have received more attention from those who devote attention to the lower forms of life, the construction of which, for the purpose of maintaining a continuous supply of fresh water to objects under observation, and for sustaining their vital energy for a long period, is of some importance. The employment of live-cells is resorted to by microscopists, as doubtless there is much to be discovered concerning the metamorphoses which some of the lower micro-organisms, both of plant and animal life, pass through.

Fig. 218.—Frog-plate.

Holman's life slide consists of a 3 × 1 inch glass slide, with a deep oval cavity in the middle to receive the specimen for observation. A shallow oval is ground and polished around the deep cavity, forming a bevel. From this bevel a fine cut extends, to furnish fresh air to the living low forms of life which invariably seek the bevelled edge of the cavity, thus bringing them within reach of the highest powers. He also contrived a convenient form of "moist chamber," or animalcule-cage (Fig. 220), for the purpose of studying the growth of minute organisms, without in any way disturbing them for a lengthened period. This is also found useful as a dry chamber for holding minute insects.

Fig. 219.—Holman's Life Slide. Full size.

Fig. 220.—Holman's Moist Chamber.

Zentmayer's Holman Syphon Slide is used either as a hot or cold water cell. It should be deep enough to hold a small fish or newt, and retain it without any undue pressure. When in use it is only necessary to place the animal into it (as shown in Fig. 221), with some water, and secure it with a glass cover; then immerse the upper tube in a jar of water, while another, at a lower level, maintains a current. When the slide is on the stage of the microscope, one jar should stand on a lower level than the other, the slide being made the highest part of the syphon. The pressure of the atmosphere is sufficient to keep the cover-glass in its place.

The examination of the various kinds of infusorial life—rotifers, for instance—is facilitated by the addition of the smallest particle of colouring matter, either carmine or indigo. A small quantity of either of these colours should be rubbed up in a little water in a watch-glass, and a portion taken up on the point of a brush, and the brush run along the edge of the cover-glass; sufficient will be left behind to barely tinge the water with the colour, and this gradually distributes itself over the rotifers. Under the microscope this minute quantity will be seen like a rising cloud of dust, and as it approaches a rotifer it is whirled round in different curves, showing at once the action of its wonderfully rapid cilia. This colouring matter appears to be devoured, as it may be traced from the mouth to the digestive canal. Monads may be detected by this means, and the smaller forms of *algæ*, *Euglena viridis* and *Protococcus pluvialis*.

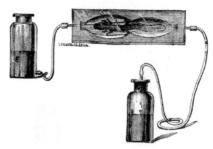

Fig. 221.—Holman's Syphon Slide.

Dipping-tubes.—In dealing with infusorial or monad life it is convenient to keep a stock-bottle ready for their reception, and in a light favourable to health. When a live specimen is required for examination, the dipping-tube is brought into requisition. These tubes are open at both ends, and vary in length and diameter. Their ends should be nicely rounded off in the flame of a blow-pipe; in form either straight, or bent and drawn out to a fine point, as represented in Fig. 222. When any special specimen is required for examination, then one of the tubes must be passed down into the water, the upper orifice having been previously closed by the forefinger, and kept tightly pressed, until its lower orifice comes in contact with the object. On the finger being removed, the water rushes up and carries the creature sought for with it. The finger is once more replaced at the top of the tube; it is then lifted out, and the contents deposited in one or other of the glass cells described. Tubes with india-rubber covers can be had.

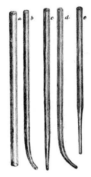

Fig. 222.—Dipping-tubes.

Fig. 223.—Stock-bottle.

Moist and Warm Stages.—In addition to the moist cells and chambers described it is often found necessary in working out the histories of minute organisms to keep them for some time under observation, and as far as possible in an undisturbed condition, and it is equally necessary to prevent evaporation of the water in which they are immersed. One of the best warm stages is that known as Maddox's growing stage; this can be had of any optician. More elaborate adaptions are required for the study of special organisms, and for experimental research.

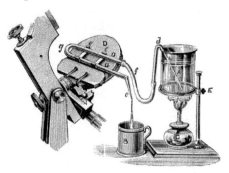

Fig. 224.—Bartley's Warm Stage.

In that case *Bartley's Warm Stage* (Fig. 224) is recommended. There are other forms of warm stages in use, many of an inexpensive kind and readily adaptable to any stage. Bartley's has proved useful; it consists of a vessel, E, three parts filled with water and supported on a ring stand. This may be kept at any temperature by the small spirit-lamp, C; a syphon tube d conveys the warm water along f, and through the bent tubing which surrounds the object under observation on the stage, D, and then passes off through the open end, C, into the receptacle, B, placed to receive the overflow. Steam can be used for heating, or iced water for observing the effects of cold upon the organism.

A simple form of warm stage may be made of an oblong copper plate, two inches long by one wide, from one side of which a rod of the same material projects. The plate has a round aperture, the centre half an inch in diameter, and is fastened to an ordinary slide with sealing-wax. The drop or object to be examined is placed on a large-sized cover-glass and covered over with a smaller one. Olive oil or vaseline is painted round the edge of the smaller one to prevent evaporation, and the preparation is placed over the aperture in the plate. The slide bearing the copper plate is clamped to the stage of the microscope. The flame of the spirit-lamp is applied to the extremity of the rod, and the heat is conducted to the plate and thence transmitted to the specimen. In order that the temperature of the copper plate may be approximately that of the body, the lamp is so adjusted that a fragment of cacao butter and wax placed close to the preparation is melted.

Professors Stricker and Schäfer have constructed warm stages for accurate observations, and which fully answer every purpose.

Fig. 225.—Stricker's Warm Stage.

Stricker's Stage (Fig. 225) consists of a rectangular box with a central opening, C, permitting the passage of light through the specimen under examination. The water makes its exit and entrance at the side tubes B B', and the temperature is indicated by a thermometer in front. In this apparatus either warm or cold water can be continuously used.

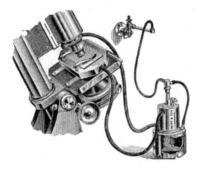

Fig. 226.—Schäfer's Warm Stage.

Schäfer's apparatus (Fig. 226) consists of a vessel filled with water (seen near the stage) which has been first boiled to expel the air, and then heated by means of a gas flame. The warm water ascends the india-rubber tubing to the brass box on the stage. The box is pierced by a tubular aperture to admit light to the object, and has an exit tube by which the cooled water from the stage returns by another piece of tubing to be reheated by the gas flame. There is a gas-regulator, by means of which any temperature can be maintained.

Methods of Preparing, Hardening, Staining and Section Cutting.

Numerous methods are employed for the preparation, hardening, staining, and section cutting of animal and vegetable tissues for the microscope, the details of which are modified, or varied as may be found needful, from time to time, by those whose intimate acquaintance with the subject entitles them to make innovations and changes in this very important department of microscopy. In the hands of the original worker, formulæ and methods will only be regarded as finger-posts pointing out a means of saving time in turning over pages to find this or that special method of staining. For this particular reason I have collected all the most accredited formulæ together in an Appendix at the end of the book, and arranged them alphabetically for ready reference.

As to section cutting, the student will do well to practise himself in making dissections, thick and thin sections, of vegetable and animal substances. The medical student will require no advice on this point, as the use of the scalpel, and those instruments needed for microscopical work, form an important part of his education. Of all the instruments contrived for delicate dissections, none are more serviceable than those which the student may make for himself out of ordinary needles. These may be fixed in handles as represented in Fig. 229, in addition to which, a pair of scissors and forceps, and a few small knives, such as those used in eye-operations, will prove most suitable. The double-bladed scissors represented in Fig. 227, with curved blades, are brought into use for cutting vegetable and other soft structures, the disadvantage attendant upon the use of which is owing to the curvature of the blades; when dealing with flat surfaces, the middle of the section is left too thick to exhibit structure.

The double-bladed knife of Professor Valentin was formerly held in high estimation by the microscopist, but this has been almost superseded by the microtome, which has taken the place of all other instruments, since by its aid uniform series of nearly all substances can be cut. The standard unit of a perfect section cutter, of any kind, has been fixed by the Royal Microscopical Society at the one-thousandth of a millimetre.

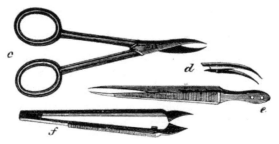

Fig. 227.—Section Scissors and Forceps.

The use of the razor for cutting sections has not been wholly abandoned, the method of using which is as follows:—Take the tissue between the thumb and finger of the left hand, hold the finger horizontally, so that its upper surface may form a rest for the razor to glide upon, take the razor firmly, and keep the handle in a line with the blade, then draw it through the tissue from heel to point and towards yourself. While cutting keep the razor well wetted with diluted methylated spirit.

Fig. 228.—Dissecting Knives.

Some preparation is required for cutting sections with the single microtome. The substance to be cut must be embedded in some other material, as carrot, turnip, potato, alder pith, paraffin, or thick gum, with either of which the cylinder or well of the microtome must be so nearly filled as to leave only an excavation in the centre for the specimen to be operated upon to occupy. The various forms of microtomes in use, and the selection of the most suitable, is therefore a matter of some difficulty. I must content myself by particularising two or three typical forms in general use. As all the substances intended for cutting require preparation, it will be first necessary to attend to the following directions given by one experienced in section cutting, Mr. M. J. Cole[44]:—(1) Always use fresh tissues. (2) Cut the organs into small pieces with a sharp knife. (3) Never wash a specimen in water; when it is necessary to remove any matter, allow some weak salt solution to flow over the surface of the tissue, or wash it in some hardening re-agent. (4) All specimens should be hardened in a large quantity of the re-agent; too many pieces should not be put into the same bottle, and keep them in a cool place. (5) In all cases the hardening process must be completed in spirits. (6) Label the bottles, stating the contents, the hardening fluid used, and when changed. Attention to details is necessary, as if hardening is neglected, good sections cannot be made.

Embedding in Paraffin Wax or Lard.—Melt together, by the aid of gentle heat, four parts of solid paraffin and one part of lard. A quantity of this may be made and kept ready for use. Melt the paraffin mass over a water bath, take the specimen, and dry it between the folds of a cloth to remove the spirit, so that the paraffin may adhere to its surface, place it in a small chip-box, in the desired position, and pour in enough melted paraffin to cover it, then set aside to solidify; when quite cold break away the box, and cut sections from the embedded mass with a sharp razor.

To infiltrate a tissue with paraffin, place the specimen in absolute alcohol or chloroform for an hour or two, then transfer to a bath of melted paraffin, at its melting point (about 110° F.), and keep it at this temperature for several hours, so that the paraffin may penetrate to the middle of the tissue. Then remove the specimen from the paraffin and put it into a small chip-box, pour in enough paraffin to cover it, and set aside to cool. When quite cold, make sections as before, with a razor, or fix it into a microtome, with a little melted paraffin. The sections when cut must be placed in turpentine to remove the paraffin, and then into absolute alcohol to remove the turpentine, and finally in distilled water to remove the alcohol, when they may be forthwith stained. It is often found better to stain the tissue in bulk before embedding. In this case the sections will only require the turpentine to dissolve away the paraffin, and may then be mounted in Canada balsam.

Hardening and Preparing Animal Tissues for section cutting and microscopical examination.—Fresh tissues are not well suited for microscopical examination, but it is sometimes advisable to observe the appearances of a fresh specimen, especially if it is suspected to contain amaloid bodies or parasites. It will then be necessary to *tease* out a small portion of the tissue immersed in a weak solution of salt and water by the aid of a pair of fine needles (Fig. 229) and the dissecting microscope (Fig. 230).

Fig. 229.—Needles for teasing out Sections.

Fig. 230.—Dissecting Microscope.

The most important point in connection with an instrument of this kind is, that it affords firm and convenient rests for the hands, and should not be raised too high from the table.

The stage should either be made of glass, or provided with a glass dish for dissecting under water, or preservative fluid. A pair of aplanatic lenses, mounted on a focussing bar as shown in Fig. 230, will be found the most convenient to work with.

Investigations of this nature should be always carried out in the manner described, but preparations of the kind cannot be preserved any length of time, unless properly hardened in spirit or Formalin solution. The method of teasing out under the light of a condensing lens is shown in Fig. 231.

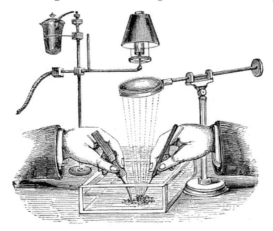

Fig. 231.—Method of teasing out Muscular Fibre, &c., in a fluid medium under Condensed Light.

It may be as well to state at the outset that physiological and pathological tissues can be hardened by immersion in methylated spirit alone, or a saturated solution of picric acid in methylated spirit in about a week, and it is said to yield satisfactory results, even some of the tissues being ready in twenty-four hours. The only drawback is that sections thus quickly hardened must be stained with picro-carmine. But, whatever method of hardening adopted, the tissue should be washed by means of a stream of water for half an hour, to remove all traces of the hardening agent, and on its removal pressed between folds of cotton cloth or fine Swedish filtering paper.

The principal hardening re-agents usually kept in bulk ready for use are the following:—

Absolute Alcohol.—This is suitable for the internal organs of animals, glands, &c. These organs must be perfectly fresh, and should be cut into small pieces, so that the alcohol may penetrate them as quickly as possible. The hardening is usually complete in a short time.[45]

Chromic Acid and Spirit.—Chromic acid one-sixth per cent., water solution two parts, and methylated spirit one part. This reagent hardens in about ten days. Then transfer to methylated spirit, which should be changed every day until all colour is discharged from the tissue. This is a suitable reagent for the preparation of cartilage, nerve trunks, heart, lips, blood vessels, trachea, lungs, tongue, intestines, and gullet.

Potassium Bichromate.—-Make a two per cent. water solution of this salt. This will harden specimens in about three weeks. Then transfer the preparation to methylated spirit, and change it every day until all colour is discharged. This is suitable for spinal cord, medulla, cerebellum, and cerebrum.

Müller's Fluid.—Bichromate of potash 30 grains, sulphate of soda 15 grains, distilled water 3½ ounces. This hardens in from three to six weeks. Then transfer, as before, to methylated spirits, and change it every day until colour ceases to appear. Most suitable for lymphatic glands, eye-ball and its internal structures, as well as for tendons, and thymus gland.

Methylated Spirit may be generally employed, but it has a tendency to shrink some tissues too much; it hardens in about ten days. It is usual to change the spirit daily, for the first three days at least. Skin, mammary gland, supra-renal glands, tonsils, and all injected organs may be hardened in it. (See note on the adulteration of methylated spirit with rack-oil, which utterly spoils it for use.)

Decalcifying solution for bones and teeth. Take one-sixth per cent. watery solution of chromic acid, and to every measured ounce add five drops of nitric acid. This reagent will soften the femur of any small animal in about three weeks; larger require a longer time. Change the fluid several times, and test its action by running a needle through the thickest part of the bone. Should it not pass through easily, then continue the process until it does. When soft enough transfer to water, let it soak for an hour or two, then pour off the water and add ten per cent. solution of carbonate of soda, and soak for twelve hours to remove all trace of acid. Wash again in water, and transfer to methylated spirit until required. Teeth require a large quantity of the decalcifying solution for softening.

Microtomes.—The simplest form of "hand-cutting machine" is that worked by a screw, which raises the preparation, and at the same time regulates the fineness of the section. When a number of sections are required, or when a complete series of sections of an organ is desired, Cole's simple microtome (Fig. 233) is in every way adapted.

Fig. 232.—Hand Section Cutter.

Fig. 233.—Cole's Section Cutting Microtome.

The method of using it is as follows:—Screw the microtome firmly to the table, and with the brass tube supplied with the microtome, punch out a cylinder of carrot to fit into the well. Cut this in half longitudinally, and scrape out enough space in one half of the carrot to take the specimen; then place the other half of carrot in position, and make sure that the specimen is held firmly between them, but it must not be crushed. Now put the cylinder of carrot and specimen into the well of the microtome and commence cutting the section. A good razor will do, but it is better to use the knife which Messrs. Watson supply with the microtome. While cutting keep the knife and plate of the microtome well wetted with dilute methylated spirit, and as sections are cut place them in a saucer of dilute spirit. A number of sections may be cut and preserved in methylated spirit until required for examination or mounting.

When a specimen has a very irregular outline, it cannot be very successfully embedded in carrot; paraffin will then be found to be more suitable. Place the tissue in the well of the microtome in the proper position, pour in enough melted paraffin to cover it, and put it by to get cold and hard before attempting to cut sections.

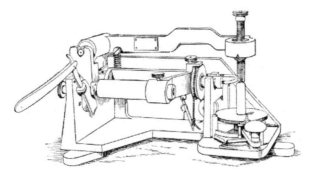

Fig. 234.—The Cambridge Rocking Microtome.

Cambridge Rocking Microtome.—This new pattern Cambridge Rocking Microtome (Fig. 234) possesses advantages over other instruments in use for cutting flat sections, and not parts of a cylindrical surface. The tube containing the paraffin is 30 millimetres in internal diameter instead of 20 millimetres, as in the earlier forms. The forward movement is also increased, so that an object 12 millimetres long can be cut throughout its whole length. It is provided with a dividing arc for reading off the thickness of the section in thousandths of a millimetre. The razor may be fixed either with its edge at right angles to the direction of motion of the object, or diagonally, for giving a slicing cut. The object can also be raised and fixed in position clear of the razor.

This microtome has both steadiness and stiffness in its geometrical arrangement and bearings, while the simplicity and efficiency of its mechanism for advancing the section between each stroke of the razor is remarkable. Although it may appear more complicated at first sight, it is found not to be so when brought into use.

Fig. 235.—Cathcart's Microtome.

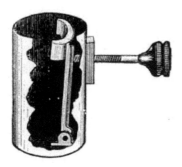

Fig. 235a.—Section Cutting Holder for Microtome.

Cathcart's Freezing Microtome.—This is a convenient and useful microtome for freezing purposes. Since its first introduction it has been much improved. The clamping arrangements give steadiness, and the principal screw is more effective; the freezing-plate is circular, and the arrangements made for preventing the ether from reaching the upper plate secures the object in view. This instrument can now be used for embedding as well as freezing. The directions for freezing are as follows:—

1. Place a few drops of mucilage (one part gum to three parts water) on the zinc plate.

2. Take a piece of the tissue to be cut, of about a quarter of an inch in thickness, and press it into the gum.

3. Fill the ether bottle with anhydrous methylated ether, and push the spray points into their socket. All spirit must of course have been previously removed by soaking for a night in water. The tissue should afterwards be soaked in gum for a like time before being cut.

Work the spray bellows briskly until the gum begins to freeze; after this work more gently. Be always careful to brush off the frozen vapour which, in a moist atmosphere, may collect below the zinc plate. If the ether should tend to collect in drops below the plate, work the bellows slower.

5. Raise the tissue by turning the milled head, and cut by sliding the knife along the glass plates.

6. After use, be careful to wipe the whole instrument clean.

7. Should the ether point become choked, clear by means of the fine wire provided for the purpose.

8. The instrument is intended for use with methylated sulphuric ether.

9. In clamping the instrument to a table, or other support, care should be taken that the zinc plate is in a horizontal position. If the plate be not horizontal, the gum will tend to run to one side.

The arrangement made for cutting and embedding sections consists of a cylindrical tube (Fig. 235a) fitting into the principal well of the microtome, within which is a hinged plate, upon which the screw acts, as in an ordinary vice. To bring this into use the freezing apparatus must be first removed, and the embedding tube placed in the well, and firmly pressed into place.

Staining Animal Structures.

Specific stains are chiefly employed to assist the eye in distinguishing one elementary tissue from another. It is therefore necessary to stain all structures, as certain parts are seen to have a special affinity for one colouring agent rather than another, whereby they become more deeply stained, and consequently more clearly differentiated. For staining animal structures, borax, carmine, and hæmatoxylin are more frequently employed than others. The formulæ for each will be found in the Appendix "Formulæ and Methods."

Staining Process.—Place the section in distilled water to wash away the alcohol; place a little of the carmine in a watch glass, and immerse the section in it for four or five minutes; then remove it to a solution composed of methylated spirit five parts, hydrochloric acid one part; shake well together. This solution should be kept ready for use. Immerse the section in this solution and leave it to soak for about five or ten minutes if over-stained, until the desired tint has been obtained. Sections of skin and fibrous tissue may be left until nearly all colour is removed, the glands and hair follicles will then be brought out more clearly. The section must be transferred to methylated spirit to remove all traces of acid, then to oil of cloves contained in a watch glass, lift the section from the methylated spirit by one of the *lifters* (Fig. 250), and carefully float it on the oil, in which it should be allowed to remain for about five minutes. This is the clearing process, the object of which is to remove the spirit and prepare the section for mounting in Canada balsam. First, however, place the section in filtered turpentine to wash away the oil of cloves; this is found to answer better than another plan adopted, that of removing the section from the oil of cloves and mounting it in balsam direct. The oil, however, has a tendency to darken the balsam.

Logwood or Hæmatoxylin Stains (see Appendix for the several formulæ). Staining by this agent is effected as follows:—

After the specimen has been hardened in any of the chromic acid solutions in use, transfer it to a seven per cent. watery solution of bicarbonate of soda for about five minutes, then wash well in distilled water. Spirit prepared preparations do not require to be transferred to the soda solution, but all sections must be washed before they are transferred to the logwood stain. To a watch glass nearly full of distilled water add ten or twenty drops of the logwood stain, in which it should remain for twenty or thirty minutes. Wash well with the ordinary tap water, which will fix the dye and cause it to become blue. Dehydrate in methylated spirit, clear in clove oil, and mount in dammar or Canada balsam.

Double-staining with Hæmatoxylin and Rosin.—Stain the section as directed above, then place it in an alcoholic solution of rosin, about one gramme of rosin to an ounce of methylated spirit, and let it soak for a few minutes; wash well in methylated spirit, clear in oil of cloves, and mount in balsam.

Canada balsam should be prepared for use as follows:—One ounce of dried balsam to one fluid ounce of pure benzole; dissolve, and keep in an *outside* stoppered bottle. Clear the section in clove oil, and place it in turpentine, clean a cover-glass and slide, place a few drops of balsam on the centre of the latter, take the section from the turpentine on a *lifter*, allow the excess of turpentine to drain away, and with a needle-point lift the section on to the balsam slide. Now take up the cover-glass with a pair of forceps (Fig. 236), and bring its edge in contact with the balsam, ease it down carefully as shown in Fig. 237, so that no air bubbles are enclosed, and with the needle point press the surface of the cover until the section lies quite smoothly and flat, and the excess of balsam is pressed out. The slide should now be transferred to the *warm-chamber*, and there allowed to remain for a day or two, or until set and hardened.

Fig. 236.—Forceps for Mounting.

Any exuded balsam may be washed away with benzole and a soft camel's hair brush; then dry the slide with an old piece of linen cloth, and apply a ring of cement or Japanner's gold size. Other methods for staining and mounting will be found to answer quite as well—that of Beneke's is a useful one for staining connective tissue.

Fig. 237.—Mode of placing Glass Cover on Object.

For staining connective tissue a modification of Weigert's method of staining fibrine is resorted to. Portions of tissue that have been fixed in alcohol having been embedded in paraffin and cut, the sections are detached and placed on glass slides, and stained for ten or twenty minutes with gentian violet, ten parts, well shaken with water 100 parts; filter, and add five to ten parts of a concentrated alcoholic gentian violet solution. Afterwards treat for one minute with lugol solution, of a port wine tint, dry with filter paper and decolourise with aniline xylol (aniline oil two parts and xylol three parts). Decolourisation having been stopped at the right point (judged from experience) mount the sections in xylol balsam. The fibres of the connective tissue should appear stained of various shades of violet.

Double Staining nucleated blood corpuscles. Two kinds of staining agents are required. Stain A: dissolve five grammes of rosin in half an ounce of distilled water, and add half an ounce of rectified alcohol. Stain B: dissolve five grammes of methyl green in an ounce of distilled water. Place a drop of frog's blood on a glass slide, and with the edge of another slide spread it evenly over the centre of the slip, and put it away to dry; when quite dry flood the slide with stain A for three minutes, and wash with water, now flood the slide with Stain B for five minutes, wash again with water, and allow the slide to dry. Apply a drop of the prepared Canada balsam and a cover-glass.

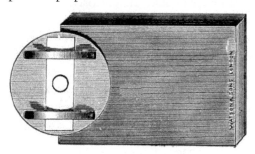

Fig. 238.—Shadbolt's Turn-table.

The blood of such mammals as are non-nucleated should be treated in a slightly different way. Spread a drop or two of blood on a slide and dry it quickly; then put the slide on Shadbolt's turn-table (Fig. 238) and run a ring of cement around it; allow this time to dry, and then apply a second coating, and before this becomes quite dry place on it a clean glass cover, and press it down gently with one of the fine needles (Fig. 229), until firmly adherent.

Epithelium.—Remove from the mouth of a frog by scraping some *squamous* epithelium; the columnar must be taken from the stomach; place it in glycerine, or Farrant's solution on the slide; apply a cover-glass, and with the point of the needle press it down until the epithelium cells are separated and spread evenly over the slide. Set this aside for a day or two, then wash away any of the medium which may have escaped; dry the slide, and run a ring of cement around the edges, on the turn-table. Portions of the intestine of a rabbit or other animal may be treated in the same way. If it is wished to make permanent specimens of such structures, the intestine must be hardened in a two per cent. solution of bichromate of potash for a couple of days, then washed until all colour is discharged, and removed to a solution of picro-carmine for twenty-four hours, after which allow the stain to drain away, when it will be ready for mounting.

By the aid of the handy little spring clip (Fig. 239), objects of delicacy when mounted may be left to dry and harden for any length of time.

Fig. 239.—Spring-clip for Mounting.

Striped muscular fibre, taken from the pig, must be teased out in a two per cent. solution of bichromate of potash, in which it should remain for two or three weeks, when it may be transferred to methylated spirit, and allowed to remain until required for mounting. Soak a piece in water to remove the spirit, place a small fragment on a slide in a few drops of water, and with a couple of needles tease the tissue up, so as to separate the fibres. Drain away the water, and apply a drop or two of Farrant's medium and a cover-glass, which cement down as before directed.

Fibrous tissue may be served in the same way. *Yellow elastic tissue* must be first placed in a solution of chromic acid and spirit for ten days, and then treated as directed for muscular fibre.

Non-striated Muscle.—A piece of the intestine of a rabbit should be steeped in chromic acid and spirit for ten days, then washed in water; strip off a thin layer of the muscular coat, and stain in hæmatoxylin solution. Well wash in ordinary water until the colour changes to blue, when it will be fit for mounting. Place a fragment on a slide and a drop of water, and carefully separate the fibres with a pair of needles. Drain off the water, as it is now ready for mounting, place on slide, and add a drop or two of Farrant's medium, and place on the cover-glass.

Nerve Tissue.—Dissect out the large sciatic nerve from a frog's thigh, and stretch it on a small piece of wood, to which pin both ends of the nerve, and transfer it to a one per cent. solution of osmic acid for an hour or two. Wash in distilled water; tease up a small fragment on a slide (as shown in Fig. 240), and apply a drop or two of Farrant's solution and cover-glass.

Tissues containing air should be soaked in water that has been boiled for ten minutes; this will displace the air. (For Farrant's medium, see Appendix.)

Glycerine Jelly.—Dissolve one ounce of French gelatine in six ounces of distilled water, and melt together in a hot-water bath. When quite dissolved, add four ounces of glycerine, and a few drops of creosote or carbolic acid. Filter through white filtering paper while warm, and keep in a capped bottle. This may be used instead of Farrant's solution.

Fig. 240.—Method of Teasing out Tissue.

Nitrate of silver darkens by exposure; it is used in a half per cent. watery solution. Specimens to be acted upon should be washed in distilled water, to remove every trace of sodium chloride, and then steeped in the silver solution for some two or three minutes, after which they should be again washed until they cease to turn milky; then place them in glycerine and expose them to the action of light until they assume a dark brown colour, when they should be mounted in glycerine or glycerine jelly.

By means of this stain the endothelial cells of the lymphatics, blood vessels, &c., and the nodes of Ranvier, constrictions in medullary nerves, are rendered visible. Sections of any of these may subsequently be stained by logwood or carmine.

Several methods have been adopted for staining with gold chloride. Dr. Klein's and Professor Schäfer's are among the best.

Dr. Klein's method of showing the nerves of the cornea is as follows:—Remove the cornea within fifteen minutes of death; place it in a half per cent. chloride of gold solution for half an hour, or an hour; wash in distilled water, and expose to the light for a few days; in the meantime occasionally change the water. Then immerse it in glycerine and distilled water, in the proportion of one to two; lastly, place it in water, and brush gently with a sable pencil to remove any precipitate, when it will be fit for mounting in glycerine. The colour of the cornea should be grey-violet.

Schäfer adopts another method—a double chloride of gold and potassium solution.

Osmic acid, first used by Schultze, is useful for the demonstration of fatty matters, all of which it colours black; it is also valuable for certain nerve preparations. Specimens should be allowed to remain in a one or two per cent. aqueous solution of the acid from a quarter to twenty-four hours, when the staining will be completed; but if it is desired to harden specimens at the same time, they should remain in it for some few days. Osmic acid does not penetrate very deeply, therefore small portions should be selected for immersion. This is a useful stain for infusorial animals.

Chloride of palladium, another of Schultze's staining fluids, is used to stain and harden the retina, crystalline lens, and other tissues of the eye, the cornified fat and connective tissues remaining uncoloured. The solution should be used very weak:—Chloride of palladium, one part; distilled water, 1,000 parts. Specimens should be mounted in glycerine at once, or further stained with carmine.

Dr. Schäfer employs a silver nitrate and gelatine solution for demonstrating lung epithelium; this is made as follows:—Take of gelatine ten grammes, soak in cold water, dissolve, and add warm water to 100 cc. Dissolve a decigramme of nitrate of silver in a little distilled water, and add to the gelatine solution. Inject this with a glass syringe into the lung until distension is pretty complete. Leave it to rest in a cool place until the gelatine has set; then cut sections as thin as possible, place them on a slide with glycerine, and expose to light till ready for mounting.

Of the double stains Mr. Groves prefers only those where the double colour is produced by a single process—or stains in which one colour is first employed, and then another. Single stains are picro-carmine, carmine and indigo carmine, aniline blue and aniline red.

Picro-carmine is specially useful for staining sections hardened in picric acid. It is prepared in several ways:—

1. Add to a saturated solution of picric acid in water a strong solution of carmine in ammonia to saturation.

2. Evaporate the mixture to one-fifth its bulk over a water bath, allow it to cool, filter from deposit, and evaporate to dryness, when picro-carmine is left as a crystalline powder of red-ochre colour.

Sections can be stained in a one per cent. aqueous solution, requiring only ten minutes for the process; wash well in distilled water, and transfer them to methylated alcohol, then to absolute alcohol, after which they are rendered transparent by immersing in oil of cloves or benzole, before mounting in balsam or dammar.

To summarise Mr. Groves' recommendations:—

1. Let the material be quite fresh.

2. (*a*) Take care that the hardening or softening fluid is not too strong. (*b*) Use a large bulk of fluid in proportion to the material. (*c*) Change the fluid frequently. (*d*) If freezing be employed, take care that the specimen is thoroughly frozen.

3. (*a*) Always use a sharp razor. (*b*) Take it with one diagonal sweep through the material. (*c*) Make the sections as thin as possible; and (*d*) Remove each one as soon as cut, for if sections accumulate on the knife or razor they are sure to get torn.

4. (*a*) Do not be in a hurry to stain, but (*b*) Remember that a weak colouring solution permeates the section better, and produces the best results; and (*c*) That the thinner the section the better it will take the stains.

5. (*a*) Always use glass slips and covers free from scratches and bubbles, and chemically clean. (*b*) Never use any but extra thin circular covers, so that the specimens may be used with high powers. (*c*) Always use cold preservatives, except in the case of glycerine jelly, and never use warmth to hasten the drying of balsam or dammar, but run a ring of cement round the cover.

6. Label specimens correctly; keep them in a flat tray, and in the dark.

Double and Treble Staining.

Dr. W. Stirling[46] furnishes a brief but useful account of the methods he has employed with much success.

Osmic Acid and Picro-carmine.—Mix on a glass slide a drop of the blood of newt or frog and a drop of a one per cent. aqueous solution of osmic acid, and allow the slide to stand by. This will fix the corpuscles without altering their shape. At the end of five minutes remove any excess of acid with blotting-paper, add a drop of a solution of picro-carmine, and a trace of glycerine to prevent evaporation, and set aside for three or four hours to see that no overstaining takes place. At the end of this time the nucleus will be found to be stained red, and the perinuclear part yellow.

Picric Acid and Picro-carmine.—Place a drop of the blood of a frog or newt on a glass slide, and add a drop of a saturated solution of picric acid: put the slide aside and allow it to remain for five minutes; at the end of that time, when the acid has fixed the corpuscles (that is, coagulated their contents), any excess of acid should be removed as before. A drop of solution of picro-carmine should now be added, and a trace of glycerine, and the preparation set aside for an hour. At the end of that time remove the picro-carmine solution by means of a narrow slip of blotting-paper, and add a drop of Farrant's solution of glycerine and apply glass-cover. The perinuclear part of the corpuscles will be seen to be highly granular and of a deep orange colour, whilst the nucleus is stained red. Some of the corpuscles will appear of a delicate yellow colour, and threads are seen extending from the nucleus to the envelopes. The preparation should be preserved and mounted in glycerine.

Picro-carmine and Aniline Dye.—For glandular tissue, none of the aniline dyes answer so well as iodine green, used in the form of a one per cent. watery solution. Stain the tissue in picro-carmine, wash it in distilled water acidulated with acetic acid, and stain it in a solution of iodine green. As it acts rapidly, care must be taken not to overstain. Wash the section in water, and then transfer it to alcohol; finally clear with oil of cloves. The washing should be done rapidly, as the spirit dissolves out the green dye. All preparations stained with iodine green must be mounted in dammar.

Picro-carmine and Iodine Green.—Stain a section of the cancellated head of a very young bone (fœtal bone) in picro-carmine, wash it in distilled water, and stain it with iodine green, and mount in dammar. All newly-formed bone is stained red; that in the centre of the osseous trabeculæ, the residue of the calcified cartilage in which the bone is deposited, is stained green. Many of the bone corpuscles are also stained green.

Ossifying cartilage, the back part of the tongue, Peyer's Patches, solitary-glands, trachea, and bronchus, may all be treated in the same way. In preparing the skin, take a vertical section from the sole of the foot of a fœtus. The cuticle and superficial layers of the epithelium are dyed yellow, the rete Malpighii green; and the continuation of these cells can be traced into the ducts of the sweat-glands, which are green, and form a marked contrast to the red stained connective tissue of the cutis vera, through which they have to ascend to reach the surface. The outer layer of the grey matter of the cerebellum with Purkinge's cells is, when double stained, red, while the inner or granular layer is green. Logwood and iodine green stains the mucous glands of the tongue green, and the serous glands, lilac logwood stain.

Eosin and Iodine Green.—Eosin is used as the ground colour. Stain the tissue in an alcoholic solution of eosin, which will colour it very rapidly, usually in a few seconds. Wash the section thoroughly in water acidulated with acetic or hydrochloric acid, a one per cent. solution, and stain with iodine green. This will double stain bone and cerebellum; but if logwood is substituted for the latter, the cerebrum and general substance become stained by the eosin, while the logwood colours the nerve-cells a lilac.

Gold Chloride and Aniline Dyes.—The tissue must be impregnated with chloride of gold, and then stained with either aniline blue, iodine green, or rosin. The tail of a young rat, containing as it does so many different structures, is an excellent material for experimenting upon. Remove the skin from the tail, and place pieces half an inch long into the juice of a fresh lemon for five minutes, wash it to get rid of the acid. The fine tendons swell up under the action of the lemon acid, and permit of the more ready action of the chloride of gold solution. Place the piece for an hour or more in a one per cent. solution of gold, remove it and wash it thoroughly, and then place it in a twenty-five per cent. solution of formic acid for twenty-four hours. This reduces the gold. During the process of reduction the preparation must be kept in the dark. The osseous portion has then to be decalcified in the ordinary way, with a mixture of chromic and nitric acid. After decalcification preserve the whole in alcohol. Transverse sections of the decalcified tail are made, and may be stained with a red dye, as rosin, and afterwards with a watery solution of iodine green. Mount in dammar.

Injecting Small Animal Bodies.

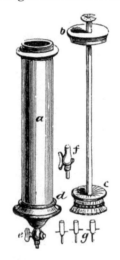

Fig. 241.—Injecting Syringe.

Fig. 242.—Water Bath and Melting Vessels.

The injection of animal bodies practised by the older anatomists, to render the vascular system more apparent, has not been superseded by the more modern methods of staining. The method of injecting even small bodies requires some skill, and a few pieces of apparatus made expressly for the purpose. First, a special form of brass syringe of such a size that it may be grasped with the right hand, the thumb at the same time covering the button at the top of the piston-rod when drawn out to the full. In Fig. 241 the piston rod is seen withdrawn, *a* is the body, with a screw at the top for firmly screwing down the cover, *b*, after the piston, *c*, is replaced; *e* is a stop-cock, to the end of which either of the smaller cannulæ, *g*, is affixed. The transverse wires are for securing them tightly with thread to the vessels into which they are to be inserted. In addition to the syringe, two or three tinned vessels are required to contain size, injecting fluid, and hot water.

The size must be kept hot by the aid of a water bath; if a naked fire be used there is danger of burning it. A convenient form of apparatus for melting the size, and afterwards keeping it at a proper temperature, is Fig. 242.

Fig. 243.—Artery Needle.

A pair of strong forceps for seizing the vessel, and a small needle (Fig. 243) is also necessary for passing the thread round the vessel into which the injection pipe has been inserted. These complete the list of apparatus. To prepare the material for opaque injections, take one pound of the finest and most transparent glue, break it into small pieces, put it into an earthen pot, and pour on it three pints of cold water; let it stand twenty-four hours, stirring it now and then with a stick; set it over a slow fire for half an hour, or until all the pieces are perfectly dissolved, skim off the froth from the surface, and strain through a flannel for use. Isinglass and cuttings of parchment make an excellent size, and are preferable for particular injections. If gelatine be employed an ounce to a pint of water will be sufficiently strong, but in very hot weather it is necessary to add a little more gelatine. It must be first soaked in part of the cold water until it swells up and becomes soft, when the rest of the water, made hot, is to be added. The size thus prepared may be fixed with finely levigated vermilion, chrome-yellow, blue salts, or flake white.

To prepare the subject, the principal points to be attained are: to dissolve the fluids and completely empty the vessels; relax the solids; and prevent the injection from coagulating too soon. For this purpose it is necessary to place the animal, or part to be injected, in warm water, as hot as the operator's hand will bear. This should be kept at nearly the same temperature for some time by occasionally adding hot water. The length of time required is in proportion to the size of the part and the amount of its rigidity.

Injecting the systems of Vessels with different colours: Carmine and Gelatine Injection.— Carmine 30 grains, strong liquid ammonia 60 drops, glacial acetic acid 43 drops, gelatine solution (one ounce in six ounces of water) two ounces, water one ounce: dissolve the carmine in the ammonia and water in a test tube, and mix it with one half of the warm gelatine, add the acid to the remaining half of gelatine, and drop it little by little into the carmine mixture, stirring it well with a glass rod during the mixing; filter through flannel, and add a few drops of carbolic acid to make it keep. It is very important that the stain should be quite *neutral*, the test of which is the colour and smell of the fluid. It should be a bright red, and all trace of smell of ammonia must be removed.

Prussian or Berlin Blue and Gelatine.—Take 1½ ounces of gelatine, place it in a vessel and cover it with water; allow it to stand until all the water is absorbed and the gelatine is quite soft, then dissolve in hot water. Dissolve one drachm (60 grains) of Prussian or Berlin blue in six ounces of water, and gradually mix it with the gelatine solution, stirring well with a glass rod during the mixing; then filter as before.

Watery Solution of Berlin Blue.—Dissolve 2½ drachms of the blue in 18 ounces of distilled water, and filter. This staining fluid is used for injecting the lymphatic system.

Directions for Injecting.—The animal to be injected must be first killed by chloroform, and injected while still warm; to secure this place the body in a water bath, at a temperature of 104° Fahrenheit. Expose the main artery of the parts to be injected, clear a small portion of it from the surrounding tissues, and place a ligature of thin tissue or silk round it, by means of the small artery needle (Fig. 243). With a pair of sharp-pointed scissors make an oblique slit in the wall of the vessel, insert the cannula, and tie the ligature firmly over the artery behind the point of the cannula, into which put the stop-cock. Fill the syringe with injection fluid, which must not be too warm, and take care not to draw up any air-bubbles; insert the nozzle of the syringe into the stop-cock and force in a little fluid; remove the syringe so that the air may escape, re-insert the syringe, repeat the process until no air-bubbles escape, and then proceed slowly with the injection. Half an hour will be required to complete the process in an animal the size of a rabbit. To judge of the completeness of the injection, examine the vascular parts of the lips, tongues and eyes; if satisfactory, tie the ligature round the artery and withdraw the syringe; place the animal in cold water for an hour to consolidate the injection fluid. When cold dissect out the organs, cut them up, and place them in methylated spirit to harden. Change the spirit every twenty-four hours for the first three days. The hardening process will be complete in ten days.

To inject lymphatics by the puncture process, a small-sized subcutaneous syringe should be used, filled with a watery solution of the prepared stains. Thrust the nozzle into the pad of the foot, (or tongue), and then rub the limb to cause the injection fluid to flow along the lymphatic vessels into the glands.

When the blue stain is used add a few drops of acetic acid to the spirit while the hardening process is going on.

Of Injecting Different Systems of Vessels with Different Colours.—It is often desirable to inject different systems of vessels distributed to a part with different colours, in order to ascertain the arrangement of each set of vessels and their relation to each other. A portion of the gall-bladder in which the veins have been injected with white lead, and the arteries with vermilion, forms an attractive preparation. Each artery, even to its smallest branches, is seen to be accompanied by two small veins, one lying on either side of it. By this method four different sets of tubes have been injected—the artery with vermilion, the portal vein with white lead, the duct with Prussian blue, and the hepatic vein with lake. There are also opaque colouring matters which may be employed for double injections.

Injecting the Lower Animals.—The vessels of fishes are exceedingly tender, and require great caution in filling them. It is often difficult or quite impossible to tie the pipe in the vessel of a fish, and it will generally be found a much easier process to cut off the tail of the fish, and put the pipe into the divided vessel which lies immediately beneath the spinal column. In this simple manner beautiful injections of fish may be made.

Mollusca (slug, snail, oyster, &c.).—The tenuity of the vessels of the mollusc often renders it impossible to tie the pipe in the usual manner. The capillaries are, however, usually very large, so that the injection runs very readily. In different parts of the bodies of these animals are numerous lacunæ or spaces, which communicate directly with the vessels. Now, if an opening be made through the integument of the muscular foot of the animal, a pipe may be inserted, and thus the vessels may be injected from these lacunæ with comparative facility.

Insects.—Injections of insects may be made by forcing the injection into the general abdominal cavity, when it passes into the dorsal vessel and is afterwards distributed throughout the system. The superfluous injection is then washed away, and such parts of the body as may be required removed for examination.

Natural injection of Medusæ may be effected without injuring the vessels, with an opening at the side remote from it. The medusa must be placed in a glass vessel, with the bell downwards, and a bell-jar ending in a narrow tube above is placed over it and made air-tight; the medusa is then covered with the injection-mass, the air in the glass is exhausted, and as the sea-water runs out by slits in the lower side of the annular canal, the coloured fluid runs in. In the case of leeches and large species of earthworms, the natural injection is made from the ventral sinus. In all cases a glass tube is used, with a finely drawn-out point. The injection is complete when the injection issues from the counter-opening. Besides the animals mentioned, large caterpillars, beetles, and larvæ of various kinds are favourable objects for injection; the glass cannula being introduced into the posterior end of the dorsal vessel, and the counter-opening made in the ventral vessel, and *vice versâ*.

Staining Living Protoplasm with Bismarck Brown.—Henneguy having treated *Paramœcium aurelia* with an aqueous solution of aniline brown (known as "Bismarck Brown"), found that they assumed an intense yellow-brown colour. The colour first appears in the vacuoles of the protoplasm, and then in the protoplasm itself, the nucleus generally remaining colourless, and becoming more visible than in the normal state. If a yellow-tinted paramœcium be compressed so as to cause a small quantity of the protoplasm to exude, it is seen that it really is the protoplasmic substance which becomes coloured. All the Infusoria may be stained with Bismarck brown, but no other aniline colour employed exhibits the same property— they merely stain the Infusoria after death, and are in fact poisonous. Living protoplasm does not as a rule absorb colouring matters, and as Infusoria are chiefly composed of protoplasm, attempts have been made to ascertain whether protoplasm in general, of animal or vegetable origin, behaved in the same way in the presence of aniline brown. A tolerably strong solution of Bismarck brown was therefore injected under the skin of the back of several frogs. After some hours the tissues became uniformly tinted a deep yellow; the muscular substance especially had a very marked yellow tint. The frogs did not appear in the least incommoded. Small fry of trout placed in a solution stained rapidly and continued to swim about. Finally, a guinea-pig, under whose skin some powder of Bismarck brown had been introduced, soon presented a yellow staining of the buccal and anal mucous membranes and of the skin. Seeds of cress sown on cotton soaked with a concentrated solution of the Bismarck brown sprouted, and the young plants were strongly stained brown; but on crushing the tissues and examining them under the microscope, it was ascertained that the protoplasm of the cells was very feebly coloured: the vessels, on the contrary, showed a deep brown stain up to their termination of the leaf. The mycelium of a mould developed in a solution of Bismarck brown was clearly stained after having been washed in water, whilst it is known that the mycelium, which frequently forms in coloured solutions, picro-carmine, hæmatoxylin, &c., remained perfectly colourless. Other aniline colours injected under the skin of frogs stained the connective tissue as deeply as did the Bismarck brown; but the striæ of muscle remained colourless. We may conclude, then, that Bismarck brown possesses the quality of colouring living protoplasm both in plants and in animals.

Cutting, Grinding, and Mounting Hard Structures.

Take the femur of cat, or rabbit, remove as much of the muscle as possible and macerate it in water until quite clean; on removal hang it up to dry. With a fine saw make transverse and longitudinal sections. File the section down until flat, and smooth. Take some Canada balsam, place a piece on a square of glass and warm gently over a lamp until the balsam is plastic enough to allow of the section being pressed into it, and set it aside to consolidate. Take a hone ("Water-of-Ayr" stone), moisten it with water, and rub one side of the section upon it until quite smooth, then place the glass slip, with the section still attached, into methylated spirit, and in a very short time the section will be separated; wash it and remount it on the reverse side, and proceed to rub it down on the hone until it appears to be thin enough for mounting. Polish both sides on a polishing strop with Tripoli powder, and mount in Canada balsam.

Fig. 244.—Small Lathe for cutting and polishing Sections of Teeth.

Teeth.—The enamel of the teeth is a much harder structure than that of bone, consequently it is found necessary to have recourse to a cutting machine. Hand machines have been introduced for this purpose, but the small lathe described in the earlier editions of my book has in no way been superseded by later cutting machines. Fig. 244 represents the small lathe used for cutting and polishing every kind of hard substance. With regard to the teeth, two sections should be made perpendicular to one another through the middle of the crown and fang of the tooth from before backwards, and from right to left, which will show the peculiar structure of the enamel. The section must be cemented to the carrier of the stock of the lathe, or to the metal plate *a*, and kept in position by the steel holder *b*; the wheel being set in motion by the first treadle. The embedding materials in use are either gum-shellac or Canada balsam. The former is more generally employed by the lapidary and grinder of lenses than the latter. As the enamel is liable to fracture under the saw, it will be necessary to lessen the friction by dripping water on the saw as it is made to revolve. Thick sections can be quickly ground down against the corrondum wheel. The final polishing of the section may be done on the lathe, or by rubbing the flattened surface with water upon a "Water-of-Ayr" stone, and ultimately set up in Canada balsam, which must not be too fluid, or it will penetrate the *lacunæ* and *canaliculi*, fill up the interspaces, and cause them to become quite invisible. As the flatness of the polishing surfaces is a matter of importance, the stones themselves should be tested from time to time, and when found to present an uneven surface must be rubbed down on a granite stone with fine sand, or on a lead plate with emery powder. If it is decided to use Canada balsam as the embedding material, this must be prepared in the following manner:—The section of tooth or bone must be attached to a slip of well-annealed glass by hardened Canada balsam, and its adhesion effectually secured by placing the slide on the cover of a water bath, or in the hot-chamber (Fig. 256), when the balsam, a thick drop of which should be used, will spread out by liquefaction. The slide should then be removed and allowed to cool in order that the hardness of the balsam may be tested. If too soft, as indicated by its readily yielding to the pressure of the thumb-nail, the heating process must be repeated, care being taken not to cause it to boil and form bubbles; if too hard, which will be shown by its chipping, it must be remelted and diluted with fluid balsam, and then set aside as before. When it is found to be of the right consistence, the section must be laid upon its surface with the polished side downwards; the slip of glass is next to be gradually warmed until the balsam is softened, care being taken to avoid the formation of bubbles, then press the section gently down with a needle upon the liquefied balsam, the pressure being just applied on one side rather than over the whole surface, so as to drive the superfluous balsam towards the opposite side; finally, an equable pressure over the whole will secure a perfect attachment of the section without air bubbles. If, however, these should present themselves in drying, and they cannot otherwise be expelled by pressure, it will be found better to take the section off and relay it as before. The thickness of the layer of balsam may be reduced by rubbing it down before applying the glass-cover.

Rock Sections.—Small pieces of rock may be ground down by the aid of the lathe, or on a zinc plate, with emery powder and water, until one side is rendered smooth and flat. Then fasten the polished side of the section to a square of glass on the metal holder of the lathe, with dried Canada balsam, as directed for bone, and allow it time to become consolidated. When moderately thin take a piece of plate-glass and some fine emery or putty-powder and rub the section down as thin as possible. When found to be thin enough wash it well in water, and put it aside to dry, or warm it over a spirit-lamp, and with a needle push the section off the glass into a watch-glass of benzole or turpentine, and allow it to soak until all the balsam is dissolved out. Wash again in turpentine, and mount in Canada balsam, with or without a cover-glass. Sections of echinus spines, shells, stones of fruits, &c., are prepared in the same way as those of bones and teeth; but when the grinding is finished, the sections must be passed through alcohol into oil of cloves, after which they should be mounted in Canada balsam. If tolerably thin, sections of these substances can be cut in the lathe; in the first instance, there will be no actual occasion to attach them to glass at all, except for the purpose of obtaining a hold upon the specimen for polishing, but the surface thus attached must afterwards be completely removed in order to bring into view a stratum which the Canada balsam may not have penetrated.

With regard to smaller bodies, these can scarcely be treated in any other way than by attaching a number of them to slips of glass at once, and in such a way as to make them mutually support each other. Thus in making horizontal and vertical sections of *foraminifera*, it would be impossible to slice them through unless they were laid close together in a bed of hardened Canada balsam, and first grinding away one side and then turning and rubbing down the other. My friend, Dr. Wallich, many years ago communicated to me the ingenious plan adopted by himself when mounting and turning a number of these minute objects together. The specimens being cemented with Canada balsam, in the first instance, to a thin film of mica, and then attached to a glass slide by the same means, when ground down to the thinness desired, the slide must be gradually heated just sufficiently to allow of the detachment of the mica-film and the specimen it carries; a clean slide with a thin layer of hardened balsam having been prepared, the mica-film is transferred to it with the ground surface downward. Its adhesion by drying having been complete, the grinding and polishing should be proceeded with; and as the mica-film will yield to the stone without any difficulty, the specimen now reversed in position may be further reduced to the requisite thickness for mounting as a permanent object.

Staining and Mounting Vegetable Tissues.—Bacteria I propose to treat of in a separate section. Vegetable tissues generally will first receive attention, and their differentiation is based on the employment of delicate gradations of colour stains. The more striking results are obtained by *Multiple Staining*, while the cell contents are rendered more palpable. On this account colouring media have been divided into *nuclear*, *plasmic*, and *specific*. The first are chiefly valued in proportion as they prove to have a selective affinity for the nuclei of cells, and leaving the protoplasm comparatively unstained. Such stains are needful for fresh and young tissues. On the other hand, *plasmic* stains colour tissue uniformly, and are used to give a ground colour by way of contrast; and *specific* stains are chiefly employed to distinguish certain elementary structures from the mass of cellulose which forms the basis of vegetable tissue, and which is also met with to a slight extent in animal membranes.

Cellulose, as it occurs in plant life, presents a variety of physical properties: sometimes it is soft, as in young plants, and again quite dense in older structures. This fact accounts for the varying results obtained when cellulose is subjected to the action of staining fluids, and whether the cellulose occurs in a nearly pure form, as in cotton fibre, or in the modified form of lignine or woody-fibre. Stains which readily attack young tissue have little or no effect upon it in its maturer form. It is of much importance, then, in the staining of fibres, as well as sections for the microscope, that the cellulose should take the stain uniformly.

The staining of tissues may be effected in four ways. First, when the stain has sufficient affinity for the tissue to be retained by it without the intervention of any outside agent. Second, when the stain and mordant are mixed and applied to the tissue in one solution. These two are the simplest and easiest methods of staining. Third, when the tissue is first immersed in the staining liquid and then transferred to some other liquid which shall fix the colour upon the tissue. Fourth, when the tissue is first impregnated with the mordant, or fixing agent, and then immersed in the stain. The last method is the one usually followed in commercial works, and it is to be recommended in the staining of microscopical preparations which do not readily take the stain.

Nuclear Stains.—As in both vegetable and animal sections it is generally the nuclei which form the landmarks of the structure, so the most important class of reagents which are used in any of the branches of microscopical work are the "nuclear stains." There are several of these stains, the most important of which is the hæmatoxylin, and when proper solutions are used the results are very satisfactory. Many formulæ have been given, but there are three only reliable, Delafield's, Kleinenberg's, and Ehrlich's, in all of which alum is present as an ingredient; the idea being that the alumina forms with the colouring matter an insoluble lake, and so acts as a mordant.

In *Delafield's* solutions a large proportion of alum to hæmatoxylin is used, and methylic alcohol (wood-spirit in the place of rectified spirit).

For *Kleinenberg's* solution many different formulæ exist. Squire's improved formulæ for both stains is given in the Appendix, "*Formulæ and Methods.*"

Hæmatoxylin solutions stain the nuclei violet, and in order to change this into blue, the sections should be transferred to water taken from the house supply, not distilled water; but as the alkalinity of the water varies in different localities, a better and more uniform result is obtained by using a weak solution of bicarbonate of sodium (half a grain to the ounce).

Carmine is also much in vogue as a nuclear stain, and the two solutions more generally employed are Greenacher's alcoholic borax carmine, and Orth's lithium carmine. Under ordinary circumstances they act as general stains, affecting the ground tissue as well as the nuclei. By subsequent treatment with acidulated alcohol or acidulated glycerine the colour is discharged from the ground tissue without seriously affecting the nuclei. Used in this way, carmine becomes a good nuclear stain. It should be remembered that the sections must not be washed in pure water, as the colour will to a great extent be discharged; nor in acidulated water, as the carmine will be precipitated.

Alum carmine and alum cochineal are useful nuclear stains, not requiring after-treatment.

Picro-carmines are also largely used. The following formulæ will be found the most useful:—

Ammonia Picro-carmine.—Carmine, one gramme; strong solution of ammonia, three cc.; distilled water, five cc. Dissolve the carmine in the ammonia and water with a gentle heat, then add saturated aqueous solution of picric acid, 200 cc.; heat to boiling, and filter.

Picro-Lithium Carmine.—The following is generally preferred for use— Lithium carmine solution, 100 cc.; saturated solution of picric acid, 270 cc.

There are several aniline dyes which are used for nuclear staining: methylene blue, methyl green, safranine, gentian violet, vesuvine, fuchsine, and Hoffmann's blue.

The usual process is to stain in ¼ or ½ per cent. aqueous solutions and wash in methylated spirit. Methylene blue and methyl green have the reputation of being so readily washed out in the methylated spirit as to be worthless. This is obviated by washing the sections (when removed from the stain) in distilled water, previous to the differentiation in methylated spirit. Treated in this manner, the nuclear staining is very beautiful. This also applies to Hoffmann's blue and partly to vesuvine; with the latter, however, it is not a necessity. Safranine and gentian violet worked better by transferring the sections directly from the stain into 90 per cent. alcohol.

Contrast Stains.—Very frequently other stains are used to dye the ground a colour which is in contrast to that employed for the nuclei. Brown, orange, or pink are used after nuclear blue or green. Carmine is generally counterstained yellow or indigo-blue; and fuchsine red, as in tubercle bacilli, is counterstained with nuclear blue. It is important that the ground stain should be made weaker than the principal stain, so that the whole tissue may be shown without detracting from the nuclei. The following colours are used as counterstains for animal sections, but they prove less useful for vegetable sections: benzo-purpurine, eosin, erythrosine, orange, acid rubin, and picric acid.

Examples of *specific* stains are fuchsine, methylene blue, and gentian violet for bacteria; osmic acid for fatty elements; victoria blue and rose bengale, for demonstrating elastic tissue; methyl violet, iodine, and safranine, for amyloid degeneration. Methylene blue is one of the most useful of aniline dyes, and one of the most variable in composition.

Iodine green, or methyl green, has long been in use as a reagent for amyloid, starchy matters, in ignorance of the fact that the reaction is due to the methyl violet, contained as an impurity in the iodine green. It is exceedingly difficult to obtain a green quite free from violet. As nuclear stains they are identical, and the amyloid reaction, being dependent wholly upon the contained violet, varies, not with the formula of the green, but with the extent to which it has been purified.

Cellulose reactions.—After the nuclear stains, the most important reagents to the botanist are those which affect cellulose and its several modifications. Pure cellulose is coloured yellow by iodine, the colour being changed to a blue on the addition of slightly dilute sulphuric acid, or a strong solution of zinc. Solutions containing iodine, iodide of potassium, and chloride of zinc, give a violet reaction with unaltered cellulose, and yellow with lignine.

Schulze's zinc re-agent must be used with a certain amount of caution, as the chloride of zinc and potassium undergo decomposition. The formula now in use is as follows: Take of zinc chloride solution (sp. gr. 1·85) 70 cc., potassium iodide 10 grammes, iodine 0·1 gramme; but this solution can only be employed as a re-agent and not as a dye, and structures stained with it cannot be mounted in any of the ordinary media, and the only fluid for ringing them down is caoutchouc cement.

Cellulose can be stained permanently by carmine, hæmatoxylin, nigrosine, methylene blue, safranine, and fuchsine. The aniline dyes are used in dilute aqueous solutions containing one-eighth or one-fourth per cent. of dye. When the cellulose undergoes the change known as lignification its reactions are altered. It is coloured yellow by chloro-zinc iodine, red by phloroglucin, yellow by aniline chloride. The two latter are much assisted by hydrochloric acid. The results of these reactions also cannot be preserved in the usual mounting media.

Sections containing mixed tissue, partly unaltered cellulose and partly lignified, give striking results with aniline dyes, and with this additional advantage can be preserved for years.

Double Staining.—When a section is passed through methyl green solution and afterwards one of carmine, the lignified portion is coloured green and the unlignified red. Acid green may be used in the place of methyl green, with a similar result. When picric acid is used with carmine, ingrosine, or Hoffmann's blue, the picric acid dyes the ligneous portion and the others colour the unlignified structure, red, black, and blue respectively.

Eosin stain is the most useful for sieve-tubes and plates. Make a strong solution of eosin in equal parts of water and alcohol, and stain the section for five or ten minutes. Wash well in methylated spirit, dehydrate, clean in oil of cloves, and mount in Canada balsam.

Bleaching Process.—The bleaching and clearing of vegetable structures before staining is a very necessary process, especially so if starch be present in any quantity. Clearing agents are of two kinds—those which act by virtue of their property of strongly refracting light, and those which disintegrate and dissolve the amyloid cell contents. To the first class belong the essential oils, as oil of cloves, Canada balsam, glycerine, and other similar bodies; to the second class, solutions of potash, phenol, and chloral hydrate. The actual value of some of these agents is questionable. The process usually preferred is as follows: Place the sections in a fresh clear solution of chlorinated lime, allowing them to remain until quite bleached, say from two to four or five minutes; then gently warm in a test-tube for a few seconds, and quickly replace the solution with distilled water and boil for two or three minutes; repeat the treatment with boiling water three times; wash with a one per cent. solution of acetic acid, and finally with distilled water. The sections are then quite ready for staining operations.

When the stem is hard and brown, a solution of chloride of lime should be used—a quarter of an ounce of chloride dissolved in a pint of water, well shaken and stood by to settle down, then pour off the clear fluid for use. For hard tissues this solution answers well, but it is not suitable for leaves, as they require not only bleaching, but the cell contents should be dissolved out to render them transparent. A solution of chlorinated soda answers well for both stems and leaves. It is prepared as follows:—

To one pint of water add two ounces of fresh chloride of lime, shake or stir it well two or three times, then allow it to stand till the lime has settled. Prepare meanwhile a saturated solution of carbonate of soda—common washing soda. Now pour off the clear supernatant fluid from the chloride of lime, and add to it, by degrees, the soda solution, when a precipitate of carbonate of lime will be thrown down; continue to add the soda solution till no further precipitate is formed. Filter the solution, and keep it in a well-stoppered bottle in the dark, otherwise it speedily spoils.

Sections bleached in chlorinated soda must, when white enough, be washed in distilled water, and allowed to remain in it for twenty-four hours, changing the water four or five times, and adding a few drops of nitric acid, or at the rate of eight or ten drops to the half-pint, to the water employed before the final washing takes place. From water transfer them to alcohol, in which they must remain for an hour or more.

Although alkaline glycerine has been recommended for several purposes in micro-technique, it is not so well known as it should be how serviceable it is as an extempore mounting solution in vegetable histology. The best mixture for general use is composed of glycerine 2 ozs., distilled water 1½ oz., solution of potash, B.P., ½ oz. This combines the refringent property of the glycerine with the clearing action of the caustic potash, while the swelling action of the potash is considerably diminished.

Cutting Sections of Hard Woods.—The lathe and circular saw will be found as useful for cutting sections of the harder kinds of woods, as for bone structure. It may be necessary to subject the older and consequently harder pieces of wood to the action of steam for a few hours to soften them, and afterwards transfer them to methylated spirit, before making an attempt to cut sections. But the more open woods, of one, two, or three years' growth, will show all that may be required, and these can be cut by hand, or with the microtome, as already described.

With a little practice the finest and thinnest possible slices may be cut by hand. It is usual to take off the first slice to give a smooth and even surface to the specimen. Then turn the screw to raise it a little, sprinkle the surface with spirit and water, and cut with a light hand. Remove the cut sections with a fine camel's-hair brush or a section lifter (Fig. 250) to a small vessel containing water, when the thinnest will float on the surface, and remove to methylated spirit and water, where they should remain until they can be mounted. Sections of hard woods, and those containing gum-resins, or other insoluble material, must first be kept in methylated spirit or alcohol, and finally transferred to oil of cloves, to render them sufficiently transparent for mounting in Canada balsam.

If the structure of an exogenous wood is required to be examined, the sections should be made in at least three different ways: the transverse, the longitudinal, and the oblique, or, as they are sometimes called, the horizontal, vertical, and tangential, each of which will exhibit different appearances, as seen in Fig. 245: *b* is a vertical section through the pith of a coniferous plant, and exhibits the medullary rays known to the cabinet-maker as the silver grain; *e* is a magnified view of a part of the same; the woody fibres are seen with their dots *l*, and the horizontal lines *k* indicating the medullary rays cut lengthwise; *c* is a tangential section, and *f* a portion of the same; the medullary rays *m m*, and the woody fibres with vertical slices of the dots, are shown. Instructive preparations will be secured by cutting oblique sections of the stem. The sections seen are made from the pine. All exogenous stems, however, exhibit three different appearances, according to the direction in which the section is made.

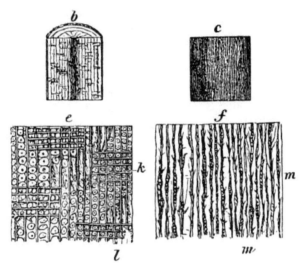

Fig. 245.—Sections of Wood.

Bacteria Cultivation, Sterilising, and Preparing for Microscopical Examination.

That branch of mycology which is now looked upon as a separate department of science, termed bacteriology, took shape in the years 1875-9, when its founder, the veteran botanist Cohn, who recognised that the protoplasm of plants corresponded to the animal sarcode, published his exact mode of studying bacteria. But it was a pupil of his, Dr. Koch, who a year later discovered that a specific cattle disease, anthrax, was due to a bacillus, and it was he also who gave us the useful modification of gelatine as a medium in which to grow bacteria; he hit upon the method of pouring melted gelatine containing distributed germs on to plates, and thus isolating the colonies and ensuring the further isolation of the spores, and so facilitate the preparation of pure cultures on a large scale, and with great saving of time.

The difficulty of isolating a bacterium and tracing its life history under the microscope must at first sight appear great. A further objection that such work is slow and difficult has no more weight here than in any other department of science, as will be seen on proceeding to follow out the directions I am about to furnish for the use of the student.

Apparatus, Material, and Reagents employed in Bacteriological Investigations.

A good microscope with a wide-angled sub-stage condenser, and objectives of an inch, ¼-inch, or ⅙-inch, and a 1/12-inch homogeneous oil-immersion.

A large bell-glass for covering the same when fuming acids are in use in the laboratory.

About a square foot of blackened plate-glass.

A white porcelain slab, or a shallow photographic dish of some size.

Glass bottles with ground stoppers for alcoholic solutions and aniline dyes.

Glass bottles with funnels for filtering solutions of stains, with pipettes.

A specialised form of pipette for the micro-chemical filtration of solutions (Fig. 246).

A small stoppered bottle of cedar oil (Fig. 247).

Set of small glass dishes or watch-glasses for section staining.

Stock of glass slides sterilised, together with round thin glass-covers, in boxes (Fig. 248).

Needle holders and platinum needles, with a packet of ordinary sewing needles (Fig. 249).

Platinum, or plated copper section-lifters (Fig. 250).

Glass rods, drawn out to a fine point, for manipulating sections when acids are employed.

Fig. 247.—Bottle and Dipper for Cedar Oil.

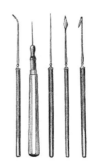

Fig. 246.—Pipette for Micro-chemical Filtration.

Fig. 248.—Box for keeping Glass-covers.

Fig. 249.—Needle Holders, fine Lifter and Hook for Manipulating Structure.

Fig. 250.—Section Lifters.

Fig. 251.—Spring Flat Forceps.

Fig. 251a.—Forceps with fine Points.

A pair of small spring steel platinum-pointed forceps for holding glass-covers (Fig. 251).

One or two pairs of fine-pointed forceps (Fig. 251a).

Collapsible tubes for containing Canada balsam and dammar.

Soft rags or old pocket handkerchiefs for removing cedar oil from lenses and cover-glasses. Chamois leather for wiping lenses and removing dust.

Reagents, alcohol, bergamot oil, *celloidin,* dissolved in equal parts of ether and alcohol.

Ebner's solution. (See Appendix.)

Formalin, glycerine, gelatine, *Klebs'* and *Kleinenberg's* solutions. (See Appendix.) The latter consisting of a watery solution of picric acid 100 parts; strong sulphuric acid two parts; filter, and add distilled water 300 parts.

Muller fluid. (See Appendix.)

Osmic acid, a five per cent. solution.

Paraffin, spermaceti and *xylol, acetic acid, hydrochloric acid,* a one per cent. solution with *alcohol.*

Ammonia liquid, *ether, picro-lithium carmine, potash solution.*

Safranine, concentrated alcoholic solution of, and a watery solution.

Turpentine, vesuvin, water distilled and sterilised.

Aqueous solutions of the several dyes may be kept in bottles ready for use.

To both aqueous and alcoholic solutions a few drops of phenol, or a crystal of thymol, should be added as a preservative. For the rapid staining of cover-glass preparations, it is convenient to have the most frequently used stains—fuchsine, methyl-violet, &c.—in bottles provided with pipette stoppers.

Clearing Agents.—Oils of cedar wood, cloves, origanum, aniline, terebene, toluol and xylol, benzol and spirits of turpentine.

Mounting Media.—Acetate of potash solution concentrated, benzole, balsam, glycerine jelly, Fanant's medium, dammar and mastic, Canada balsam in xylol, Hollis's glue, zinc white.

Cement for fixing small specimens temporarily to a glass slide. Remove all traces of moisture, place upon it a drop or two of a medium prepared as follows:—Dissolve over a water bath 15 grammes of white lac in 100 grammes of absolute alcohol, decant off the clear liquid, and stand it by for a while.

As the alcohol evaporates from the warmed surface of the glass slide a hard transparent coating is left. This may be slightly softened at any time by means of a drop of oil of lavender. After arranging the objects the heat of a spirit-lamp will cause the oil to evaporate, leaving them firmly attached. Objects may be mounted on cover-glasses in a similar way. A resinous mounting medium may then be employed in the usual manner. If glycerine or glycerine jelly is the mounting medium employed, collodion diluted with two or three times its volume of oil of lavender may be found preferable as the fixing agent. The section should be placed in position before the preparation dries and the oil is evaporated.

Methylated spirit is often so largely adulterated with rock-oil as to render it unsuitable for technical purposes. Even to varnishes it imparts a fluorescent appearance as it dries off.

Fig. 252.—Iron Box for holding Sterilised Instruments and Glass Plates.

The needles and instruments used must not be passed through a Bunsen burner flame, which is most destructive, but enclosed in a sheet-iron box made for the purpose (Fig. 252), and placed in the hot-air steriliser for an hour at 150°C. The box can be opened at the side, and each instrument withdrawn with a pair of sterilised forceps when required for use.

Glass plates are sterilised in the same iron box, and the *platinum needles* for inoculating nutrient media, examining cultivations, &c., are served in the same manner before being used. The needles consist of two or three inches of platinum wire fixed to the end of a glass rod. Several of these needles should be made by fixing pieces of wire into a glass rod about six inches long. The glass rod must be heated at the extreme end in the flame of a Bunsen burner, or blow-pipe, and the platinum wire held near one extremity with forceps, and fused into the end of the glass rod. Some of these rods should be straight, and some bent, and others provided with a loop, and kept especially ready for inoculating test-tubes of nutrient jelly.

Fig. 253.—Damp Chamber for Plate-cultivations.

Glass Dishes.—Several shallow glass dishes are required for preparing damp chamber cultivations, the upper covers fitting over the under (as in Fig. 253), in the centre of which culture-plates are stacked one above the other, and when necessary placed in the incubator.

Apparatus for Incubation and Cultivations in Liquid Media.

Lister's Flasks.—Lister devised a globe-shaped flask with two necks, a vertical and a lateral one, the lateral being a bent spout, tapering towards the extremity. When the vessel is restored to the erect position after pouring out some of its contents, a drop of liquid remains behind in the end of the nozzle, and thus prevents the regurgitation of air through the spout. A cap of cotton-wool is tied over the orifice, and the residue left in the flask for future use. The vertical neck of the flask is plugged with sterilised cotton-wool in the ordinary way.

Fig. 254.—Pasteur's Bulb Pipette.

Fig. 255.—Storing Cultivation Tube.

Sternberg advocates the use of a glass bulb, provided with a slender neck drawn out to a fine point and hermetically sealed. Special forms of tubes, bulbs, and pipettes were devised by Pasteur, and are still in use at the Bacteriological Institute, Paris, and known as the Pasteur's bulb pipette (Fig. 254).

Others are provided with lateral or with curved arms, one of which is drawn out to a fine point, and the slender neck plugged with cotton-wool, as in Fig. 255.

THE WARM CHAMBER, STERILISER, AND INCUBATOR.

Fig. 256.—Pfeiffer's Warm Chamber.

The Warm Chamber.—This is an accessory of importance in bacteriological work. For the continuous heating of specimens during cultivation it is an absolute necessity. Pfeiffer's warm chamber (Fig. 256) is suitable for microscopical work generally. It consists of a hard-wood box, made air-tight, with doors and glass windows to allow of the specimen being moved from time to time, and kept under constant observation. The box is mounted on a metal plate tripod stand, and is heated from below by a small gas burner, with a thermo-regulator. A paraffin lamp will do as well, so long as it maintains a temperature of from 25° to 45°C., and without danger of injury to the stand and lenses of the microscope. A thermometer is placed in the air space to mark the temperature.

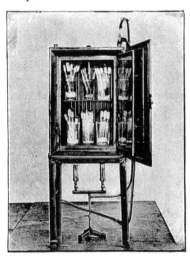

Fig. 257.—Crookshank's Incubator.

Hot-air Incubators and Sterilisers are usually made of sheet-iron, in the form of a cubical chest, with double walls, supported on four legs, as that of Dr. Crookshank's (Fig. 257). They are heated by gas or a lamp from below, while the temperature is indicated by a thermometer inserted through a hole in the top, as in that of the Hearson's incubator. Test-tubes, flasks, funnels, cotton-wool, &c., must be sterilised by exposure to a temperature of 150°C. for an hour or more.

Wire Cages or crates are used for containing test-tubes, especially when they are to be sterilised in the hot-air steriliser, or for lowering tubes of nutrient jelly into the steam steriliser. All instruments, needles, scalpels, &c., before using must be carefully sterilised.

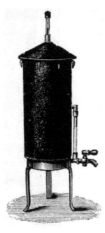

Fig. 258.—Dr. Koch's Steam Steriliser.

Steam Sterilisers are made either of iron or tin, jacketed with thick felt, and provided with a conical cap or lid perforated at the apex to receive a thermometer (Fig. 258). Inside the vessel is an iron grating or diaphragm about two-thirds of the way down, which divides the interior into two chambers, the upper or steam chamber, and the lower or water chamber. A gauge outside marks the level of the water in the lower chamber; this should be kept about two-thirds full. The apparatus stands upon three legs, and is heated from below with a Bunsen burner or a lamp. It is employed for sterilising nutrient media in tubes or flasks, for cooking potatoes or hastening the filtration of agar-agar. When the thermometer indicates 100° C. the lid is removed, and test-tubes are lowered in a wire-basket by means of a hook and string, and the lid quickly replaced. Potatoes or small flasks are lowered into the cylinder in a tin receiver with a perforated bottom, which rests upon the grating, and admits of the contents being exposed to the steam generated.

One of the most efficient forms of incubators introduced into the bacteriological laboratory is that known as Hearson's (Fig. 259). This consists of a chamber surrounded by a water-jacket, with water space below, to afford room for the pipe, L, which conveys the heated products from the flame of the lamp, T, through the water and back again to the lantern. A is the water-jacket surrounding the chamber containing the cultures; O, the pipe through which the water supply is admitted; N, the tap for employing the same; M, the overflow pipe; S, the capsule in a case attached by a tube to the lower plate outside; D, a lever pivoted on the left, carrying at its free end a damper, F, which, when resting on the chimney, V, effectually closes it; P, a screw for adjusting the damper when starting the apparatus; H, a lead weight for bringing more pressure on the capsule; K, a thermometer, the bulb of which is inside and the scale outside the chamber.

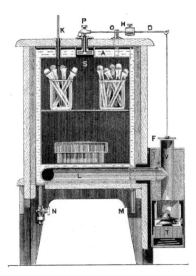

Fig. 259.—The Baird-Hearson Biological Incubator.

The treated products of combustion move in the direction indicated until the water and chamber are sufficiently heated to distend the capsule. When this point is reached the wire between S and P is pushed up by the capsule, and the lever causes the damper to rise more or less off the chimney, V, and on examining the thermometer the inside of the chamber is at length found to remain steadily at the required temperature.

When the thermometer registers the desired temperature, the lead weight must be damped to the lever by means of the milled-head screw which goes through it. After having been once adjusted the heat in the interior will remain constant, notwithstanding the utmost changes of temperature occurring in these latitudes, nor will very great alterations in the size of the lamp-flame seriously interfere with the results. The milled-head screw, P, must be turned, after the first adjustment, during the whole time that the incubator is in use. Observe the temperature before opening the door; observations taken afterwards are worthless.

Preparation of Nutrient Media—Separation, and Cultivation of Bacteria.

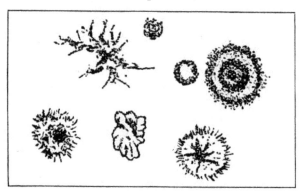

Fig. 260.—Plate Cultivation Showing Colonies.

To cultivate micro-organisms artificially they must be supplied with the proper nutrient material, perfectly free from pre-existing organisms. The secret of Koch's methods greatly depends upon the possibility, in the case of starting with a mixture of micro-organisms, of being able to isolate them completely one from another, and to obtain an absolutely pure growth of each cultivable species. When sterile nutrient gelatine has been liquefied in a test-tube and inoculated with a mixture of bacteria in such a way that the individual micro-organisms are distributed throughout it, and the liquid is poured out on a glass plate and allowed to solidify, the individual bacteria, instead of moving about freely as in a liquid medium, are fixed to one spot, where they develop their own species. In this way colonies are formed, each possessing its own biological characteristics and morphological appearances (Fig. 260).

To maintain individuals isolated from each other during growth, and free from contamination, it is only necessary to thin out the cultivation to protect the plates from the air, and to have facilities for examining them from time to time, and observing the characteristic microscopical appearances. The colonies on nutrient gelatine examined with a low power (Fig. 260), if micro-organisms such as *Bacillus anthraces* and *Proteus mirabilis*, the naked eye appearances in test-tubes of the growth of the bacilli of anthrax and tubercle, and the brilliant growth of micro-coccus prodigiosus, may be given as examples in which the appearances are often very striking and sometimes quite characteristic. I must, however, first direct attention to a well-recognised fact, that bacteriology only touches animal pathology at a few points, and that so far from bacteria being synonymous with *disease germs*, the majority of these remarkable organisms appear to be beneficent rather than inimical to man. This is of immense importance to science, as I shall attempt to show further on; although even a brief description of all the useful ferments due to bacteria and brought into use would occupy a volume to themselves, and call for a school of bacteriology quite apart from that involved in the medical aspect of the question, for the purpose of fully investigating problems raised by the agriculturist, the forester, the gardener, the dairyman, brewer, dyer, tanner, and other industries, which open up vistas of practical application, and to some extent are already being taken advantage of in commerce.

The Preparation of Nutrient Gelatine and Agar-agar.—Take half a kilogramme (one pound) of beef as free as possible from fat, chop finely, transfer to a flask or cylindrical vessel, and shake up well with a litre of distilled water. Place the vessel in an ice-pail, or ice-cupboard, or in winter in a cold cellar, and leave for the night. Next morning commence with the preparation of all requisite apparatus. Thoroughly wash and rinse with alcohol about 100 test-tubes, and allow them to dry. Plug the mouths of the test-tubes with cotton-wool, place them in their wire cages in the hot-air steriliser, to be heated for an hour at a temperature of 150°C. In the same manner cleanse and sterilise several flasks, and a small glass funnel. In the meantime, the meat infusion must be well shaken, and the liquid portion separated by filtering and squeezing through a linen cloth or a meat press. The red juice thus obtained must be brought up to a litre by transferring it to a large measuring glass and adding distilled water. It is then poured into a sufficiently large and strong beaker, and set aside after the addition of ten grammes of peptone, five grammes of common salt, and 100 grammes of best gelatine.

In about half an hour the gelatine is sufficiently softened, and subsequent heating in a water bath causes it to be completely dissolved.

The next process requires the greatest care and attention. Some micro-organisms grow best in a slightly acid, others in a slightly alkaline, medium. For example, for the growth and characteristic appearances of the *comma bacillus* of Asiatic cholera a faintly alkaline soil is absolutely essential. This slightly alkaline medium will be found to answer best for most micro-organisms, and may be obtained as follows:—With a clean glass rod dipped in the mixture, the reaction upon litmus-paper may be obtained, and a concentrated solution of carbonate of soda must be added drop by drop until red litmus-paper becomes faintly blue. If it is too alkaline, it can be neutralised by the addition of lactic acid.

Finally, the mixture is heated for an hour in the water-bath. Ten minutes before the boiling is completed the white of an egg beaten up with the shell is added, and the liquid is then filtered while hot.

During filtration the funnel should be covered over with a plate of glass, and the process of filtering must be repeated, if necessary, until a pale straw-coloured, perfectly transparent filtrate results. The sterilised test-tubes are filled to about a third of their depth by pouring in the gelatine carefully and steadily. The object of this care is to prevent the mixture touching the part of the tube with which the plug comes into contact; otherwise, when the gelatine sets, the cotton-wool adheres to the tubes and becomes a source of embarrassment to subsequent procedures. As the tubes are filled they are placed in a basket, and then sterilised. They are either lowered into the steam steriliser, when the thermometer indicates 100 cc., for twelve minutes, for four or five successive days, or they may be transferred to the test-tube water-bath, and heated for an hour or two for three successive days.

If the gelatine shows any turbidity after, it must be poured back into a flask, boiled for ten minutes, and filtered again, and the process of sterilisation repeated.

Nutrient Agar-agar is a substance prepared from seaweed which grows on the coasts of Japan and India, and is supplied in long crinkled strips. It boils at 90° C., and remains solid up to a temperature of about 45° C. It is therefore substituted for gelatine in the preparation of a jelly for the cultivation of those bacteria which will grow best in the incubator at the temperature of the blood, and also at ordinary temperature for bacteria which lignify gelatine. The preparation is conducted on much the same principles as those already described. Instead, however, of 100 grammes of gelatine, only about twenty grammes of agar-agar (1·5 to 2 per cent.), and to facilitate the solution it must be allowed to soak in salt water overnight. Flannel is substituted for filter paper. The hot-water apparatus is invariably employed. The final results, when solid, should be colourless and clear; but if slightly milky, it may still be employed.

Wort-gelatine is used in studying the bacteria of fermentation. It is made by adding from five to ten per cent. of gelatine to beer-wort.

Glycerine Agar-agar.—This is made by adding five per cent. of glycerine to nutrient agar-agar, after the boiling and before the filtration.

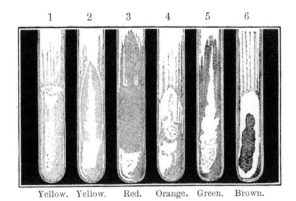

| 1 | 2 | 3 | 4 | 5 | 6 |

Yellow.　Yellow.　Red.　Orange.　Green.　Brown.

Fig. 261.—Pure Cultivation in Tubes (Crookshank).

Test-tube Cultivations.—To inoculate test-tubes containing nutrient jelly, the cotton-wool plug is removed. A sterilised needle, charged, for example, with blood or pus containing bacteria, is thrust once in the middle line into the nutrient jelly, and steadily withdrawn. The tube should be held horizontally or with its mouth downwards, and the plug replaced as quickly as possible, and an india-rubber cap fitted over the mouth of the tube.

The appearance produced by the growths in the test-tubes can be in most cases sufficiently examined with the naked eye (Fig. 261). In some cases the jelly is partially liquefied, while in others it remains solid. The growths may be abundant or scanty, coloured or colourless. When liquefaction slowly takes place in the needle tracts, the appearances which result are often very delicate and in some very characteristic. The appearance of a simple white thread with branching lateral filaments, of a cloudiness, or of a string of beads in the track of the needle, may be given as examples. In some cases much may be learnt by means of a magnifying-glass.

Beneke recommends that gelatine culture tubes should be inoculated by making a puncture quite at the side of the medium, close to the glass. The advantage of this method over the plan of inoculating the mass in the middle is that the growing culture can be microscopically examined from the outside, and various details made out, such as the nature of the growth, the comparative appearance of colonies near the surface and those situated more deeply, and the presence of one or more distinct organisms. If the tubes used have the opposite sides flat and parallel, such examinations will be still further facilitated.

Plate Cultivations.—By this method a mixture of bacteria, whether in fluids, excreta, or in cultivations on solid media, can be so treated that the different species are isolated one from the other, and perfectly pure cultivations of each of the cultivable bacteria in the original mixture established in various nutrient media. We are enabled also to examine under a low power of the microscope the individual colonies of bacteria. The same process, with slight modification, is also employed in the examination of air, soil, and water.

In order to spread out the liquid jelly evenly on the surface of a glass plate, and to hasten its solidification, it is necessary to place the plate upon a level and cool surface. The glass plates are sterilised in an iron box placed in the hot-air steriliser, at 150° C., from one to two hours.

The damp chambers for the reception of the inoculated plates are prepared by cleansing and washing out with one in twenty carbolic acid the shallow glass dish and bell-cover (Fig. 253). A piece of filter-paper should cover the bottom of dish, moistened with the same solution.

"In a glass-beaker with pad of cotton-wool at bottom place tube containing cultivation, the three tubes to be inoculated, three glass rods which have to be sterilised, and a thermometer. Liquefy the gelatine in the three tubes by placing them in a beaker containing water 30° C. Keep the tubes, both before and after the inoculation, in the warm water to maintain the gelatine in a state of liquefaction. Remove the plug from the culture and also the plug of test-tube with liquefied jelly. With the needle take up a droplet of the cultivation and stir it round in the liquefied jelly. Replace both plugs, and set aside the cultivation. Hold the freshly-inoculated tube almost horizontally, then raise it to the vertical, so that the liquid gelatine gently flows back. By repeating this motion, and rolling the tube, the micro-organisms which have been introduced are distributed throughout the gelatine. Any violent shaking, and consequent formation of bubbles, must be carefully avoided. Inoculate the second tube, and also third, in the same way, but with three droplets from a sterilised needle. The next process consists in pouring out the gelatine on glass plates and allowing it to solidify.

"Remove cover of box containing sterilised plates, withdraw a plate with sterilised forceps, and rapidly transfer it to the filter-paper under the bell-glass and quickly replace cover of box. Remove plug from the test-tube which was first inoculated, and the contents are poured out on the plate. With a glass rod the gelatine must be then rapidly spread out in an even layer within about half an inch of the margin of the plate, the bell-glass is replaced, and the gelatine is allowed to set. Meanwhile a glass bench is placed in damp chamber, upon which the plate is placed when the gelatine is quite solid; precisely the same process is repeated with the other tubes.

"The colonies will be found to develop in the course of a day or two, the time varying with the temperature of the room. The lower plate will contain a countless number of colonies, which, if the micro-organisms liquefy gelatine, speedily commingle, and produce in a very short time a complete liquefaction of the whole gelatine. On the middle plate the colonies will also be very numerous, but retain their isolated positions for a longer time; while on the uppermost plate the colonies are completely isolated from one another, with an appreciable surface of gelatine intervening.

"The microscopical appearances of the colonies are best studied by placing the plate on a slab of blackened glass, or on a porcelain slab if the colonies are coloured. A small diaphragm is used, and the appearances studied principally with a low power. A much simpler method of plate-cultivation is to pour the liquefied jelly into shallow flat dishes; they take up much less room, and in many ways are more convenient.

"Nutrient agar-agar can also be employed for the preparation of plate-cultivations, but it is much more difficult to obtain satisfactory results."

Microscopical Examination of Bacteria.

Bacteria in Liquids, Cultures, and Fresh Tissues.—In conducting bacteriological researches, the importance of absolute cleanliness cannot be too strongly insisted upon. All instruments, glass vessels, slides, and cover-glasses should be thoroughly cleansed before use. The same applies to the preparation and employment of culture media; any laxity in the processes of sterilisation, or insufficient attention to minute technical details, will be followed with disappointing results by contamination of the cultures, resulting in the loss of much time.

For the preparation of microscopical specimens it will be found convenient to use a platinum inoculating needle, sterilised, as before directed, in the sheet-iron box; in a few moments it will be cool enough not to destroy the bacteria with which it is brought into contact.

Unstained Bacteria.—The bacteria in liquids, such as blood and culture-fluids, can be investigated in the unstained condition by transferring a drop with a looped platinum needle, or a capillary pipette, to a slide, covering it with a clean cover-glass, and examining without further treatment. If it is desirable to keep the specimen under prolonged observation, a drop of sterilised water or salt solution must be run in at the margin of the cover-glass to counteract the tendency to dry.

Cultures on the solid media can be examined by transferring a small portion with a sterilised needle to a drop of sterilised water on a slide, thinning it out, and covering with cover-glass as already described. Tissues in the fresh state may be teased out with needles (Fig. 249) in sterilised salt solution, and pressed out into a sufficiently thin layer between the slide and cover-glass. Glycerine may in many cases be substituted for salt solution, especially for such as actinomyces and mould fungi.

Very small bacilli and micro-cocci are distinguished from granular matter or fat-crystals, or *vice versâ*, by the fact that the latter are altered or dispersed by the addition of acetic acid, and changed by solution of potash; ether dissolves out fatty particles, while micro-organisms remain unaffected. Baumgarten demonstrated tubercle bacilli in sections by treating them with potash, which clarified the tissues and brought the bacilli clearly into view. In examining unstained bacteria the iris-diaphragm should be used, and the sub-stage condenser carefully centred and focussed.

His's Method of Staining.—A slide is prepared as for bacteria in the fresh state; the reagents are then applied by placing them with a pipette drop by drop at a margin of the cover-glass, and causing them to flow through the preparation by means of a strip of filter-paper placed at the opposite margin.

Babès' Method is as follows: A little of the growth spread out on a cover-glass into as thin a film as possible; when almost dry, apply a drop or two of a weak aqueous solution of methyl-violet from a pipette to the film; any excess of the stain must be removed by gentle pressure with a strip of filter-paper.

Cover-glass Preparations.—A cover-glass is smeared with the substance to be examined spread out into a sufficiently thin layer; in the case of cultures on solid media, diffuse the bacteria in a little sterilised water. By means of another cover-glass the juice or fluid is squeezed out from between them into a thin layer, and on sliding them apart each cover-glass bears on it a thin film of the material. The cover-glass is then placed with its film side upwards and allowed to dry. After a few minutes it is passed from above downwards through the flame of a Bunsen burner three times. Apply two or three drops of an aqueous solution of fuchsine or methyl-violet to cover the film, wash away any surplus stain after a few minutes with distilled water. The cover-glass is then allowed to dry, when the preparation may be mounted in Canada balsam, or while still wet, turned over on a slide, and the excess of water removed with filter-paper.

If necessary to apply stain for a much larger period, pour staining solution into a watch glass and allow cover-glass to swim on surface with prepared side downwards.

Crookshank, instead of watery solutions of aniline dyes, prefers to use stronger solutions, and to reduce the staining by a momentary immersion in alcohol. The method is as follows: cover-glass preparations are stained with carbolised fuchsine (*Neelsen's solution*) for about two minutes, rinsed in alcohol for a few seconds, and quickly washed in water. This method is specially valuable for sarcinæ and streptococci.

Gram's Method.—The whole film is first stained violet with gentian-violet, fixed by a solution of iodine, in iodide of potassium in the bacilli, but not in any débris, pus cells, or tissue elements present. Transfer cover-glass to alcohol, the bacilli alone remain stained, the violet colour being changed to blue. By employing a contrast colour, such as eosin, a double staining is obtained.

For staining preparations with gentian-violet Crookshank employs the following useful method:—Place four or five drops of pure aniline in a test-tube, add distilled water to three-quarters full, close mouth with thumb, shake thoroughly. Filter the emulsion twice, pour filtrate into watch-glass. To the perfectly clear aniline water thus obtained, add, drop by drop, a concentrated alcoholic solution of gentian-violet till precipitation commences. Cover-glasses must be left in this solution ten minutes, transferred to iodine-potassic-iodide until the film becomes uniformly brown, then rinsed in alcohol. The decolourisation may be hastened by dipping the cover-glass in clove oil and returning to alcohol. Again immerse cover-glass in clove oil, dry by gently pressing between two layers of filter-paper, and mount in Canada balsam.

Double-staining of cover-glass preparations.—They can be treated by Ehrlich's method for staining tubercular sputum, or by Neelsen's modification, or by staining with eosin after treatment by the method of Gram.

Ehrlich's Method is as follows: Five parts of aniline oil are shaken up with one hundred parts of distilled water, and the emulsion filtered through moistened filter-paper. A saturated alcoholic solution of fuchsine, methyl-violet, or gentian-violet, is added to filtrate in watch-glass, drop by drop, until precipitation commences. Cover-glass preparations are floated in this mixture for fifteen minutes to half an hour, then washed for a few seconds in dilute nitric acid (one part of nitric acid to two of water), then rinsed in distilled water.

Neelsen's Solution and Methylene Blue.—Ziehl suggested the use of carbolic acid as a substitute for aniline blue. Neelsen recommended a solution of carbolic acid, absolute alcohol and fuchsine. (See Appendix.)

Gram's Solution and Eosin.—After using Gram's method as above and decolourising in alcohol, the cover-glass is placed in a weak solution of eosin for two or three minutes, washed in alcohol, immersed in clove oil, dried, and mounted in balsam.

Staining of Spores.—The cover-glass preparation must be heated to 210° C. for half an hour, or passed about twelve times through the flame of a Bunsen burner, or exposed to the action of strong sulphuric acid for several seconds, then a few drops of a watery solution of aniline dye applied in the usual way.

To double-stain spore-bearing bacilli the cover-glass preparation must be floated from twenty minutes to an hour on Ehrlich's fuchsine-aniline-water, or on the Ziehl-Neelsen solution. The stain must be heated until steam arises.

Staining of Flagella.

Koch first stained flagella by floating the cover-glass on a watery solution of hæmatoxylin, transferring them to a five per cent. solution of chromic acid, or to Müller's fluid, by which they obtained a brownish-black coloration.

Löffler's Method.—Add together aqueous solutions of ferrous-sulphate and tannin (twenty per cent.) until the mixture turns a violet-black colour, then add three or four cc. of a one-in-eight aqueous solution of logwood; a few drops of carbolic acid may be added before transferring to a stoppered bottle; that is the mordant. The dye consists of 1 cc. of a one per cent. solution of caustic soda, added to 100 cc. of aniline water, in which four or five grammes of either methyl-violet, methylene blue, or fuchsine, are dissolved. A cover-glass preparation is made in the usual way, then the film is covered with mordant, and cover-glass held over flame until steam rises, the mordant is then washed off with distilled water. The stain is filtered and a few drops allowed to fall on film, after a few minutes the cover-glass is again warmed until steam rises. The stain is then washed off with distilled water, and the preparation is ready to be mounted for examination.

As Löffler's process is somewhat complicated, a modification has been said to afford more satisfactory results. A specimen is taken from a recent gelatine culture and diluted with water. A little of the fluid is then transferred to a warm cover-glass by means of a pipette and allowed to dry, after which a drop of the following mordant is applied:—Aqueous solution of tannin (twenty per cent.), ten cc.; cold saturated solution of ferrous sulphate, five cc.; saturated solution of fuchsine in absolute alcohol, one cc. The cover is next heated gently for a short time until vapours are given off, then washed carefully. This process is repeated two or three times, and the specimen washed after each application. Subsequently, staining is effected by means of Ziehl's fuchsine solution, the cover is afterwards warmed once or twice for about fifteen seconds, then washed, and the specimen examined in water to ascertain if the colour is sufficiently intense. If satisfactory, the preparation may then be dried and finally mounted in Canada balsam or dammar.

Preservation of Preparations.—After examining a cover-glass preparation with an oil-immersion objective the cedar oil must be carefully wiped off, and the slide set aside for the Canada balsam to set. At a convenient time these preparations should be sealed with a ring of Hollis's glue.

Bacteria in Sections of Tissues.

Method of Hardening and Decalcifying Tissues.—To harden small organs, such as the viscera of a mouse, they should be placed on a piece of filter-paper at the bottom of a small wide-mouthed glass jar, and covered with about twenty times their volume of absolute alcohol. Larger organs are treated in the same way, but must be cut up into small pieces. Müller's fluid, methylated spirit, or formalin may be used.

Teeth, or osseous structures, must first be placed in a decalcifying solution, as Kleinenberg's. When sufficiently softened, soak in water, to wash out picric acid, and transfer to weak spirit. Ebner's solution gives good results.

Methods of embedding, fixing, and cutting.—Crookshank finds that after hardening, the pieces of tissue are embedded in a mixture of ether and alcohol for an hour or more, then transferred to a solution of celloidin in equal parts of ether and alcohol, and left there for several hours.

The piece of tissue is then placed in a glass capsule, and some of the celloidin solution poured over it. The capsule can be placed bodily in 60 to 80 per cent. alcohol, and left there until the following morning. The celloidin should be of the consistency of wax. The piece of tissue is next cut out, and after trimming is put into water until it sinks, then transferred to gum, and cut with the freezing microtome.

Sections of fresh tissues are to be floated in ·8 per cent. salt solution, and then carefully transferred by a platinum lifter to a watch-glass containing absolute alcohol.

Staining Bacteria in Tissue Sections.—Weigert's method is as follows:—Place sections for from six to eighteen hours in a one per cent. watery solution of any of the basic aniline dyes. To hasten, place the capsule containing solution in the incubator, or heat it to 45° C., or a stronger solution may be used. In the latter case the sections must be treated with a half-saturated solution of carbonate of potash, as they are easily over-stained. In either case the sections are next washed with distilled water, passed through sixty per cent. alcohol into absolute alcohol. When almost decolourised, spread out on a platinum lifter and transfer to clove oil, or stain with picro-carmine solution (Weigert's) for half an hour, wash in water, alcohol, and treat with clove oil, and transfer to clean glass slide.

Gram's Method.—Sections are stained for ten minutes in a capsule containing aniline-gentian-violet solution, then placed in the iodine and iodide solution until uniformly brown, then placed in absolute alcohol, and washed by carefully moving sections in the liquid with a glass rod. When completely decolourised, they are transferred to clove oil and then to a slide.

Double-staining is obtained by transferring the sections after decolourisation to eosin, Bismarck brown, or vesuvin (Crookshank).

Formalin is an excellent preservative fluid; one part to 20,000 is sufficient to prevent fermentation. For the preservation of vegetable sections, a one per cent. solution is required; even the fresh appearance of vegetable structures is preserved for some time when immersed in it. In the nutrient gelatine for biological specimens, if used early, will arrest the liquefaction of the gelatine by bacteria. For hardening it saves time, and is even better than alcohol, chromic acid, pot. bich., and many others. It does not cause shrinkage of the cells. Tissue ½ to ¾ inch thick hardens in twenty-four hours in pure formalin; five to ten per cent. is best for loose tissue. In another method, by which time can be saved, instead of placing the specimen in the *formalin* and afterwards in mucilage, prior to cutting sections, make the mucilage with two per cent. (or stronger) formalin water, and it will then answer both purposes at the same time.

Preparing, Mounting, Cementing and Collecting Objects.

Various materials are required for preparing and mounting microscopic objects, as slips of glass, patent flatted plate measuring 3 × 1 inch, thin glass covers, glass cells, preservative media, varnishes, cements, a glazier's diamond, and a Shadbolt's turn-table.

The glass slides and covers, although sent out packed ready for use, should be immersed in an alkaline solution to ensure perfect freedom from any greasiness derived from touching by the fingers. Dr. Seller recommends a particular solution for this purpose. (See *Formulæ*, Appendix.)

Varnishes and cements must be selected with care, as these are not only expected to adhere firmly to the glass slide, but also to resist the action of the preservative fluid in which the specimen may be mounted. Among the numerous preparations employed, I may enumerate Canada balsam, gum dammar, Venice turpentine, Japanners' gold size, used for closing up cells, asphalte varnish, Brunswick black, shellac, glue and honey, Hollis' liquid glue, and marine glue. To give a finish to the mounted specimen, coloured varnishes are sometimes resorted to. A red varnish of sealing-wax is made by digesting powdered sealing-wax in strong alcohol. Filter, and place the solution in a dish, and evaporate by means of a sand bath to reduce it to a proper consistency. This is said to resist the action of cedar oil. For white, zinc, cement is the best. This is made of benzole, gum dammar, oxide of zinc, and turpentine. Cole gives another formula, but either of these may be obtained of Squire, who supplies every kind of staining and mounting material.

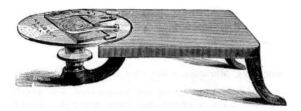

Fig. 262.—Walmsley's Cell-making Turn-table.

Cells for Mounting.—The minuter forms of life should be mounted in thin cells, which may be readily made with Japanners' gold size, dammar or asphalte, and a Shadbolt or Walmsley's turntable. The glass slide being placed under the metal springs in such a manner that its two ends shall be equi-distant from the centre (a guide to the position is afforded by the circles traced out on the brass), take a camel's hair pencil and dip it into the Japanner's gold-size, holding it firmly between the finger and thumb, and set the wheel in motion, when a perfect circle will be formed; put it aside to dry, or place it in the warm chamber to harden. To cut cover-glasses place a sheet of thin glass under the brass springs, and substitute for the pencil a cutting diamond. A cutting diamond is not only useful to the microscopist for the above purpose, but also for writing the names of mounted objects on one end of the slide.

It will be found convenient to make a number of such cells, and keep a stock ready for use. There are many objects whose structure is very transparent. These should be mounted dry. Scales from the wings of butterflies and moths, of the podura and lepisma, and some of the diatomaceæ are of this class. All that is necessary in preparing objects for dry mounting is to take care that they are free from extraneous matter, and fix them permanently in the position in which their structure will show to the best advantage.

For mounting specimens of greater thickness it is desirable to use deeper cells. It will then be found convenient to make a second or a third application of the gold-size, allowing sufficient time between applications for the varnish to dry. Cells of a still deeper kind are made up by cementing rings of glass or metal to the glass-slides with marine glue or Brunswick black. The latter will be rendered more durable by mixing in a small quantity of indiarubber varnish (made by dissolving small strips of caoutchouc in gas-tar). The process of mounting in glass-cells is similar to that employed in making varnish-cells, except that a somewhat larger quantity of cementing medium is required. Objects mounted in this way should be kept for a time in the horizontal position, and a little fresh varnish must be applied if the cement shows a tendency to crack. In mounting objects in balsam, care must be taken to have the specimen *quite dry* before transferring it to turpentine. Objects mounted in cells should become *perfectly saturated* with the mounting fluid before being finally cemented down.

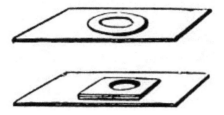

Fig. 263.—Glass-cells for Mounting.

It is preferable to mount and preserve specimens of animal tissues in shallow cells, to avoid undue pressure on the preparation. Cells intended to contain preparations immersed in fluid must be made of a substance impervious to the fluid used, such as here represented (Fig. 263). The surface of the fixed glass-circle should be slightly roughened before applying the cement.

Different modes of mounting may be employed with advantage; for instance, entomological specimens, as legs, wings, spiracles, tracheæ, ovipositors, stings, tongues, palates, corneæ, should be mounted in balsam; the trachea of the house-cricket, however, should be mounted dry. Sections of bone may either be mounted dry or in a fluid. Other objects, as sections of wood and stones of fruit, exhibit their structure best in Canada balsam.

In mounting entomological specimens, the first thing, of course, is the dissection of the insect. This is best accomplished by the aid of a dissecting microscope, a pair of small brass forceps, and finely-pointed scissors; the parts to be prepared and mounted should first be carefully detached from the insect with the scissors, then immersed in a solution of caustic alkali (*liquor potassæ*) for a few days, to soften and dissolve out the fat and soft parts. The length of time necessary for their immersion can only be determined by experience, but, as a general rule, the objects assume a certain amount of transparency when they have been long enough in the alkali; when this is ascertained, the object must be placed in a proper receptacle and put by to soak for two or three hours in soft or distilled water. It should then be placed between two slips of glass, and gently pressed till the softer parts are removed. Should any adhere to the edge of the object, it will be necessary to wash the specimen carefully in water, a process that will be much assisted by the delicate touches of a camel's-hair brush. Place the object now and then under the microscope to see that all extraneous matter is removed, and when this is accomplished take the specimen up carefully with the camel's-hair brush, or a lifter, and place it on a piece of very smooth paper (thick ivory note is the best for the purpose), arrange it carefully with the brush and a finely pointed needle, place a second piece of paper over it, and press it flat between two slips of glass, and compress it by a small spring clip (Fig. 264). A dozen clips may be had for a few pence. When *thoroughly* dry (which it will probably be in about twenty-four hours, if in a warm room), separate the glasses, and gently unfold the paper; then, with a little careful manipulation, the object may be readily detached, and placed in a little spirit of turpentine, where it should be allowed to remain until rendered transparent and fit for mounting. The time during which it should remain in this liquid will depend on the structure; some objects, such as wings of flies, will be quickly permeated, while horny and dense objects require an immersion of a fortnight or even longer. A pomatum pot with a *concave* bottom and well-fitting lid will answer admirably for conducting the soaking process in; and it is well, in preparing several specimens at a time, to have two pots, one for large and medium, the other for very small objects, otherwise the smaller will adhere to the larger.

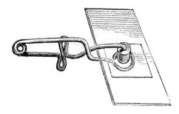

Fig. 264.—Spring Clip for Mounting.

In mounting objects in fluid, the glass cover should come nearly, but *not quite*, to the edge of the cell, a slight margin being left for the cement, which should project slightly over the edge of the cover, in order to secure it to the cell.

Media for Preserving Algæ.—The most useful preservative media for algæ are chrome-alum, formalin, and camphor water. The solution should consist of one per cent. of chrome-alum and one per cent. of formalin; this will render the gelatinous sheath and matrix form clear, while it will retain the colour of the algæ in most cases. The Chlorophyceæ do well in any of these media; but other species, as *Ulva Lactuca*, are rendered somewhat brittle. For such use formalin alone. The Phæophyceæ should be placed while fresh in the formalin; the larger forms are better fixed by placing them for an hour or two in chrome-alum solution. The Florideæ do well in any of the three solutions, but the more delicate species, *Griffithsia*, require a two per cent. formalin solution in sea-water; the plant preserves its natural appearance in this medium.

To preserve and mount diatomaceæ in as nearly as possible a natural condition, they should be first well washed in distilled water and mounted in a medium composed of one part of spirits of wine to seven parts of distilled water. The siliceous coverings of the diatoms, however, which show various beautiful forms under the higher powers of the microscope, require more care in preparation. The guano, or infusorial earth containing them, should first be washed several times in water till the water is colourless, allowing sufficient time for precipitation between each washing. The deposit must then be put into a test tube and nitro-hydrochloric acid (equal parts of nitric and hydrochloric acids) added to it, when a violent effervescence will take place. When this has subsided, the whole should be subjected to heat, brought nearly to the boiling point for six or eight hours. The acid must now be carefully poured off, and the precipitate washed in a *large* quantity of water, allowing some three or four hours between each washing, for the subsidence of some of the lighter forms. The sediment must be examined under the microscope with an inch object-glass, and the siliceous valves of the diatoms picked out with a coarse hair or bristle.

Dr. Rezner's Mechanical Finger (Fig. 265) for selecting and arranging diatoms, adaptable to any microscope, is made to slip on to the objective far enough to have a firm bearing, and so that the bristle point can be brought into focus when depressed to its limit. It is clamped in its place by a small thumb-screw. The bristle holder slides into its place, and is carefully adjusted to the centre of the field. When using the finger, the bristle is first raised by means of the micrometer screw till so far within focus as to be nearly or quite invisible, then the objective is focussed on to the slide, and the desired object sought for and brought into the centre of the field; the bristle point is then lowered by the screw until it reaches the object, which usually adheres to it at once, and can then be examined by rotating the bristle wire by means of the milled head.

Fig. 265.—Rezner's Mechanical Finger.

The medium used for mounting diatomaceæ is of considerable importance, inasmuch as their visibility is either diminished or much increased thereby. Professor Abbe, experimenting with the more minute test objects, diatoms, &c., found monobromide of naphthaline gave increased definition to most of them. This liquid is colourless, somewhat of an oleaginous nature, and is soluble in alcohol. Its density is 1·555, and refractive index 1·6. Its index of visibility is about twice that of Canada balsam.

Taking the refractive index of air as 1·0, and diatomaceous silex as 1·43, the visibility may be expressed by the *difference* ·43.

The following table may be constructed :—

Refractive indices (taken approximately).			Visibility of silex (Refr. index = 1·43).
Water	.. =	1·33 ..	10
Canada balsam	.. =	1·54 ..	11
Bisulphide of carbon	.. =	1·68 ..	25
Sol. of sulphur in bisulph. ..	=	1·75 ..	32
"phosphorus"	.. =	2·11 ..	67

These data relating to visibility must be taken in connection with the numerical aperture of the objectives and of the illuminating pencil. The effect produced on diatoms is very remarkable, the markings on their siliceous frustules being visible under much lower powers.

So that the visibility of the diatom mounted in phosphorus as compared with balsam is as sixty-seven to eleven; in other words, the image is six times more visible. Mr. Stephenson's phosphorus medium is composed of a solution of solid or stick phosphorous dissolved in bisulphide of carbon. Great care is required in preparing the solution owing to the very inflammable nature of the materials. So small a quantity of the bisulphide of carbon is required to dissolve the phosphorus that the diatom may be said to be mounted in nearly pure phosphorus. Remarkable enough, this medium has the reverse effect upon such test-objects as podura and lepisma scales. These lose their characteristic markings.

For mounting minute objects, carbolic acid solution will be found a useful medium—the purest crystals of carbolic acid dissolved in just sufficient water to render them fluid. No more should be dissolved than may be wanted for the time being, as if left standing exposed to the light it changes colour. Small crustacean foraminifera, the palates of moluscs, after boiling a short time in liquid potash and well washing to remove all traces of alkali, may be preserved in carbolic acid solution. Should the specimens appear cloudy gently warm the slide over a spirit lamp.

Preserving and Killing Rotatoria with cilia in situ.—Mr. C. Rousselet's method of preserving and mounting the Rotatoria[47] has been attended with so much success that the old difficulty attendant upon the preservation of these various beautiful forms of infusorial life has been practically overcome. The process resorted to consists of four stages, namely, narcotising, killing, fixing, and preserving. In dealing with rotifers hitherto, the difficulty has been that of successfully killing them with their rotating organs fully extended. It has been found needful to have recourse in the first instance to a narcotising agent, and one that acts slowly. The most suitable is a weak solution of the hydrochlorate of cocaine, a one per cent. solution, or even weaker. This was first proposed by Mr. Weber for keeping these active little bodies quiet while under observation. Mr. Rousselet carries this agent further; he applied it to narcotise them prior to killing, and this it does most effectually. The rotifers are seen to sink to the bottom of the live-cell, and the cilia gradually to slacken in motion, and the time for killing has arrived. This is effected by Flemming's chromo-aceto-osmic acid. A rather weak solution must be employed—consisting of 1 per cent. solution of chromic acid, 15 parts; 2 per cent. osmic acid, 4 parts; glacial acetic acid, 1 part—which is at the same time a killing and fixing medium. The word "fixing" must not be taken to imply simply fixing, as it includes rapidly *killing* and *hardening* and preventing further change in the tissues of the rotifers by subsequent treatment, as mounting. The animal, therefore, must remain quietly for a few minutes, and then taken out and washed in five or six changes of distilled water, and hence transferred to the preservative fluid. All this must be effected with great care. The best preservative fluid is simply distilled water, rendered antiseptic by a trace of the fixing solution (about eight drops to an ounce of water) giving the slightest tinge of yellow to the solution. This slight tinge of colour is imparted to the rotifers, otherwise they remain transparent and unchanged, while the nervous tissue throughout the body is brought out to perfection.

Some slight difference in treatment is required by certain species, as that of *Asplanchna priodonta*; after the application of the cocaine solution, which should be added slowly, that is, by letting a few drops trickle down the side of the live-trough; this, being heavier than water, sinks to the bottom, thus narcotising the rotifers, and assisting to kill them with the cilia fully expanded. They should be left quietly for fifteen minutes, then thoroughly washed with distilled water. On further experimenting, Mr. Rousselet found that a weaker solution of osmic acid alone, $\frac{1}{4}$ per cent., answers quite as well as, if not better than, Flemming's fluid; even this must be allowed to act for only a very short time—a minute at most; the rotifers then remain white and transparent, excepting the ova, in which a fat-like substance, *lecithene*, is secreted. If they become too much stained, they may be decolourised by passing them through peroxide of hydrogen. For narcotising the following solution has been found most useful:—Take a 2 per cent. solution of cocaine hydrochlorate, 3 parts; methylated spirit of wood naphtha, 1 part; and distilled water, 6 parts. This must be added as before directed, drop by drop, watching the effect upon the rotifers under the microscope.

All the rotatoria may be killed and preserved in the same way. For mounting, Mr. Rousselet prefers a slightly *hollowed-out* glass cell, the advantage of which is that the rotifers are kept to the centre, and cannot move to the edge. A little difficulty at first presents itself to exclude air-bubbles, but this, with a little care, can be overcome by placing a drop of a two or three per cent. solution of formalin, just sufficient to fill the cell. Then transfer the rotifers with a dipping pipette to the cell, and lower the cover-glass down very gently, removing any excess of fluid by blotting-paper. The best cement for the cover-glass is gold-size.

Method of Cementing.—After many years' experience, I have arrived at the conclusion that for cementing down the cover-glass there is nothing better than either gold size or gum dammar varnish. The latter, for some preparations, will be improved by the addition of a small proportion of indiarubber dissolved in naphtha. (See Appendix.)

Should glycerine be preferred, carefully wash away any surplus quantity by gently syringing; then apply a ring of waterproof cement round the cover-glass. An inexpensive one can be made by dissolving ten grains of gum-ammoniac in an ounce of acetic acid, and adding to this solution two drachms of Cox's gelatine. This liquid flows easily from the brush and is waterproof, rendered more so if subsequently brushed over with a solution of ten grains of bichromate of potash in an ounce of water. An especial recommendation to this cement is its adhesiveness to glass, even should there be a little glycerine left behind on the cover. After the gelatine ring is thoroughly dry any kind of cement may be employed.

A useful cement for fixing minute objects, diatoms, &c., temporarily to thin glass covers, before permanently mounting them in Canada balsam, is made as follows:—Dissolve, without heat, two or three grains of gum arabic in one ounce of distilled water, then add glacial acetic acid, three minims, and the least trace of sugar. Filter carefully through filter paper, and repeat this in the course of three or four weeks. This cement will be unaffected by the balsam.

Mounting Chara.—It is often found difficult to preserve and mount the fruit of chara, but this can be successfully accomplished in glycerine jelly, by taking the following precautions. After cleaning the specimen place it in 92 per cent. of alcohol for several hours, then transfer it to a mixture of equal parts of spirit and glycerine for several hours longer, pour off nearly all the mixture, and add pure glycerine at intervals till the glycerine becomes concentrated. The specimen is then mounted in glycerine jelly in a cell just deep enough to take it without pressure.

There are some objects much more difficult to prepare than others, and which tax the patience of the beginner in a manner which can hardly be imagined by any one who has never made the attempt. The structure of many creatures is so delicate as to require the very greatest care to prevent mutilation, and consequent spoliation, of the specimen. The beginner, therefore, must not be discouraged by a few failures in commencing, but should persevere in his attempts, and constant practice will soon teach him the best way of managing intricate and difficult objects. The room in which he operates should be free from dust, smoke, and intrusion, and everything used should be kept scrupulously clean, since a very small speck of dirt, which may be almost invisible to the naked eye, will assume unpleasant proportions under the microscope, and not only mar, but possibly spoil a fine and delicate preparation.

Few students on commencing to work with the microscope will fully realise the fact that under medium or high powers the natural appearance of almost all objects is changed by the refractive nature of the fluid medium in which they are immersed and which enters more or less into their composition. The remarkable changes effected by the law of diffusion, when alkaloid substances enter into their composition, show the necessity of taking every precaution in the employment of preservative fluids. Glycerine affords an example of the chemical change induced, should the preparation have been passed through an alkaline solution.

Air Bubbles are a constant source of annoyance both in preparing and mounting. These may be removed from the specimen by gently warming the under part of the slide over a spirit lamp, or placing the slide in the warm chamber, when the bubbles will move towards the edge of the cover-glass and ultimately disappear. The air-pump is preferred by many microscopists.

Collection of Objects.

Infusorial Life, with all its fascinations, was fully unveiled to naturalists by the celebrated Ehrenberg. It was he who termed it infusorial, because he first met with the more interesting forms of minute life in infusions of hay and other vegetable substances. Since his day it is a well-known experience of those who take up the microscope that the most interesting objects to commence with are infusorial living creatures of sufficient dimensions to be easily understood and seen with moderate magnifying powers. Moreover, infusoria are more readily found in almost any pool or running stream of water, either near the surface or clinging to the under surfaces of aquatic plants. At one time all the small shallow pools in the neighbourhood of London—Hampstead Heath, Clapham, Wandsworth, and other commons—abounded in the most interesting forms of life, were famous hunting grounds for the marvellous volvox, the charming dismid and diatom, the wonderful budding and self-dividing hydra. A few hours' ramble furnished the microscopist with a bountiful supply of these and many other forms of life. Now all is changed; our commons have been devoted to other purposes, and with the general *levelling* up all the little pools have disappeared, and the microscopist has been warned off and driven further afield, or seeks the good offices of a country friend for an occasional peep into pond life.[48]

A teaspoonful, however, judiciously taken from a well-chosen locality will often be found to contain a variety of living forms, every one of which will deserve a careful and patient study.

Of the microscopic organisms, the collection of which requires no other methods than those ordinarily pursued by the naturalist, most of them must be sought for in pools or running waters, basking in the sunshine, clinging to leaves and rootlets of all aquatic plants; some freely moving about, others clinging to stones or pieces of wood at the bottom. Dismids congregate in shallow waters or rise to the surface in a quiet nook, while the diatomaceæ are seen covering the bottom of clear water, to which they give a yellowish-brown tinge of colour.

Infusorial animal life, as vorticellæ, stentors, rotifers, and various polyzoa, cling, as also do hydra, in colonies to vallisneria, duck-weed, frogbit, or small branches dipping down under water; and if some of the water-weed is brought home the little creatures will live and thrive for several weeks. No waters, however, are so full of minute animal life as the sphagnum bog. A number of species of diatoms, as well as protozoids and the smaller molluscs, will be found in all peat bogs. It is remarkable, too, that the same species, everywhere, are associated with this kind of moss. Lord Sidney Godolphin Osborn supplied his friends with moss growing in a damp part of the garden walk of his rectory; this always furnished the same species of rotifers. These proved to be most interesting objects to my friends, and in an early communication I described them as *indestructible*, since they will bear any amount of desiccation; nevertheless, they were revived when a drop of water was introduced into the glass-cell.

Fig. 266.—Collecting Stick, Bottle, Hook, and Net.

The Thames mud always furnishes a number of beautiful forms of triceratum. Lower down the river, as brackish water is reached, greater varieties of diatoms appear. But to secure them the collector must be provided with a collecting stick. A convenient form is furnished by Messrs. Baker (Fig. 266). This consists of an ordinary walking-stick, together with a lengthening rod, a cutting hook to clear away weeds, ringed bottles with screw tops, and a net with a glass tube attached. Their uses are too obvious to need further description.

The siliceous skeletons of diatoms are met with in the fossil state. Among the first discovered of the infusorial strata were the polishing slates of Bilin and Tripoli, the berg-mehl or mountain meal, the entire mass of which is composed of the siliceous skeletons of different species of diatoms. Richmond, Virginia, is rich in the same organisms, while the great mass of our chalk cliffs are composed of foraminiferous shells, xanthidiæ, &c. One remarkable fact in connection with fossil infusoria is that most of the forms are still found in the recent state. The beautiful engine-turned discs, *Coscinodisci*, so abundant in the Richmond earth, may be met with in our own seas, and in great profusion in the deposits of guano on the African and American coasts, and in the stomachs of the oyster, scallop, and other salt-water molluscous animals common to our shores.

A great number of infusorial earths may be mounted as dry objects, while others require careful washing and digesting in appropriate media. The finer portions of the sediments will be found to contain the better and more perfect siliceous shells.

Preparing and Mounting Apparatus.

Fig. 267.—Mounting Apparatus.

1.—Ross's instrument for cutting thin covering-glass for objects. This apparatus consists of a bent arm supporting the cutting portion of this apparatus, which consists of a vertical rod with a soft cork at one end. A brass arm at right angles carries the diamond parallel with and close to the main rod.

2.—Covering-glass measurer. To measure the thickness of covering-glass, place it between the brass plate and the steel bearing; the long end of the lever will then indicate the thickness on the scale, to $\frac{1}{50}$-th, $\frac{1}{100}$-th, or $\frac{1}{1000}$-th inch.

3.—Brass table on folding legs, with lamp for mounting objects.

4.—Whirling table with eccentric adjustment for making cells and finishing off slides.

5.—Air-pump with glass receiver, $3\frac{1}{2}$-inch brass plate for mounting objects and withdrawing air-bubbles.

6.—Improved table with knife for cutting soft sections. This consists of an absolutely flat brass table, with a square hole to receive the wood, or other matter, on a movable screw, which adjusts the thickness of the section.

7.—Smith's holder with spring and screw for adjusting pressure when mounting objects.

8.—Cutting diamonds for cell-making and cutting slips of glass.

9.—Writing diamonds for cutting thin covering-glass and naming objects.

10.—Page's wooden forceps, for holding glass slips or objects when heated, during mounting.

PART II.

CHAPTER I.

Microscopic Forms of Life—Thallophytes—Pteridophyta, Phanerogamæ—
Structure and Properties of the Cell.

The time has long since passed by since the value of the microscope as an instrument of scientific research might have been called in question. By its aid the foundation of mycology has been securely laid, and cryptogamic botany in particular has, during the last quarter of a century, made surprising progress in the hands of those devoted to pursuits which confer benefits upon mankind.

Little more than thirty years ago practically nothing was known of the life history of a fungus, nothing of parasitism, of infectious diseases, or even of fermentation. Our knowledge of the physiology of nutrition was in its infancy; even the significance of starches and sugars in the green plant was as yet not understood, while a number of the most important facts relating to plants and the physiology of animals were unknown and undiscovered. When we reflect on these matters, and remember that bacteria were regarded merely as curious animalculæ, that rusts and smuts were supposed to be emanations of diseased states, and that spontaneous generation still-survived among us, some idea may be formed of the condition of cryptogamic botany and the lower forms of animal life some eight or ten years after my book on the microscope made its first appearance (1854).

Indeed, long prior to this time, dating from that of even the earliest workers with the microscope, it was known that the water of pools and ditches, and especially infusions of plants and animals of all kinds, teem with living organisms, but it was not recognised definitely that vast numbers of these microscopic living beings (and even actively moving ones) are plants, growing on and in the various solid and liquid matters examined, and as truly as visible and accepted plants grow on soil and in the air and water. Perhaps the most important discovery in the history of cryptogamic botany was initiated here. The change, then, that has come over our knowledge of microscopic plant life during this last busy quarter of a century has been almost entirely due to the initiation and improvement, first in methods of growing them, and in the methods of *"Microscopic Gardening"*; and secondly, to the greater knowledge gained in the use of the microscope.

"If we look at the great groups of plants from a broad point of view, it is remarkable that the fungi and the phanerogams occupy attention on quite other grounds than do the algæ, mosses, and ferns. Algæ are especially a physiologist's group, employed in questions on nutrition, reproduction, and cell division and growth; the Bryophyta and Pteridophyta are, on the other hand, the domain of the morphologist. Fungi and Phanerogams, while equally or even more employed by specialists in morphology and physiology, appeal widely to general interest on the ground of utility.

"It is very significant that a group like the fungi should have attracted so much scientific attention, and aroused so general an interest at the same time. But the fact that fungi affect our lives directly has been driven home; and whether as poisons or foods, destructive moulds or fermentation agents, parasitic mildews or disease germs, they occupy more interest than all other cryptogams put together, the flowering plants alone rivalling them in this respect. A marked feature of the period in which we live will be the great advances made in our knowledge of the uses of plants, for, of course, this development of economic botany has gone hand in hand with the progress of geological botany, the extension of our planting, and the useful applications of botany to the processes of home industries."[49]

The intimate organic structure of the vegetable world is seen to consist of a variety of different materials indeterminable by unassisted vision, and for the most part requiring high magnification for their discrimination. Chemical analysis had, however, shown that vegetables are composed of a few simple substances, water, carbonic acid gas, oxygen, nitric acid, and a small portion of inorganic salts. Out of these simple elements the whole of the immense variety of substances produced by the vegetable kingdom are constructed. No part of the plant contains fewer than three of these universally distributed elements, hence the greater uniformity in their chemical constituents. It will be seen, then, that the methods of plant chemistry are of supreme interest both to the chemist and the physiologist, or biologist. Plants, while they borrow materials from the inorganic, and powers from the physical world, whereby they are enabled to pass through the several stages of germination, growth, and reproduction, could not accomplish these transformations without the all-important aid of light and heat, the combined functions of which are indispensable to the perfect development of the vegetable world.

Light, then, enables plants to decompose, change into living matter, and consolidate, the inorganic elements of carbonic acid gas, water, and ammonia, which are absorbed by the leaves and roots from the atmosphere and earth; the quantity of carbon consolidated being exactly in proportion to the intensity of the light. Nevertheless, light in its chemical character is a deoxidising agent, by which the numerous neutral compounds common to vegetables are formed. It is the principal agent in preparing the food of plants, and it is during the chemical changes spoken of that the specific heat of plants is slowly evolved, which, though generally feeble, is sometimes very sensibly evolved, especially so when flowers and fruits are forming, on account of the increase of chemical energy at this period.

The action of heat is measurable throughout the whole course of vegetable life, although its manifestations take on various forms—those suited to the period and circumstances of growth. Upon the heat generated depends the formation of protein and nitrogenous substances, which abound more directly in the seed buds, the points of the roots, and in all those organs of plants which are in the greatest state of activity. The whole chemistry of plant life, in fact, is manifest in this production of energy for drawing material from its surroundings; therefore the organising power of plants bears a direct ratio to the amount of light and heat acting upon them.

The living medium, then, which possesses the marvellous property of being primarily aroused into life and energy, and which either forms the whole or the greater portion of every plant, is in its earliest and simplest form nothing more than a microscopic cell, consisting of one or two colourless particles of matter, in closest contact, and wholly immersed in a transparent substance somewhat resembling *albumen* (white of egg), termed *protoplasm*, but differing essentially in its character and properties. This nearly colourless organisable matter is the life-blood of the cell. It is sufficiently viscid to maintain its globular form, and under high powers is seen to have a slightly consolidated film enclosing semi-transparent particles, together with vacuoles which are of a highly refractive nature. These small bodies are termed nuclei, and they appear to be furnished with an extremely delicate enveloping film. In a short time the nuclei increase in number and split up the parent body. The protoplasmic mass, however, is undoubtedly the true formative material, and is rightly regarded as "the physical basis of life" of both the vegetable and animal kingdoms.

There are, however, certain members of the vegetable kingdom which somewhat resemble animals in their dependence upon receiving organic compounds already formed for them, being themselves unable to effect the fixation of the carbon needed to effect the first stage in their after chemical transformations. Such is the case with a large class of flowering plants, among Phanerogams, and the leafless parasites which draw their support chiefly from the tissues of their hosts. It is likewise the case with regard to the whole group of fungi; the lower cryptogams, which derive the greater portion of their nutritive materials from organic matter undergoing some form of histolysis; while others belonging to this group have the power of originating decomposition by a fermentative (*zymotic*) action peculiarly their own. There are many other protophytes which live by absorption, and which appear to take in no solid matter, but draw nourishment from the atmosphere or the water in which they exist.

With regard to motion, this was at one time considered the distinctive attribute of animal life, but many protophytes possess a spontaneity of power and motion, while others are furnished with curious motile organs termed *cilia*, or whip-like appendages, *flagella*, by which their bodies are propelled with considerable force through the water in which they live.

Henceforth this protoplasmic substance was destined to take an important position in the physiological world. It is, then, desirable to enter somewhat more fully into the life history of so remarkable a body. It has a limiting membrane, composed of a substance somewhat allied to starch, termed *cellulose*, one of the group of compounds known as carbo-hydrates. The mode of formation and growth of this cell wall is not yet definitely determined; nevertheless, it is the universal framework or skeleton of the vegetable world, although it appears to play no special part in their vital functions. It merely serves the purpose of a protecting membrane to the globular body called the *"primordial cell,"* which permanently constitutes the living principle upon which the whole fundamental phenomena of growth and reproduction depend.

Sometimes this protoplasmic material is seen to constitute the whole plant; and so with regard to the simplest known forms of animal life—the amœba, for example. That so simple and minute an organism should be capable of independent motion is indeed surprising. Dujardin, a French physiologist, termed this animated matter *sarcode*. On a closer study of the numerous forms of animal life it was found that all were alike composed of this sarcode substance, some apparently not having a cell wall. The same seemed to hold good of certain higher forms of cells, the colourless blood corpuscles for instance, which under high powers of the microscope are seen to change their shape, moving about by the streaming out of this sarcode. At length the truth dawned on histologists that the cell contents, rather than the closing wall, must be the essential structure. On further investigation it became apparent that a far closer similarity existed between vegetables and animals than was before supposed. Ultimately it was made clear that the vegetable protoplasm and the animal sarcode were one and the same structure. Max Schultz found this to be the case, and to all intents and purposes they are identical.

We have now to retrace our steps and look somewhat more closely into the discovery of that important body, the *cell-nucleus*. It was an English botanist, Dr. Robert Brown, who, in 1833, during his microscopical studies of the epidermis of orchids, discovered in their cells "an opaque spot," to which soon afterwards he gave the name of *nucleus*. Schleiden and Schwann's later researches led them to the conclusion that the nucleus is the most characteristic formative element in all vegetable and animal tissues in the incipient phase of existence. It then began to be taught that there is one universal principle of development for the elementary parts of all organisms, however different, and that is the formation of cells. Thus was enunciated a doctrine which was for all practical purposes absolutely new, and which opened out a wide field of further investigation for the physiologist, and led up to a fuller knowledge of the cell contents. In fact, it became a question as to whether the cell contents rather than the enclosing wall should not be considered the basis of life, since the cell at this time had by no means lost its importance, although it no longer signified the minute cavity it did when originally discovered by Schwann. It now implied, as Schultz defined it, "a small mass of viscid matter, protoplasm, endowed with the attributes of life." The nucleus was once more restored to its original importance, and with even greater significance. In place of being a structure generated *de novo* from non-cellular substance, and disappearing as soon as its function of cell formation is accomplished, the nucleus is now known as the central permanent feature of every cell, and indestructible while the cell lives, and the parent, by division of its substance, of other generations of nuclei and cells. The word *cell* has at the same time received its final definition as "a small mass of protoplasm supplied with a nucleus." In short, all the activities of plant and animal life are really the product of energy liberated solely through *histolysis*, or destructive processes, amounting to the combustion that takes place in the ultimate cells of the organisms.

But there are other points of especial interest involved in the question of cell formation beside those already mentioned.

The cell and its contents collectively are termed the *endoplasm*, or when coloured, as in algæ, *endochrome*. With regard to the outer layer of the cell and its growth nothing satisfactory has been clearly determined and finally accepted.

The cell as a whole is a protoplasmic mass, and not an emulsion, as some observers would have us suppose. It is, in fact, a reticulated tissue of the most delicate structure, made up of canaliculate spiral fibrils with hyaline walls capable of expansion and contraction. These fibrils are probably composed of still finer spirals. The visible granulated portion of the protoplasm, the only part that takes a stain under ordinary circumstances, is simply the contents of these canals. It is the chromatin of Flemming, and is capable of motion within the canals. The nucleus, then, is probably nothing more than a granule of the extra-cellular net, and is formed by the junction of the several bands of wall-threads which traverse it in different directions. The cell wall of plants possesses the same structure as protoplasm, and is probably protoplasm impregnated by cellulose.

It is this portion of the protoplasmic mass that is now recognised under the term *octoplasm*, or primordial utricle, and is of so fine and delicate a nature that it is only brought into view when separated from the cell wall either by further developmental changes, or by reagents and certain stains or dyes. It was, in fact, discovered to be a slightly condensed portion of the protoplasmic layer corresponding to the *octosare* of the lower forms of animal life. The octoplasm and cell wall can only be distinguished from each other by chemical tests. Both nucleus and nucleoli are only rendered visible in the same way, that is, by staining for several hours in a carmine solution, and washing in a weak acetic acid solution.

With the enlargement of the cell by the imbibition of water, clear spaces, termed vacuoles, are seen to occupy a small portion of the cell, while the nucleus and nucleoli lie close to the parietal layer.

The interesting phenomenon of cyclosis, to which I shall have occasion to refer further on, is now believed to be due to the contractility of certain wall-threads stretching from the nucleus to the outermost layers of the cell. An intimate relationship is thereby established between the nucleus, the nucleolus, and the parietal layer. This much has been made clear by the more scientific methods of investigation pursued in the use of the microscope. Nevertheless a large and important class of cells, forming a kind of borderland between the vegetable and animal kingdoms, still remains to be dealt with, in which the cell contents are only imperfectly differentiated, while numerous other unicellular organisms, owing to their extreme minuteness, tenuity, and want of all colour, are apparently devoid of any nucleus, and when present can only be differentiated by a resort to a specially conducted method of preparation and staining. There is, however, a remarkable feature in connection with many micro-organisms—that certain of these protophytes possess motive organs, cilia or flagella, bodies at one time supposed to be characteristic of, and belonging to, the protozoa.

This being the case, the methods of plant chemistry are of supreme interest, the more so because physiologists are in a position to isolate a single bacterial cell, grow it in certain media, and thus devote special attention to it, and keep it for some time under observation. In this way it has become possible to further grasp facts in connection with cell nutrition and the nature of its waste products. We have, then, arrived at a stage when the history of the chemical changes brought about by bacteria can be more definitely determined, as we have here to do with the vegetable cell in its simplest form. The chemical work performed by these micro-organisms has as yet occupied only a few years; nevertheless, the results have been of the most remarkable and encouraging character.

At an earlier period an interesting discovery in connection with the pathogenic action of these bodies was, by the labours of Schöenlein, Robin, and others, brought to the notice of the medical profession, viz., that certain diseases affecting the human body were due to vegetable parasites. In 1856 an opportunity offered itself for a thorough investigation, and the microscopical part of the work fell into my hands, with the result that I was able to add considerably to Schöenlein's list of parasitic skin diseases. My observations were in the first instance communicated to the medical journals. But the generalisation arrived at was that "If there be any exceptions to the law that parasites select for their sustenance the subjects of debility and decay, such exceptions are rarely to be found among the vegetations belonging to fungi, which invariably derive nutrition from matter in a state of lowered vitality, passing into degeneration, or wherein decomposition has already taken place to a certain extent.... It scarcely admits of a doubt that all diseases observed of late years among plants have been due to parasites of the same class favoured by want of vigour of growth and atmospheric conditions, and that the cause of the various murrains of which so much has been heard is also due to similar causes."[50]

Herein, then, is to be found the solution of a difficulty that so long surrounded the question, but which subsequently culminated in the specialisation and scientific development of bacteriology, due to the unceasing labours of Pasteur, whose solid genius enabled him to overcome the prejudices of those who were at work on other lines, and who had no conception of the functions that parasitic organisms fulfil in nature.

Going back to my earlier experimental researches to determine the part taken by saccharomycetes and saprophytes in fermentation, I find, from correspondence in my possession, that in 1859 I demonstrated to the satisfaction of Dr. Bell, F.R.S., the then head of the chemical laboratory of Somerset House, that a very small portion of putrefactive matter taken from an animal body, a parasitic fungus (*Achorion Schöenleinii*), a mould (*Aspergillus* or *Penicillium*), and a yeast (*Torula cerevisiæ*) would in a short time, and indifferently, set up a ferment in sweet-wort and transform its saccharine elements into alcohol, differing only in degree (quantitative), and not in kind or quality. This, then, was the first step in the direction towards proving symbiotic action between these several parasitic organisms. The only apparent difference observed during the fermentative processes was that putrefactive (saprophytic) action commenced at a somewhat earlier stage, and that the percentage of alcohol was also somewhat less.[51]

In 1856, also, the ærobic bacteria attracted my attention, and, together with the late Rev. Lord Sidney Godolphin Osborne, I exposed plates of glass (microscopical slides), covered with glycerine and grape sugar, in every conceivable place where we thought it possible to arrest micro-organisms. The result is known, viz., that fungoid bodies (moulds and bacterial) were taken in great numbers, and varying with the seasons. The air of the hospital and sick-room likewise engaged attention, each of which proved especially rich in parasitic bodies. During the cholera visitation of 1858 the air was rich in ærobic and anærobic bacteria, while a *blue mist* which prevailed throughout the epidemic yielded a far greater number than at any former period (represented in Plate I., No. 13). This blue mist attracted the especial attention of meteorologists. At a somewhat later period a more remarkable fungoid disease, the fungus foot of India, *mycetoma*, came under my observation, a detailed description of which I contributed to the medical journals, and also, with further details, to the "Monthly Microscopical Journal" of 1871. Interlacing mycelia, ending in hyphæ, in this destructive form of parasitic disease were seen to pervade the whole of the tissues of the foot, the bony structures being involved, and it was only possible to stay the action of the parasite by amputation.

So far, then, the study of parasitic organisms had at an early period shared largely in my microscopical work, extending over several years, and with the result that these micro-organisms were found to exhibit on occasions great diversity of character, and that different members of the bacteria in particular flourish under great diversity of action, and often under entirely opposite conditions; that they feed upon wholly different materials, and perform an immense variety of chemical work in the media in which they live.

The study of the chemistry (*chemotaxis*) of bacteria has, however, greatly enlarged our conception of the chemical value and power of the vegetable cell, while it is obvious that no more appropriate or remunerative field of study could engage the attention of the microscopist, as well as the chemist, than that of bacterial life, and which is so well calculated to enlarge our views of created organisms, whether belonging to the vegetable or animal kingdom.

Pathogenic Fungi and Moulds.

It is scarcely necessary to go back to the history of the parasitic fungi to which diseases of various kinds were early attributable. The rude microscopes of two and a half centuries ago revealed the simple fact that all decomposable substances swarmed with countless multitudes of organisms, invisible to ordinary vision. Leuwenhoek, the father of microscopy, and whose researches were generally known and accepted in 1675, tells of his discovery of extremely minute organisms in rain-water, in vegetable infusions, in saliva, and in scrapings from the teeth; further, he differentiated these living organisms by their size and form, and illustrated them by means of woodcuts; and there can be no doubt that his figures are intended to represent leptothrix filaments, vibrios, and spirilla. In other of his writings attempts are made to give an idea of the size of these "animalcules"; he described them as *a thousand times smaller than a grain of sand*. From his investigations a belief sprung up that malaria was produced by "animalcules," and that the plague which visited Toulon and Marseilles in 1721 arose from a similar cause. Somewhat later on the natural history of micro-organisms was more diligently studied, and with increasing interest. Müller, in 1786, pointed out that they had been too much given to occupy themselves in finding new organisms, he therefore devoted himself to the study of their forms and biological characters, and it was on such data he based a classification. Thus the scientific knowledge gained of these minute bodies was considerably advanced, and the subject now entered upon a new phase: the origin of micro-organisms. It further resolved itself into two rival theories—spontaneous generation, and development from pre-existing germs—the discussion over which lasted more than a century. Indeed, it only ended in 1871, when the originator of the Abiogenesis theory withdrew from the contest, and the more scientific investigations of Pasteur (1861) found general acceptance. This indefatigable worker had been investigating fermentation, and studying the so-called diseases of wines and a contagious disease which was committing ravages among silkworms. Pasteur in time was able to confirm the belief that the "muscadine disease" of silkworms was due to the presence of micro-organisms, discernible only by the microscope. The oval, shining bodies in the moth, worm, and eggs had been previously observed and described by Nägeli and others, but it was reserved for Pasteur to show that when a silkworm whose body contained these organisms was pounded up in a mortar with water, and painted over the leaves of the tree upon which healthy worms were fed, all took the disease and died.

PLATE IX.

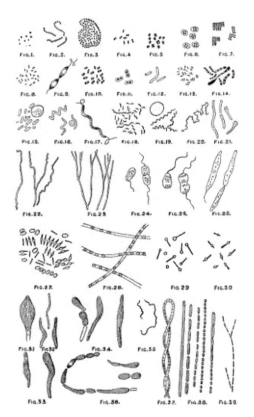

AFTER DR CROOKSHANK *J. T. Balcomb. del.*

TYPICAL FORMS OF BACTERIA, SCHIZOMYCETES, OR FISSION-
FUNGI.

As the contagious particles were transmitted to the eggs, the method adopted
for preventing the spread of the disease was as follows:—Each female moth
was kept separate from the others, and allowed to deposit her eggs, and after
death her body was crushed up in a mortar as before, and a drop of the fluid
examined under the microscope. When any trace of muscadine was found
present, the whole of the eggs and body were burnt. In this way the disease
was combated, and ultimately stamped out.

Pasteur also pointed out that one form or cause of disease must not be
confounded with another. For example, muscadine, a true fungus (*Botrytis
bassiana*), should not be confounded with another disease known to attack
silkworms, termed *pebrin*, this being caused by a bacterium, and, according to
the more recent researches of Balbiani, by a Psorospermia. Botrytis is a true
mould, belonging to the Oomycetes, and allied to the potato fungus,
Peronospora. It is propagated by spores, which, falling on a silkworm,

germinate and penetrate its body. A mycelium is then developed, which spreads throughout the body. Hyphæ appear through the skin, and bear white chalky-looking spores; these become detached, and float in the air as an impalpable dust-like smoke. Damp further develops the fungus.

Insects suffer much from the ravages of fungi. The house-fly sticking to the window-pane is seen to be surrounded by the mycelia of *Penicillium racemosum* (*Sporendonema muscæ*, or *Saprolegnia feræ*). In other cases Cordiceps attacks certain caterpillars belonging to the genera Cossus and Hepialus when they are buried in the sand and before their metamorphosis into chrysalides; they are killed by the rapid development of hyphæ and mycelium in their tissues.

Sphæria miletaris, a parasite of *Bombyx pilyocarpa*, the caterpillar of which is found on pine-trees, is one of the few fungi which may be regarded as beneficial to man, since it aids in the destruction of multitudes of these caterpillars, which otherwise would devour the young shoots and pine needles. Giard specialises other parasites of insects, which he terms Entomophoreæ. Others, *E. rimosa*, attack grasshoppers and the diptera, enveloping them in a dense coating of mycelium and spores, which speedily kills the victim.

The study, then, of the life-history of germs, microbes, micro-organisms, or bacteria (as they are indifferently termed), opened up a new science, that of Bacteriology. By the more recent advances in this science we are enabled to understand the very important part these minute organisms fill in the great scheme of Nature, for almost exclusively by their agency the soil is supplied with the requisite nutritive material for plant life. And, as already pointed out, wherever organic matter is present—that is, the dead and useless substances which are the refuse of life—such material is promptly seized upon by micro-organisms, by means of which histolysis is rapidly accomplished.

Bacteria require a power of from 600 to 1,000 diameters or more for the determination of the species to which they belong. The number of species has been so much increased of late that a bulky volume is found to be insufficient for their enumeration. I am, however, by the courtesy of Professor Crookshank, enabled to present my readers with the typical forms of thirty-nine species of Bacteria, Schizomycetes, or fission-fungi, a selection, it will be seen, chiefly taken from among pathogenic organisms—those believed to originate disease. But many of the supposed *Saprophytic* forms often described as originating disease are merely accidental associates, that is, living in companionship for a time.

Size.—In ordinary terms of measurement, bacteria are on an average from $\frac{1}{25000}$th to about $\frac{1}{5000}$th of an inch long. These measurements do not convey a definite impression to the mind. It is calculated that a thousand million of them could be contained in a space of $\frac{1}{25}$th of an inch. The best impression of the size of the bacteria is, perhaps, obtained when it is stated that a $\frac{1}{25}$-inch immersion objective gives a magnification of nearly 2,200 diameters, and that under this power the bacteria appear to be about the size of very small print. The standard of measurement accepted by bacteriologists is the micro-millimeter. One millimeter is equal to about $\frac{1}{25000}$th an English inch. The number of micrococci in a milligramme of a culture of *Staphylococcus pyogenes aurens* has been estimated by Bujwid by counting at eight thousand millions. Not only do various species differ in dimensions, but considerable differences may be noted in a pure culture of the same species. On the other hand, there are numerous species which so closely resemble each other in size and shape that they cannot be differentiated by microscopic examination alone, and we have to look to other characteristics, as colour, growth in various culture media, pathogenic power, chemical products, &c., in order to decide the question of identity.

Reproduction.—The reproduction of bacteria takes place for the most part by fission and by spore formation. *Fission* is a process of splitting up or division, whereby an organism divides into two or more parts, each of which lives and divides in its turn. If certain organisms are watched under the microscope, a coccus or bacillus will be seen to elongate and at the same time become narrower, until its two halves become free, the two individual organisms again dividing and subdividing in their turn. This kind of reproduction is more readily seen in a higher class of unicellular organisms, the desmids. If, however, the new organisms do not break away from each other, but remain connected in groups or clusters, they are termed Staphylococci; if they remain connected in the form of a chain, or like a string of beads, they are termed Streptococci. If the division takes place in one plane, Diplococci are formed; if in two directions Tetracocci, or Tablet-cocci, are formed. On account of this multiplication by fission, the generic name of Schizomycetes, or fission-fungi, has been given to bacteria.

Spores.—A second method by which bacteria propagate is by spores. These bodies are distinguished by their remarkable power of resistance to the influence of temperature and the action of chemical reagents. Some of them will resist their immersion in strong acid solutions for many hours; also freezing and very high temperatures. Spore formation may take place in two ways: firstly, by "endogenous spores" (internal spores); secondly, by "arthrospores."

Endogenous Spores.—When the formation of the spores takes place in the mother-cell, the protoplasm is seen to contract, giving rise to one or more highly refractive bodies, which are the spores. The enclosing membrane of the organism then breaks away, leaving the spores free.

Arthrospores.—When the spore is not formed in the parent bacillus, but when entire cells (owing to lack of favourable conditions of growth) become converted into spores, the formation is known as "arthrogenous," the single individual being called an arthrospore. When the conditions are again favourable, spores germinate, giving rise to new bacilli. The germinating spore becomes elongated, and loses its bright appearance, the outer membrane becomes ruptured, and the young bacillus is set free. Certain conditions, such as the presence of oxygen in the case of the anthrax bacillus, give rise to the formation of spores; while various kinds of bacteria secure continuous existence by developing spores when there is lack of proper food material.

With reference to the incredible rapidity with which the bacteria multiply under conditions favourable to the growth and development, Cohn writes as follows:—"Let us assume that a microbe divides into two within an hour, then again into eight in the third hour, and so on. The number of microbes thus produced in twenty-four hours would exceed sixteen and a half millions; in two days they would increase to forty-seven trillions; and in a week the number expressing them would be made up of fifty-one figures. At the end of twenty-four hours the microbes descended from a single individual would occupy $\frac{1}{40}$th of a hollow cube, with edges $\frac{1}{25}$th of an inch long, but at the end of the following day would fill a space of twenty-seven cubic inches, and in less than five days their volume would equal that of the entire ocean."

Again, Cohn estimated that a single bacillus weighs about 0·000,000,000,024,243,672 of a grain; forty thousand millions, 1 grain; 289 billions, 1 pound. After twenty-four hours the descendants from a single bacillus would weigh $\frac{1}{2666}$th of a grain; after two days, over a pound; after three days, sixteen and a half million pounds, or 7,366 tons. It is quite unneccessary to state that these figures are purely theoretical, and could only be realised if there were no impediment to such rapid increase.

Fortunately, however, various checks, such as lack of food and unfavourable physical conditions, intervene to prevent unmanageable multiplication of these bodies.

These figures show, however, what a tremendous vital activity micro-organisms do possess, and it will be seen later at what great speed they increase in water, milk, broth, and other suitable media.

The following bacilli, among others, have numerous flagella distributed over the whole of the organism: the bacillus of blue milk (*Bacillus cyanogenus*)[52]; the bacillus of malignant œdema; the hay bacillus (*Bacillus subtilis*); *Proteus vulgaris*, &c.

The following have only one or two flagella at the poles: the *Bacillus pyocyaneus*, the *Spirillum finkleri*, the *Spirillum choleræ Asiaticæ*, &c.

The *Spirillum undala*, *Spirillum rubrum*, *Spirillum concentricum*, and *Sarcinæ*, pocket-cocci, have several flagella.

Micrococcus agilis have also several flagella; these possibly arise from one point. As I have already pointed out, the *classification* of the bacteria is one of great difficulty, since new kinds are being constantly discovered, and at present any attempt made in this direction can only be considered as quite of a provisional nature.

The difficulties which stand in the way may be surmised from the fact that *Sarcinæ*, pocket-cocci, were originally believed to be a single species, described by me, under the name of *Sarcina ventriculi*, in the fourth edition of my book, "as remarkable bodies invading the human and animal stomach, and seriously interfering with its functions."

Fig. 268.—Sarcinæ.

The original woodcut of these curious parasites is reproduced in Fig. 268, also in Plate IX., No. 7, and which evidently belong to a different species, numbering thirty-nine altogether. Quite recently Mr. G. H. Broadbent, M.R.C.S., Manchester, sent me a supply of these interesting bodies lately discovered by him in an infusion of cow manure. On examining a drop with a power of 1500 diameters they were discovered moving over the field of the microscope with a gyrating motion by the aid of flagella projecting from each corner of the pocket. After some days, having attained their full growth of four, eight or sixteen in a pocket, they break up, and recommence the formative process. Sarcinæ are certainly pathogenic in their nature. Cocci in groups, or asso-cocci, are similarly associated. These several forms of spiro-bacteria are enclosed in a transparent cell-wall, and are sometimes described as zooglæa.

Of bacteria the most characteristic groups are bacillus, bacterium, and a species of clostridium, a bottle-shaped bacillus. It is, however, difficult to draw a sharp line between so-called *species*.

Spiro-bacteria, or *spirilla*, possess short or long filaments, rigid or flexible, and their movements are accordingly rotatory, or in the long axis of the filaments. These bodies are again divided into comma bacilli, or vibrios—a name invented by the older microscopists who first described them—some species of which have a flagellate appendage, to which their movements are due.

Anthrax, Splenic Fever, has been long known to be prevalent among cattle at certain seasons of the year, and is believed to originate from peculiar conditions of climate and soil. This view of splenic fever on microscopical examination proved an entire fallacy. Bollinger in 1872 discovered that the blood of the affected animal was still virulent after death, owing to the presence of the *spores* of the bacillus, and that the soil also became infected and impregnated by the disease germs wherever the fever first broke out. In 1877 Dr. Koch made a more careful investigation into the source of the disease, and was able to give a complete demonstration of the life-history of the splenic fever bacillus, and to offer definite proofs of its pathogenic properties. He pointed out that the rods grew in the blood and tissues by lengthening and by cross division. Further, that they not only grew into long leptothrix filaments but they produced enormous numbers of seeds or spores. He watched the fusion of the rods to the formation of spores and the sprouting of fresh rods. He furthermore inoculated a mouse, watched the effect through several generations, and fully demonstrated that in the blood and swollen spleen of the animal the same rods were always present. Pasteur and Paul Bret pursued the same course of investigations, which were always followed with precisely similar results. It was, however, principally due to the researches of Koch that the doctrine of *contagium vivum* was placed on a scientific basis.

Subsequently Koch formulated methods of cultivation, and dictated the microscopical apparatus needful. Furthermore, he furnished postulates for proving beyond doubt the existence of specific pathogenic micro-organisms.

"The chain of evidence regarded by Dr. Koch as essential for proving the existence of a pathogenic organism is as follows:—1. The micro-organism must be found in the blood, lymph, or diseased tissue of man or animal suffering from, or dead of the disease. 2. The micro-organism must be isolated from the blood or tissue, and cultivated in suitable media—*i.e.*, outside the animal body. These pure cultivations must be carried on through successive generations of the organism. 3. Pure cultivation thus obtained must, when introduced into the body of a healthy animal, produce the disease in question. 4. In the inoculated animal the same micro-organism must again be found. The chain of evidence will be still more complete if, from artificial culture, a chemical substance is obtained capable of producing the disease quite independently of the living organism. It is not enough to merely detect, or even artificially cultivate, a bacterium associated with disease. An endeavour must be made to establish the exact relationship of the bacteria to disease processes. In many instances disease bacteria regarded as the actual contagia have been found, on a further searching inquiry, to be entirely misleading. It is almost needless to remind the enthusiast that the actual contagion of the disease must be fully demonstrated."

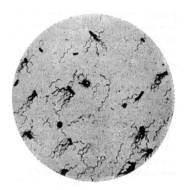

Fig. 269.—Micro-Photograph of Typhoid Fever Bacteria. Magnified 1000 ×.
Taken by Leitz's oil immersion ½₁₂-inch ocular No. 4, and sunlight exposure
of one minute.

Typhoid Bacillus (Fig. 269).—Rods 1 to 3μ in length, and ·5 to ·8μ in breadth,
and threads. Spore-formation has not been observed, but the protoplasm
may be broken up, producing appearances which may be mistaken for
spores. Actively motile, provided, some with a single and others with very
numerous flagella, which are from three to five times as long as the bacillus
itself. They stain readily in aqueous solutions of aniline dyes; and grow rapidly
at a temperature of about 60° Fahr. In plate cultivations minute colonies are
visible in thirty-six to forty-eight hours; they are circular or oval, with an
irregular margin. On agar they form a whitish transparent layer, and they
flourish in milk.

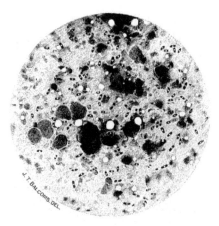

Fig. 270.—Plague Bacillus, Bombay, 1897. Magnified 1200 ×.

The Plague (Pestis Bacillus).—The Bombay plague of 1897-98 will ever be
remembered as one of the most appalling visitations ever known. The
number of deaths will never be accurately determined, as the native
population, among whom the disease chiefly prevailed and became so fatal,

concealed their dead or carried them away by night. The outbreak from the first proved to be most infectious, its incubation lasting from a few hours to a week only. It prevailed in all the over-crowded native quarters of the city. The rats and mice that infested the dwellings of the poor were found to be equally susceptible with human beings, and these vermin also died by hundreds. Those that survived left their holes and made off, in this way helping to spread the infective virus. On examining the bodies of dead rats, they were found to have swollen legs, the blood being filled by bacilli and curious monads, with whip-like appendages. The bacillus of plague was discovered by Kitasato in 1894; it is characterised by short rods with rounded ends, and a clear space in the middle. The bacilli stain readily with aniline dyes, and when cultivated on agar, white transparent colonies are formed which present an iridescent appearance when examined by reflected light. In addition to the bubonic swellings, the neighbouring lymphatic glands were also swollen and blocked by bacilli.

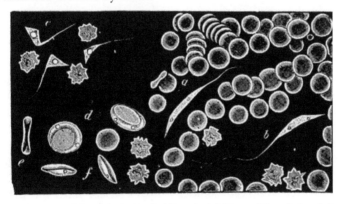

Fig. 271.—Monads in Rat's Blood, 1,200 ×. (Crookshank.)

a. Monad threading its way among the blood-corpuscles; *b*. Another with pendulum movement attached to a corpuscle; *c*. Angular forms; *d*. Encysted forms; *e* and *f*. The same seen edgeways.

My illustration (Fig. 270) is from a micro-photograph taken in 1897, when the death rate stood very high. The general distribution of the bacilli, together with phagocytes and the contents of swollen lymphatic glands, magnified 1,200 ×, is from a preparation made in hospital. The monads from the rat's blood, 1200 ×, seen threading their way among the blood corpuscles of a rat, and represented in Fig. 271, are somewhat larger than those found in the Bombay rats, but the flagella in the latter were quite as marked, while the encysted forms were wholly absent and the blood corpuscles less crenated. The white bodies (Fig. 270) were in some preparations, together with the lymphatic bodies, more numerous and more swollen.

With regard to the conditions of life of the bacteria, they may be divided broadly into two classes. When the organisms draw their nourishment from some living body or "host," they are known as "parasites." These are further termed "obligate" parasites if they exclusively live on their "host." If the bacteria draw their nourishment from dead organic matter, they are called "saprophytes." These are also divided into "obligate" and "facultative" saprophytes. Thus it will be apparent that a parasite under certain circumstances may readily become a saprophyte.

Some of the more important saprophytes are those organisms which play an important and useful part in our every-day life, such as, for instance, in the phenomena associated with fermentation, and putrefaction agents which transform dead and decomposing organic matter into their simpler elements, thus completing the great life cycle, and rendering the dead and effete matter again ready for the vital processes.

Among other life manifestations of certain bacteria may be mentioned those which have the property of generating colouring matter, though not chlorophyll. The bacteria themselves are colourless and transparent, and the pigment is merely formed as a product of their metabolism, especially under the influence of light. Many of the bacteria give rise to various gases and odours, particularly the anærobic organisms, which originate those foul putrefactive gases (ammonia, sulphuretted hydrogen, &c.). The blood-rain, *Micrococcus prodigiosus*, gives off an odour resembling trimethylamin. Micro-organisms have the property of producing various changes in the medium on which they are grown. In many cases albuminous bodies are peptonized and gelatine is liquefied. Many bacteria have the faculty of resolving organic bodies into their simplest elements; others, again, have the property of converting ammonia into nitric and nitrous acid. Certain microbes have the property of becoming phosphorescent in the dark. These phosphorescent bacteria are often seen on decaying plants and wood; sometimes in tropical climates the sea becomes luminous owing to the presence of countless numbers of these organisms. Again, they are frequently seen on the surface of dead fish, particularly mackerel, which often become so bright as to strongly illuminate the cupboard in which they lie.

The particular class of fungi that produce disease in man and the higher animals are generally known as "pathogenic." These pathogenic organisms may exert their pernicious power in several ways. They may be injurious on account of their abstracting nourishment from the blood or tissues, or for the purely mechanical reason of their stopping up the minute capillaries and blood-vessels by their excessive multiplication. But the poisonous action of most of the pathogenic bacteria is due to the chemical products secreted by the organisms, and it is to the circulation and absorption within the body of these poisons that the disturbances of the animal system, which characterise disease, decay, and dissolution of every organism, must be traced.

Parasitic Diseases of Plants.

The subject of fungoid diseases and fungus epidemics are of worldwide interest, if only because of the annual losses to agriculturists from parasitic diseases of plants, amounting to millions of pounds sterling. The history of wheat-rust, and that of oats and rye, each equally susceptible to the ravages of the same Rufus, can be traced back to Genesis. A description of it was given in 1805 by Sir Joseph Banks. He suggested that the germs entered the stomata, and he warned farmers against the use of *rusted* litter, and made important experiments on the sowing of rusted wheat-grains. A great discussion on the barberry question followed, Fries particularly insisting on the difference between *Æcidium berberidis* and *Puccinia graminis*. Tulasne confirmed the statement made by Henslow that the uredo and puccinia stages belong to the same fungus, and are not mixed species. De Bary's investigations in 1860-64 proved that the *sporidia* of some Uredinieæ (*e.g.,* *Coleosporium*) will not infect the plant which bears the spores, and that the æcidia of certain other forms are stages in the life-history of species of Uromyces and Puccinia. Furthermore, De Bary in 1864 attacked the question of wheat rust, and by means of numerous sowings of the telentospores on barberry proved that they bring about the infection.

This led to the discovery of the phenomenon of *Heterœcism* (colonisation), introducing a new idea, and clearing up many difficulties. In 1890 the rust question entered on a new phase: it was taken up by men of science all over the world, and active inquiries were set on foot. The result has been the confirmation of De Bary's results, but with the further discovery that our four common cereals are attacked by no less than ten different forms of rust belonging to five separate species or "form species," and with several physiological varieties, capable of turning the table upon the barberry by infecting it. Some of these are found to be strictly confined to one or other of the four common cereals, infecting two or more of them, while others can infect various kinds of our common wild grasses.

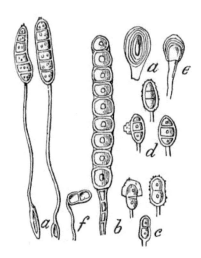

Fig. 272.—*Puccinia*, displaying *uredospores* and *telentospores*.

a. Aregma speciosum; b. Xenodochus paradoxus; c. P. Amorphæ; d. Triphæmium dubens; e. Younger spores; *f. P. lateripes;* magnified 450 diameters.

The fact is, that what has usually gone by the name of *Puccinia graminis* is an aggregate of several species, and that varietal forms of this exist so especially adapted to the host, that, although no morphical differences can be detected between them, they cannot be transferred from one cereal to another, pointing to physiological variations of a kind met with among bacteria and yeasts, but hitherto unsuspected in these higher parasitic fungi. It now appears we must be prepared for similar specialisation of varietal forms among Ustilagineæ as well as among Uredineæ.

Moreover, it has been found that different sorts of wheat, oats, barley, and rye are susceptible to their particular rusts in different degrees, at the bottom of which, it is suggested, there must be some complex physiological causes. De Bary gave proof, in 1886, that Peziza (Plate I., Nos. 1, 4, 5, 6) succeeds in becoming parasitic only after *saprophytic* culture to a strong mycelium, and that its form is altered thereby—probably by the excretion of a poison. Professor Marshall Ward showed that similar results took place in the case of the lily disease. Reinhardt, in 1892, showed that the apical growth of a peziza is disturbed and interrupted if the culture solution is employed concentrated; and Büsgen, in 1893, showed that *Botrytis cinerea* excretes poison at the tips of the hyphæ, thus confirming Professor Ward's results with the lily disease in 1888, and of later years, that a similar excretion occurs in rust-fungus. He further found that the water contents of the infected plant exercises an influence, as in the case of *Botrytis* attacking chrysanthemums and other plants in the autumn, and that cold increases the germinating capacity of the spores.

Pfeiffer, in his work on "*Chemotaxis*," shows that bacteria will congregate in the neighbourhood of an algal cell evolving oxygen. He also found that many motile antherozoids, zoospores, bacteria, &c., when free to move in a liquid, are attracted towards a point whence a given chemical substance is diffusing. He was concerning himself less with the evolution of oxygen or movements of bacteria than with a fundamental question of stimulation to movement in general. He found the attractive power of different chemical substances vary with the organism, and that various other bodies beside oxygen attract bacteria—peptone, dextrose, potassium salts, &c.; that swarm spores of the fungus *Saprolegnia* are powerfully attracted towards the muscles of a fly's leg placed in the water in which they are swimming about; also, that in many cases where the hyphæ of fungi suddenly and sharply bend out of their original course to enter the body of a plant or animal, the cause of the bending lies in a powerful chemotropic action, due to the attraction of some substance escaping from the body. Professor Ward has seen zoospores of a *Pythium* suddenly dart out on to the cut surface of a bean-stem, and there fix themselves.

This will be better understood by referring to the course pursued by these bodies generally. When the spore of a parasitic fungus settles on a plant, it frequently behaves as follows:—The spore germinates and forms a slender tube of delicate consistency, blunt at the end, and containing colourless protoplasm, as shown, highly magnified in Fig. 272, and in Figs. 273 and 274 much less magnified. De Bary long ago showed that such a tube—the germinal-hypha—only grows for a short time along the surface of the organ, and its tip soon bends down and enters the plant, either through one of the stomata or by boring its way directly through the cell-walls. Professor Ward says these phenomena suggested to himself that the end of the tube is attracted in some way, and by some force which brings its tip out of the previous direction, and De Bary has suggested that this attraction is due to some chemical substance excreted by the host plant. It is remarkable with what ease the tube penetrates the cell-walls, and which Ward believes to be due to the solvent action of an enzyme, capable of dissolving cellulose.

"Miyoshi carried these observations a step further when, in 1894, he showed that if a leaf is injected with a substance such as ammonium-chloride, dextrine, or cane-sugar (all substances capable of exerting chemotropic attraction on fungus-hyphæ), and spores of a fungus which is *not parasitic* are then sown on it, the hyphæ of the fungus penetrate the stomata and behave exactly as if the fungus were a true parasite.

"So surprising a result lets in a flood of light on many known cases of fungi, which are, as a rule, *non*-parasitic, becoming so, in fact, only when the host plant is in an abnormal condition, *e.g.*, the entry of species of Botrytis into living tissues when the weather is cold and damp and the light dull; the entry of Mucor into various fruits, tomatoes, apples, pears, &c., when the hyphæ meet with a slight crack or wound, through which the juices are exposed. It is exceedingly probable that the rapid infection of potato leaves in damp weather in July is traceable not merely to the favouring effect of the moisture on the fungus, but that the state of super-saturation of the cell-walls of the potato leaf—the tissues of which are now unduly filled with water and dissolved sugars, &c., owing to the dull light and diminished transpiration— is the primary factor which determines the easy victory of the parasite, and, as Professor Ward suggested some time ago, that the suppressed life of Ustilagineæ in the stems of grasses is due to the want of particular carbo-hydrates in the vegetative tissues, but which are present in the grain. A year later Miyoshi carried proof to demonstration, and showed that a fungus-hypha is actually so attracted by substances on the other side of a membrane, and that its tip pierces the latter; for the hyphæ were made to grow through films of artificial cellulose, of collodion, of cellulose impregnated with paraffin, of parchment paper, and even the chitinous coat of an insect, simply by placing the intact films on gelatine impregnated with the attracting substance, and laying the spores on the opposite side of the membrane.

"Now this is obviously a point of the highest importance in the theory of parasitism and parasitic diseases, because it suggests at once that in the varying conditions of the cells, the contents of which are separated only by membranous walls from the fungus-hyphæ, whose entrance means ruin and destruction, there may be found circumstances which sometimes favour and sometimes disfavour the entrance of the hyphæ; and it is, at least, a remarkable fact that some of the substances which experiments prove to be highly attractive to such hyphæ—e.g., sugars, the sap of plums, phosphates, nitrates, &c.—are just the substances found in plants; and the discovery that the action depends upon the nature of the substance as well as on the kind of fungus, and is affected by its concentration, the temperature, and other circumstances, only confirms us in this idea."

Moreover, there is one other fact which it is important to notice, viz., that there are substances which repel instead of attract the hyphæ. Is it not, then, asks Professor Ward, natural to conclude that the differences in behaviour of different parasites towards different host-plants, and towards the same host-plant under different conditions, probably depend on the chemotropic irritability of the hyphæ towards the substance formed in the cells on the other side of the membranous cell-walls? And when, as often happens, the effusion of substances, such as the cells contain, to the exterior is facilitated by over-distension and super-saturation, or by actual wounds, we cannot be surprised at the consequences when a fungus, hitherto unable to enter the plant, suddenly does so. To this proposition my answer is emphatically in the affirmative, since in my investigations into the "fungus-foot disease"

("*Mycetoma*"), 1871, of India, the entry of the fungus was in almost every case shown to be through an abrasion of the skin or a direct open wound; the majority of the cases reported were among the agricultural classes. When, then, as often happens, the effusion of substances, such as the cells contain, to the exterior is facilitated by over-distension and super-saturation, or by actual wounds, we cannot be surprised at the consequences when a fungus, hitherto unable to enter the plant, suddenly does so. Nevertheless, it must be admitted that the knowledge gained of parasites does not satisfactorily account for epidemic visitations over large areas.

Habitat of Fungi and Moulds.

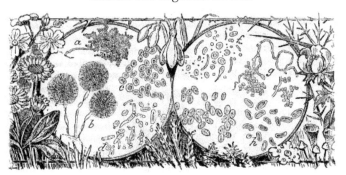

Fig. 273.—Fungi and Moulds.

Description of Figures.—*a.* Fungi Spores, taken in a sick chamber; *b.* *Aspergillus glaucus*; *c.* Yeast, recent state; *d.* Exhausted yeast, budding; *e.* Penicillium spores more highly magnified; *g.* Aerobic spores and mould mycelium; *h.* Aspergillus spore, grown on melon.

Habitat, Specialised Forms of Parasites.

Habitat.—The habitat of vegetable parasitic fungi is extremely variable. Fungi are found everywhere, living and flourishing on all the families of the vegetable and animal kingdoms. They attack our houses, foods, clothes, utensils of every kind, wall papers and books, the paste of which, to my astonishment, affords a sufficient supply of nourishment. Members of the parasitic tribe of bacteria, by a combined effort of countless myriads, have given rise to a sense of supernatural agency. *Bacillus prodigiosus*, described also as *Palmella mirifica* and *Zoogalactina imetropia*, from its attacking milk and other alimentary substances, the spores of which are often of a deep red colour, have been found to cover whole tracts of country in a single night with what is called a "*gory dew*," changing in daylight to a deep green colour. This was at one time regarded with superstitious awe as a miracle, as it has been known to attack bread and even the sacred wafer, and which in mediæval ages was described as the "bleeding-host." This parasitic plant belongs to anærobic bacteria, and is only developed in the dark. The nitrogen required for nutrition must be derived from the air. An algal form gives rise to the red scum seen in ponds and reservoirs in the autumn. The discharge from wounds is coloured blue by *Bacterium pyocyanine*. There are many other forms, some of which have an orange colour, and the genus is recognised as "*chromogenic microbes.*"

Fig. 274.—Fungi and Moulds.

Description of Figures.—*d. Puccinia graminis* on wheat; *c.* Polycystis spore of rye-smut; *f.* Alder fungus spores, *Microspheria penicellula*; *g. Dactylium roseum*, rose-coloured mould; *h. Verticillium distans*, whorled mould found on herbaceous plants; *i. Botrytis*, vine and lily fungus; *j, j'. Peronospora infestans*, potato fungus; *k. P. gangliformis*, mould of herbaceous plants; *l.* Various *Penicillium* and other spores taken in a bean-field.

A cryptogam belonging to anærobic bacteria, described as *Protococcus invalis*, on being set aside in a bottle, and a little rain water added, was seen to set up spontaneous fermentation, and in a very short time exhibited remarkable activity. The colour of the infusion changed, it assumed a delicate pink hue in direct light, which deepened to a red in reflected light. The fluid contents were now observed to be dichoric, and the spectroscopic appearance subsequently presented was one of much interest. The spectrum was a well-marked one, and might be taken to determine the presence of a nitrogenous element or of glucose.

Among all the various plants known to suffer from the attacks of parasites, the vine has been the greatest sufferer. The oïdium, or *Erysiphe Tuckeri*, so called from the name of the discoverer by whom it was first described, has been longest known to the vine grower. This really belongs to the group Ascomycetes, and appears to have been brought from America in 1845, whence it was passed on to France, where it soon threatened to entirely destroy the vineyards. This was followed by another parasite, belonging in this instance to the animal kingdom, *Phylloxera vastatrix*. This oïdium appears on the grape in the form of greyish filaments, terminating in an enlarged head, which contains an agglomeration of spores, not free or in a chaplet, as in Aspergillus (Fig. 273). These spores when ripe burst from the capsule as fine dust, and are diffused by the air in all directions, thus spreading the disease far and away. Another of the parasitic moulds, *Peronospora viticola*, is a kind of mildew, differing from oïdium. The hyphæ penetrate more deeply than that of oïdium. On the upper surface of the leaf brown patches appear; these branch out and ramify as seen in the potato-fungus, *P. infestans* (Fig. 274). The parasite destroys the tissue of the leaf, and it withers and dies. There are other well-known parasites, the black-rot, *Phomauvicola*, belonging to the Ascomycetes. This appears in early shoots in the form of round black spots, and gradually spreads over leaves and young fruit. This same rot, one year, devastated the American vineyards.

Fig. 275.—Fungi, Moulds.

a. Clustered Spores, *Gonatobotrys simplex*; *b.* Spore of *Puccinia coronata*, the mildew of grapes; *c.* Barley smut; *d. Puccinia althœa*; *e. Penicillium glaucum*; *m. Ixodes farinæ*, found in damaged flour together with smut.

Cereals, wheats and grasses, suffer from other well-known forms of microscopic fungi termed *rusts* and *smuts*, which cover the blades or infect the full ear of the fruit. The name given indicates their colour, and these belong, for the most part, to the genus Uredo and the family of the Basidiomycetes. They have no endogenous spores but as many as four forms of exogenous. This is also the case with wheat and barley, whereby they are distinguished as *Uredo* or *Puccinia graminis* (see Figs. 273 and 274, and Plate I., Nos. 19 and 22, *Æcidium berberidis*). For a long time it was believed that *Uredo linearis* and *Puccinia graminis* were so many distinct species, but it is now known that there are only three successive phases of the developmental stages of a single species—that, as a matter of fact, puccinia presents the phenomenon of alternation of generations, that is, that the complete development of the fungus is only effected by its transference from one plant to another. Other uredines, Ustilago and Tilletia smuts, are more apt to affect the ears of wheat, rye, and other grasses than puccinia. Bread made from wheat affected by smut has an acrid and bitter taste, while that made from rye flour often produces a serious form of disease. The propagation of either, then, should be stopped as quickly as possible by destroying all barberry bushes growing near or within the vicinity of corn fields, and by other means. The ergot of rye is due to distinct species of fungi having endogenous spores enclosed in a sac or *ascus*, hence the name of the family, Ascomycetes or *Tuberaceæ*, which are reproduced by the spores contained in these asci. Truffles belong to this family. But other members of the same family have several forms of spores, and these again present us with the phenomenon of alternation of generations.

Fig. 276.—Fungi, Moulds.

p. Spores of *Tilletia caries*; *q.* Spores of *Tilletia caries*, when germinating, produce a fœtid olive-coloured spore in cereal grains; *r.* Telentospores of *Puccinia graminis*; *s. Crystopus candidus*, spores growing in chains; *t. Petronospora infestans*, mildew of turnips, &c.; *u.* A transverse section of ergot of rye, showing spores in masses; *v. Claviceps purpuræ*, associated with ergoted rye.

Ergot of rye is used in medicine, but if not used with care it will produce a dangerous disease. This parasitic fungi consists of minute microscopic masses of spores, which cover the young flower of the rye with a white flocculent mass, formerly termed *sphacelium*. The mycelium formed spreads over the ear of corn in thick felt-like masses, termed *sclerotis*. The sphacelium changes its form in the following spring. Other changes are brought about, and it seems to pass through a cycle of alternations of generations.

Bread made from rye so infested is known to produce grave consequences, soon to become fatal if not detected in time. The disease is termed ergotism, and gangrene of the extremities takes place among people of the north of France and Russia, who consume bread made from rye flour. Ergot of maize will also cause similar diseases. Fowls and other animals fed upon this cereal become in a short time poisoned, and the cause of death is not rightly suspected. There is another fungus belonging to the same group of Ascomycetes, known as *Eurotium repens*, which appears upon leather when left in a damp place, and also upon vegetable or animal substances if badly preserved, and gradually destroys it. This mould is of a darkish green colour.

The minute spores display themselves as rows of beads when fully ripe on the erect mycelium. *Aspergillus glaucus* represents the white exogenous spores of the sphacelium of the ergot of rye; and those subsequently produced in the yellow balls correspond with the asci developed in sclerotis, the endogenous species. Many of the parasitic species belonging to the genera *Erysiphe, Sphæria, Sordaria, Penicillium,* &c., have a similar mode of propagation, and affect a large number of plants.

Parasitic Fungi of Men and Animals.

In the microscopical examinations especially given to the elucidation of parasitic diseases of the skin, previously referred to, I discovered more varieties of spores and filaments of certain cryptogamic plants associated with a larger number of specific forms of fungi than any previous observer. I did not, however, feel justified in concluding, with Küchenmeister, Schœnlein, and Robin, that these fungoid growths were the primary cause of the diseases referred to. Indeed, the foremost dermatologists of the period utterly refused to entertain the specific germ theory of the German investigators. Nevertheless, I contended, "the universality of their distribution is in itself a fact of very considerable importance, and one pointing to the belief that they are scavengers ever ready to fasten on decaying matter, and, on finding a suitable soil, spread out their invisible filaments in every direction in so persistent a manner as to arrest growth and overwhelm the plant in destruction."[53]

Special forms of fungi are given in Plate I., Nos. 10-14, and those of the ascomycetes in Nos. 17-21.

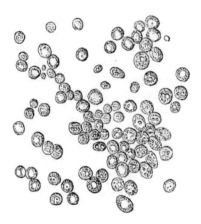

Fig. 277.—Healthy fresh Yeast, from a large Brewery, in an active stage of formation, × 400.

Oïdium albicans affects both animals and plants. It often attacks the mucous membrane of the mouths of young children. The spores become elongated and converted into hyphæ, and ramify about in all directions, producing a troublesome form of disease. This parasitic fungus is better known under another name, *Saccharomyces mycoderma*. Oïdium resemble algæ in their mode of life, as they are mostly found in a liquid media. The structure of all ferments is very simple: each plant is composed of a single cell, either of a spherical, elliptical, or cylindrical form, varying in size, and filled with protoplasmic and nucleated matter. This grows, and is seen to bud out and divide into two or more parts, all resembling the mother cell.

Fig. 277 represents the healthy cells of yeast, *Saccharomyces cerevisiæ*, freshly taken from a brewer's vat, and in an active stage of growth. The mode of multiplication continues as long as the plant remains in a liquid favourable to its nutrition.

The changes from one stage to another are rapid, as will be noticed on reference to the consecutive formative processes the cells are known to pass through, Fig. 278 (1859).

If the development of the plant is arrested by want of a saccharine or nitrogenous substance, and the liquid dries up, the protoplasm contained in the cell contracts, and the spores, or endogenous reproductive organs, of the plant will remain in a state of rest, become perfectly dry, and yet retain life. They are not easily killed, even when subjected to a very high or low temperature, they do not lose the power of germination when favourable conditions present themselves, and at once take on a new birth.

There are, however, many other ferments besides that of beer-yeasts, such as alcoholic and wine ferments, the commonest of which, according to Pasteur, is *Saccharomyces ellipsoideus*.

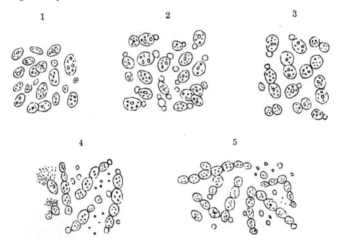

Fig. 278.—Development of Yeast Cells.

1. When first taken; 2. One hour after introducing a few cells into sweet-wort; 3. Three hours after; 4. Eight hours; 5. Forty-eight hours, when the cells become elongated.

But yeast-fungi and mould-fungi, like bacteria or fission-fungi, are micro-organisms, belonging to two specific orders, the Saccharomycetes and the Hyphomycetes, which are intimately related to each other, but quite distinct from bacteria. Their germs occur widely distributed in air, soil, and water. Many species are of hygienic, while others are of pathological interest and importance in being either accidentally associated with, or the cause of, disease processes, while others are fermentations of very essential service in various industrial processes. The making of beers, wines, and spirits, as we understand them, constitutes but a small part of the province of fermentation. The life activities of ferments open out a study of vast importance to mankind, and while they have only been regarded in their worst aspect—that of a bane—they are, nevertheless, a boon to mankind. The first clear view we obtained of this was that of Reess, who in 1870 showed there were several species or forms of the yeast-fungus. Hansen followed up this discovery in 1883, and, taking advantage of the strict methods of culture introduced by bacteriologists, found that by cultivating yeast on a solid media from a single spore it was quite possible to obtain constant types of pure yeasts, each possessing its own peculiar properties. One consequence of Hansen's labours was that it now became possible for every brewer to work with a yeast of uniform type instead of with haphazard mixtures, in which serious disease forms might predominate and injure the beer. Among other things made clear was that a true yeast may have a mycelial stage of development. Furthermore, there is the influence exercised by the nucleus of the yeast cell. Many other points of interest arose out of these investigations; one was, that many higher fungi can assume a yeast-like stage of development if submerged in fluids, as, for instance, various species of Mucor, Ustilago, Exoascus, and numerous others. Ascomycetes, and Basidiomycetes as well, are known to form budding cells, and it was thought that the yeasts of alcoholic fermentation are merely reduced forms of these higher fungi, which have become habituated to the budding condition—a conclusion supported by Hansen's discovery that a true Saccharomyces can develop a feeble, but a true, mycelium.

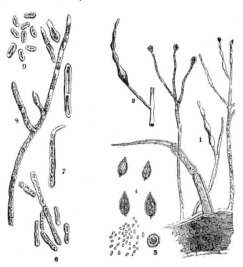

Fig. 279.—Saccharomyces and Moulds.

1. Section from a tomato, showing spores growing from cuticle; 2. Portion detached to show budding-out process; 3. Lateral view of spore sac with oospores issuing forth; 4. Apiculated ferment spores; 6 and 7. *Mycoderma cerivisiæ* in different stages of growth, as seen on wine bottles; 8 and 9. *Torulæ diabeticæ*, torulæ and fission spores.

"This view has been entirely confirmed by an inquiry into the mode of brewing *saké* by the Japanese, by the aid of the Aspergillus fungus. Further researches established the fact that other forms of fungi, *e.g.*, those on the surface of fruits, developed endogenous spores, which cause alcoholic fermentation. More recently, and by further experimental inquiry, partly by pure cultures of separate forms, and partly by well-devised cultures on ripening fruits still attached to the plant but imprisoned in sterilised glass vessels, it has been found that yeast and moulds are separate forms, not genetically connected, but merely associated in nature, as are so many other forms of yeasts, bacteria, and moulds. Further, Hansen has discovered that several yeasts furnish quite distinct races or varieties in different breweries in various parts of the world, so that we cannot avoid the conclusion that their race characteristics have been impressed on the cells by the continued action of the conditions of culture to which they have so long been exposed—they are, in fact, domesticated races."

The environments of yeasts are peculiar. Sauer found that a given variety of yeast, whose activity is normally inhibited when the alcohol attains a certain degree of concentration in the liquid, can be induced to go on fermenting until a higher degree is attained by the addition of a certain lactic acid bacterium. The latter, indeed, appears to prepare the way for the yeast. It has been shown, also, that damage may be done to beers and wines by allowing plant germs to gain access with the yeast; there are, too, several forms of yeast that are inimical to the action of the required fermentation. Other researches show that associated yeasts may ferment better than any single yeast, and such symbiotic action of two yeasts of high fermenting power has given better results than either alone. English ginger-beer furnishes a curious symbiotic association of two organisms—a true yeast and a true bacterium—so closely united that the yeast cells become imprisoned in the gelatinous meshes of the bacterium; and it is a curious fact that this symbiotic union of yeast and bacterium ferments is far more energetic than either when used alone, and the product is different, large quantities of lactic and carbonic acids being formed, and little or no alcohol.

Many years ago I gave an account of similar curious symbiotic results obtained by introducing into a wort-infusion a small proportion of *German yeast*, an artificial product composed of honey, malt, and a certain proportion of spontaneously-fermented wheat flour. This, to my astonishment, produced ten per cent. more alcohol than any of its congeners, and did not so soon exhaust itself as brewer's yeast.[54]

In the hephir used in Europe for fermenting milk, another symbiotic association of yeast and a bacterium, it is seen that in this process no less than four distinct organisms are concerned. I have already instanced the fermentation of rice to produce saké, which is first acted upon by an Aspergillus that converts the starch into sugar and an associated yeast, and this is also shown to be a distinct fungus, symbiotically associated in the conversion. "Starting, then, from the fact that the constitution of the medium profoundly affects the physiological action of the fungus, there can be nothing surprising in the discovery that the fungus is more active in a medium which has been favourably altered by an associated organism, whether the latter aids the fungus by directly altering the medium, or by ridding it of products of excretion, or by adding gaseous or other body. It is not difficult to see, then, that natural selection will aid in the perpetuation of the symbiosis, and in cases like that of the ginger-beer plant it is extremely difficult to get the two organisms apart, a difficulty similar to that in the case of the soredia of lichens."

Buchner discovered that by means of extreme pressure a something can be extracted from yeast which at once decomposes sugar into alcohol and carbon-dioxide. This something is regarded as a kind of incomplete protoplasm—a body, as we have already seen, composed of proteid—and in a structural condition somewhere between that of true soluble enzymes like invertin and a complete living protoplasm. This reminds me of an older experiment of mine, the immediate conversion of cane-sugar into grape-sugar. If we take two parts of white sugar and rub it up in a mortar with one part of a perfectly dry solid, the German yeast before spoken of, it is immediately transformed as if by magic into a flowing liquid mass—a syrup. This process of forming "invert sugar" can be watched under the microscope; the liberation of carbonic acid gas in large bubbles is seen to go on simultaneously with the assimilation of the dextrose, and the breaking up of the crystals of sugar; the cell at the same time increasing in size as well as in refractive power; a curious state of activity appears to be going on in the small mass, which is very interesting to watch throughout.

However, the enzymes of Buchner are probably bits off the protoplasm, as it were, and so the essentials of the theory of fermentation remain, the immediate agent being not that of protoplasm itself, but of something made by or broken off from it. Enzymes, or similar bodies, are known to be very common in plants, and the suspicion that fungi do much work with their aid is abundantly confirmed. It seems, indeed, that there are a whole series of these bodies which have the power of carrying over oxygen to other bodies, and so bringing about oxidations of a peculiar character. These curious enzymes were first observed owing to studies on the changes which wine and plant juice undergo when exposed to the action of the oxygen of the air.

The browning of cut apples is known to be due to the action of an oxydase, that is, an oxygen carrying ferment, and the same is claimed for the deep colouring of certain lacs obtained from the juice of plants, such as Anacardiaceæ, which are pale and transparent when fresh drawn, but which gradually darken in colour on exposure to the air. Oxydases have been isolated from beets, dahlia, potato-tubers, and several other plants. This fact explains a phenomenon known to botanists, and partly explained by Schönbein as far back as 1868, that if certain fungi (*e.g.*, *Boletus beridies*) are broken or bruised, the yellow or white flesh at once turns blue; this action is now traced to the presence in the cell sap of an oxydase.

It is the diastatic activity of Aspergillus which is utilised in the making of saké from rice, and in the preparation of soy from the soja bean in Japan. Katz has recently tested the diastatic activity of Aspergillus, of Penicillium, and of *Bacterium megatherium*, in the presence of large and small quantities of sugar, and found all are able to produce not only diastase, but also other enzymes; as the sugar accumulates the diastase formed diminishes, whereas the accumulation of other carbo-hydrates produces no such effect. Harting's investigation on the destruction of timber by fungi derives new interest from the discovery of an emulsion-like enzyme in many such wood-destroying forms, which splits up glucosides, amygdalin, and other substances into sugar, and that hyphæ feed on other carbo-hydrates. The fact, also, that Aspergillus can form inverts of the sucrase and maltase types, as well as emulsin, inulate, and diastase, according to circumstances of nutrition, will explain why this fungus can grow on almost any organic substance it may happen to alight upon. The secretion of special enzymes by fungi has a further interest just now, for recent investigations promise to bring us much nearer to an understanding of the phenomena of parasitism than it was possible when I was at work upon them some forty or fifty years ago.

It was De Bary who impelled botanists to abandon older methods, and he who laid the foundation of modern mycology. Later on he pointed out that when the infecting germinal tube of a fungus enters a plant-cell, two phenomena must be taken into account, the penetration of the cell-walls and tissues, and the attraction which causes the tips of the growing hypha to face and penetrate these obstacles, instead of gliding over them in the lines of apparent least resistance. The further development of these two factors shows that in the successful attack of a parasitic plant on its victim or host these fungi can excrete cellulose-dissolving enzymes, and that they have the power of destroying lignine. Zopf has also furnished examples of fungi which can consume fats. There is, however, one other connection in which these observations on enzymes in the plant-cell promise to be of considerable importance, viz., the remarkable action of certain rays of the solar light on bacteria. It has been known for some time past that if bacteria in a nutrient liquid are exposed to sunlight they quickly die. The further researches of Professor Marshall Ward and other workers in the same direction have brought out the fact that it is really the light rays, and not high temperatures, that it is especially the blue-violet and ultra-violet rays, which exert the most effective bactericidal action. This proof depended upon the production of actual photographs in bacteria of the spectrum itself. Apart from this, the Professor demonstrated that just such spores as those of anthrax, at the same time pathogenic and highly resistant to heat, succumb soonest to the action of these cold light-rays, and that under conditions which preclude their being poisoned by a liquid bath. It is in all probability the action of these rays of light upon the enzymes, which abound in the bacterial cells, that bring about their death.

The sun, then, is seen to be our most powerful scavenger, and this apparently receives confirmation in connection with Martinaud's observations, that the yeasts necessary for wine-making are deficient in numbers and power on grapes exposed to intense light, and to this is due that better results are obtained in central France as contrasted with those in the south. "When we reflect, then, that the nature of parasitic fungi, the actual demonstration of infection by a fungus spore, the transmission of germs by water and air, the meaning and significance of polymorphism, heteræcism, symbiosis, had already been rendered clear in the case of fungi, and that it was by these studies in fermentation, and in the life-history of the fungus Saccharomyces, that the way was prepared for the ætiology of bacterial diseases in animals, there should be no doubt as to the mutual bearings of these matters."

Industrial uses of Fungi and Saccharomycetes.

There are many industrial processes which are more or less dependent for success on bacterial fermentations. The subject is young, but the results already obtained are seen to be of immense importance from a scientific point of view, and to open up vistas of practical application already being taken advantage of in commerce, while problems are continually being raised by the forester, the agriculturist, the gardener, the dairyman, the brewer, dyer, tanner, and with regard to various industries, which will eventually confer great advantages in their economic application.

The remarkable discovery made by Alvarez of the bacillus, which converts a sterilised decoction of the indigo plant into indigo sugar and indigo white, the latter then oxidising to form the valuable blue dye, whereas the sterile decoction itself, even in presence of oxygen, forms no indigo, plainly proves how these minute organisms may be turned to a good account. There are, however, important points to be determined as to the action of the fermentation brought about by these enzymes, and the appearance of certain mysterious diseases in the indigo vats. Again, certain stages in the preparation of tea and tobacco leaves are found to depend upon very carefully regulated fermentations, which must be stopped at the right moment, or the product will be spoilt. Regarding the possible *rôle* of bacteria, the West Indian tobacco has a special bacterium, which has been isolated and found to play a very important part in its flavour. Every botanist knows that flax and hemp are the best fibres of Linum and Cannabis respectively, separated by steeping in water until the middle lamella is destroyed and the fibres isolated; but it is not so well known that *not every water* is suitable for this "retting" or steeping process; and for a long time this was as much a mystery as why some waters are so much better than others for brewing. Quite recently Fribes has succeeded in isolating the bacillus upon which the dissolution of the middle lamella depends. This investigation brought out other interesting details as to the reaction produced by living micro-organisms, and which can be utilised in deciding questions of plant chemistry too subtile for testing with ordinary re-agents. One other important fact connected with these researches is that botanists have now discarded the view that the middle lamella of the plants referred to is composed of cellulose, and know that it consists of pectin compounds. Fribes' anærobic bacillus is found to dissolve and destroy pectins and pectinates, but does not touch cellulose or gum. It is well known that the steeping of skins in water in preparation for tanning involves bacterial action, owing to which the hair and epidermal coverings are removed, but it also appears that in the process of swelling the limed skins, the gases evolved in the substance of the tissues, and the evolution of which causes the swelling and loosens the fibre so that the tanning solutions may penetrate, are due to a particular fermentation caused by a bacterium, which, according to some investigators, is identical with a lactic ferment introduced by the pine bark, and which is responsible for the advantageous acidification of the tanning solutions.

Hay is made in different ways, and in those where a "spontaneous" heating process is resorted to the fermentation is no doubt dependent upon the presence of thermogenic bacteria. But probably no other subject has attained to so much importance as the bacteriology of the dairy: the study of the bacteria found in milk, butter, and cheese in their various forms.

Of milk, especially, much has been written and said as a disease-transmitting medium, and with every good reason, and, if the statement of a Continental authority may be accepted that each time we eat a slice of bread and butter we devour a number of bacteria equal to the population of Europe, we have sure grounds for seeking for further information as to what these bacteria are and what they are doing. And similarly so with cheese, which teems with millions of these minute organisms.

"Some few years ago it was found that the peculiar aroma of butter was due to a bacterium. There are two species of bacteria, one of which develops an exquisite flavour and aroma, but the butter keeps badly, while the other develops less aroma, but the butter keeps better. In America, however, they have isolated and distributed pure cultures of a particular butter bacillus which develops the famous 'June' flavour, hitherto only met with in the butter made in a certain district during a short season of the year. This fine-flavoured butter is now constantly manufactured in a hundred American dairies; and the manufacture of pure butter with a constant flavour has become a matter of certainty.

"Properly considered, the manufacture of cheese is a form of 'microscopic gardening' even more complex and more horticultural in nature than the brewing of beer. From the first moment, when the cheesemaker guards and cools his milk, till his stock is ready he is doing his best to keep down the growth of micro-organisms rushing about to take possession of his milk. He therefore coagulates it with rennet—an enzyme of animals, but also, as we have seen, common in plants—and the curd thus prepared is simply treated as a medium, on which he grows certain fungi and bacteria, with every needed precaution for favouring their development, and protecting them against the inroads of other pests and against unsuitable temperature, moisture, and access of light. Having succeeded in growing the right kind of plants on his curd, his art then demands that he shall stop their growth at the critical moment, and his cheese is ready for market.

"Furthermore, the particular flavour and peculiar odours of cheeses, as Camembert, Stilton, and Roquefort, have to be obtained, and this is secured, for instance, by cultivating a certain fungus, Penicillium, on bread, and purposely adding it to Roquefort. This is found to destroy the lactic and other acids, and so enables certain bacteria in the cheese to set to work and further change the medium; whereas in another kind of cheese the object is to prevent this fungus paving the way for these bacteria. Another kind of bacillus has been discovered which gives a peculiar clover aroma to certain cheeses.

"It is thought that more definite results will be obtained by the investigation of the manufacture of the vegetable cheeses of China and Japan, which are made by exposing the beans of the leguminous plant, *Glycine*—termed soja-beans—to bacterial fermentations in warm cellars with or without certain mould-fungi. Several kinds of bean-cheeses are made in this way, known by special names. They all depend upon the peculiar decompositions of the tissues of the cotyledons of the soja-beans, which contain 35 to 40 per cent. of proteids and quantities of fatty matter. The softened beans are first rendered mouldy, and the interpenetrating hyphæ render the contents accessible to certain bacteria, which peptonise and otherwise alter them. There is the further question of the manufacture of vinegar by fermentation, of the preparation of soy from a brine extract of mouldy and fermented soja-beans, of bread-making, and other equally interesting manufactures."

Results of De Bary's Investigations in Parasitism.

"When the idea of parasitism was rendered definite by the fundamental distinction drawn by De Bary between a *parasite* and a *saprophyte*, it soon became evident that some further distinction must be made between *obligate facultative* parasites and saprophytes respectively. De Bary, when he proposed these terms for adoption, was clearly alive to the existence of transitions which we now know to be numerous and so gradual in character that we can no longer define any such physiological groups. Twenty years ago penicillium and mucor would have been regarded as *saprophytes* of the most obligate type, but we now know that under certain circumstances these fungi can become parasites, and the borderland between facultative parasites and saprophytes on the one hand, and between the former and true parasites on the other, can no longer be recognised."

In 1866 the germ of an idea was sown which has taken root and extended. De Bary pointed out that in the case of lichens we have either a fungus parasite on an algæ, or else certain organisms hitherto accepted as algæ are merely incomplete forms.

"In 1879 the same observer definitely launched the new hypothesis of *symbiosis*. The word itself is due to Frank, who, in a valuable paper on the biology of the thallus of certain lichens, very clearly set forth the existence of various stages of life in common among all the lower forms of plants. The details of these matters are now principally of historical interest. We now know that lichens are dual organisms, composed of various algæ, symbiotic with Ascomycetes, with Basidiomycetes, and, as Massee has shown, even with Gastromycetes. The soil contains also bacterio-lichens. Hence arose a new biological idea—that a fungus may be in such nicely-balanced relationship with the host from which it derives its sustenance, that it may be attended with nearly equal advantage to both.

"In the humus of forests we find the roots of beeches and other Cupuliferæ (willows, pines, and so forth) clothed with a dense mantle of hyphæ, and swollen into fleshlike masses of mycorhiza. In similar soils, and in moorlands, which abound in the slowly decomposing root-fibres and other vegetable remains so characteristic of these soils, the roots of orchids, heaths, gentians, &c., are similarly provided with fungi, the hyphæ of which penetrate further into the tissues, and even send haustoria into the living cells, but without injuring them. As observations multiplied it became clear that the mycorhiza, or fungus-root, was not to be dismissed as a mere case of roots affected by parasites, but that a symbiotic union, comparable to that of the lichens, exists, and we must assume that both tree and fungus derive benefit from the connection.

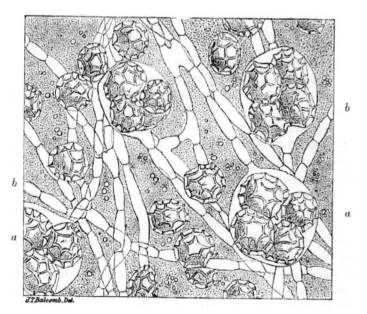

Fig. 280.—Fine Section through Truffle.

a. Asci filled with spores; *b.* Mycelia, × 250.

"Frank stated, as the result of his experimental research, that seedling forest-trees cannot be grown in sterilised soil, where their roots are prevented from forming mycorhiza; and he concluded that the fungus conveys organic materials to the roots, which it obtains by breaking down the leaf-mould and decaying plant remains, together with water and minerals from the soil, and plays the especial part of a nitrogen-catching apparatus. In return for this import service the root pays a tax to the fungus by sparing it certain of its tissue contents. It is a curious fact then that the mycorhiza is only formed where humus or vegetable mould abounds."

These instructive investigations offer an intelligible explanation of the growth of that well-known subterranean fungus, the truffle (*Tuber cibarium*), the microscopic appearances of a section of which formed the subject of a paper I contributed to "The Popular Science Review" some years ago (1862). The fungus, as will be seen by the fine section cut through a truffle, Fig. 280, consists of flocculent filaments, which in the first instance cover the ground at the fall of the leaf in autumn, under oak or beech trees, the hyphæ of which penetrate the ground, through the humid soil to the *root-hairs* of the tree. Filaments (mycelia) are again given off which terminate in asci or sacs filled with minute spores of about $\frac{1}{2500}$th of an inch in size, while the interspaces are filled up by mycelia, that become consolidated into a firm nut-like body.

What happens, then, is this: Trees and plants with normal roots and root-hairs, when growing in ordinary soil, can adapt their roots to life in a soil heavily charged with humus only by contracting symbiotic association with the fungus and paying the tax demanded by the latter in return for its supplies and services. If this adaptation is impossible, and no other suitable variation is evolved, such trees cannot grow in such soils. The physiological relations of the root to the fungus must be different in details in the case of non-green, purely saprophytic, plants, Neottia, Monotropa, &c., and in that of green plants like Erica, Fagus, and Pinus. It is, however, a well-known fact that ordinary green plants cannot utilize vegetable débris directly, and forest trees do so in appearance only, for the fungi, yeasts and bacteria there are actively decomposing the leaves and other remains. A class of pseudo-symbiotic organisms are, however, being brought into the foreground, where the combined action of two symbionts results in the death of or injury to a third plant, each symbiont alone proving harmless. Some time ago Vuillemin showed that a disease in olives results from the invasion of a bacillus (B. *oleæ*), which can, however, only obtain its way into the tissues through the passages driven by the hyphæ of a fungus (Chætophoma). The resulting injury is a sort of burr. This observer also observed the same bacillus and fungus in the canker burrs of the ash.

Among many similar cases well worth further attention are the invasion of potato-tubers by bacteria, these making their way down the decaying hyphæ of pioneer fungi. Professor Marshall Ward has seen tomatoes infected by similar means, and other facts show that many bacteria which quicken the rotting of wood are thus led into the tissues by fungi.

Probably no subject in the whole domain of cryptogamic botany has wider bearings on agricultural science than the study of the flora and changes on and in manure and soil. Nitrifying bacteria play a very important part by providing plant life with a most necessary food. They occur in the soil, and two kinds have been described—the one kind converting ammonia into nitrous acid, and the other changing nitrous into nitric acid. We are principally indebted to Winogradsky for our knowledge of these bacteria; he furnishes instances of the bearing of bacteriological work on this department of science, and explains, not only the origin of nitre-beds and deposits, but also the way the ammonia compounds fixed by the soil in the neighbourhood of the root-hairs are nitrified, and so rendered directly available to plant life. The investigations of other observers show that the nitrifying organism is a much more highly-developed and complex form than had been suspected; that it can be grown on various media, and that it exhibits considerable polymorphism—*i.e.*, it can be made to branch out and show other characteristics of a true fungus. "I have," writes Professor Ward, "for some time insisted on the fact that river water contains reduced forms of bacteria—*i.e.*, forms so altered by exposure to light, changes of temperature, and the low nutritive value of the water, that it is only after prolonged culture in richer food media that their true nature becomes apparent." Strutzer and Hartleb show that the morphological form of the nitrifying organism can be profoundly altered by just such variations of the conditions described by Ward, and that it occurs as a branched mycelial form; as bacilli or bacteria; or as cocci of various dimensions, according to the conditions.

"These observations, and others made on variations in form (polymorphism) in other fungi and bacteria, open out a vast field for further work, and must lead to advancement in our knowledge of these puzzling organisms; they also help us to explain many inconsistencies in the existing systems of classification of the so-called 'species' of bacteria as determined by test-tube culture."

Algæ.—The algals have a special charm for microscopists. I am free to confess my interest in these organisms, and for several reasons. In this humid climate of ours they are accessible during the greater part of the year; they can be found in any damp soil, in bog, moss, and in water—indeed, wherever the conditions for their existence seem to be at all favourable for development. Should the soil dry up for a time, when the rain returns algæ are seen to spring into life and give forth their dormant spores, which once more resume the circle of formation and propagation. In the earliest stage of development the spore or spore cell is so very small when in a desiccated state, that any number may be carried about by the slightest breath of air and borne away to a great distance. To all such organisms I originally gave the name of Ærozoa; now recognised as ærobic and anærobic organisms (Fig. 281).

Fig. 281.—Ærobic Spores × 200.

1. Ærobic fungi caught over a sewer; 2. Fragments of Penicillium spores; 3. Ærobic fungi taken in the time of the cholera visitation, 1854.

With reference to the ærobic bacteria I have only to add that in addition to the simple mode of taking them on glass slides smeared over with glycerine, special forms of æroscopes are now in use for the purpose, consisting of a small cylinder in which a current of air is produced by an aspirator and diffused through a glass vessel containing a sterilised fluid. These are in constant use in all bacteriological laboratories. The results obtained are transferred to sterilised flasks or tubes as those shown in a former chapter.

Miquel, who has given considerable attention to the subject of ærobic and anærobic bacteria, reckons that the number of spores that find their way into the human system by respiration, even should health be perfectly sound, may be estimated at 300,000 a day.

One of the most commonly met with forms of micro-organisms is *Leptothrix buccalis*. It chiefly finds its nutritive material in the interstices of the teeth, and is composed of short rods and tufted stems of vigorous growth, to which the name of *Bacillus subtilis* has been given (Fig. 282). Among numerous other fungoid bodies discovered in the mouth, Sarcinæ have been found. See Plate IX., No. 7.

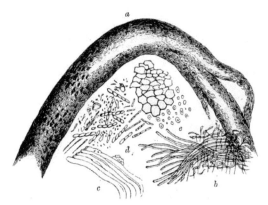

Fig. 282.—Section of the Mucous Membrane of the Mouth, × 350.

Showing: *a.* The denser connective tissue; *b.* Teased out tissue; *c.* Muscular fibre; *d. Leptothrix buccalis*, together with minute forms of bacteria and micrococci; *e.* Ascomycetes and starch granules.

The Beggiatoa, a sewage fungus, found by me in the river Lea water of 1884 growing in great profusion, consists chiefly of mycelial threads and a number of globular, highly refractive bodies, and may be regarded as evidence of the presence in the water of an abnormal amount of sulphates which set free a gas, sulphuretted hydrogen, of a dangerous and offensive character. Another curious body closely allied to *Beggiatoa alba* is Cladothrix; this assumes a whitish pellicle on the surface of putrefying liquids.

These saprophytes obtain nourishment from organic matter; nevertheless they are not true parasites in the first stage of their existence, during which they live freely in the water or in damp soil; they, however, become pathogenic parasites when they penetrate into the tissues of animals, and necessarily live at the expense of their host.

FUNGI, ALGÆ, LICHENS, ETC.

Tuffen West, del. Edmund Evans.

PLATE I.

Bacteria, as I have said, were for a long time classed with fungi under the name of Schizomycetes. But the more recent researches into their organisation, and more especially into their mode of reproduction, show that they rather more resemble a group of algæ devoid of chlorophyll. Zopf asserts that the same species of algals may at one time be presented in the form of a plant living freely in water, or in damp ground, in association with chlorophyllaceous protoplasm, and at another in the form of a bacterium devoid of green colouring matter, and receiving nourishment from organic substances previously elaborated by plants or animals, thus accommodating itself, according to circumstances, to two very different modes of existence.

That widely-distributed single-cell plant, the *Palmoglœa macrococca* of Kützing, that spreads itself as a green slime over damp stones, walls, and other bodies, affords an example. If a small portion be scraped off and placed on a slip of glass, and examined with a half or a quarter-inch power, it will be seen to consist of a number of ovoid cells, having a transparent structureless envelope, nearly filled by granular matter of a greenish colour. At certain periods this mass divides into two parts, and ultimately the cell becomes two. Sometimes the cells are united end to end, just as we see them united in the actively-growing yeast plant; but in this case the growth is accelerated, apparently, by cold and damp. Another plant belonging to the same species, the *Protococcus pluvialis*, is found in every pool of water, the spores of which must be always floating in the air, since they appear after every shower of rain.

Protococcus pluvialis is furnished with motile organs—two or more vibratile flagella passing through perforations in the cell-wall—whereby, at certain stages, they move rapidly about. The flagella are distinctly seen on the application of the smallest drop of iodine. The more remarkable of the several forms presented by the plant is that of naked spores, termed by Flotow *Hæmatococcus porphyrocephalus*. These minute bodies are usually seen to consist of green, red, and colourless granules in equal proportions, and occupying different portions of the cell. They seem to have some share in the after subdivision of the cell (Fig. 283). There are also *still*-cells, which sub-divide into two, while the motile cells divide into four or eight. It is not quite clear what becomes of the motile zoospores, B, but as they have been seen to become encysted, they doubtless have a special function, or become *still*-cells under certain circumstances.

It appears that both longitudinal and transverse division of the primordial cell takes place; and that the vibratile flagella of the parent cell retain to the last their function and their motion after the primordial cell has become detached and transformed into an independent secondary cell (Fig. 283, G).

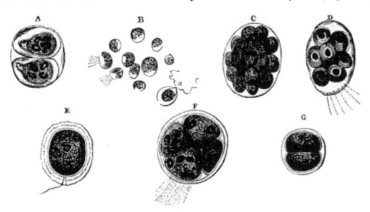

Fig. 283.—Cell Development. (*Protococcus pluvialis*.)

Protococcus pluvialis, Kützing. *Hæmatococcus pluvialis*, Flotow. *Chlamidococcus versatilis*, A. Braun. *Chlamidococcus pluvialis*, Flotow and Braun.

A. Division of a simple cell into two, each primordial vesicle having developed a cellulose envelope; B. Zoospores, having escaped from a cell; C. Division of an encysted cell into segments; D. Division of another cell, with vibratile flagella projecting through cell-wall; E. An encysted flagellate cell; F. Division of an encysted nucleated cell into four parts, with vibratile filaments projecting; G. Fission of a young cell.

The most striking of the vital phenomena presented by Protococcus is that of periodicity. Certain forms—for instance, encysted zoospores, of a certain colour, appear in a given infusion, at first exclusively, then they gradually diminish, become more and more rare, and finally disappear altogether. After some time their number again increases, and this may be repeated. Thus, a cell which at one time presented only still forms at another contained only motile ones. The same may be said with respect to segmentation. If a number of motile cells be transferred from a larger vessel into a smaller one, in the course of a few hours most of them will have subsided to the bottom, and in the course of the day observed to be on the point of sub-division. On the following morning division will have become completed; on the next day the bottom of the vessel will be found covered with a new generation of self-dividing cells, which, again, will produce another generation. This regularity, however, is not always observed. The influence of every change in the external conditions of life upon the plant is very remarkable. It is only necessary to pour water from a smaller into a larger or shallower vessel to at once induce segmentation of cells. The same phenomenon occurs in other algals; thus Vaucheria almost always develops zoospores at whatever time of year they may be brought from their natural habitat into a warm room. Light is conducive to the manifestation of vital action in the motile spores; they usually collect in great numbers on the surface of the water, and at that part exposed to the strongest light.

But in the act of propagation, on the contrary, and when about to pass into the still condition, the motile Protococcus cell seems to shun light, and falls to the bottom of the vessel. Too strong sunlight, as when concentrated by a lens, quickly kills the young zoospores. A temperature of undue elevation is injurious to the development of their vital activity and the formation of the zoospores. Frost destroys motile, but not still zoospores.[55]

Stephanosphæra pluvialis is a conspicuous variety of the fresh-water algals, described by Cohn. It consists of a cell containing eight primordial cells filled with chlorophyll, uniformly arranged (see Plate I., No. 24 *d*). The globular mother-cell rotates, somewhat in the same way as the volvox, by vibratile flagella, two of which are seen projecting from each cell and piercing the transparent outer cell wall. Every cell divides first into two, then four, and lastly eight cells, each one of which again divides into a number of micro-gonidia, which have a motion within the mother-cell, and ultimately escape from it. Under certain circumstances each of the eight young cells is observed to change places in the interior of the cell; eventually they escape, lose their flagella, form a thicker membrane as at *b*, and for a time remain motionless, and sink to the bottom of the vessel in which they are contained. If the vessel is permitted to become thoroughly dry, and then again has water poured into it, motile cells reappear; from which circumstance it is probable that these represent the resting spores of the plant. When in the condition of greatest activity its division into eight is perfected during the night, and early in the morning light the young cells escape and pass through similar changes. It is calculated that in eight days, under favourable circumstances, 16,777,216 families may be formed from one resting-cell of Stephanosphæra. In certain of the cells, and at particular periods, remarkable amœboid bodies (Plate I., No. 24 *c*) make their appearance. There is a marked difference between Stephanosphæra and Chlamydococcus, for while in the latter the individual portions of a primordial cell separate entirely from one another, each developing its own enveloping membrane, and ultimately escaping as a unicellular individual; in the former, on the other hand, the eight portions remain for a time living in companionship.

Volvocineæ.—A fresh-water unicellular plant of singular beauty and interest to the microscopist is the *Volvox globator* (Plate I., No. 15). No. 16 represents a portion of another cell, with brownish amœboid bodies enclosed in the protoplasmic web. It is common to our fresh-water pools, and attains a diameter of about $\frac{1}{20}$th or $\frac{1}{30}$th of an inch. Its movement is peculiar, a continued roll onwards, or a rotation like that of a top; at other times it glides along smoothly. When examined under a sufficiently high power, it is seen to be a hollow sphere, studded with green spots, and traversed by green threads connecting each of the spots or spores with the maternal cell. From each of the spores proceed two long flagella, lashing filaments, which keep the globular body on the move. After a time the sphere bursts, and the contained sporules issue forth and speedily pass through a similar stage of development. These interesting cells were long taken to be animal bodies. Ehrenberg described them as *Monads*, possessing a mouth, stomach, and an eye.

The setting free of the young volvox is essentially a process of cell division, occurring during the warmer periods of the year, and, as Professor Cohn shows, is a considerable advance upon the simpler conjugation of two smaller cells in desmids; it more closely resembles that which prevails among the higher algæ and a large number of cryptogams. As autumn advances the volvox spherules usually cease to multiply by the formation of zoosporanges, and certain of their ordinary cells begin to undergo changes by which they are converted, some into male or sperm-cells, others into germ-cells, but the greater number appear to remain sterile. Both kinds of cells at first so nearly resemble each other that it is only when the sperm cells begin to undergo sub-division that they are seen to be about three times the size of the sterile cells. Then the primary cell resolves itself into a cluster of peculiar secondary cells, each consisting of an elongated body containing an orange-coloured endochrome and a pair of long flagella, as seen in the antherozoids of the higher cryptogams. As the sperm-cells approach maturity the clusters may be seen to move within them; the bundles then separate and show an independent active movement while still within the cavity of the primary cell, and finally escape through a rupture in the cell-wall, rapidly diffusing themselves as they pass through the cavity. The germ-cells continue to increase in size without undergoing sub-division, at first showing large vacuoles in their protoplasm, but subsequently becoming filled with a darker coloured endochrome. The form of the cell also changes from its flask-like shape to the globular, and at the same time seems to acquire a firmer envelope. Over this the swarming antherozoids diffuse themselves and penetrate the substance to the interior, and are then lost to view. The product of this fusion, Cohn tells us, is a reproductive cell, or "oospore," which speedily becomes enveloped in another membrane with a thicker external coat, beset with conical-pointed processes; and now the chlorophyll of the young cell gives place, as in Palmoglæ, to starch and reddish or orange-coloured, and a more highly refractive, fluid. As many as forty of such oospores have been counted in a single sphere of volvox, which then acquires the peculiar appearance observed by Ehrenberg, and described by him under the name of *Volvox stellatus*. The further history of this wonderful spheroid unicellular plant has been traced out by Kirchner, who found that their germination commences in the early months of the year—in February—with the liberation of the spherical endospore from its envelope and its division into four cells. A remarkable phenomenon has been observed by Dr. Braxton Hicks—the conversion of an ordinary volvox cell into a moving mass of protoplasm that bears a striking resemblance to the well-known amœba. "Towards the end of the autumn the endochrome mass of the volvox increases to nearly double its ordinary size, but instead of undergoing the usual sub-division so as to produce a macrogonidium, it loses its colour and regularity of form, and becomes an irregular mass of colourless protoplasm, containing a number of brownish granules." The final change and the ultimate destination of these curious amœboid bodies have not been satisfactorily made out, but from other observations on the protoplasmic contents of the cells of the roots of mosses, which in the course of two hours become changed into ciliated bodies, it is believed that this is the mode in which these fragile structures are enabled to retain life and to resist all the external conditions, such as damp, dryness, and the alternations of heat and cold.

It would be quite impossible to deny the great similarity there is between the structure of volvox and that of the motile cell of *Protococcus pluvialis*. The influence of reagents will sometimes cause the connecting processes of the young cells, as in Protococcus, to be drawn back into the central mass, and the connecting threads are sometimes seen as double lines, or tubular prolongations of the membrane. At other times they appear to be connected by star-like prolongations to the parent cell (Plate I., No. 15), presenting an almost identical appearance with *Pediastrum pertusum*. Another body designated by Ehrenberg *Sphærosira volvox* is an ordinary volvox in a different stage of development; its only features of dissimilarity being that a large proportion of the green cells, instead of being single, are double or quadruple, and that the groups of flagellate cells form by their aggregation discoid bodies, each furnished with a single flagellum. These clusters separate themselves from the parent cell, and swim off freely under the forms which have been designated Uvella and Syncrypta by Ehrenberg. Mr. Henry Carter, F.R.S., who made a careful investigation of unicellular plants, described Sphærosira as the male, or spermatic form of *volvox*.

Among other organisms closely allied to volvox and included in Volvocineæ, affording the microscopist many interesting transitional forms in their various modes of fructification, are the Eudorina, still-water organisms that pass through a similar process of reproduction as the volvox. In the *Pandorina morum*, its reproduction is curiously intermediate between the lower and the higher types; as within each cell is a mulberry-like mass, composed of cells possessing a definite number of swarm spores, sixteen usually, which rupture the mother cell, and swim off furnished with a pair of flagella. A similar process takes place in some of the Confervaceæ and other fresh-water algæ. The Palmella, again, consist of (Plate I., No. 21) minute organisms of very simple structure, which grow either on damp surfaces or in fresh water. The stonework of some of our churches is often seen to be covered with a species of Palmella, that take the form of an indefinite slimy film. The "red snow" of Arctic or Alpine regions, considered to be a species of Protococcus, is frequently placed among Palmella. A more characteristic form of the *P. cruenta* is the *Hæmatococcus sanguinis*, the whole mass of which is sub-divided by partitions enclosing a larger or smaller number of cells, which diffuse their granular contents through the gelatinous mass in which their several changes take place. The albuminoid envelope of these masses is seen to contain parasitic growths, which have given rise to some discussion, especially when their filaments are observed to radiate in various directions.

The *Oscillariaceæ* constitute a genus of Confervaceæ which have always had very great interest for the microscopist in consequence of their very remarkable animal-like movements, and from which they derive their generic name. For more than a century these Bacillaria have excited the curiosity of all observers without any one having derived more than an approximate idea of their remarkable rhythmical movements. The frustule consists of a number of very fine short threads attached together by a gelatinous sheath, in one species all of equal length. Their backward and forward movement is of a most singular character; the only other conferva in which I have seen a motion of a similar kind is the Schizonema. In this species the frustules are packed together in regular series, the front and side views being always in the same direction. These several bodies move along within the filamentous sheath without leaving their respective places. On carefully following the movement, it is seen at first much extended, and then more compressed, while the frustules become more linear in their arrangement, and present a closer resemblance to *Bacillaria paradoxa*, augmented by the circumstance that the frustules are seen to move in both directions. A frustule of Schizonema can move independently of the sheath, and so will a detached frustule of bacillaria. This peculiar and exceptionally anomalous phenomenon as that of the movements of bacillaria can hardly be confined to a solitary species. The movements of the frustules are much accelerated by warmth and light. The longer filaments of other minute species only slightly exhibit any motion of the kind, but have peculiar undulating motions.

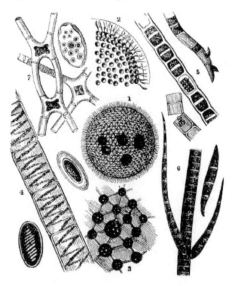

Fig. 284.—Confervaceæ.

1. *Volvox globator*; 2. A section of volvox, showing the flagellate margin of the cell; 3. A portion more highly magnified, to show the young volvocina, with their nuclei and thread-like attachments; 4. Spirogyra, near which are spores in different stages of development; 5. *Conferva floccosa*; 6. *Stigeoclonium*

protensum, jointed filaments and single zoospores; 7. *Staurocarpus gracilis*, conjugating filaments and spores.

Confervaceæ are a genus of algals. The species consist of unbranched filaments composed of cylindrical or moniliform cells, with starch granules. Many are vesicular, and all multiply by zoospores generated in the interior of the plant at the expense of the granular matter. They are, for the most part, found in fresh water attached or floating, some in salt water, and a few in both, in colour usually green, but occasionally olive, violet, and red. The Confervaceæ proper are often divided into four families: 1. *Hydrodictidæ*; 2. *Zygnemidæ*; 3. *Confervidæ*; 4. *Chætophoridæ*. To the microscopist all the plants of this genera are extremely interesting as subjects for the study of cell multiplication. The process usually takes place in the terminal cell, the first step in which is the division of the endochrome, and then follows a sort of hour-glass contraction across the cavity of the parent cell, whereby it is divided into two equal parts. This is better seen in some of the desmids than in Fig. 284, Nos. 4, 5, and 6. Some species are characterised by a different mode of reproduction; these possess a number of nuclei, and multiply by zoospores of two kinds, the largest of which have either two or four cilia, which germinate directly the smaller are biciliated; conjugation has been seen to take place in a few instances.

Allied to the Confervaceæ is an interesting plant, *Sphæroplea annulina*, which has received careful attention from Cohn. The oospores of this plant are the product of a process partaking of a sexual nature, and when mature are filled with reddish fat vesicles which divide by segmentation.

The *Ædogoniaceæ* also closely resemble Confervaceæ in habits of life, but differ in some particulars, especially so in the mode of reproduction (only a single large zoospore being set free from each cell) and by the almost complete fission of the cell-wall or one of the rings which serve as a hinge. The zoospores are the largest known among algals, and each is described as having a red eye-spot. The *Chætophoraceæ* form an interesting group of confervoid plants, and are usually found in running streams, as they prefer pure water. One of the characteristics of the group is that the extremities of the branches are prolonged into an acute-shaped termination, as represented in Fig. 284, No. 6. A very pretty object under the microscope is *Draparnaldia glomerata*, belonging to this species. It consists of an axis composed of a row of cells, and at regular intervals whorls of slender prolongations, containing chlorophyll or endochrome of a deeper green; these attain to an extraordinary length.

The *Batrachospermæ* bear a strong resemblance to frog-spawn, from which they derive their name, and are chiefly a marine group of algals allied to the Rhodespermeæ or red seaweeds. The late Dr. A. Hassall first described them;

they have since received more careful attention from M. Sirodot. They are reddish-green, extremely flexible, and nothing can surpass the grace of their movements in water; but when removed from their element they lose all form, and resemble a jelly-like substance without a trace of organisation; but if allowed to remain quiet they regain their original shape.

The presence of the cell-membrane will be best demonstrated by breaking up the filaments, either by moving the thin glass cover, or by cutting through a mass of them in all directions with a fine dissecting knife. On now examining the slide, in most instances many detached empty pieces of the cell-membrane, with its striæ, will be seen, as well as filaments partly deprived of protoplasm. On the application of iodine all these appearances become more distinguishable in consequence of the filament turning red or brown, while the empty cells remain either unaffected, or present a slight yellowish tint, as is frequently the case with cellulose when old.

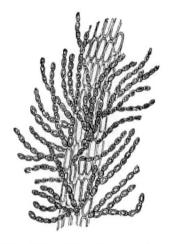

Fig. 285.—*Mesoglia vermicularis.*

With regard to the contents of the cell, the endochrome is coloured in the Oscillatoriæ, and is distinguishable by circular bands or rings around the axis of the cylindrical filament. Iodine stains them brown or red, and syrup and dilute sulphuric acid produce a beautiful rose colour. As to their mode of propagation, nothing positive is known. If kept for some time they gradually lose their green colour; a portion of the mass, becoming brown, sinks to the bottom of the vessel, and presents a granular layer.

Mesoglia vermicularis (Fig. 285) consists of strings of cells cohering and held together by their membranous covering. In the lowly organised plant Vaucheria (Plate I., No. 23, *V. sessilis*)—so named after its discoverer Vaucher, a German botanist—a genus of Siphonaceæ, we have an example of true processes of sexual generation. The branching filaments are often seen to bear at their sides peculiar globular bodies or oval protuberances, nipple-shaped buddings-out of the cell-wall, filled with a dark-coloured endochrome and distributed in pairs, one of which curves round to meet the other, when conjugation is seen to take place. Near these bodies others are found with pointed projections, which have been described as "horns," but these, Pringshelm says, are "antherids which produce antherozoids in their interior," while the capsule-like bodies constituting the oospores become, when fertilised, a new generation, which swarm out through a cavity or aperture in the parent cell-wall.

The fruit of fresh-water and most olive-green algals is enclosed in spherical cavities under the epidermis of the frond, termed conceptacles, and may be either male or female. The zoids are bottle-shaped and have flagella; the transparent vesicle in which they are contained is itself enclosed in a second of similar form. In monœcious and diœcious algals the female conceptacles are distinguished from the male by their olive colour. The spores, when developed, are borne on a pedicle emanating from the inner wall of the conceptacle. They rupture the outer wall at its apex; at first the spore appears simple, but soon after a series of changes takes place, consisting in a splitting up of the endochrome into six or eight masses of spheroidal bodies. A budding-out occurs in a few hours' time, and ultimately elongates into a cylindrical thread. The Vaucheria present a double mode of reproduction, and their fronds consist of branching tubes resembling in their general character that of the Bryophyta, from which indeed they differ only in respect of the arrangement of their green contents. In that most remarkable plant *Saprolegnia ferox*, which is structurally so closely allied to Vaucheria, though separated from them by the absence of green colouring matter, a corresponding analogy in the processes of development takes place. In the formation of its zoospores, an intermediate step is presented between that of the algæ and a class of plants formally placed among fungi.

The Ulvaceæ.—The typical form of seaweeds is the *Ulva lactuca*, well known from its fronds of dark-green "laver" on every coast throughout the world. Ulvæ are seen to differ but little from the preceding group of fresh-water algals. The specific difference is that the cells, when multiplied by binary subdivision, not only remain in firm connection with each other but possess a more regular arrangement. The frond plane of the algal is either more simple or lobed, and is formed of a double layer of cells closely packed together and producing zoospores. The whole group is chiefly distinguished from Porphyra by their green colour, the latter being roseate or purple. Ulvæ are mostly marine, with one or two exceptions. One species (*U. thermalis*) grows in the hot springs of Gastein, in a temperature of about 117° Fahr. The development of Ulvæ is seen in Fig. 286. The isolated cells, A, resemble in some points those of the Protococcus; these give rise to successive subdivisions determining the clusters seen at B and C, and by their aggregation to the confervoid filament shown at D. These filaments increase in length and breadth by successive additions, and finally take the form of fronds, or rows of cells.

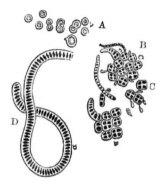

Fig. 286.—Successive Stages of Development of Ulvæ.

A. Isolated spores; B and C. Clusters of cells; D. Cells in the filamentous stage.

Fig. 287.—*Sphacelaria cirrhosa*, with spores borne at the sides of the branchlets.

The marine greenish-olive algæ present a general appearance which might at first sight be mistaken for plants of a higher order of cryptogams. Their fronds have no longer the form of a filament, but assume that of a membranous expansion of cells. The cells in which zoospores are found have an increased quantity of coloured protoplasm accumulated towards one point of the cell-wall; while the zoospores are observed to converge with their apices towards the same point. In some algæ, which seem to be closely related in form and structure to the Bryophyta, we notice this important difference, that the zoospores are developed in an organ specially destined for the purpose, presenting peculiarities of form and distinguishing it from other parts of the branching tubular frond. In the genus Derbesia distinct spore cases develop, a young branch of which, when destined to become a spore case, instead of elongating indefinitely, begins, after having arrived at a certain length, to swell out into an ovoid vesicle, in the cavity of which a considerable accumulation of protoplasm takes place. This is separated from the rest of the plant, and becomes an opaque mass, surrounded by a distinct membrane. After a time a division of the mass takes place, and a number of pyriform zoospores, each of which is furnished with flagella, are set free.

DESMIDIACEÆ, DIATOMACEÆ, ALGÆ.

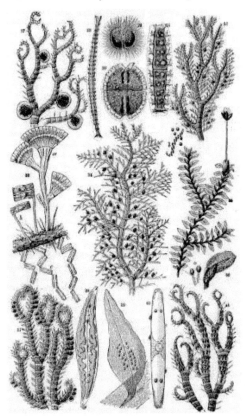

Tuffen West, del. Edmund Evans.

PLATE II.

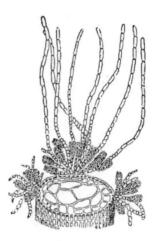

Fig. 288.—*Cutleria dichotoma.* Section of lacinia of a frond, showing the stalked eight-chambered oosporanges growing on tufts with intercalated filaments. Magnified 50 diameters.

In *Cutleria* (Fig. 288) we have a special feature of interest with two kinds of organs, seemingly opposed to each other with regard to their reproductive functions. The sporangia not only differ from those of other species, but the frond consists of olive-coloured irregularly-divided flagella, on each side of which tufts (*sori*) consisting of the reproductive organs, intermixed with hair-like bodies, are scattered. The zoospores are divided by transverse partitions into four cavities, each of which is again bisected by a longitudinal median septum. When first thrown off they are in appearance so much like the spores of Puccinia that they may be mistaken for them, although so very much larger than those of other olive-coloured algæ.

Florideæ, the red algæ (Plate II.), present many varieties of structure, although less appears to be known of their reproductive processes than of lower forms of cryptogamic plants. These are, however, of three kinds. The first, to which the term polyspore has been applied, is that of a gelatinous or membranous pericarp or conceptacle, in which an indefinite number of zoospores are contained. This organ may be either at the summit or base of a branch, or it may be concealed in or below the cortical layer of the stem. In some cases a number of spore-bearing filaments emanate from a kind of membrane at the base of a spheroidal cellular perisporangium, by the rupture of which the zoospores formed from the endochrome of the filaments make their escape. Other changes have been observed; however, they all agree in one particular, namely, that the zoospore is developed in the interior of a cell, the wall of which forms its perispore, and the internal protoplasmic membrane endochrome, the zoospore itself, for the escape of which the perispore opens out at its apex.

Fig. 289.—*Dasya kutzingiana*, with seed vessel and two rows of tetraspores. Magnified 50 diameters.

The second form is more simple, and consists of a globular or ovoid cell, containing a central granular mass; this ultimately divides into four quadrate-shaped spores; these, on attaining maturity, escape by rupture of the cell-wall. Another organ, called a tetraspore, takes its origin in the cortical layer. The tetraspores are arranged either in an isolated manner along the branches, or in numbers together; in some instances the branches that contain them are so modified in form they look like special organs, and have been called stichidia; as, for example, in Dasya (Fig. 289). Of the third kind of reproductive organ a difference of opinion exists as to the signification of their antheridia; although always produced in precisely the same situations as the tetraspores and polyspores, they are agglomerations of little colourless cells, either united in a bunch, as in Griffithsia, or enclosed in a transparent cylinder, as in Polysiphonia, or covering a kind of expanded disc of peculiar form, as in Laurencia. According to competent observers, the cells contain spermatozoids. Nägeli describes the spermatozoid as a spiral fibre, which, as it escapes, lengthens itself in the form of a screw. Thuret, on the contrary, says the contents are granular, and offer no trace of a spiral filament, but are expelled from the cells by a slow motion. The antheridia appear in their most simple form in Callithamnion (Plate II., Nos. 32 and 34), being reduced to a small mass of cells composed by numerous little bunches which are sessile on the bifurcations of the terminal branches. The spores are simpler structures than the tetraspores, and mostly occupy a more important position. They are not scattered through the frond, but grouped in definite masses, and generally enclosed in a special capsule or conceptacle, which may be mistaken for a tetraspore case. The simplest form of the spore fruit consists of spherical masses of spores attached to the wall of the frond, or imbedded in its substance, without a proper conceptacle; such a fruit is called a *favellidium*, and occurs in Halymenia; the same name is applied to the fruits of similar structures not perfectly immersed, as those of Gigartina, Gelidium,

&c., where they form tubercular swellings on the lobes. In some, the tubercles present a pore at the summit, through which the spores emerge forth. In other cases, as in Ceramium (Plate II., Nos. 27 and 37), the spores occupy a more conspicuous place; a characteristic species is Delessaria (Plate II., No. 39), the coccidium either occurring on lateral branches, or is sessile on the face of the frond, when it consists of a case filled with angular-shaped spores attached to the wall of the case. The general external appearance of the red algæ is very varied, but it seems to attain to its deepest colouring in the Red Sea, which, it is said, is entirely due to the peculiarly vivid red seaweed. They are all exquisite objects for the microscope, as may be surmised from the few varieties presented in Plate II. The Floridæ of the warmer seas exhibit most elegantly formed fronds, as will be seen on reference to the "Phycologia Australica" of the late Dr. William Harvey, F.R.S.

The Characeæ may be placed among the highest of the algals, if only for the complexity of their reproductive organs, which certainly offer a contrast in their simplicity of structure. *Chara vulgaris*, stonewort, is a simple fresh-water plant, preferring still freshwater ponds or slow-moving rivers running over a chalky soil. It thus derives the calcareous matter found in the axis of the plant, together with a small portion of silica. Its filaments (or branches, as some botanists prefer to call them) are given off in whorls. The Characeæ are a small family of acrogens, consisting of only two or three at most. They are monœcious and diœcious, the two kinds of fruit being often placed close together. They may easily be grown in a tall glass jar for observation. All that is necessary is to put the jar occasionally under the house tap and let the water run slowly over the top for a short time, thus renewing the contents without disturbing the plant. The hard water supplied to London suits chara better than softer water. Both chara and nitella are objects of great interest to microscopists, since in the former the important fact of vegetable circulation was first observed. A portion of the plant of the natural size is shown in Fig. 290, No. 1.

Characeæ.

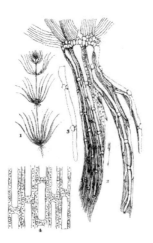

Fig. 290.—Diagrammatic sketch of Chara.

1. A stem of *Chara vulgaris*, natural size; 2. Magnified view (arrows indicating the course taken by the chlorophyll); 3. A limb, with buds protruding; 4. Portion of a leaf of *Vallisneria spiralis*, showing cyclosis of chlorophyll granules.

Each plant is composed of an assemblage of long tubiform cells placed end to end, with fixed intervals, around which the branchlets are disposed with great regularity. In nitella the stem and branches are composed of simple cells, which sometimes attain to several inches in length. Each *node*, or zone, from which the branches spring, consists of a single plate, or layer, of small cells, which are a continuation of the cortical layer of the internode (Fig. 290, No. 3) as an outgrowth. Each cell is partially filled with chlorophyll granules, and it is these that are seen under the microscope taking the course shown by the arrows (Fig. 290, No. 2). The rate of movement of the granules is accelerated by moderate warmth and retarded by cold. It is in viewing the circulation in water plants that the warm stage of the microscope is brought into use. Borne along with the protoplasmic stream are a number of solid particles consisting of starch granules and other matters. The method of viewing the circulation is by cutting sections off a portion of the plant with a very sharp knife, and arranging them in a growing cell with a few drops of water, and covering over with a thin cover-glass.

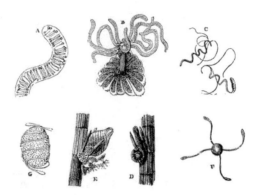

Fig. 291.—The Fructification of *Chara fragilis.*

A. Portion of filament containing "antheroids"; B. A group of antheridial filaments, composed of a series of cells, within each of which antherozoids are formed; C. The escape of mature antherozoids, with whip-like prolongations, about to swim off; D. Antherid supported on flask-shaped pedicle; E. Nucule enlarging, and seen to contain oospores; F. Spores and elaters of Equisetum; G. Spores surrounded by elaters of Equisetum.

The reproductive process of Chara is effected by two sets of bodies, both of which are placed at the base of the branches (Fig. 291, E and D) either on the same or different plants, one set known as globules or *antherids*, and the other as nucules, containing the oospores or *archegones*. These are often of a bright red colour, and have covering plates, or shields (B and E), curiously marked, and the central portion is composed of a number of filaments rolled up (as in E) or free (as seen at B), projecting out from the centre of the sphere. The antherid is supported on a short flask-shaped pedicle, which projects into the interior. At the apex of each of the eight manubria is a roundish hyaline cell, termed a capitulum, and at its apex again six smaller or secondary capitula. The long whip-shaped filaments are divided by transverse septa into a hundred or more compartments, every one of which is filled with an antherozoid (as at A), consisting of a spiral thread of protoplasm packed into two or three coils; these escape and become free (as seen at C), each having two long fine flagella. The young antherozoid swims off with a lashing action, and the whole field appears for a time filled with life. They swim about freely, but their motion gradually ceases, and soon they arrive at a state of inaction.

Nitella appears to have a somewhat different mode of fructification to that of its congener. It puts forth a long filamentous branch from one of its joints, which, on reaching the surface of the water, terminates in a whitish fruit-like cluster. It is even a more delicate and less robust algal than chara, and every care should be taken to imitate the still water in which it grows. It delights in shady woods and in calcareous open pools.

Similar care is requisite with regard to Vallisneria; and a more equal temperature is better suited to the growth of this aquatic plant. It should be planted in the middle of the jar or aquarium, about two inches deep in mould, closely pressed down, then gently fill the jar with water. When the water requires changing, a small portion only should be run off at a time. It appears to thrive in proportion to the frequency of changing the water, and taking care that the water added rather increases the temperature than lowers it.

The natural habitat of the *Frog-bit*, another water-plant of much interest, is found on the surface of ponds and ditches; in the autumn its seeds fall, and become buried in the mud at the bottom during the winter; in the spring these plants rise to the surface, produce flowers, and grow throughout the summer. Chara may be found in many places around London, and in the upper reaches of the Thames.

Anacharis alsinastrum.—This remarkable plant is so unlike any other water-plant that it may be at once recognised by its leaves growing *in threes* round a slender stem. It is also known as "Waterthyme," from a resemblance it bears to that plant.

The colour of the plant is deep green; the leaves are nearly half an inch long, by an eighth wide, egg-shaped at the point, with serrated edges. Its powers of increase are prodigious, as every fragment is capable of becoming an independent plant, producing roots and stems, and extending itself indefinitely in every direction. The specific gravity of it is so nearly that of water, that it is more disposed to sink than float. A small branch of the plant is represented, with a hydra attached to it, in a subsequent chapter.

The special cells in which the circulation is most readily seen are the elongated cells around the margin of the leaf and those of the midrib. On examining the leaf with polarised light, the cells are observed to contain a large proportion of silica, and present a very interesting appearance. A bright band of light encircles the leaf, and traverses its centre. In fact, the leaf is set, as it were, in a framework of silica. By boiling the leaf for a short time in equal parts of nitric acid and water, a portion of the vegetable tissue is destroyed, and the silica rendered more distinct, without changing the form of the leaf.

It is necessary to make a thin section or strip from the leaf of Vallisneria for the purpose of exhibiting the circulation in the cells, as shown in Fig. 290, No. 4. Among the cell granules, a few of a more transparent character than the rest, are seen to have a nucleolus within.

The phenomenon of cell cyclosis occurs in other plants beside those growing in water. The leaf of the common plantain or dock, Plantago, furnishes a good example, the movement being seen both in the cells of the plant and hairs of the cuticle torn from the midrib.

Cell-division.—In order to study the process of cell-division the hairs on the stamens of Tradescantia should be taken. Remove one from a bud on a warm day and let a drop of a one per cent. sugar solution fall upon it, and cover it with a thin glass cover. Place it for a short time in a *moist-chamber* (Fig. 256), and then examine it with a magnifying power of 500 diameters. The nucleus of the cell will be seen, near its terminal position, to gradually elongate in the direction of the longer axis of the cell and become more granular, while the protoplasm moves towards the extreme end; the nucleus at the same time will present a striated appearance, with the fibrilla arranged parallel to the longer axis of the nucleus, and at length approach each other at the poles. A nuclear spindle will now be produced, and the fibres ruptured in the equatorial plane, so that two nuclei will be found in place of the one. The best preparations of nuclei are obtained by making thin longitudinal sections of actively-growing plants (young rootlets of Pinus, for example), and staining them with hæmatoxylin in the manner described in a former chapter.

Desmidiaceæ and Diatomaceæ.

The two groups of Desmidiaceæ and Diatomaceæ differ so little in their general characters that they may be spoken of as members or representative families of microscopic and unicellular algæ alike in their remarkable beauty and bilateral symmetry, and of such peculiar interest as to call for special notice. Desmids differ from diatoms chiefly in colour, in lacking a non-silicious skeleton, and in their generative process, which for the most part consists in the conjugation of two similar cells. Diatoms, on the other hand, have dense silicious skeletons and a general absence of green colouring matter. Ralfs, in his systematic monograph, enumerates twenty genera of desmids. The limiting membrane is alike firm and flexible, since it exhibits some elasticity and resistance to pressure, and is not readily decomposable. Traces of silica are found in only a few of the desmids, while the frustule of the diatom is chiefly composed of this substance; both have an external membranous covering, so transparent and homogeneous in structure as to be in danger of being entirely overlooked, unless some staining material is used, together with a high-power objective possessing considerable penetration. In some species, however, the mucous covering is more clearly defined, as in Staurastrum and *Didymoprium Grevelli*. Openings occur in the outer membrane of other species, as the Closterium.

PLATE X.

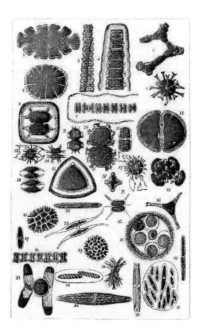

DESMIDIACEÆ.

Many species of desmids have a power of motion, the cause of which must be due either to cilia or a flagellate organ. This, however, is denied by some observers, who regard their movements as due to an exudation of the mucilaginous contents of the cell, to exosmose, or diffusion, neither of which hypotheses will at all help us to understand the gliding movements of the Oscillariæ or the sharp jerky movement of the Schizonema. The movements of desmids are especially exerted when in the act of dividing, and by sunlight, towards which they are always observed to move. The force with which some diatoms move about is very great, and this can only be satisfactorily explained by admitting a specialised organ.

The appearance of the Desmidiaceæ (Plate X.) is much modified by their eminences, depressions, and processes, as well as that of the surface, the margin of the fronds, and the depth and width of the central constriction. The surfaces may be dotted over irregularly, the dots themselves being elevated or depressed points in their structural character. The margins of some have a dentate appearance, as in Cosmarium. In the elongated forms, such as Penium, the puncta are disposed in lines parallel to the length. In several these lines are either elevations or furrows, it is not always easy to say which; they are peculiar, however, to the elongated forms of Closterium. When the lines are fine they produce a striation of the surface, but in order to discover this the fronds should be viewed when empty and by a fairly good power. The modification of surface in several genera seems to be due, not to

- 387 -

mere simple appendages, but to expansion of the limiting membrance into thickened processes, and which may terminate in spines, as in Xanthidium and Staurastrum (Plate X., Nos. 8-19 and 22). A general distribution over the surface is characteristic of the former, but in Euastrum the surfaces are very irregular, and therefore described as "swellings or inflations." Micrasterias has its margin deeply incised into lobes, which in some have a radiating arrangement; when the lobes on the margin are small they constitute crenations or dentations. The fronds of *Euastrum binatum* are bicrenate on the sides, as are those of Desmidium and Hyalotheca and other species. Another variety of margin exists, known as undulating or wavy, while the general concavity or convexity of the margins furnish other specific characteristics.

Pediastreæ (Plate X., Nos. 24-29).—The members of this family formerly included the Micrasterias and Arthrodesmius of Ehrenberg. From their arrangement of cells in determinate numbers and definite forms, it has been thought by some observers that they should be removed from the desmids to a special or sub-family. The points of difference consist in the firmness of the outer covering, in the frequent interruptions on the margin of the cells, and in the protrusion of "horns," or rather a notch more or less deep. It is true that the cells are not made up of two symmetrical halves, and that they are in aggregation, which is not (except in the Scenedesmus, a genus that distinctly connects this group with desmids) in linear series, but in the form of discoidal fronds. They, however, divide into 8, 16, or 32 gonidia, and these move about for some time before the formation of a new frond. It was Nägeli who first instituted a sub-genus of Pediastrum, under the designation of Anomopedium, the chief characteristic of which is the absence of bilobed peripheral cells. In Cœlastrum the cells are hexangular, the central ones very regularly so; in Sorastrum they are wedge-shaped, or triangular, with rounded-off angles. Viewed laterally the cells appear oblong. The cells of Pediastrum are considerably compressed, so that when aggregated they form a flattened tubular structure; in figure they are polygonal, frequently hexagonal, a shape owing, in all probability, to mutual lateral pressure during growth. There is a pervading uniformity in the contents of the cells of the different genera, which consist of protoplasmic endochrome. At first the colour is pale green, but it becomes deeper with full maturity, while the decaying cells are seen to change to a deep reddish-yellow or brown. The protoplasm is also clear and homogeneous, but in time granules appear, enlarge, and multiply in number; moreover, each cell presents a single bright green vesicle, around which are collected clear circular spaces or globules, recalling those of Closterium, and varying in number from two to six or more, their position not being regulated by the partition wall as in Palmellæ, but by the centre of the entire frond. Oil globules are also contained in the cells; their presence is indicated by the addition of a drop of tincture of iodine. On one occasion Nägeli saw in *Pediastrum boryanum* the endochrome disposed in a radiating manner, an arrangement which often obtains in algals and in other vegetable cells with a central nucleus. The cells of Pediastreæ are always united together in compound fronds, as represented in Plate X., Nos. 24 and 29.[56]

The differences pointed out in no way constitute a claim to remove Pediastreæ from among Desmidiaceæ, certainly not to rank as a distinct species.

Reproduction of Desmidiaceæ.—A true reproductive act is presented by the conjugation or coupling of two fronds, and by the resulting development of a sporangium and subsequent interchange of the contents of the two cells. At another time self-division is frequently seen to take place in all respects as in the cells of other algæ. The proceeding is varied in some essential particulars by the form of the fronds and by other circumstances; as in fission of Euastrum, for instance (seen in Plate X., Nos. 1, 2, and 12), when the narrow connecting bands between the two segments of the fronds are rapidly pushed aside by growth and finally divide. Two modes of conjugation of fronds are represented in Plate X., Nos. 25 and 33, in Closterium and Penium. The act of conjugation admits of variations in character, as shown in Staurastrum and Microsterias; the contents of both fronds are discharged into a delicate intermediate sac; this gradually thickens and produces spines (Plate X., Nos. 8 and 19). In Didymoprium the separate joints unite by a narrow process pushed out from each other, often of considerable length, through which the endochrome of one cell is transferred to the other, and thus a sporangium is produced within one of two cells, just as in the conjugatæ (No. 5). In *Penium Jennereri* the conjugation takes a varied form; the fronds do not open and gape at the suture, but couple by small but distinct cylindrical tubes (No. 27).

Among those enumerated, the compressed and deeply constricted cells of Euastrum offer the more favourable opportunities for studying the manner of their division; for although the frond is really a single cell, in all its stages it appears like two, the segments being always distinct, from the earliest stage. The segments, however, are separated by a connecting link, which is subsequently converted into two somewhat round hyaline bodies. These bodies gradually increase and acquire colour, and as they grow the original segments are further divided, and at length become disconnected, each taking a new segment to supply the place of that from which it is separated. It is curious to trace the progressive development of the newer portions, which at first are devoid of all colour; but as they become larger a faint green tint is observed, which gradually darkens, and then assumes a granular appearance. Soon the new segments attain their normal size, while the covering in some species shows the presence of puncta. In Xanthidium, Plate X., Nos. 9, 10, and Staurastrum, Nos. 15-18, the spines and processes make their appearance last, beginning as mere tubercles, and then lengthening until they attain their perfect form and size, armed with setæ; but complete separation frequently occurs before growth is fully completed. This singular process is repeated again and again, so that the older segments are united successively, as it were, with many generations. When the cells approach maturity, molecular movements may be at times noticed in their contents, precisely similar to what Agardh and others aptly term "swarming." Meyen describes this granular matter as starch.[57] Closterium, early in the spring, when freshly secured and exposed to light, presents a wonderful appearance, these bodies being kept continually in motion at both ends of the frustule by the ciliary action within the cell, and the whole frond is seen brilliantly glittering with active cilia. When a gleam of stronger light is allowed for a moment to fall on the frond, the rapid undulations of the cilia produce a series of most delicate prismatic Newton's rings. The action and distribution of the cilia, together with the cyclosis of the granular bodies in the frond, are better seen by the aid of Wenham's parabola or a good condenser with a central stop. One of the wide angular objectives shows the circulation around the marginal portions of the whole frond. The stream is seen to be running up the more external portion, internal to which is another stream following a contrary direction; this action, confined to the space between the mass of endochrome and the outer portion of the cell-wall, is seen to pass above or around the space in which cyclosis of the spores is taking place.

During the summer of 1854, the late Rev. Lord Sidney Godolphin Osborne and myself became much interested in the remarkable family of Closteria. Fig. 292 is a highly magnified view of *Closterium lunula* which I drew by the aid of the camera-lucida at the time. There could be no doubt about the ciliary action within the frond: it was in every way similar to that of the branchiæ of the muscle, the same wavy motion, which gradually became slower as the death of the desmid drew near. This was brought about earlier when the cell was not kept supplied with fresh water.

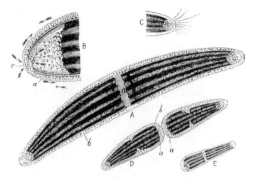

Fig. 292.—*Closterium lunula.*

In diagram A, line *b* points to a cluster of ovoid bodies; these are seen at intervals throughout the endochrome within the investing membrane. These bodies are attached to the membrane by small pedicles, and are occasionally seen in motion about the spot, from which they eventually break away, and are carried off, by the circulating fluid, to the chambers at the extremities of the frond; there they join a crowd of similar bodies, in constant motion within the chambers, when the specimen is quite fresh. That the action of these free granules or spores is "Brownian," as surmised by some writers, is in my opinion entirely fallacious. It is doubtless in a measure due to the current brought about by the ciliary motion of the more fluid contents of the cell.

The circulation, when made out over the centre of the frond, for instance at *a*, is in appearance of a wholly different nature from that seen at the edges. In the latter the matter circulated is that of granules, passing each other in distinct lines, but in opposite directions; in the circulation as seen at *a*, the streams are broad, tortuous, of far greater body, and passing with much less rapidity. To see the centre circulation, use a Gillett's illuminator and a ⅛th or a ¹⁄₁₀th immersion; work the fine adjustment so as to bring the centre of the frond into focus, then almost lose it by raising the objective; after this, with great care, work the milled head until the darker body of the endochrome is clearly brought out.

At B is an enlarged sketch of one extremity of the frond. The arrows within the chamber pointing to *b* denote the direction of a strong current of fluid, which can be occasionally followed throughout. It is acted upon by cilia at the edges of the chamber, the greater impetus appearing to come from the centre of the endochrome. The fluid is here acting in positive jets, that is, with an almost arterial action; and according to the strength with which it is propelled at the time, the loose floating bodies are sent to a greater or less distance from the end of the frustule; the fluid is thus impelled from a centre, and kept in activity by the lateral cilia, that create a rapid current and give a turning motion to the free bodies. The line—*a*, in this diagram, denotes the outline of the membrane which encloses the endochrome; on both sides cilia can be seen. The circulation exterior to it passes and repasses in opposite directions, in three or four distinct courses; these, when they arrive at—*c*, seem to encounter a stream making its way towards an aperture at the apex of the chamber; then they appear to be driven back again by a stronger force. Some, however, do occasionally enter the chamber, but very rarely will one of the bodies escape into the outer current, and should it do so, is carried about until it becomes adherent to the side wall of the frond.

With regard to the propagation of the *C. lunula*, I have never seen anything like conjugation; but I have repeatedly seen self-division (shown at D *a a*). This act is chiefly the work of one half of the frond. Having watched for some time, one half is seen to remain passive, while the other has a lateral motion from side to side, as if moving on an axis at the point of juncture; the motion increases, is more active, until at last with a jerk one segment separates itself from the other, as seen at E. It will be noticed that each end of the segment is perfectly closed before separation finally takes place; there is, however, only one perfect chamber, that belonging to the extremity of the original entire frond. The circulation continues for some time previous to and after subdivision, in both fronds, and by almost imperceptible degrees increases in volume. From the end of the endochrome symptoms of elongation of the frond take place, the semi-lunar form gradually changes, elongates, and is more defined, until it takes the form and outline of the fully-formed frustule at the extremity. The obtuse end—*b* of the other portion of frond is at the same time elongating and contracting, and in a few hours from the division of the one segment from the other the appearance of each half is that of a nearly perfect frustule, the chamber at the new end is complete, the globular circulation exterior to it becomes affected by the circulation from within the said chamber, and, shortly afterwards, some of the free bodies descend, and become exposed to the current already going on in the chamber. E is a diagram of one end of a *C. didymotocum*, in which the same process was well marked, and completed while it was under observation.

It will appear to most observers that if the continuation of the widely-spread family of Desmidiaceæ was wholly dependent upon conjugation and subdivision of their frustules, a process requiring several hours for its completion, the whole species must have long ago disappeared. It may be presumed then that some other mode of reproduction must prevail. In the fresh-water algæ the two more general methods of multiplication are clearly governed by the conditions of the seasons; the resting-spores securing continuity of life during the winter, the swarm-spores spreading the plant profusely during the warmer portion of the year, when rapid growth is possible. I therefore regard the actively swarming bodies seen in continuous motion at the two extreme portions of the frustule of *Closterium lunula* as being either oospores or zoospores, by means of which reproduction takes place.

Diatomaceæ, commonly called brittleworts, Plate XI., are chiefly composed of two symmetrical valves, narrow and wand-like, navicular, miniature boat-shaped, hence their name *Navicula* (little ship). Hitherto they have excited the deepest interest among microscopists because of their wonderfully minute structure, and the difficulty involved in determining their exact nature and formation. Each individual diatom has a silicious skeleton, spoken of as a frustule, frond, or cell, having a rectangular or prismatic form, which mostly obtains in the whole family, the angles of the junction of the two united valves being, as a rule, acute, and enclosing a yellowish-brown endochrome.

Deeply-notched frustules, like those of the Desmidiaceæ, do not occur, and the production of spines and tubercles so common in that family is rare in the Diatomaceæ. Great variety of outline prevails, so much so that no rule in this respect can be formulated.

The frustules, however, are usually composed of two equal and similar halves, but exceptions to this are found in the Actinomtheæ, Cocconcidæ, and one or two other families. The extremities of some species, *e.g.*, Nitzshia and Pleurosigma, are extremely elongated, forming long, filiform, tubular processes; in Biddulphia and Rizoselenia, short tubular processes from their margins. Great variety of outline may prevail in a genus, so considerable indeed that no accurate definition can be given, the characteristics shading off through several species until the similarity to an assumed typical form is much diminished, which may again be modified by accidental circumstances that surround the development of the silicious frustule. It must not be forgotten that the figure is greatly modified or entirely changed by the position of the valves, whether seen in one position or another, as already explained in connection with "Errors of Interpretation." Again, in the genera Navicula, Pinnularia (Plate II., Nos. 33, 38, and 40), and others, the frustules are in one aspect boat-shaped, but in the other either oblong with truncated ends, or prismatic. In the genus Triceratium (Plate XI., No. 10), the difference of figure is very remarkable as the front or side view is examined.

The sudden change in appearance presented to the eye as the frustule is seen to roll over is rather peculiar. As a rule, therefore, we must examine all specimens in every aspect, to accomplish which very shallow cells should be selected, say of $\frac{1}{100}$th of an inch deep, and covered with glass $\frac{1}{250}$th of an inch thick. A good penetrating objective should be used, and careful illumination obtained. The Diatomaceæ are perhaps more widely distributed than any other class of infusorial life; they are found in fresh, salt, and brackish water; many grow attached to other bodies by a stalk (Plate II., No. 33, Licmophora and Achnanthidium); while others, as Pleurosigma, No. 40, swim about freely.

PLATE XI.

DIATOMACEÆ, RECENT AND FOSSIL.

There are a considerable number of Diatomaceæ which, when in the young state, are enclosed in a muco-gelatinous sheath; while others are attached by stipes or stalk to algæ. It would be vain, in a limited space, to attempt a description of this numerous and extensive family. Nägeli and other observers describe a "mucilaginous pellicle on the inner layer of the valves," while, as Menghine observes, "an organic membrane ought to exist both inside and outside, for the silica could not become solid except by crystallizing or depositing itself on some pre-existing substance." The surface of the frustules is generally very beautifully sculptured, and the markings assume the appearance of dots (puncta), stripes (striæ), ribs (costæ), pinnules (pinnæ), of furrows and fine lines; longitudinal, transverse, and radiating bands; canals or canaliculi; and of cells or areolæ; whilst all present striking varieties and modifications in their form, character, and degree of development. Again, the fine lines or striæ of many frustules are resolvable into rows of minute dots or perforations, as occur in *Pleurosigma angulatum*, delineated in the accompanying microphotograph (Fig. 294), taken for the author purposely to show the markings on this especially selected test diatom.

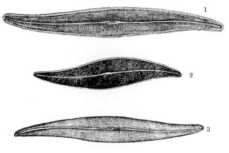

Fig. 293.

1. *Pleurosigma attenuatum*; 2. *Pleurosigma angulatum*; 3. *Pleurosigma Spencerii.* Magnified 450 diameters.

The nature of the markings on the diatom valves is one of considerable interest, and attempts have been made to produce them artificially, but without success.

Fig. 294.—*Pleurosigma angulatum*, magnified 4500 diameters.

(From a microphotograph taken by Zeiss with the 2 mm. aprochromatic objective, 1·30 numerical aperture, and projection eye-piece, No. 4.)

Professor Max Schultze devoted a great amount of time to the investigation of the subject, and has recorded in a voluminous paper[58] the results of his observations. He says, "Most of the species of the Diatomaceæ are characterised by the presence on their outer surface of certain differences of relief, referable either to elevations or to depressions disposed in rows. The opinions of microscopists with respect to the nature of these markings are still somewhat divided. Whilst in the larger forms, and those distinguished by their coarser dots, the appearance is manifestly due to the existence of thinner spots in the valve, we cannot so easily explain the cause of the striation or punctation in *Pleurosigma angulatum* and similar finely-marked forms."

Dr. R. Zeiss some time ago furnished me with a microphotograph of a frustule magnified 4500 diameters that seemed to confirm Mr. T. F. Smith's view of the structure of these valves. Dr. Van Heurck has also made a study of this diatom, and concludes that the valves consist of two membranes of thin films, and of an intermediate layer, the outer being pierced with openings. The outer membrane is, he believes, "so delicate that it is easily destroyed by acid or by friction, and the several processes employed in cleaning and preparing it for microscopical examination. When the openings or apertures of the internal portion are arranged in alternate rows they assume the hexagonal form; when in straight rows, the openings are seen to be square or oblong." A description hardly in accord with Fig. 294.

Movements of Diatoms.

The late Professor Smith, in his "Synopsis of Diatoms," refers to their movements in the following terms: "I am constrained to believe that the movements observed in the Diatomaceæ are due to forces operating within the frustule, and are probably connected with the endosmotic and exosmotic action of the cells. The fluids which are concerned in these actions must enter, and be emitted through the minute foramina at the extremities of the silicious valves." Schultze's researches, which were made at a later date, carried this debatable question somewhat further. He is of opinion "that a sarcode (protoplasmic) substance envelops the external surface of the diatoms, and its movements are due to this agent exclusively." His investigations were mainly confined to *P. angulatum*, and to the larger *P. attenuatum* (Fig. 293, 1 and 2), as the transverse markings on the frustule do not impede to so great an extent the observation of what is going on within. The living specimen of *P. angulatum* under the microscope usually has its broad side turned to view, with one long curved "raphe" uppermost, and the other in contact with the glass cover (Fig. 293). Within the frustule the yellow colouring matter, "endochrome," fills the cavity more or less completely. In the broader part of the frustule these bands of endochrome describe one or two complicated windings. It is only possible in those specimens in which the bands are narrow to properly trace their foldings, and determine their number. The next objects which strike the eye on examining a freshly-gathered Pleurosigma are numerous highly refractive oil-globules. These are not, however, all in the same place, and one globule appears nearer the observer than the other; their relative position is best seen when a view of the narrow side of the frustule can be obtained, so that one raphe is to the left and the other to the right. The blue-black colour which is assumed by these globules after treating with acid demonstrates their oleaginous nature. The middle of the cavity of the frustule is occupied, in the larger navicula, by two large oil-globules (seen in the diagrammatic Fig. 295), and by a colourless finely granular mass, whose position in the body is not so clearly seen in the flat view as in the side view. Besides the central mass, the conical cavities at either end of the frustule are seen to enclose granular substance, and two linear extensions from each of three masses are developed, closely underlying the raphæ. In the side view, therefore, they appear attached to the right and left edges of the interior of the frustule. This colourless granular substance carries in its centre, near the middle part of the diatom, an imperfectly developed nucleus which is not very easy to see, but may be demonstrated by the application of an acid. The colourless substance is protoplasm, and encloses numerous small refractive particles; this, on adding a drop of a one per cent. solution of osmic acid, is coloured blue-black, and proves to be fat. It is, however, exceedingly difficult to determine the exact limitations of the protoplasm, on account of the highly refractive character of the silicious skeleton, and the obstruction to the light presented by the endochrome.

At a short distance the protoplasm reappears, contracted into a considerable mass, within the terminal ends of the frustule. Schultze observed in this part of the protoplasm a rapid molecular movement, "cyclosis," such as occurs in Closterium, and also a current of the granules of the protoplasm along the raphe. "*Pleurosigma angulatum* 'crawls,' as do all diatoms possessing a raphe, along this line of suture. To crawl along, it must have a fixed support." "There is obviously," adds Schultze, "but one explanation; it is clear that there must be a band of protoplasm lying along the raphe, which causes the particles of colouring matter to adhere, and gives rise to a gliding movement. For there is but one phenomenon which can be compared with the gliding motion of foreign bodies on the Diatomaceæ, and that is, the clinging to and casting off of particles by the pseudopodia of the rhizopod, as observed, for instance, on placing a living Gromia or Miliolina in still water with finely-powdered carmine. The nature of the adhesion and of the motion is in both cases the same. And since, with diatoms as unicellular organisms, protoplasm forms a large part of the cell (in many cases two distinctly moving protoplasms), this implies that the external movements are referable to the movements of the protoplasm." It is quite evident to those who have studied the movements of diatoms that they are surrounded by a sarcode structure of a more pellucid character than that of Amœba. Six years before Schultze's observations were published, I wrote in a third edition of my book, page 307, "The act of progression favours the notion of contractile tentacular filaments—*pseudopodia*—as the organs of locomotion and prehension."

Since my former observations on the movements of diatoms, I have given much attention to two forms, *P. angulatum* and *Pinnularia*. The powers used were Hartnack's No. 8, and Gunlack's $\frac{1}{16}$-inch immersion; Gillett's condenser illumination, with lamp flame edge turned to mirror and bull's-eye lens; a perforated slide with a square of thin glass ·006 cemented to it, and a cover-glass of ·005. So far as I could satisfy myself, no terminal space, as in the Closteria, could be seen, otherwise the course of the gemmules is as freely traced as in that form. They are more minute than the *Closterium lunula* granules, more steadily or slowly seen to pass up and down one half the frustule towards the extremity, one half of the current seeming to turn round upon its axis and descending towards the other. The granules were thickly scattered at the apex, but gradually became fewer, and the ascending and descending current tapered away towards the central nodule, which became more filled up or closed in.

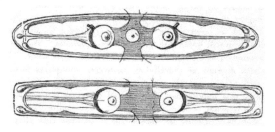

Fig. 295.—Outline sketches of Pinnulariæ, showing vesicles.

Fig. 296.—*Gomphonema constrictum.* (From a microphotograph.)

This beautiful sight was not confined to one frustule, but was exhibited in all that were in a healthy condition. I examined several, and watched them for a long time. The phenomenon described depends much upon the healthy condition of the frustule at the time; as the movements of the diatoms became sluggish, the circulation gradually slackens and then ceases altogether. I also saw a somewhat similar action in the more active specimens of *P. hippocampus* and *Navicula cuspidata*, but the coarser markings and thickness of the wall of these diatoms seemed to place greater difficulties in the way of observation than the finer valves of the *P. angulatum*. One thing I believe is certain, that the circulation described is precisely similar to that seen in the Closteria, or, on a much larger scale, in Chara and the leaf of the Anacharis, bearing in mind also that in the Closterium the cell is divided by a transverse suture, and in *P. angulatum* by a longitudinal one (Plate II., Nos. 38-40). About the same time some very lively specimens of the Pinnulariæ were sent to me, and the movements of these frustules were more closely observed. One or two of the more active would attack a body relatively larger than itself, it would also force its way into a mass of granular matter, and then recede from it with a jerky motion. In more than one instance a cell of Palmoglæa was seized and carried away by the Pinnularia, the former at the time being actively engaged in the process of cell division. Other diatoms present among my specimens were also in an active condition, and the circulation of granular matter in all was distinctly visible. In the Pinnulariæ two large colourless vesicles were seen on either side of the median nodule, each having a central nucleus, as represented in the accompanying sketch, made while under observation in two positions. The central portion of each frustule was closely packed with a rich yellowish-brown coloured endochrome, interspersed with a few fat globules. The phenomenon of cyclosis was not seen in any of these diatoms, but I have satisfied myself, by staining, of the presence of a delicately fine external protoplasmic covering in many diatoms. That their movements resemble the gliding movements exhibited by the Amœba can scarcely be doubted. Numerous forms of Diatomaceæ are found growing on or attached to water-plants or pieces of detached stalks, which, although generally simple, are sometimes compound, dividing and subdividing in a beautiful ramous manner. Pinnulariæ, Nitzschia, &c., are seen adherent by one extremity, about which they turn or bend themselves as on a hinge. By the process of cell-division, groups of Synedræ become attached by a point, in a fan-like form. The fan-like collection of frustules is said to be flabellate, or radiate. In Licmophora, Achnanthes and other species (Plate II., Nos. 29-33) the double condition of union of frustules and of attachment by a pedicle are illustrated. When a stipe branches it does so normally in a dichotomous manner, each new individual being produced by a secondary pedicle. This regular dichotomy is seen in several genera: Cocconema and Gomphonema, the latter more perfectly in Fig. 296, from a microphotograph, in which a branching, or rather longitudinal, rupture of the pedicle takes place at intervals, and the entire organism presents a more or less complete flabella, or fan-like cluster, on the summit of the branches, and imperfect or single frustules irregularly scattered throughout the whole length of the pedicle.

Isthmia enervis (Fig. 297).—The unicellular frustule of this species is extremely difficult to define, owing to the large areolations of the valves; it has a remarkable internal structure. The olive-brown cell contents are found collected, for the most part, into a central mass, from which radiating, branched, granular threads extend to and unite with the periphery. When viewed by a magnifying power of 600 or 700 diameters, these prolongations are seen to be composed of aggregations of ovate or spindle-shaped corpuscles, held together by protoplasmic matter. These bodies are sometimes quiescent, but more often travel slowly to and fro from the central mass. The general aspect under these conditions so nearly corresponds to the characteristic circulation in the frustules of unicellular plants and of certain rhizopoda, that it is difficult to realise that the object when under examination is an elegant marine diatom.

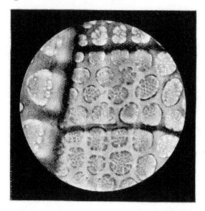

Fig. 297.—*Isthmia enervis*. Microphotograph.

There is a large section of diatoms in which the frustules are diffused throughout a muco-gelatinous envelope in a definite manner. Histologically this is homologous with the pedicles and connecting nodules thrown out during the act of self-division, and in some species (Cocconeis, Fragillaria, &c.) it often persists after that act is complete.

Diatomaceæ, Recent and Fossil.

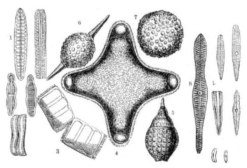

Fig. 298.—Fossil Diatoms from Springfield (Barbadoes).

1, Achnanthidium; 2, *Diatoma vulgare*, side view and front view; 3, Biddulphia; 4, 5, 6, 7, *Amphitetias antediluviana*, front view, with globular and oval forms; *Gomphonema elongatum* and *capitatum*.

Fossilised Diatomaceæ.—Dr. Gregory was of opinion that a large number of diatoms separated into species are only transition forms, and more extended observations have proved that form and outline are not always to be trusted in this matter. Species-making is a modern invention, and can hardly apply to the indestructible fossilised forms of the frustules of Diatomaceæ, with their beautiful sculpturings and geometrical constructions, which have not been materially changed since they were first deposited. Startling and almost incredible as the assertion may appear to some, it is none the less a fact established beyond all question, that some of the most gigantic mountain-ranges, as the mighty Andes, towering into space 25,250 feet above the level of the sea, their base occupying vast areas of land; as also massive limestone rocks; the sand that covers boundless deserts; and the soil of many wide-extended plains, are each and all principally composed of Diatomaceæ. And, as Dr. Buckland once observed: "The remains of such minute animals have added much more to the mass of materials which compose the exterior crust of the globe than the bones of elephants, hippopotami, and whales."

In 1841 the late Mr. Sollitt, of Hull, discovered the beautiful longitudinal and transverse *striæ* (markings) on the *Pleurosigma hippocampus*. A curved graceful line runs down the shell, in the centre of which is an expanded oval opening. Near to the central opening the dots elongate crossways, presenting the appearance of small short bands.

In the vicinity of this town many interesting varieties of Diatomaceæ have been found, the beauty of the varied forms of which are constantly under investigation; at the same time some of them are highly useful, as forming that class of *test objects* which are better calculated than many others for determining the excellence and powers of certain objectives. Mr. Sollitt carefully measured the markings on some of the frustules and found they ranged between the $\frac{1}{30000}$th and $\frac{1}{130000}$th of an inch; the *Pleurosigma strigilis* having the strongest markings, and the *Pleurosigma acus* the finest.

Mr. J. D. Sollitt not only first proposed their use, but he also furnished the measurements of the lines of the several members of this family, as follows:—

Amphipleura pellucida, or Acus, 130,000 in the inch, cross lines.
" sigmoidea, 70,000 in the inch.
Navicula rhomboides, 111,000 in the inch, cross lines.
Pleurosigma fasciola, fine shell, 86,000 in the inch, cross lines.
"" strong shell, 64,000 in the inch, cross lines.
" strigosum, 72,000 in the inch, diagonal lines.
" angulatum, 51,000 in the inch, diagonal lines.
" quadratum, 50,000 in the inch, diagonal lines.
" Spencerii, 50,000 in the inch, cross lines.
" attenuatum, 42,000 in the inch, cross lines.
" Balticum, 40,000 in the inch, cross lines.
" formosum, 32,000 in the inch, diagonal lines.
" strigilis, 30,000 in the inch, cross lines.

PLATE XII.

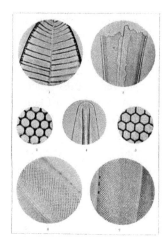

MICRO-PHOTOGRAPH OF TEST DIATOMS.

Lichenaceæ.

The lichens are a family of autonomous plants, an intermediary group of algals or cellular cryptogams, drawing their nourishment from the air through their whole surface medium, and propagating by spores usually enclosed in asci, and always having green gonidia in their thallus. Their gonidia, bright coloured globular cells, form layers under the cortical covering of the thallus, and generally develop in the form of incrustations, which cover stones, wood, and the bark of trees, or penetrate into the lamellæ of the epidermis of woody plants. The gonidia of lichens partake of both the character of vegetative and reproductive cells.

The thallus in the fructicose group attaches itself by a narrow base, growing in the form of a miniature shrub. Another group is met with in a slimy condition—the gelatinous lichens. These species, for the most part, furnished dyes before the discovery of the coal-tar dyes. In many of the *Palmella cruenta*, commonly found growing on the walls and roofs of houses, a colourless acid liquid is found, which, on being treated with alkali, produces a bright yellow colour; and another, *Avernia vulpina*, furnishes a brown dye; the *Rocella fuciformis* and *R. tinctoria* yield the purple dye substance known as orchil, or archil, from which the useful blue paper of the chemist for testing acidity is manufactured. Usnic acid, combined with green and yellow resins, seems to be more or less a constituent of many lichens.

A vertical section of *Palmella stellata* is given in Plate I., No. 26, in which the emission of the ripe spores of the lichens is seen to be not unlike that which takes place in some of the fungi, Pezizæ, Sphæriæ, &c. If a portion of the thallus be moistened and placed in a common phial, with the apotheca turned toward one side, in a few hours the opposite surface of the glass will be found covered with patches of spores, easily perceptible by their colour; or if placed on a moistened surface, and one of the usual glass slips laid over it, the latter will be covered in a short time. As to the powers of dissemination of these lowly organised plants, an observation led to the conclusion that the gonidia of lichens have greater powers in this direction than was formerly supposed. It is found that by placing a clean sheet of glass in the open air during a fall of snow, and receiving the melting water in a tube or bottle, quantities of what has been looked upon as a "unicellular plant" can be taken, the cells of which may be kept in a dormant condition for a long time during cold weather, but upon the return of spring warmth and moisture they begin to increase, by a process of subdivision, into two, four or eight portions; these soon assume a rounded form, and burst the parent cell-wall open; these secondary cells then begin to divide and subdivide again, and the process may go on without much variation for a long time. The phenomena described may be watched by taking a portion of the bark of a tree on which Chlorococcus has been deposited, and placing it under a glass to keep it in a moderately moist atmosphere; the only difference being a change in colour, caused by the growth of the fibres, as may be seen on microscopical examination. "And this," says Dr. Hicks, who first observed this phenomenon in plant life, "is an instructive point, because it will be found that the colour varies notably according to the lichen prevalent in its neighbourhood."[59] He believes there can be no doubt that what has been called Chlorococcus is nothing more than the gonidia of a lichen; and that under suitable conditions, chiefly drought and warmth, the gonidium often throws out from its external envelope a small fibre, which, adhering and branching, forms a "soridium." "The soridia remain dormant for a very long time, and do not develop into thalli unless in a favourable situation, in some cases it may be for years. It will be perceived that the soridium contains all the elements of a thallus in miniature; in fact, a thallus does frequently arise from one alone, and the fibres of neighbouring soridia interlace; thus a thallus is matured very rapidly. This is one of the causes of the variation of appearance so common in many species of lichens, more readily seen towards the centre of the parent thallus. When the gonidia remain attached to the parent thallus, the circumstances are, of course, more favourable, and they develop into secondary thalli, attached more or less to the older one, which, in many instances, decays beneath them. This process being continued year after year gives an apparent thickness and spongy appearance to the lichen, and is the principal cause of the various modifications in the external aspect of the lichens which caused them formerly to be misunderstood and wrongly classified."[60]

The erratic lichens are found among the genus Palmella, some of which grow among boulders of the primary and metamorphic formations, curled up into a ball, and only fixed to their matrix by a slender thread. The globular *Lecanora esculenta* will at times suddenly cover large tracts of country in Persia and Tartary, where it is eaten by the cattle. During a scarcity of food a shower of these lichens, Mr. Berkeley tells us, fell at Erzeroum, and saved the cattle from starvation.[61]

Another group of the Palmella, or Peltigeri, so named from the target-like discs on their surface, spread their foliaceous fronds over the ground, and as the fruit is marginal, it gives the thallus a digitate appearance. These are often spotted over by a little red fungus. The Lecidinei contains numerous species of the most varied habits, and always crustaceous, and so closely adherent to the hard rocks and stones on which they grow, that at length they disintegrate them. From this low species a higher form arises, with erect branching stems, and clothed with foliaceous, brightly-coloured scales.

The Coccocarpei is mainly distinguished by having orbicular discs entirely deprived of the cortical envelope called an excipulum. The discs spring at once from the medullary stratum, and contain asci and sporidia similar to those of the minute fungi Sphæriæ. Some of the lichens are themselves parasitic, and begin existence under the thick skin of the leaves of tropical plants, and spread encrusting thallus over their surface, the excipulum and perithecia being black; but in most cases these are beautifully sculptured, and are interesting objects for the microscope. Indeed, the sphere-bearing lichens, with upright stems bearing globular fruit at the extremity of their branches, are at first indicated by a swelling, but in time the outer layer bursts and exposes sporidia, which are beautiful objects under the microscope on account of their spherical form and more or less deep blue tint. Humble and lowly as lichens may appear to be, they have been divided into fifty-eight or more genera and 2,500 species. The brothers Tulasne, De Bary, the Rev. Mr. Berkeley, and others, devoted great attention to the peculiarities of their structure and natural history.

Hepaticæ.—An intermediary group of much interest to the microscopist are the Hepaticæ (liverworts). These are found growing on damp rocks in the neighbourhood of springs and dripping banks. The scale-moss, the *Marchantia polymorphia* (Fig. 299), may be taken as typical of this little group, with its gemmiparous conceptacles and lobed receptacles, bearing archegones on transparent glass-like fruit stalks, carrying on their summits either round shield-like discs or radiating bodies with a striking resemblance to a wheel without its tyre.

Fig. 299.—*Marchantia polymorphia.*

The liverworts are closely allied to the mosses, and as much difficulty was experienced in dividing the two, Hooker placed the whole under one genus, the Jungermannia. More recently, however, they have been divided into those with a stem and leaves confluent in a frond, Marchantia; those with stem and leaves distinct, Jungermannia; and those with a solitary capsule, filiform, bivalved, stalked, with a free central placentation, Anthocotaceæ. Some botanists have further divided them, but they are all extensively propagated by gemmæ.

The fronds carry the male organs, or *antherids*, and the disc, in the first instance, bears the female organs, or *archegones*, and after a time gives place to the *sporanges*, or spore cases. It is these bodies which are of so much interest to microscopists; if the plant is brought into a warm room, they suddenly burst open with some violence the moment a drop of water is applied to them, and the sporanges are dispersed in a small cloud of brownish dust. If this dust is examined under a medium power, it is seen to consist of a number of chain-like bodies, somewhat like the spring of a small watch; and if the process of bursting be closely watched, these minute springs will be found twisting and curling about in every direction. The structure of the frond itself will be seen to be interesting when cut in the vertical direction and placed under the microscope.

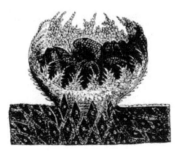

Fig. 300.—Gemmiparous conceptacle of *Marchantia polymorphia*, expanding and rising from the surface of a frond. In the interior are seen gopidial gemmæ already detached by the splitting of the epiderm.

The gemmæ of *Marchantia polymorphia* are produced in elegant membranous cups, with a toothed margin growing on the upper surface of the frond, especially in very damp courtyards between the stones, or near running water, where its lobed fronds are found covering extensive tracts of moist soil. At the period of fructification the fronds send up stalks, which carry at their summit round shield-like radiating discs, which bear upon their surface a number of little open basket-shaped "conceptacles." These again expand into singularly graceful cups (as in Fig. 300), and are found in all stages of development. When mature, the basket contains a number of little green round or oblong discs, each composed of two or more layers of cells; the wall itself being surmounted by a glistening fringe of teeth, whose edges are themselves regularly fringed with minute outgrowths. The cup seems to be formed by a development of the superior epidermis, which is raised up, and finally bursts and spreads out, laying bare the seeds.

The archegones of Marchantia are very curious bodies, while the elater and spores are even still more so. These are elongated cells, each containing a double spiral fibre coiled up in the interior. It is the elasticity of this which tears apart the cell-membrane, and sends forth the spores with a jerk, and thus assists in their dispersion. Marchantia is the type of the malloid Hepaticæ.

Musci, Bryophyta.

Mosses are a beautiful class of non-vascular cryptogams. Linnæus called them *servi*, servants or workmen, as they seem to labour to produce vegetation in places where soil is not already formed. The Bryophyta form three natural divisions: the Bryinæ, or true mosses; the Sphagnaceæ, or peat-mosses; and the Hepaticæ, or liverworts. The two first are commonly united. In these the sexual organs consist of antheridia and archegonia, but they are of simpler structure than will be found in ferns; and the first generation from the spore is asexual.

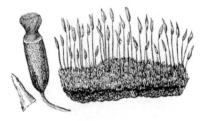

Fig. 301.—Screw-moss.

The common or wall screw-moss (Fig. 301) grows almost everywhere, and if examined closely, is seen to have springing from its base numerous very slender stems, each terminating in a dark brown case, which encloses antheroids. If a patch of the moss is gathered when in this state, and the green part of the base is put into water, the threads of the fringe will uncoil and disentangle themselves in a most curious and beautiful manner; from this circumstance the plant takes its popular name of screw-moss. The leaf usually consists of either a single or a double layer of cells, having flattened sides, by which they adhere one to another. The leaf-cells (Fig. 302) of the Sphagnum or bog-moss exhibit a curious departure from the ordinary type; they are large, polygonal, and elongated, and contain spiral fibres loosely coiled in their interior. The young leaf does not differ from the older; both are evolved by a gradual process of differentiation.

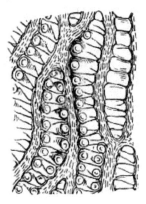

Fig. 302.—Section of leaf of Sphagnum moss, showing large cells of spiral fibres and connecting apertures.

Mosses, like liverworts, possess both antheridia and pistillida, which are engaged in the process of fructification. The fertilized cell becomes gradually developed into a conical body elevated upon a footstalk, the walls of the flask-shaped body carrying the higher part upwards as a *calyptra* or hood upon its summit, while the lower part remains to form a kind of collar round the base. These spore-capsules are closed on their summit by *opercula* or lids, and their mouths when laid open are surrounded by a beautiful toothed fringe, termed the *peristome*. This fringe is shown in Fig. 303, in the centre of a capsule of Funaria, with its peristome *in situ*. The fringes of teeth are variously constructed, and are of great service in discriminating the genera. In *Neckera antipyretica* the peristome is double, the inner being composed of teeth united by cross bars, forming a very pretty trellis. The seed spores are contained in the upper part of the capsule, where they are clustered round the central pillar, termed the *columella*; and at the time of maturity, the interior of the capsule is almost entirely occupied by spores.

Fig. 303.—Mouth of Capsule of Funaria, showing Peristome.

Fig. 304.—Hair-moss in Fruit.

The undulating hair-moss, *Polytrichum undulatum* (Fig. 304), is found on moist, shady banks of pools and rivulets. The seed-vessel has a curious shaggy cap; but in its construction it is very similar to that of the screw-moss, except that the fringe around its opening is not twisted. The reproductive organs of mosses are of two kinds; the capsule containing minute spores, *archegonia*, and the *antheridia*, or male efflorescence. The capsule, *theca*, or sporangium, is lateral or terminal, sessile, or on a fruit stalk (*seta*) of various shapes, indehiscent, or bursting by four valves at the sides, or more commonly by a deciduous cup, *operculum*. When this falls the mouth of the capsule becomes exposed. The rim is crowned with tooth-like or cilia-like appendages in sets of four or multiples of that number—*peristome*. These are often brightly coloured and hydroscopic. By simply breathing upon them they suddenly fly open, and are endowed with motion, that is, if they contain spores. The spores on germination produce a green confervoid-like mass of threads, from which the young plant arises.

The Sphagnaceæ, or "bog mosses," have been separated from true mosses from the marked differences they present. The stem is more widely differentiated, and throughout its structure a rapid passage of fluid takes place. It has the power of absorbing moisture from the atmosphere, so that if a plant be placed dry in a glass of water with its rosette of leaves hanging over the edge, it acts like a syphon, and the water will drop from it until the glass is emptied. As may be supposed, the leaf is composed of large open cells, and it absorbs more water than the root. The antherids or male organs of Sphagnaceæ resemble those of liverworts, rather than those of mosses, both in form and arrangement; they are grouped in "catkins" at the tips of the lateral branches, each of the imbricated perigonal leaves enclosing a single globose antherid on a slender foot-stalk, and surrounded by long branched paraphyses of cobweb-like tenuity. The female organs, or archegones, do not differ materially in structure from those of mosses; they are grouped together in a sheath of deep green leaves at the end of the shorter lateral branchlets at the side of the rosette or terminal crown of leaves. The sporange is very uniform in all the species, and the spores are in groups of fours, as in mosses, around a hemispherical columella. These plants grow so rapidly that they soon cover a pool with thin matted bundles of branches, and as they decay they fall to the bottom, and become the foundation of the future bog or peat moss.

Felices.—Of all the spore-bearing families the ferns are the more universally known. They constitute an exceedingly numerous genera and species, and vary from low herbaceous plants of an inch in height to that of tree ferns, which attain a height of fifty or more feet, terminating in a graceful coronet of fronds or leaves. Of whatever size a fern may be, its spores are, for the most part, microscopic, produced within the sporangium by cell division, and are therefore free and variously shaped.

The true mode of development of ferns from their spores was that furnished by Nägeli, who announced the existence of antheridia. On the spore starting into life it sends out from the cell-wall of its outer coat a white tubular projection, or root fibre (Fig. 305, A, B, and C), which passes through the cell-wall of its outer coat. This attracts sufficient moisture to burst open the outer, and then it begins to increase by the subdivision of its cells, until the primary green prothallus D is formed. This falls to the ground, and, being furnished on its under side with thread-like fibres, fixes itself to the earth, and thus is developed the rhizome, or root of the future plant. In each of the antheridia, which are numerous, a cell is formed, chiefly filled with albuminous matter and free spores, each having attached a flat ribbon-like filament, or stermatoid, curled in a spiral manner. These are ultimately set free by the rupture of the cell-wall, and commence revolving rapidly by the agency of the whip-like appendage at the larger end.

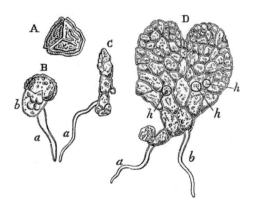

Fig. 305.—Development of the Globular Antheridium and Spermatoids of *Pteris serrulata*.

A. Spores; B, C. Early stages of development; D. Prothallus with radial fibres; *a, a* and *a, b* are stermatoids; and *h, h*. Enclosed antheridia.

The sporangia, or spore-cases, are, for the most part, globular in form, and are nearly or quite surrounded by a strong elastic ring, which in some cases is continued to form a stalk. When the spores are ripe, this ring, by its elastic force, tears open the sporangia and gives exit to a quantity of microscopic filaments, curled in corkscrew-like fashion (Figs. 305 and 307). The ring assumes various forms; in one group it passes vertically up the back of the sporangium, and is continued to a point termed the stomata, where the horizontal bursting takes place. This form is seen in Fig. 306, *a, b*. In other groups it is vertical, as in *c, c*; in others transverse, as in *d*; or apical, as at *e*; and in a few instances it is obsolete, as in *f*. These are the true ferns, and their systematic arrangement is chiefly founded on the peculiarity of the sori and sporangia, characters which become quite intelligible by the aid of the microscope.

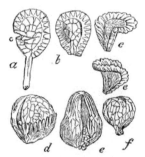

Fig. 306.—Sporangia of Polypodiaceous Ferns.

a, b. Polypodiaceæ; *c*. Cyantheineæ; *d*. Gleichenineæ; *e*. Schizeineæ; *f*. Osmundineæ.

Fig. 307.—Spores of *Deparia prolifera*.

The beautiful ringed sporangium of the fern (Fig. 307) when ruptured gives exit to the dust-like spores; these, examined under a moderate power, are seen to be sub-globose and pyramidal, the outer coat or exospore being a coloured hyaline cell with nuclei similar to the spores of mosses, but in which chlorophyll soon begins to form, and from this little green embryonic growth the organs of reproduction are formed.

In all ferns the pistillidia or archegonia are analogous to the ovules or nascent seeds of flowering plants, and contain, like them, a germinal vesicle, which becomes fertilized through the agency of the spiral filaments, and then gradually develops into an embryo plant possessing a terminal bud. This bud begins at once to unfold and push out leaves with a circinate vernation, of a very simple form at first, and growing up beneath the prothallium, coming out at the notch; single fibrous roots are at the same time sent down into the earth, the delicate expanded prothallium withers away, and the foundation of the perfect fern plant is laid. When a fern acquires a considerable stem, as in a tree fern, it consists of cellular tissue and an external cortical portion forming fibro-vascular bundles, scalariform ducts, and woody fibre. Fig. 308, *b*, shows an oblique section of the footstalk of a fern leaf with its bundle of scalariform ducts.

These observations on ferns have acquired increased interest from subsequent investigations made on the allied Cryptogams, and on the processes occurring in the impregnation of the Conifers. Not only have later researches furnished a satisfactory interpretation of the archegonia and antheridia of the mosses and liverworts, but they have made known and co-ordinated the existence of analogous phenomena in the Equisetaceæ, Lycopodiaceæ, and Rhizocarpeæ, and prove, moreover, that the bodies described by Dr. Brown in the Conifers under the name of "corpuscles" are analogous to the *archegonia* of the Cryptogams; so that a link is hereby formed between these groups and the higher flowering plants.

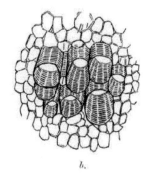

a.   b.

Fig. 308.—*a.* Vertical section of Fern-root, showing spiral tissue and cells filled with granular bodies; *b.* Section of Footstalk.

Equisetaceæ.—The development of *Horse-tails* (Fig. 309), the name by which they are commonly known, corresponds in some respects with that of ferns. They comprise a little group, and the whole of their structure is composed in an extraordinary degree by silex, so that even when the organic portion has been destroyed by prolonged maceration in strong acid, a consistent skeleton still remains. It is this flinty material that constitutes their chief interest for microscopists. A portion of their silicious particles is distributed in two lines, arranged parallel to the axis of the plant, others are grouped into oval forms, and connected by a chain as in a necklace. The form and arrangement of the crystals are better seen under polarised light. Plate VIII., No. 170, a portion of the epidermis, forms an extremely beautiful object. Sir David Brewster pointed out that each silicious particle has a regular axis of double refraction. What is usually said to be the fructification of the Equisetaceæ forms a cone or spike-like extremity to the top of the stem (Fig. 309), the whole resembling a series of spike-like branches (the real stem being a horizontal rhizome), and a cluster of shield-like discs, each of which carries a circle of sporanges that open by longitudinal slits to set free the spores which are attached to it in two pairs of elastic filaments (shown in Fig. 291, F, G), *elaters*; these are at first coiled up around the spore in the manner represented at G, but on their liberation they extend themselves as shown at F. The slightest moisture will close them up again, and their purpose having been served in the distribution of the spores, they are no longer required. If a number of spores be spread out on a glass-slip under the microscope and, while watching, a bystander breathes upon them, they immediately respond, are set in motion, presenting a curious appearance, but as soon as the hydroscopic effect has passed off they return to their previous condition. These spores can be mounted in a cell with a movable cover, and made to exhibit the same effect over and over again.

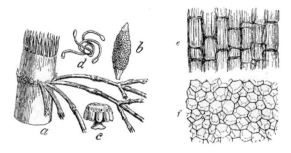

Fig. 309.—Equisetum giganticum.

a. Fragment of stem showing mode of branching out; *b.* Cone or spike of fructification; *c.* Scale detached from cone; *d.* Spore with elastic filaments; *e.* Vertical section of stem; *f.* Transverse section showing hexagonal cells.

The vascular tissue of the Equisetaceæ (Fig. 309, *e, f*) shows them to be of a higher grade than the ferns. More recently discovered Horse-tails, of Brazil, grow to a gigantic size, but even these are comparatively small when compared with the Calamites, and other fossil Equisetaceæ of the coal measures and new red sandstone. They all require a calcareous flinty soil for growth. A spring water-course making its way to the sea, as in the Chines of the Isle of Wight, is very favourable, the author having gathered them more than once in Bramble Chine.

Nearly allied to ferns is a little group of small aquatic plants, the Rhizocarpeæ (pepperworts), which either float on the water or creep along shallow bottoms. These are chiefly curious from having two kinds of spores produced from separate sporanges; smaller and larger "microspores" undergoing progressive sub-division without the formation of a distinct prothallium; each cell giving origin to an antherozoid, a generative process said to belong exclusively to flowering plants, corresponding indeed to the pollen grains of higher plants.

Structure of Phanerogamiæ or Flowering Plants.

The two great divisions of the vegetable kingdom are known as Cryptogamia and Phanerogamia. It does not follow, however, that there is any abrupt break between the two, as will appear from the context. Although it is customary to speak of the flowering plants as a higher grade of life, yet there is an intermediary class of Phanerogamiæ in which the conspicuous parts of the generative system partake of a condition closely resembling those of the higher Cryptogamiæ, observed in Gymnosperms, Coniferæ, and Cycadæ. So it may be said the distinctive character of the former is that of reproduction by seeds rather than flowers. The progress of botanical science during the latter half of the Victorian reign has been quite as remarkable as that of histology; while the comparative physiology and morphology of plants have perhaps advanced even more rapidly because the ground was newer. The consequence is that the specialisation of botanical science has been brought about con-currently with a more comprehensive nomenclature. The chief cause in this instance of modern specialisation is utility. "If we look at the great groups of plants from a broad point of view, it will be seen that the fungi and the phanerogams occupy public attention on other grounds than do the algæ, mosses and ferns. Algæ are especially a physiologist's group, employed in questions on nutrition, reproduction, and cell division and growth. The Bryophyta and Pteridophyta, are, on the other hand, the domain of the morphologist concerned with such questions as the alternations of generations and the evolution of the higher plants.

"Fungi and phanerogams, while equally or even more employed by specialists in morphology and physiology, appeal widely to general interest, and evidently so on the ground of utility. Without saying that this enhances the importance of either group, it certainly attracts scientific attention to them. However, the histology of the minute cell, in addition to its importance from an academical point of view, has a special interest for the microscopist."

It would be impossible to find anything more remarkable in histology than the detailed agreement in the structure and behaviour of the nucleus in the higher plants and the higher animals, an agreement which is conspicuously manifest in those special divisions which take place during the maturation of the sexual cells.

So with regard to the question of "alternation of generations." We have known since the important discoveries of Hofmeister that the development of a large part of the vegetable kingdom involves a regular alternation of two distinct generations, the one which is sexual being constantly succeeded, so far as the normal cycle is concerned, by the other which is asexual. This alternation is most marked in the mosses and ferns. In the Bryophyta the ordinary moss or liverwort plant is the sexual generation of the ovum, which, when fertilised, gives rise to the moss-fruit, and represents the asexual stage. The latter is once more seen to form spores from which the sexual plant is again developed.

In the Pteridophyta the alternation is equally regular, but the relative development of the two generations is totally different, the sexual form being the insignificant prothallus, while the whole fern-plant, as we ordinarily know it, is the asexual generation.

The thallus of some of the lower Bryophyta is quite comparable with the prothallus of a fern, so as regards the sexual generation there is no difficulty in seeing the relation of the two classes; but when we come to the asexual generation or sporophyte the case is totally different. There is no appreciable resemblance between the fruit of any of the Bryophyta and the plant of any vascular Cryptogam.

"It is now known that in the higher plants a remarkable numerical change takes place in the constituents of the nucleus of the cell shortly before fertilisation. In angiospermous plants a reduction of the chromosomes occurs shortly before differentiation of the sexual cells. Thus, in the case of the lily, fertilisation is not the simple fusion of nuclear bodies. These spheres are seen to fuse in pairs, and then by position to determine the plane of first cleavage of the ovum; agreeing, in fact, closely with what is observed to take place in the animal kingdom."

In the higher grades of plants it will be evident that the several tissues that compose their bodies are not found in the root, stem, and leaf without definite order and purpose, but that they are grouped into systems for the performance of different kinds of work. In all flowering plants at least three different systems may be clearly distinguished. These are the epidermal or boundary tissue system, the fundamental or ground tissue system, and the fibro-vascular or conducting system. All three systems of tissue originate from meristem cells, located at the growing point of the stem and root.

Although these systems characterise the higher types of plants, the elementary tissues (represented in Plate XIII. and in other figures) enter alike into the several component parts of nearly all plants. The stem, the branch, and the root, are alike constituted of an outer coating which affords a mechanical support, and once formed takes no further share in the economy of the plant, excepting that of assisting to convey fluid from the roots to the branches and leaves, an action more of a capillary nature than vital. The nourishment of the plant is brought about by other material structures, as the pith, the cortex, the cambium, and so forth, all of which greatly assist in the formative process. The woody portion of the plants is especially concerned in furnishing support to the softer pulpy textures, while the tissues of leaves and flowers are chiefly composed of cells compactly held together by protoplasmic or albuminoid matter. Water, of course, enters largely into the constituents of all plants. Beneath the epidermis is another layer of importance, the parenchymatous, which becomes more or less solid with the growth of the pith and cellular wall. In the pulpy substance of some leaves the epidermis presents a thin lamina of palisade-tissue, the bulk of the mesophyll consisting of spongy parenchyma or sclerenchymatous fibres (seen in Fig. 310), which also serve to show the disposition of the several layers about to be brought under notice.

Development of the Tissue Systems.—In the growing plant the embryonic cells soon become differentiated into three primary meristem layers, known as dermatogen, periblem, and phloem, from which are developed respectively the primary cortex, epidermis, and the stele or vascular cylinder. The dermatogen forms the outermost layer of cells at the growing point, and when present always develops into true epidermal tissue. In stems the dermatogen is always single-layered, while in roots it consists of several layers and develops a many-layered epidermis.

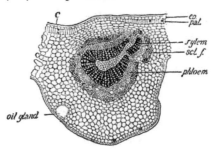

Fig. 310.—Section of Leaf of Piper.

c. Cortex; *ep.* Epidermis; *pal.* Palisade-tissue; *scl f.* Sclerenchymatous fibres of pericycle; *o.* Oil gland.

The periblem occurs immediately beneath the dermatogen, forming a hollow cylinder of tissue, which surrounds the phloem. From the periblem is developed the fundamental tissue of the primary cortex. When no dermatogen is present in the growing-point (stems of vascular cryptogams) the external layer of the periblem develops cells which perform epidermal functions. The phloem occupies the centre of the growing-point, and consists of a solid mass of somewhat elongated cells. From the phloem are developed the fibro-vascular and fundamental tissues of the vascular-cylinder or stele.

PLATE XIII.

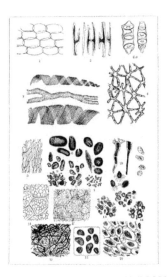

ELEMENTARY PLANT TISSUES.

Epidermal or Boundary Tissue System.—This system constitutes the external covering of the plant, and is commonly called the epidermis. It includes, besides the ordinary epidermal cells, the guard-cells of the stomata and water pores, the plant hairs or trichomes, and the epidermal or external glands. The epidermal tissues are chiefly protective in function, serving to prevent excessive evaporation from the interior tissues of the plant.

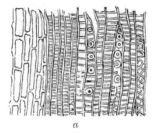

a *b*

Fig. 311.

a. Epidermis, reticulated ducts, and conjunctive palisade cells; *b.* Vertical section of alder root, woody layer, and boundary ducts.

In stems the external layer of cells, whatever its origin, is known as the epidermis, while in roots it is called the epiblema. The epidermis usually consists of a single layer of cells, but in some cases it is two or three-layered, as in the leaves of figs and begonias.

In land plants the epidermis is usually strongly cutinised, while in submerged plants it is never cutinised. The epidermis of land plants is also often waxy, the wax occurring on the surface as minute grains, rods or flakes, constituting the so-called bloom of leaves and fruits, and giving to them their glaucous appearance. Chlorophyll bodies are usually absent from the ordinary epidermal cells of land plants, while they commonly occur in the epidermal cells of aquatic plants.

Ordinary epidermal cells are usually thin-walled and transparent, and contain a nucleus and colourless watery protoplasm, but are destitute of both chlorophyll-bodies and starch-grains.

The external layers of the outer walls constitute the cuticle of the plant, while the internal layers and the radial and inner walls are composed of cellulose. The cells of the epidermis are always very compactly arranged, having their walls so closely adherent that the intercellular spaces are entirely obliterated except at the stomata and water-pores.

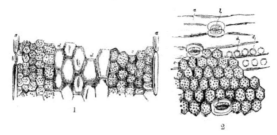

Fig. 312.

1. Vertical section of leaf of *Iris germanica*; *a, a.* Elongated cells of the epiderm; *b.* Stomata cut through longitudinally; *c, c.* Green cells of the parenchyma; *d, d.* Colourless tissue of the interior of the leaf. 2. Portion of leaf torn from its surface; *a.* Elongated cells of the cuticle; *b.* Cells of the stomata; *c.* Cells of the parenchyma; *d.* Limiting wall of the epidermic cell; *e.* Lacunæ or openings in the parenchyma corresponding to the stomata.

There are exceptions to this rule, as, for example, in *Cinchona calisaya*, which shows no trace of epidermis, this being replaced by a corky layer of tubular cells. Where this occurs in a plant to any extent, the whole of the outer tissues are displaced, and the bark consists exclusively of phloem tissues. This, although of constant occurrence in *C. calisaya*, is not so common in other species, as *C. succirubia*, the middle structure of which consists of parenchyma in which appear more or less numerous isolated store-cells, and when these are absent there is a formation of rhytidoma and displacement of the tissues containing the store-cells and ducts. The chlorophyll of *C. succirubia* is very marked, and its spectrum presents seven distinct absorption bands.

The epidermal system of plants in general includes other tissues than those already named, as the guard-cells of the stomata, the water-pores, plant-hairs or trichomes, and the external or epidermal glands, all of which are but modifications of ordinary epidermal tissue.

The Stomata or Breathing Pores are apertures in the epidermal which lie over large intercellular spaces (Fig 312, 2, *b*). These are usually bordered by two modified epidermal cells, called guard-cells. Stomata are formed in the following manner: A young epidermal cell divides into two equal portions by the formation of a septum across its middle, each half developing into a guard-cell; the septum now splits lengthwise and separates the guard-cells, leaving an aperture or stoma between them.

In the higher plants the guard-cells of the stomata are crescent-shaped and occur in pairs, the concave sides of the cells facing each other with the aperture between, while in mosses the stomata possesses but a single annular guard-cell which surrounds the aperture. The guard-cells of stomata usually contain chlorophyll-bodies in addition to the ordinary protoplasm. They have the power of increasing or diminishing the size of the aperture under the influence of light and moisture, thus regulating the amount of evaporation from the internal tissues of the plant.

Water Pores or Water Stomata are apertures in the epidermis, similar in structure to ordinary stomata, but differ from them both in function and distribution. Water-pores excrete water in the form of drops, and have their guard-cells fixed and immovable. They always occur at the ends of vasal bundles, and are found on the margin and at the apex of leaves.

Plant Hairs or Trichomes are modified epidermal cells prolonged externally, and may be either unicellular or multicellular. Each hair consists of a basal portion, or foot, which is embedded among the ordinary epidermal cells, and an apical portion or body, which is prolonged externally. Ordinary epidermal hairs are usually thin-walled, the inner layers of the wall being composed of cellulose, while the outer layer is more or less strongly cutinised. The walls may become hardened by deposits of lime-salts or silica. Sometimes the cells become glandular and secrete oily, resinous, or irritating matters, as in stinging-nettle hairs (Plate XIII., No. 19), when they are known as glandular hairs. The development of resin-passages may be observed in transverse sections of the stem of the ivy (*Hedera helix*) cut from a young succulent stem, and mounted in glycerine. The resin is seen scattered through the cortex and pith, and in the soft bast which lies outside the cambium in various stages of development, starting from a group of four cells without intercellular spaces.

Root hairs spring from the epiblema and are never cutinised, but are frequently more or less mucilaginous. The root-hairs are the principal absorbing organs of the plant, and are confined to the younger roots, occurring just above their tips. Root-hairs are never present in aquatic plants, and are absent from the roots of certain of the Coniferæ. It is a curious fact with regard to bell-heather growing in higher latitudes, that the plants possess a peculiar root structure as a protection against droughts. In most of them the sustentation of life depends upon the formation of a number of long thin filaments on their roots resembling root-hairs, which penetrate the root, forming nodular masses within it. These filaments belong to a fungus entirely parasitic to the root, and yet different from a common parasite, inasmuch as the plant in this way obtains so much of its nourishment, and when the fungus is not present, or is removed, the plant can no longer live on a peaty soil. The leaf-blade of the coarse moorland grass Nardus is likewise endowed with a singular property—that of rolling up cylindrically and spreading out again to adapt itself to the dry and wet weather of the moorlands of Scotland.

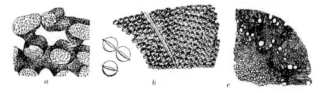

Fig. 313.

a. Section of the testa of Gourd Seed, showing communicating cells filled with colouring matter; *b.* Section of stem of Clematis, three pores separated and more highly magnified; *c.* Transverse section of same, showing medullary rays.

Fundamental or Ground Tissue System.—This system constitutes the groundwork of plants, and is the system through which the vasal bundles are distributed. The fundamental tissues are composed largely, though not wholly, of parenchyma, and are chiefly concerned in the metabolic work of plant life.

Ground tissue includes, besides ordinary parenchyma, collenchyma, selerenchymatous parenchyma, fibrous tissue, cork, laticiferous and glandular tissues. To the fundamental system also belongs the chlorophyll cells of leaves, the thin-walled cells of the pith and medullary rays, the cells of the cortex of stems and roots, and most of the soft cellular tissues in all plants.

The lower plants consist almost entirely of fundamental tissue. In the herbaceous forms of the higher plants the ground tissues largely predominate, while in woody plants they are present in much smaller proportion, the vascular tissues being the most abundant. In aquatic plants generally, the fundamental tissues constitute the principal system.

The hypoderma occurs immediately beneath the epidermis, and consists of several layers of cells. A collenchymatous hypoderma is found in the stems and petioles of most herbaceous dicotyls, and frequently occurs next the midrib of leaves, where it forms a strengthening tissue. A sclerenchymatous hypoderma occurs either as a continuous layer beneath the epidermis, as in the stems of some ferns, *Pteris aquilina*, and in leaves of the pine; or it may form numerous isolated strands beneath the epidermis, as in the stems of horsetails and in certain Umbelliferæ.

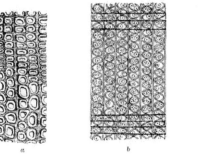

Fig. 314.

a. Tangential section of *Taxus baccata* (Yew), showing the woody fibre; *b.* Vertical section of same, spiral fibres, and ducts; *c.* Vertical section of Elm, showing ducts and dotted cells.

The endodermis is the innermost layer of the extra-stelar fundamental tissues, and always abuts on the stele or steles. In monocotyls it marks the boundary between the cortex and the central cylinder, and it is sometimes spoken of as the nucleus sheath.

In stems the endodermal cells are usually thin-walled and unlignified, having a suberous thickening band extending round the upper, lower and lateral surfaces, which in cross-section appears as a black dot on the radial wall (Fig. 314, *c.*)

According to its position in the stele, the conjunctive tissue is divided into three principal portions, viz., that portion which invests the vasal bundles, the pericycle; that portion which lies between the bundles of the stele, the interfascicular conjunctive tissue; and that which occupies the centre of the stele, the medullary conjunctive tissue. The pericycle, formerly called the pericambium, is the outermost layer of the conjunctive tissue of the stele.

The bundle-sheath of the young stem is more easily recognised than in the older stem. It is, in fact, a continuous layer of cells, whose radial walls have a characteristic dark spot on each radial wall. The bundle-sheath lies immediately outside the vascular bundles, curving slightly towards the centre of the stem in the spaces between the bundles. It is more prominent in the stem when very young, as the cells are then filled with starch granules. This layer of cells will be readily seen in sections treated with iodine.

In dicotyls and gymnosperms the medullary rays consist essentially of interfascicular ground tissue. The medullary conjunctive tissue occupies the centre of the stele, constituting the so-called pith, and usually consists of parenchymatous cells, but may contain, in addition, either stone cells, sclerenchyma fibres, laticiferous or glandular tissues.

The Fibro-vascular or Conducting Tissue System.—This system constitutes the fibrous framework of the plant, and is the system by means of which fluids are conducted from one part of the plant to another. Its function is partly to give strength and support, but principally to conduct the crude and elaborated juices to and from the leaves. It is found only in the higher plants, constituting the tough and stringy tissues in stems and roots, and the system of veins in leaves. The fibro-vascular system consists essentially of vascular tissue (ducts, tracheids, and sieve-tubes), and forms long strands—the fibro-vascular bundles—which extend vertically through the fundamental tissues of the plant. The term "fibro-vascular," as applied to the conducting system, is not strictly correct, since fibres do not always accompany the vascular elements, hence this system is often spoken of as the vascular system, and the bundles as vascular, or more briefly as vasal bundles.

That the arrangement, and course of the vascular bundles in dicotyledous stems are connected with those of the leaves is an obvious fact. It may be seen in sections of Helianthus, but is more markedly shown in plants with regularly decussate leaves, as Cerastium, Clematis, &c. Still, the arrangement of the bundles may differ radically from that of the leaves, and is, to a certain extent, independent of them. This will be noticed in sections of *Iberis amara*, where the bundles do not run longitudinally, but in tangential spirals. These, as Nägeli pointed out, have no direct relation with the leaves; and he recommends a series of types for investigation, in which it will be seen how closely the arrangement of the bundles is connected with the arrangement of the leaves, and the number of bundles entering the stem from each leaf: *Iberis amara*, leaves alternate, leaf-trace with one bundle; Lupinus, leaves alternate, leaf-trace with three bundles; Cerastium, leaves opposite, leaf-trace with one bundle; Clematis, leaves opposite, leaf-trace with three bundles; Stachys, leaves opposite, leaf-trace with two bundles.

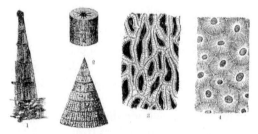

Fig. 315.

1. Transverse section of the stem of Cedar, showing xylem or wood; 2. Section of stem of Conifer, the phloem and zones of annual growth; 3. Section of an Ivory Nut, cells, and radiating pores; 4. Section of the outer or ligneous portion of same, with radiating cells.

The connection of the leaf and stem will be best seen by cutting longitudinal sections through a *young node* of Helianthus, so as to include the median plane of the leaf, or of both leaves if opposite to each other, as they often are; steep them in dilute potash for twenty-four hours and mount in glycerine. A medium power will serve for their examination. The course of the vascular bundles will appear dark through the more transparent parenchyma. The continuity of the tissues of the stem and petiole if followed will be seen to have no definite boundary between the two parts; the bundles from the petiole pass into the stem, and no bundle of the upper internode lies in the same vertical plane as that which enters from the petiole between two successive bundles of the vascular ring.

Every complete *vasal bundle* consists of xylem or wood and phloem or bast.

The former consists essentially of trachery tissue (ducts and tracheids), and may contain in addition both wood fibres and wood parenchyma. The phloem or bast consists essentially of sieve tissue, and usually contains some ordinary parenchyma. In angiosperms companion-cells always accompany the sieve-tubes in the phloem, while in gymnosperms they are absent.

According to the relative positions of the xylem and phloem elements, there are two principal kinds of conjoint bundles—the collateral and the concentric. Of these again there are three varieties, but the experiments with leaves bring out parallel facts; that in ordinary stems the staining of the wood by an ascending coloured liquid is due, not to the passage of the coloured liquid up the substance of the wood, but to the permeability of its ducts and such of its pitted cells as are united into regular canals; and the facts showing this at the same time indicate with tolerable clearness the process by which wood is formed, for what in these cases is seen to take place with dye may be fairly presumed to take place with sap.

Taking it, then, as a fact that the vessels and ducts are the channels through which the sap is distributed, the varying permeability of their walls, and consequent formation of wood, is due to the exposure of the plant to intermittent mechanical strains, actual or potential, or both, in this way. If a trunk, a bough, shoot, or a petiole is bent by a gust of wind, the substance of its convex side is subject to longitudinal tension, the substance of its concave side being at the same time compressed. This is the primary mechanical effect. The secondary is when the tissues of the convex side are stretched, and also produce lateral compression. In short, the formation of wood is dependent upon transverse strains, such as are produced in the aerial parts of upright plants by the action of the wind.

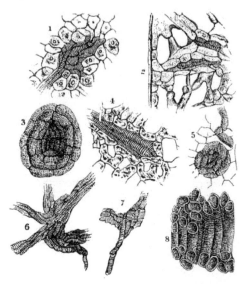

Fig. 316.—Termination of Vascular System.

1.—Absorbent organ from the leaf of *Euphorbia neriifolia*. The cluster of fibrous cells forming one of the terminations of the vascular system is here embedded in a solid parenchyma.

2.—A structure of analogous kind from the leaf of *Ficus elastica*. Here the expanded terminations of the vessels are embedded in the network parenchyma, the cells of which unite to form envelopes for them.

3.—End view of an absorbent organ from the root of a turnip. It is taken from the outermost layer of vessels. Its funnel-shaped interior is drawn as it presents itself when looked at from the outside of this layer, its narrow end being directed towards the centre of the turnip.

4.—Shows on a larger scale one of these absorbents from the leaf of *Panax Lessonii*. In this figure is clearly seen the way in which the cells of the network parenchyma unite into a closely-fitting case for the spiral cells.

5.—A less-developed absorbent, showing its approximate connection with a duct. In their simplest forms these structures consist of only two fenestrated cells, with their ends bent round so as to meet. Such types occur in the central mass of the turnip, where the vascular system is relatively imperfect. Besides the comparatively regular forms of these absorbents, there are forms composed of amorphous masses of fenestrated cells. It should be added that both the regular and irregular kinds are very variable in their numbers: in some turnips they are abundant, and in others scarcely to be found. Possibly their presence depends on the age of the turnip.

6.—Represents a much more massive absorbent from the same leaf, the surrounding tissues being omitted.

7.—Similarly represents, without its sheath, an absorbent from the leaf of *Clusia flava*.

8.—A longitudinal section through the axis of another such organ, showing its annuli of reticulated cells when cut through. The cellular tissue which fills the interior is supposed to be removed.

In concentric bundles one of the elements, either the xylem or the phloem, occupies the centre, and is more or less surrounded by the other, as seen in Fig. 310. Meristem tissue is never present, hence concentric bundles are always closed. They, however, occur in the stems of most ferns, and are always surrounded by a pericycle and endodermis, and should be regarded as steles. Concentric bundles with a central phloem occur in the rhizomes of some monocotyles, as Calamus, Iris, Convallaria, &c.

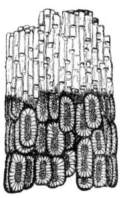

Fig. 317.—Vertical section of Sugar-cane Stem showing parachyma and crystalline cells, × 200 diameters.

The Stele, or Vascular Cylinder, is developed from the phloem of the growing plant, and consists of one or more vasal bundles imbedded in fundamental tissue, the whole being enclosed by a pericycle and an endoderm. The typical *stele* includes all the tissues evolved by the endodermis, which, however, forms no part of the vascular cylinder itself, but merely surrounds it. The pericycle is always the outermost layer of the tissues of the stele, while the endodermis is the innermost layer of the extra-stelar tissues.

The arboreus type of stem can be best followed by making sections of a twig of the elm (*Ulmus campestris*), which will be found to be cylindrical hirsute, green or brown according to age, the latter colour being due to the formation of *cork*. Small brown excrescences are scattered over its surface; these are termed *lenticels*. The cork will be seen to lie immediately below the epidermis, and to consist of cubical cells, with little or no cell contents; they are arranged in radial rows, without intercellular spaces. The walls of these cork cells will stain yellowish-brown with Schultze's solution. Treat a thin section with sulphuric acid and the walls will swell out and gradually lose their sharpness of outline, with the exception of the cuticularised outer wall of the epidermis and the *cork*. This material is occasionally found developed in the twigs of the elm, so that it can be separated as thick radial plates of tissue.

"By comparing sections of twigs cut of various ages, the following information may be gleaned: That cork cambium, or *phellogen*, appears as a layer of cortical cells below the epidermis, and that these divide parallel to the surface of the stem. The result of successive divisions in this direction is the formation of secondary tissue, which develops externally as cork, internally as phelloderm. The true cork cambium consists of only a single cell in each radial row, from which, by successive division, all these secondary tissues are derived—*i.e.*, cambium of vascular bundles. As stems grow older, layers of cork appear successively further and further from the external surface; not only the cortex, but also the outer portions of the phloem are thus cut off from physiological connection with the inner tissue. The term *bark* is applied to tissues thus cut off, together with the cork which forms the physiological boundary. The stem of Vitis affords a good example of such successive layers of cork."

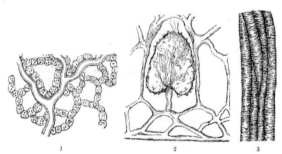

Fig. 318.

1. Laticiferous Tissue; 2. Vertical section of a Leaf of the India-rubber Tree, with a central gland; 3. Vertical cast of spiral tubes of Opuntia.

For the study of *sieve-tubes* take the vegetable marrow, in which they are of extraordinary size. Cut transverse sections of the stem and stain with eosin, and mount them in glycerine. The general arrangement will be seen to differ from that of most other herbaceous plants. Below the epidermis a thick walled band of sclerenchyma with lignified walls will be seen distinct from the vascular bundles, which readily take a stain. The vascular bundles are separate and distinct, and the structure of the bundle is abnormal, there being in each a separate central mass of xylem, with the phloem masses lying, the one central, the other in the peripheral side. Between the xylem and the phloem masses is the cambium layer. The structure being the same in both will serve for the study of the punctate sieve-plates; these are readily stained with eosin, as shown in Sach's text-book.

Laticiferous Tissues (Fig. 318).—In cutting sections of latex care must be taken to at once transfer them to alcohol so as to prevent the flow of the latex from the cells, otherwise the laticiferous vessels will be much less easily traced. The better method is to plunge the root of the dandelion (*Leontodon taraxacum*), after cleaning, into alcohol, and there let it remain until it has become hardened; then cut thin tangential sections from the phloem, and longitudinal sections through the cambium, and mount them in potash and glycerine. The laticiferous vessels appear circular in the transverse sections with brown contents; these are distributed in groups round the central xylem. Observe in such sections the presence of sphere crystals of inulin. These are formed quite irrespective of the cell-walls.

Laticiferous cells are readily seen in the cortex of *Euphorbia splendens*, cut just outside the vascular ring. Long tubes will be seen to run through the cortical parenchyma, with thick cellulose walls and granular contents. These are the laticiferous cells, the branching of which distinguishes them from the preceding structure. Included in the granular contents are starch grains of a peculiar dumb-bell form.

Leaf or Petiole.—The general morphology of leaf tissue is essentially the same as that of the stem from which it proceeds. In the typical monostotic stem of Phanerogamæ each leaf receives a portion of the stele or central cylinder of the stem. Such portion is termed a meristele, and may be either entire or split up into a number of schizosteles.

The microscopical structure of leaves should be studied in the whole organ, and by the aid of isolating elements. The whole or portion of a leaf should be soaked in chloral hydrate solution; this will render it transparent, whereby the internal structure can be studied as a whole. Sections should be prepared from fresh leaves, or dried ones softened by soaking in water. Cut them transversely, both in the direction of the mid-rib and at right angles to it. This is best effected by placing the material between two pieces of elder pith or fresh carrot. Sections of the whole are made and transferred to a dish of water. Leaf sections are easily made for examination by macerating the leaves in solution of caustic potash varying in strength from one to five per cent. The epidermis on both sides may be detached, and the elements of the mesophyll and vascular bundles isolated for separate examination.

Potassium permanganate proves to be a useful reagent. A weak solution causes the protoplasmic structures to swell up, thus assisting in the observation of the structure of the chromatophores. This solution may also be employed as a macerating fluid. Beautiful preparations are obtained in this way of the sieve-tubes of Vitis.

Special structural peculiarities are to be observed in the leaves of various plants in which the epidermis consists of more than a single layer of cells (*e.g.*, the leaves of Ficus, Peperaceæ, Begoniaceæ, &c.), cystoliths in the cells of the epidermis of Urtica; glandular structure in Ruta, Psorales; the coriaceous leaves of the Cherry Laurel, and the cylindrical leaves of Stonecrop (*Sedum acre*).

Reproductive Organs.—The development of the rudiments of flowers is of an extremely interesting nature, and the complete flower should be carefully studied. Median sections are best suited for the purpose. In the large majority of plants the calyx is developed first, then the corolla, and next the stamens. Preparations should be made from materials hardened in alcohol, or first fixed with a strong solution of picric acid and then hardened in alcohol.

Pollen-grains.—Microspores are found lying free in sections made of the reproductive organs; these may be transferred to a glycerine fluid and examined under a high power. They are mostly spherical, with granular protoplasmic contents, in which with much difficulty two nuclei can be made out. Mount and examine, as types of the various forms of granules, the pollen of Helianthus, Althœa, Cucurbita, Ænothera, Orchis, Mimosa, Tulipa, &c. Mount any of these pollen-grains in a weak solution of cane-sugar (about five per cent.), examine with a high power, and note the configuration of their walls with a medium power under polarised light. If transverse sections be made from very young buds, the development of the anther and the pollen may be traced. The material should be preserved in strong alcohol, and the sections treated with equal parts of alcohol and glycerine, and exposed in a watch-glass that the alcohol may evaporate. By this method sections may be prepared for illustrating the formation of the *tapetum*, special mother-cells, and division of the nucleus.

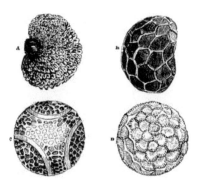

Fig. 319.—Pollen Grains.

A. Pollen-grain of Clove-pink; B. Poppy; C. Passion-flower (*Passiflora cærulea*); D. *Cobæa scandens*.

Starch Granules.—One of the most universally distributed materials found in plants is starch composed of two substances, *granulose*, which constitutes by far the largest part, and a skeleton of *farinose*. It is only the former of these that stains blue with iodine solutions; the latter partially assumes a brownish colour. The structure of starch granules is not of equal density throughout; the hilum or nuclear portion is most conspicuous, around which the rest of the material is deposited in layers, indicative of stratification. The several layers next to the hilum are less dense than those farthest from it. The position of the hilum determines the form of the grain, a few being rounded, others oval or elongated. The grain also contains different proportions of water; this conveys the appearance of concentric lines or curves about the nucleus. The latter is more conspicuous in the potato starches, as seen in Plate XIII., Nos. 6-15. Starch grains, in nearly all cases, are formed by the agency of proteid bodies, either chloroplasts or amyloplasts, and under the action of sunlight are gradually broken up and employed in the process of growth. There are some plants, however, notably the Compositæ, in which another carbohydrate, *inulin*, takes the place of starch from the first, and is used as a reserve food material. For this reason we look in vain for starch in the cells of Inula, Taraxacum, &c. From the whole group of fungi starch is absent; this seems to explain the fact that chlorophyll, or colouring matter, is rarely met with in the fungi, hence their inability to utilize, like green plants, carbon-dioxide as food.

Fig. 320.—Swollen Potato Starch, after the application of potassium hydrate. (Magnified 210 diameters.)

The tissues which most commonly contain starch, or which contain it in largest quantity, are those of the parenchymatous series, though it sometimes occurs in the latex of laticiferous tissues, and even in ducts and tracheids. In the stems of Dicotyledons it occurs chiefly in the parenchyma of the middle and inner bark, in the medullary ray cells, and in the cells of the pith. In the roots of these plants it has a similar distribution, being for the most part confined to the middle or inner bark and the medullary rays, pith not being present in these organs. In succulent stems and roots, of course, it also commonly occurs in the xylem tissues of the fibro-vascular bundles.

A study of the various kinds of starches is important, since this material is very largely used as an adulterant. Other than microscopical means of detecting frauds are practically useless; assaying is tedious and expensive, while the microscope is always available and at hand. The limits of variation should be studied in starches from the same species of plants; the variations are not very wide, but in most cases characteristic, so that the discrimination is at all times an easy task. The reagents required are simply iodine and dilute potassium hydrate, aided by polarised light.

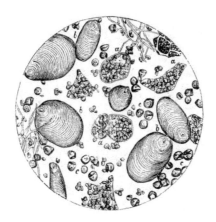

Fig. 321.

a a a. Granules and cells of cocoa; *b b b.* Arrowroot, *Tous-les-mois*; *c c c.* Tapioca starch. (Magnified 300 diameters.)

The starch grains of the potato are the best to study in the first instance on account of their large size (Fig. 320).

In arrowroot starch (Fig. 321) the stratification is almost as distinct as in that of the potato; the grains much resemble each other. Although somewhat smaller, the grains of arrowroot are more uniform in size. The starches are much used as an adulterant of drugs and various articles sold as cocoas.

Wheat-starch (Fig. 322) consists of circular flattened grains varying much in size, the central nucleus and stratification of which are very difficult to distinguish.

In the smaller starches the hilum becomes more indistinct, and without stratification, as in rice-starch, the latter being angular in shape. The hilum in other leguminous plants forms a longitudinal cleft; white rye-starch exhibits distinct cracks. Compound grains are occasionally met with, as in the oat. In Plate XIII. will be found small groups of starches taken under the same medium power for the sake of comparison. In the microscopical examination of starches first use a ⅔-inch or a ½-inch and then a ⅙-inch objective.

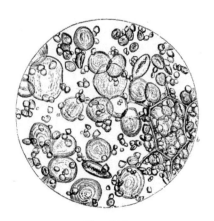

Fig. 322.

a. Husks of Wheat-starch, swollen by reagents and heat; *b.* A portion of cellulose; *c.* Rice-starch, magnified 420 diameters.

The bran of the husk of wheat when broken by grinding is seen to be composed of two coats of hexagonal cells, the outer of which is detached by the roasting process. The hexagonal cell layer is, however, so little altered as to be perfectly distinguishable under the microscope. Thus even a small admixture of roasted corn with coffee or chicory can be detected without much difficulty. As to whether starch granules should be regarded as crystalline or colloid bodies, a difference of opinion still prevails. There are, however, reasons for believing that the polarisation effects produced by starch grains are not due to crystalline structure but to stress or strain, of the same nature as the polarisation of glass when it is subject to strain. The polarising phenomena are precisely such as would be induced in any transparent solid composed of layers, the inner of which being kept in a state of stress by the compression exerted by the outer layers. Moreover, when by use of a swelling reagent, such as caustic potash solution, the outer wall of the starch is made to expand by the imbibition of water, the polarisation effects immediately disappear. Were the solid particles of crystal thus forced apart by water each particle would still exhibit polarisation phenomena.

Want of space will not permit me to further enlarge upon other micro-chemical substances that enter into the composition of plants; as, for example, the oil secreting glands. These when present take the place of starch. There is, however, one product among the cell contents of plants of some interest to the microscopist—those extremely fine crystals known as *raphides*, composed of calcium-phosphate and oxalate. Mr. Gulliver insisted upon the value of raphides as characteristic of several families of plants. Schleiden states that "needle-formed crystals, in bundles of from twenty to thirty in a cell, are present in almost all plants," and that so really practical is the presence or absence of raphides, that by studying them he has been able to pick out pots of seedling Onagraceæ, which had been accidentally mixed with pots of other seedlings of the same age, and at that period of growth when no other botanical character would have been so readily sufficient.

If we examine a portion of the layers of an onion (Plate XIV., No. 3), or a thin section of the stem or root of the garden rhubarb (No. 4), we shall find many cells in which either bundles of needle-shaped crystals or masses of a stellate form occur, not strictly raphides.

Raphides were first noticed by Malpighi in Opuntia, and subsequently described by Jurine and Raspail. According to the latter observer, the needle-shaped or acicular are composed of phosphate, and the stellate of oxalate of lime. There are others having lime as a basis, in combination with tartaric, malic, and citric acids, all of which are destroyed by acetic acid; others are soluble in many of the fluids employed in mounting. These crystals vary in size from the $\frac{1}{40}$th of an inch, while others are as small as the $\frac{1}{1000}$th. They occur in all parts of the plant; in the stem, bark, leaf, petals, fruit, root, and even in the pollen, and occasionally in the interior of cells. In certain species of aloe, as *Aloe verrucosa*, we are able to discern small silky filaments; these are bundles of the acicular form of raphides, and probably, as in sponges, act as a skeleton support to the internal soft pulpy mass.

PLATE XIV.

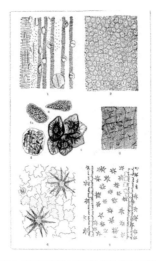

STELLATE AND CRYSTALLINE TISSUE OF PLANTS.

In portions of the cuticle of the medicinal squill (*Scilla maritima*) large cells are found full of needle-shaped crystals. These cells, however, do not lie in the same plane as the smaller cells of the cuticle. In the cuticle of an onion every cell is occupied either by an octahedral or a prismatic crystal of calcium oxalate. In some specimens the octahedral form predominates; in others, even from the same plant, the crystals are prismatic and arranged in a stellate form, as in that of the grass (*Pharus cristatus*). (Plate XIV., No. 6.)

Raphides of peculiar figure are found in the bark of certain trees. In the hickory (*Carya alba*) may be observed masses of flattened prisms having both extremities pointed. In vertical sections from the stem of *Elæagnus angustifolia*, numerous raphides of large size are embedded in the pith, and also found in the bark of the apple-tree, and in elm seeds, every cell containing two or more minute crystals.

In the Graminaceæ, especially the canes; in the *Equisetum hyemale*, or Dutch rush; in the husk of rice, wheat, and other grains, silica in some form or other is abundant. Some have beautifully-arranged masses of silica with raphides. The leaves of *Deutzia scabia*, No. 7, are remarkable for their stellate hairs, developed from the cuticle of both their upper and under surfaces; forming most interesting and attractive objects examined under polarised light. (Plate VIII., No. 173.)

Silica is found in the structure of Rubiaceæ both in the stem and leaves, and, if present in sufficient thickness, depolarises light. This is especially the case in the glandular hairs on the margins of the leaves. One of the order Compositæ, a plant popularly known as the "sneezewort" (*Archillæ ptarmica*), has a large amount of silica in the hairs found about the serratures of its leaves.

All plants are provided with hairs; some few with hairs of a defensive character. Those in the *Urtica dioica*, commonly called the *Stinging-nettle*, are glandular hairs, developed from the cuticle, and contain an irritating fluid; in other hairs a circulation is visible: examined under a power of 100 diameters, they present the appearance seen at Plate XIII., No. 19.

Fig. 323.

A. Cotton; B. Fibres of Flax; C. Filaments of Silk; D. Wool of Sheep.

The fibrous tissue of plants is of great value in many manufactures. It supplies material for our linens, cordage, paper, and other industries. This tissue is remarkable for toughness of fibre, and exhibits an approach to indestructibility, in the use it is put to in connection with the electric light. It is of importance, then, to be able to distinguish it from other fibres with which it is often mixed in various manufactures. Here the use of the microscope is found of considerable importance. In flax and hemp, in which the fibres are of great length, there are traces of transverse markings at short intervals. In the rough condition in which flax is imported into this country, the fibres have been separated, to a certain extent, by a process termed *hackling*, and further subjected to hackling, maceration, and bleaching, before it can be reduced to the white silky condition required by the spinner and weaver, and finally assumes the appearance of structureless tubes, Fig. 323 B. China-grass, New Zealand flax, and some other plants produce a similar material, but are not so strong, in consequence of the outer membrane containing more *lignine*. It is important to the manufacturer that he should be able to determine the true character of some of the textures employed in articles of clothing; this he may do by the aid of the microscope. In linen we find each component thread made up of the longitudinal, unmarked fibres of flax; but if cotton has been mixed, we recognise a flattened, more or less rounded band, as in Fig. 323 A, having a very striking resemblance to hair, which, in reality, it is; since, in the condition of elongated cells, it lines the inner surface of the pod. These, again, should he contrasted with the filaments of silk, Fig. 323 C, and also of wool, Fig. 323 D. The latter may be at once recognised by the zigzag transverse markings on its fibres. The surface of wool is covered with furrowed and twisted fine cross lines, of which there are from 2,000 to 4,000 in an inch. On this structure depends its *felting* property, in judging of fleeces, attention should be paid to the fineness and elasticity of the fibre—the furrowed and scaly surface, as shown by the microscope, the quantity of fibre in a given surface, the purity of the fleece, upon which depend the success of the scouring and subsequent operations.

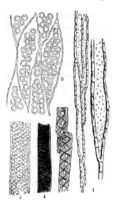

Fig. 324.

1. Woody Fibre from the root of the Elder, exhibiting small pores; 2. Woody fibre of fossil wood, showing large pores; 3. Woody fibre of fossil wood, bordered with pores and spiral fibres; 4. Fossil wood from coal.

In the mummy-cloths of the Egyptians flax only was used, whereas the Peruvians used cotton alone. By the many improvements introduced into manufacturing processes, flax has been reduced to the fineness and texture of silk, and even made to resemble other materials.

Fossil Plants.—It is well known that the primordial forests furnish a number of families of plants familiar to the modern algæologist. The cord-like plant, *Chorda filium*, known as "dead men's ropes," from its proving fatal at times to the too adventurous swimmer who gets entangled in its thick wreaths, had a Lower Silurian representative, known to palæontologists as *Palæochorda*, or ancient chorda, which existed, apparently, in two species,—a larger and a smaller. The still better known *Chondrus crispus*, the Irish moss, or Carrageen moss, has likewise its apparent, though more distant representative, in chondritis, a Lower Silurian algal, of which there seems to exist at least three species. The fucoids, or kelpweeds, appear to have also their representatives in such plants as *Fucoides gracilis*, of the Lower Silurians of the Malverns; in short, the Thallogens of the first ages of vegetable life seem to have resembled in the group, and in at least their more prominent features, the algæ of the existing time. And with the first indications of land we pass from the thallogens to the acrogens—from the seaweeds to the fern-allies. The Lycopodiaceæ, or club-mosses, bear in the axils of their leaves minute circular cases, which form the receptacles of their spore-like seeds. And when high in the Upper Silurian system, and just when preparing to quit it for the Lower Old Red Sandstone, we detect our earliest terrestrial organisms, we find that they are composed exclusively of those little spore-receptacles.

The existing plants whence we derive our analogies in dealing with the vegetation of this early period contribute but little, if at all, to the support of animal life. The ferns and their allies remain untouched by the grazing animals. Our native club-mosses, though once used in medicine, are positively deleterious; horsetails (*Equisetaceæ*), though harmless, so abound in silex, which wrap them round with a cuticle of stone, that they are rarely cropped by cattle; while the thickets of fern which cover our hill and dell, and seem so temptingly rich and green in their season, scarce support the existence of a single creature, and remain untouched, in stem and leaf, from their first appearance in spring until they droop and wither under the frosts of early winter.

The flora of the coal measures was the richest and most luxuriant, in at least individual productions, with which the fossil botanist has formed an acquaintance. Never before or since did our planet bear so rank a vegetation as that of which the numerous coal seams and inflammable shales of the carboniferous period form but a portion of the remains—the portion spared, in the first instance, by dissipation and decay, and in the second by denuding agencies. Nevertheless almost all our coal—the stored-up fuel of a world—

is not, as it is often said to be, the product of destroyed forests of conifers and flora of the profuse vegetation of the earliest periods in the history of our globe. Later investigations show that our coal measures are the compressed accumulations of peat-bogs which, layer by layer, have sunken down under the superimposed weight of the next. The vertical stems of coniferous trees became imbedded by a natural process of decay, and were subsequently overwhelmed in the erect position in which they are found. The true grasses scarcely appear in the fossil state at all. For the first time, amid the remains of a flora that seems to have had but few flowers—the Oolitic ages—do we detect, in a few broken fragments of the wings of butterflies, decided traces of the flower-sucking insects. Not, however, until we enter into the great Tertiary division do these become numerous. The first bee makes its appearance in the amber of the Eocene, locked up hermetically in its gem-like tomb—an embalmed corpse in a crystal coffin—along with fragments of flower-bearing herbs and trees. Her tomb remains to testify to the gradual fitting up of our earth as a place of habitation for creatures destined to seek delight for the mind and eye, as certainly as for the proper senses, and in especial marks the introduction of the stately forest trees, and the arrival of the charmingly beautiful flowers that now deck the earth.[62]

CHAPTER II.

The Sub-kingdom Protozoa.

The consideration of the whole special group of organisms forming the subject matter of this chapter, under the heading of Protozoa, were formerly included among Infusoria, which also embraced every kind of microscopical aquatic body, whether belonging to the vegetable or animal series. A more critical survey of the organisation and affinities of Infusoria and the members which constituted the group led to a re-arrangement, which has been very generally accepted as forming a sub-kingdom, Protozoa. This may be defined as embracing all those forms of life, referable to the lowest grade of the animal kingdom, whose members for the most part are represented by organisms possessing a single cell or aggregation of cells (and also included under the general term of unicellular organisms) the whole of which are engaged in feeding, moving, respiring, and reproducing by segmentation or fission much in the same way as that of the unicellular plants described in a previous chapter. Following out this sub-division of the entire series of Protozoa, the several groups range themselves into four readily distinguishable sections. In the first, the most lowly organised and most abundant have no oral orifice in the literal meaning of the word, food being intercepted at any point of the surface of the body. This most simple elementary type of structure of the Protozoa is represented in the Amœba and Actinophrys, the various representatives of the Foraminifera, and certain Flagellata, as Spumella and Anthrophysa. Next in the ascending scale is a group of Protozoa, in which, though differentiation has not proceeded so far as to arrive at the constitution of a distinct oral aperture, the inception of food substance is limited to a discoidal area occupying the anterior extremity of the body and is associated with the special food-arresting apparatus. To this section of the Protozoa are relegated the minuter flagellate, "collar-bearing" animals, and also the entire group of sponges or Porifera.

GREGARINIDA, POLYCYSTINA, FORAMINIFERA, ROTIFERA, ETC.

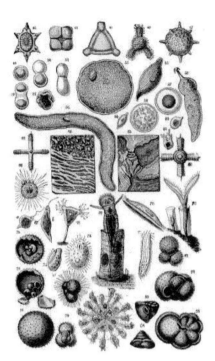

Tuffen West, del. Edmund Evans.

PLATE III.

In the third section the highest degree of organisation is arrived at. Here is represented a single, simple, often highly-differentiated oral aperture or true mouth. Associated with this section are found the majority of those organisms that collectively constitute the class Infusoria in the proper acceptation of the term, and it embraces the majority of the Ciliata, the Cilio-flagellata, as Euglena, Chilomonas, &c., in which the presence of a distinct and circumscribed oral aperture is clearly seen. With the fourth and remaining section of Protozoa, the oral or inceptive apparatus exhibits a highly characteristic structural modification. This is not restricted to a definite area, nor is it associated with the entire surface of the body, but it consists of a number of flexible, retractile, tentacle-like organs radiating from diverse and definite regions of the periphery, each of which subserves as a tubular sucking-mouth, or for the purpose of grasping food. These may be literally described as many-mouthed, and have been appropriately designated Polystomata. The true zoological position of the Spongida or Porifera is not finally settled, the members of this important section having been formerly regarded as a subordinate group of the Rhizopoda or an independent class of the Protozoa; consequently a tendency has been shown to assign to them a position more nearly approximating to that of the Cœlenterata, or zoophytes and corals, or place them among the more highly organised tissue-constructed animals, the Metazoa, these being characterised by groups of cells set apart to perform certain functions for the whole animal. A division of labour is seen to be marked in these lower animals as the organism becomes more specialised, and the number of functions a cell performs becomes more and more limited as the body becomes more complex.

It has been found convenient to adopt the following definition of the Infusoria as one more generally acceptable. The Protozoa in their adult condition are furnished with prehensile or locomotive organs, that take the form of cilia, flagella, or of adhesive or suctorial tentacula, but not of simple pseudopodia; their zooids are essentially unicellular, free swimming or sedentary; they are either naked, loricate, or inhabit a simple, mucilaginous matrix; single or united in aggregations, in which the individual units are distinctly recognisable; not united and forming a single gelatinous plasmodium, as in Mycetozoa, nor immersed within and lining the interior cavities of a complex protoplasmic and mostly spiculiferous skeleton, as in the Spongida, their food substances being intercepted by a single distinct oral aperture, or by several apertures through a limited terminal region or through the entire area of the general surface of the body. They increase by simple longitudinal or transverse fission, by external or internal gemmation or division, preceded mostly by a quiescent or encysted state, into a greater or less number of sporular bodies. Sexual elements, as represented by true ova or spermatozoa, are entirely absent, but two or more zooids frequently coalesce as an antecedent process to the phenomena of open formation.[63]

The infusorial body in its simplest type of development, as in Amœba, exhibits a structural composition substantially corresponding with that of the lowest organised tissue cell. There is no distinct bounding membrane, or cell-wall, and it is throughout, and apart from the nucleus or endopart, one continuous mass of granular matter, but otherwise homogeneous and undifferentiated protoplasm. Professor Greef, who has made a study of the Amœba, describes motor fibrils in the exoplasm which are active and large in *A. terricola*. These are readily seen by staining with osmic acid, and, after washing this out with water, immersing in a weak alcoholic solution. In Amœba so prepared and examined with a high power, the whole body will be seen to be surrounded by a distinct double integumentary layer. Highly refractive bodies may also be seen in the interior, connected together by extremely fine filaments. Professor Greef concludes that here we have to do with muscular fibrillæ, which traverse the contractile outer zone in a radial direction and there terminate for the time being. By a similar method, axial filaments can be demonstrated in Heliozoa; these, it is believed, are the true motors of their pseudopodia, and also the axial structures of the Acineta, a marine animal related to ciliate infusoria.

In the Amœba, at one time well known as the *Proteus animalcule*, Fig. 325, the marvellous body creeps onward in a flowing manner, occasionally and languidly emitting a single pseudopod first on one side, then on the other. More commonly it puts on a dendroid or palmate form; then again it assumes more or less grotesque shapes in which almost any conceivable image may be imagined. The body, as will be seen in this highly-magnified figure, is full of granules (with the exception of a thin clear outer hyaline zone), and near the centre is a globular or discoid body known as the nucleus, composed of slightly denser material than that which surrounds it. The division of the body into two is preceded by a division of this nucleus. Near the latter is a clear spherical space—the contractile vacuole—which gradually expands, and then rather suddenly collapses and reappears at the same spot, the systole and diastole being slow and continuous. The contractile vacuole contains a clear liquid which is expelled on the collapse of the vacuole. This organ probably serves the double function of respiration and excretion. The Amœba is omnivorous, chiefly a vegetarian, and, therefore, found on the ooze of ponds or on the under surface of the leaves of aquatic plants, especially among Confervæ. It can be readily produced by placing a few fibres of fresh meat in an infusion of hay.

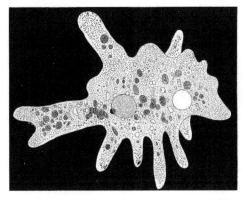

Fig. 325.—Amœba, *Proteus animalcule*; magnified 600 diameters.—(Warne).

The Gregarinæ consist of a remarkable group of organisms, but these, although unicellular, are, for the most part, confined to the intestinal tract of worms and of the higher animals, and will therefore be described among internal parasites.

Tho fungus-animals, Mycetozoa, have already been referred to in a previous chapter. The best known species, however, is found in tan yards in the form of creeping masses of naked protoplasm, termed Plasmodia. Cakes of protoplasm become segregated from the main mass, and break up into Amœba-like spores, which unite again to form Plasmodia.

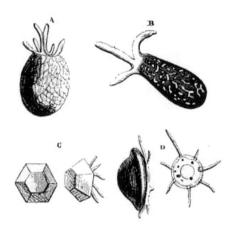

Fig. 326.—Rhizopoda lobosa.

A. *Difflugia proteiformis*; B. *Difflugia oblonga*; C, D. *Arcella acuminata* and *dentata*

The Rhizopoda, or root-footed class of animals, are among the most interesting simple organisms with which the microscope has made us acquainted. In the living state they have the power of protruding pseudopodia from the body, by which they creep about, or cling to plants when in search of food. This group, in fact, includes Amœba, Foraminifera, Sun-animalcules, and Radiolarians. In the first the pseudopodia are simple and lobose; in the second they are slender, confluent and reticulate; while in the two last they are simple, radiating and somewhat stiff, and partake of a calcareous formation.

Of the Lobosa, we may take a well-known representative of the group, the Protomyxa, found at the bottom of fresh-water pools, especially those near bog-moss, where its minute orange-coloured particles of jelly-like substance are seen creeping over stones or shells. If quietly watched the pseudopodia, some of which are broad and others slender, become quiescent spheres, which break up into numerous portions, each of which becomes a new animal.

This group is divided into the shell-less (Nuda) and shell-formed (Testacea). The brown, horny covering is often finely faceted, and is either shaped like a dome, semi-circular, or flat as a box, through which they protrude their few or many pseudopodia (seen in Fig. 326).

PLATE XV.

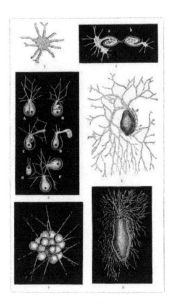

GROMIA.

In the Difflugia the lorica or shell is strengthened by the addition of silicious particles; in Euglypta it is sac-shaped, with a jagged free margin, the surface being covered by overlapping scales; while Arcella are capable of secreting vesicles of air in their interior, whereby they are enabled to rise to the surface. On some parts of our coast, if the sea sand be carefully looked over with a pocket lens, there will often be found minute grains of a porcelain oval kind, belonging to the Miliolina, segmented or strung together not quite in the same plane.

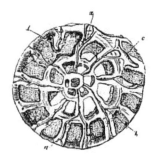

Fig. 327.—Section of Rotalia.

a,a, Radiating interceptal canals; *b*, Internal bifurcations; *c*, Transverse branch; *d*, Tubular wall of chambers.

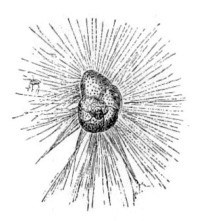

Fig. 328.—*Rosalina varians* or *Discorbina globularia*, with pseudopodia protruding.

The Foraminifera are rhizopods, whose simple protoplasmic bodies send forth, through perforations in the membrane or outer covering of calcium carbonate and silica, branching rays of pseudopodia. The order is divided into two groups, the Imperforata and the Perforata; in the former the shell or harder structure possesses only one or more apertures, whereas in the latter, in addition to the main opening, the shell has its walls perforated throughout, which admits of minute pseudopodia or fine threads being protruded (Fig. 328). (See also Plate III., Nos. 75-85.) The vast majority of Perforata form their shells, or rather skeletons, of calcium carbonate and silica, which renders them almost indestructible. Consequently the form is preserved through ages, and they present objects of the greatest interest to the microscopist.

A curious and interesting feature of the Foraminifera—often an element of difficulty to the student—is the tendency of modifications of types comprising the larger groups to run into parallel isomorphous series. Thus, if the entire class be roughly divided, as it sometimes has been, into three orders, comprising respectively the forms characterised by porcellaneous, arenaceous, and hyaline "tests," the same general conformation and arrangement of chambers will be found in each of the three series. The most remarkable example, even among the smaller groups, is the Rotaliidæ, of which three or four genera may be arranged in parallel lines, and in more or less closely isomorphous series. In the report appended to the "Challenger" scheme of classification many examples are enumerated. In Arenacea we have a small family of Foraminifera, the external surfaces of which present a ridge and furrow arrangement, and the incrustations are entirely of a sandy nature held together by a cement secreted by the animal. (Plate XV., No. 1, *Astrorhiza limicola.*)

Gromia.—Among the more remarkable of the Perforata group the Gromia have a foremost place. They are very minute globular or oval-shaped bodies, about one-twenty-fourth of an inch in length, found in fresh, brackish, and salt water. The forms brought up in Dr. Wallich's deep sea soundings of 1860 were taken attached to pieces of corallines, or found loose among Globigerina ooze. At first there appears to be nothing peculiar about these tiny specks of matter resembling the ova of a zoophyte, but presently, at the smaller end, a very fine thread is protruded, and then another, dividing into finer branches, and, ultimately, a complete network of filaments extends on all sides, and become attached to the side of the glass jar that contains them. Now, on employing magnifying power, every thread exhibits a circulatory motion, an up and down stream or cyclosis of granules suspended in a fluid mass. It is by means of these pseudopodia, as the threads are termed, that the Gromia moves its body along and clings to the glass. We may surmise, then, that these pseudopodia are either gelatinous, glutinous, or terminate in sucker-like processes. Increase in the "test," integument, is brought about, as in Difflugia, by the secretion of calcareous matter or by cementing fine silicious particles to the outer wall, as the protoplasm is seen to flow over the test, so that when it comes in contact with a diatom it is thereby drawn towards the oral opening and slowly digested.

Some considerable time elapsed between the discovery of Gromia by Mr. W. Archer, F.R.S., and the demonstration of a nucleus and contractile vesicle by Dr. Wallich. It was thought that in the whole of the Monozoa the nucleus was absent, but it is now known that this important body is embedded in the protoplasmic substance, and the reproduction of these curious animals is thereby secured. Among the better known species of Gromia is *G. Dujardinii*, chiefly distinguishable by the darker colour of the "test," by the greater quantity of silica that enters into the formation of its pseudopodia, and by the formation of isogamous zoospores, two of which are seen in conjugation in Plate XV., No. 2. An excess of protoplasm must also be secreted to admit of so large a protrusion outside the testa.

G. Lieberkühnia (of Claparède and Lachman), No. 5, differs in formation. Its shape is pyriform, and the opening whence the pseudopodia streams out is situated in a lateral depression about midway in the testa, *c, o*. Hence a trunk branch is seen to issue forth, and from this a ramification of threads, *psdp*, extends to a considerable distance in all directions.

The Micro-gromia of Hertwig, No. 4, is the minutest form of the genus yet discovered, and differs from those already described in the mode of reproduction. The individual takes the shape of a water bottle with a short neck, whence issue forth a limited number of very slender threads. The test is quite transparent, and it was in this species that the nucleus and contractile vesicle, which lie embedded near the mouth, were first clearly made out.

The zoospores of Micro-gromia have a curious habit of uniting with their neighbours to form a colony, No. 4. Their colonisation is apparently intended to facilitate multiplication. Reproduction is carried on somewhat after the manner of Volvox. The globular bodies formed sink to the bottom of the glass vessel, and there remain for a time in a quiescent state. In the course of a day or two the mass assumes a motive appearance, increases in bulk, becomes more ovoid in shape, and ultimately the nucleus shows the first sign of division. Vertical segmentation takes place, as at A, into two equal parts; each half is seen to possess its fair share of the nucleus and contractile vesicle. It then turns in the horizontal direction, and now there appears to be an upper and a lower division, the uppermost having a neck-like attachment, and this is making its way to the narrow oral opening in the parent testa, as at B. Here it is seen pressing forward, and at C the neck is protruding some distance, and the second half assumes a bottle shape; at D the greater part of the animal is nearly set free, and after a short rest it fully launches forth. It finally pulls itself together, as at E, and either develops a pair of flagella and swims off, or assumes the form of an Actinophrys. In either case, and in a very short space of time, the separated young animal is quite ready to re-unite, as at F, and assist in forming a new colony of the species.

The Polymorphina belong to a low genus of the Foraminifera. They consist of a number of forms and exhibit a rather extensive series of variations, although consisting of a few simple types, and showing transitions between forms which at first seem to be distinct. The majority of species keep to the sea bottom; some few are pelagic, and occur in abundance on the surface of the ocean. Among the latter are the Globigerina: its shell is about one-fortieth of an inch in diameter, and usually composed of seven globular chambers arranged spirally in such a manner that all are visible from above, each chamber opening by a crescentic-shaped orifice into a depression in the middle of the next. Perfect specimens bristle with long slender spines, the pores affording passage to pseudopodia, which stream out along the spines. The more carefully-conducted deep-sea investigations have brought to light the fact that the floor of the ocean, at great depths, and over a vast area, is formed of these white or pinkish coloured bodies, all containing on an average about 60 per cent. of calcium carbonate. It is a question whether the Globigerinidæ which make up the bulk of the ooze actually live at the bottom as well as the surface of the sea. This question has given rise to much discussion. Dr. Murray came to the conclusion that pelagic species do not live near the ocean floor. This opinion is partly based on the fact that the area of the Globigerina ooze coincides with the area of surface of temperature at which these bodies are found to exist. When the surface water is too cold for them, they are not to be found, neither are they found below. Major S. R. J. Owen, while dredging the surface of mid-ocean—the Indian, and the warmer portion of the Atlantic—found attached to his nets a number of these interesting bodies, and which always made their appearance just about sunset. In Plate III., Nos. 43-52, a number of these interesting and variously-formed bodies are given, and an attempt is also made to show the richly-tinted colour appearances presented by the sarcode or protoplasm of the Globigerina.

Fig. 329.—Globigerina and other bodies taken in deep sea soundings (Atlantic).

"Many of the forms," writes Major Owen,[64] "have hitherto been claimed by the geologist, but I have found them enjoying life in this their true home, the silicious shells filled with coloured sarcode, and sometimes this sarcode in a state of distension somewhat similar to that found projecting from the Foraminifera, but not in such slender threads. There are no objects in nature more brilliant in their colouring or more exquisitely delicate in their forms and structure. Some are of but one colour, crimson, yellow, or blue; sometimes two colours are found on the same individual, but always separate, and rarely if ever mixed to form green or purple. In a globular species, whose shell is made up of the most delicate fretwork, the brilliant colours of the sarcode shine through the little perforations very prettily. In specimens of the triangular and square forms (Plate III., Nos. 43, 44, 45 and 46), the respective tints of yellow and crimson are vivid and delicately shaded; in one the pink lines are concentric; while another is of a stellate form, the points and uncoloured parts being bright clear crystal, while a beautiful crimson ring surrounds the central portion. A globular form resembles a specimen of the Chinese ball-cutting—one sphere within another; this, however, appears to belong to a distinct species.

Fig. 330.—Globigerina and other bodies taken in deep sea soundings, 1856 (Atlantic).

"The shells of some of the globular forms of these Polycystina, whose conjugation I believe I have witnessed, are composed of a fine fretwork, with one or more large circular holes; and I suspect the junction to take place by the union of two such apertures. That the figures of these shells become elongated, lose their globular form after death, and present a disturbed surface is seen in some of the figures represented in Plate III., Nos. 82-85." Those without internal chambers have been described as *Orbulina universa*, Plate III., Fig. 78, while Nos. 75 and 76, although members of the same family, have been separated, but all should certainly be united under Globigerina.

"The minute silicious shells of Polycystina present wonderful beauty and variety of form; all are more or less perforated, and often prolonged into spines or other projections, through which the sarcode body extends itself into pseudopodial prolongations resembling those of Actinophrys. When seen disporting themselves in all their living splendour, their brilliancy of colouring renders them objects of unusual attraction. It will appear that they wish to avoid the light, as they are rarely found on the surface of the sea in the daytime; it is after sunset and during the twilight that they make their appearance."

Many forms of Globigerina and Foraminifera are represented in Figs. 329 and 330. These varied and beautiful forms were dredged up with soundings made in 1856 for the purpose of ascertaining the depth of the Atlantic, prior to the laying down of the electric telegraph wire from England to America, and taken at a depth of 2,070 fathoms.

Heliozoa.—Actinophrys-Sol, "sun-animalcules," belong to this group; most of them inhabit fresh water (Plate III., No. 66). The chief characteristic, and the one to which they owe their name, is the possession of long, slender, somewhat stiff pseudopodia; these radiate from all parts of the body. The living animal usually contains green-coloured particles within a minute translucent spherical globule of about $\frac{1}{250}$th of an inch in diameter. It is, therefore, variously designated the green sun-animalcule, Acanthocystis, or Actinophrys-Sol. It is commonly found amongst the weeds in clear pools of water, where desmids abound. The pseudopodia appear to be stiff; they are, however, quite flexible, and the body contains more than one clear vesicle with a nucleus; reproduction is secured by the simple division commencing in the nucleus. The little animal can move over a hard surface by the alternate relaxation and stiffening of its pseudopodia; when one of these touches a small organism, it is believed to paralyse it, then envelop, and deliberately digest it. In another species, the lattice-animalcule (Cathrulina), the pseudopodia or silicious threads are arranged tangentially. It grows on a long flexible stalk, attached to an aquatic plant, the total length of which is about $\frac{1}{200}$th an inch. The globular body is perforated in all directions, through which the fine stiff pseudopodia are thrust out; it is often known to form colonies.

In this order may well be placed the Radiolaria; they are, however, usually separated. But Radiolarians, whether seen alive or in their skeleton form, are surpassingly beautiful. By the favour of Messrs. Warne, I am enabled to append a frontispiece plate to this volume taken from their "Royal Natural History." These bodies are all marine, and live in zones of several thousand fathoms, and like their congeners, the Globigerina, they avoid a strong light, and only appear after sunset. Their bodies are supposed to emit a phosphorescent glow, but more is known of their silicious skeletons than of their living forms; yet it is not this feature that separates them from other orders of rhizopods, but the possession of a membranous central capsule enclosing the nucleus. The body substance outside this capsule is highly vacuolated in some species, especially in surface forms. A few are without a skeleton, and these consist of oval masses of protoplasm, with slender pseudopodia. In a few species the skeleton is formed of a glassy horny substance, termed acanthin, arranged in the form of radiating spines.

Radiolarians secrete a silicious skeleton, which assumes a variety of forms, as trellis-work, boxes joined by radiating spines, helmets, baskets, bee-hives, discs, rings, and numerous other forms. Haeckel has described upwards of four thousand species, and possibly as many more could be added to this number. Radiolaria are divided into two groups. In the one there is either no skeleton or one of silex; in the other the skeleton is formed of radiating spines of a horny nature. These are again subdivided according to the characters of the central capsule. In those forms with a silicious skeleton the geometrical pattern conforms more or less to the shape of the central capsule, being either spherical or conical. The central capsule is regarded as being homologous with the calcareous shell of Globigerina. Reproduction takes place by simple division into two, or by the body breaking up into spores, each provided with a flagellum, or two spores may fuse together, and the result will be an adult Radiolarian. Certain yellow corpuscles present in the outer part of their body-surface change into unicellular parasitic algals; these can be separated and cultivated independently of their host. The Radiolarians live floating at all depths from 1,000 to 2,500 fathoms, and are distributed over areas in the central Pacific and the south-eastern part of the Indian Ocean, the ooze forming the ocean bed being made up of their skeletons to an extent of 80 per cent. of the deposit; hence it has become known as Radiolarian ooze. The chalky-looking Barbadoes earth, a Tertiary formation, is composed almost entirely of their skeletons. Somewhat similar deposits exist in the Nicobar Islands, in Greece, and in Sicily.

It will have been noticed that by far the greater number of Foraminifera are of marine origin, and these occur in such widespread profusion that the finest calcareous particles which constitute the seashore in some places consist almost wholly of their microscopic remains. At former periods of the earth's history they appear to have existed even in greater profusion than at the present time. This is evidenced by their remains forming the principal constituent of our largest geological formations.

Moreover, during the Canadian Geological Survey large masses of what appeared to be a fossil organism were discovered in rocks situated near the base of the Laurentian series of North America. Sir William Dawson, of Montreal, referred these remains to an animal of the foraminiferal type; and specimens were sent by Sir W. Logan to the late Dr. Carpenter, requesting him to subject them to a careful examination. As far back as 1858 Sir W. Logan had suspected the existence of organic remains in specimens from the Grand Calumet limestone, on the Ottawa River, but a casual examination of the specimens was insufficient to determine the point. Similar forms being seen by Sir W. Logan in blocks from the Grenville bed of the Laurentian limestone were in their turn tried, and ultimately revealed their true structure to Sir William Dawson and Dr. Sterry Hunt, who named the structure *Eozoon Canadense*.

The masses of which these fossils consist are composed of layers of serpentine alternating with calc spar. It was found by these observers that the calcareous layers represented the original shell, and the silicious layers the softer parts of the once living Foraminifera. The results were arrived at through comparison of the appearance presented by the Eozoon with the microscopic structure which Dr. Carpenter had previously shown to characterise certain members of the Foraminifera. The Eozoon not only exceeded other known Foraminifera in size to an extent that might have easily led observers astray, but, from its apparently very irregular mode of growth and general external form, no help was derived in its identification, and it was only by microscopical examination of its minute structure that its true character was ascertained. Dr. Carpenter wrote:—"The minute structure of Eozoon may be determined by the microscopic examination either of thin transparent sections, or of portions which have been subjected to the action of dilute acids, so as to remove the calcareous portion, leaving only the internal casts, or models, in silex, of the chambers and other cavities originally occupied by the substance of one animal." Subsequently he found portions of minute structure so perfect that he was able to say that "delicate pseudopodial threads were originally put forth through openings in the shell wall of less than $\frac{1}{10000}$th of an inch in diameter" (Plate III., Nos. 64, 65). In a paper read at the meeting of the Geological Society he stated that he had since detected Eozoon in a specimen of ophicalcite from Bohemia, in a specimen of gneiss from near Moldau, and in specimens of serpentine limestone sent to Sir C. Lyell by Dr. Gümbel, of Bavaria. These also were found to be parts of the great formation of the "fundamental" gneiss, considered by Sir Roderick Murchison as the equivalent of the Laurentian rocks of Canada.[65]

If the remains of Foraminifera be dissolved in dilute hydrochloric acid, an organic basis is left, after the removal of the calcareous matter, accurately retaining the form of the shell with all its openings and pores. The earthy constituent is mainly calcium carbonate; but there is also a small amount of phosphate of lime in the shells of many of them.

Fig. 331.

1. Separated prisms from outer layer of Pinna shell; 2. Skeletons of Foraminifera from limestone; 3. Recent shell of *Polystomella crispa*; examined under dark-ground illumination.

Infusoria.

We are now brought face to face with animals which possess considerable variation of structure, *Infusorial animalcules*, as they are termed. It was Ehrenberg who attributed to them a highly complex organisation, but later observations negatived these views and showed them to be animals formed of one or more cells, or colonies of so-called individuals. It is true that this cell or united protoplasm may show a wonderful amount of differentiation, what with its nucleus and vacuole, mouth and gullet, its variously-arranged cilia or flagella, its contractile fibres, its separation into an outer denser and a more fluid inner protoplasm, and its horny cup and stalks.

In these few lines we have a condensed summary of the special qualities of minute forms of life that afford much interesting work for the microscope.

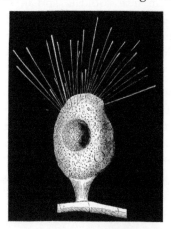

Fig. 332.—Acineta, magnified 600 diameters (*Warne*).

Among those widespread, and in some respects heterogeneous, forms of life associated under the comprehensive title of Infusoria, we encounter types that not only differ very widely from one another, but which occupy a different rank or position, so to speak, with regard to the relation they bear to each other, and also to the outlying representatives of the series—differences that permeate throughout the ranks of this extensive group. Furthermore, a considerable number of Infusorial animalcules foreshadow or typify, in a corresponding degree, the separate or associated cell elements out of which higher tissue structures—metazoic organisms—are built up. We may take the well-known example *Euglena viridis* (Plate III., No. 67), or Paramecium (No. 74), and their allies; these would appear to be the prototypes of Turbellaria. Another more lowly organised group of the Ciliata exhibits a distinct and highly-interesting affinity to the Opalinidæ. There are many other species (Acineta, Plate III., No. 68, for instance), which at first sight would seem to stand by themselves and present no marked agreement with any metazoic type. Indeed, the function of these and other polypites consists simply in seizing food and conveying it through perforations at the extremity of each separate tentaculum to its interior. In Acineta certain of the tentacles only are suctorial, and these, being the inner ones, fulfil the ingestive function, while the peripheral series are prehensile. This stalked club-shaped body (Fig. 332), which fixes itself to seaweeds or Bryozoa, is seen to have a nucleus, and also clear vesicles in the body-substance; its embryos are ciliated. It is an object of considerable interest even among curious marine animalcules; one or two species inhabit fresh water. The spiral-mouthed Spirostomum are among the largest of the class, and in sunlight are visible to the naked eye as slender golden threads of about ¹⁄₁₀th of an inch in length. The mouth slit, extending half the length of the body, is bordered on one side by cilia. The body is cylindrical and the surface covered with rows of cilia. Its multiplication takes place by transverse fission through the middle.

Flagellate Infusoria.—The characteristic of this group, as its name implies, is the possession of one or more flagella or whip-like appendages, at the base of which is an opening in the denser surface layer of protoplasm, and in the interior a nucleus and one or more contractile vacuoles, and not infrequently a brilliant red spot of pigment known to microscopists as the eye-spot. The Monads, which constitute the simplest members of the group, are commonly found in fresh-water pools and vegetable infusions. The typical form consists simply of a spherical or oval cell provided with a flagellum. The Volvox was formerly placed in this group, but as it contains chlorophyll it is properly claimed by the botanist. The collared group possesses cup-like collars, and these frequently secrete horny receptacles or cups, and form elegant tree-like colonies.

The mail-coated group are of very varied form, the body being often prolonged into spiny processes. They have two long flagella which fit into grooves purposely provided. But the most interesting and remarkable are the phosphorescent animalcules (Noctiluca), whose beautiful bluish-green luminosity on the surface of the sea has attracted attention from very early periods. It was, however, not until the first half of the present century that the luminosity was discovered to be due to the presence of multitudes of these minute jelly-like spheres.

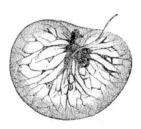

Fig. 333.—*Noctiluca miliaris*; magnified 150 diameters.

Fig. 334.—Pyrocystis; magnified 150 diameters.

The body of the Noctiluca (Fig. 333) is a nearly globular-shaped cyst, enclosed in a tough membranous wall, from a grooved opening in which a striated muscular flagellum or proboscis is projected forth, and it is by means of this the animal swims away even in rough seas. A fine whip-like flagellum is also located in the same groove. At the apex of the funnel there is a mass of protoplasm which extends itself as a widely-meshed, highly-vacuolated network to the inner wall of the cyst, whence it is believed the phosphorescent light emanates. It multiplies by self-division, first becoming encysted after withdrawing its flagellum, and then breaking up into numerous ciliated helmet-shaped swarm spores. Frequently two organisms fuse into one and then divide into spores.

Noctiluca mainly confines itself to the shallower seas, but there are related forms met with in the warmer open seas; these belong to the genus Pyrocystis (Fig. 334). In one variety the body is perfectly spherical and without the big flagellum or proboscis. Professor Butschli, however, regards this species as an encysted or resting phase of the commoner and better-known form.

The late Mr. Philip Gosse, F.R.S., was the first microscopist to describe the Noctiluca. After careful observation, he wrote in his "Naturalist's Rambles" as follows:—"I had an opportunity of becoming acquainted with the minute animals to which a great portion of the luminousness of the sea is attributed. One of my large glass vases of sea-water I had observed to become suddenly at night, when tapped with the finger, studded with minute but brilliant sparks at various points on the surface of the water. I set the jar in the window, and was not long in discovering, without the aid of a lens, a goodly number of the tiny jelly-like globules of *Noctiluca miliaris* swimming about in various directions. They swam with an even gliding motion, much resembling that of the *Volvox globator* of our fresh-water pools. They congregated in little groups, and a shake of the vessel sent them darting down from the surface. It was not easy to keep them in view when seen, owing rather to their extreme delicacy and colourless transparency than to their minuteness. They were, in fact, distinctly appreciable by the naked eye, measuring from $\frac{1}{50}$th to $\frac{1}{30}$th of an inch in diameter."

Among the numerous fresh-water members of the flagellate infusoria, there is one which especially calls for notice, Codosiga, discovered by the late Professor H. J. Clark. This minute body bears a delicate funnel-shaped protoplasmic expansion or collar, common to the several members of this organic series. The flagellum is placed at the base of the oral opening, and within the circumscribed area of the collar, which is of such extreme tenuity that its true form and nature can only be determined by a very careful adjustment of the achromatic condenser and accessory apparatus employed, together with a wide-angled objective. It is seen to greater advantage by supplying the animal with very fine particles of colouring matter. In this way it is found that the infundibuliform cup consists of protoplasm, through which the flagellum is protruded and withdrawn into the general substance of the Monad's body (Fig. 335). As many as twenty or more zooids are attached to the extremity of a slender footstalk. The length of the body, exclusive of the collar, is $\frac{1}{2500}$th to the $\frac{1}{1200}$th of an inch. The habitat of these bodies is fresh water. Mr. Saville Kent in 1869 discovered some of these interesting infusoria in the London Docks.

"The more exact significance of the special organ, the collar, is manifest by the circulatory currents or cyclosis induced, and there can be no room for doubt that this structure finds its precise homologue in the pseudopodia of the foraminiferous group of the Rhizopoda, in which a similar circulation or cyclosis of the constituent sarcode is exhibited. The whole of this highly-interesting flagellate order, a comparatively small one as yet, are remarkable for their pale glaucous green or florescent hue, such colour assisting materially in their recognition, even when the magnifying power employed is insufficient for the detection of the very characteristic collar with its enclosed flagellum."[66]

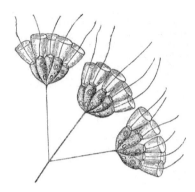

Fig. 335.—*Codosiga umbellata*; a few colonies of Zooids diverging from the parent foot-stalk with flagella extended, magnified 650 diameters.

Ciliata.—Types of Ciliata obtained from hay infusions are very numerous. Ehrenberg's animalcules were mainly of a large size, and of those belonging to the higher order of the Ciliata, pertaining to such genera as Paramecium, Colpoda, Cyclidium, Oxytricha, and Vorticella. These, however, represent but an insignificant minority of the hosts of flagellate forms which abound in our humid climate, and in hay infusions in particular. In such infusions, watched from day to day and produced from hay obtained from different localities, the number of types developed in regular sequence is found to be perfectly marvellous, commencing with the *Monas* proper, Amphimonas and Heteromita; while Bacteria, in their motile and quiescent forms, are invariably present and furnish an abundant supply of material for the microscope.[67]

Vorticellidæ constitute one of the most numerous families of the ciliate infusoria. All its members are at once recognised by their normal stationary condition, and by the structure of their oral system. In but few of the genera is there any marked divergence from this formula, and when any exists it is made manifest by an increase in development of some one of its elements at the expense of another. For instance, in the genus Spirochona, the external edge of the encircling border or peristome is suppressed, while the inner portion is abnormally developed into a transparent and highly elevated spiral membrane. The bell-animalcules usually possess stalks, and are either solitary or form branching colonies. *Conichilus vorticella* (Plate III., No. 80) is a well-known member of the colony stock, all the zooids of which are united on a slender branching pedicle, which consists of a central contractile cord enclosed within a tubular hyaline sheath. There are many other shrub-like colonies all variously modified in form and character. The *Epistylis opercularia*, or nodding-bell animalcule, is an interesting member of a numerous host of solitary short-stalked forms (Fig. 337). When the animal is disturbed, the heads drop down towards the stalk. This animalcule has been found to form a colony; and another, Carchesium, whose tiny branched tree-like colonies resemble little white globular masses of moulds, are seen at once to drop down towards the base of the colony with a jerky movement if the cell be touched. By a process of encysting, all the Vorticellæ and many of the more highly-organised ciliata have the means of what may be termed self-preservation. Should the water dry up in which they have been living, the little animal encases itself in mud at the bottom of the pool. Should this be baked by the sun not the least injury arises, for at this stage it crumbles into dust, and is carried by the wind to long distances, but the first shower of rain calls it back to active life, and soon after it is seen to issue forth as a free swimming bud.

Fig. 336.—*Vorticella microstoma.*

Thuricola valvata (Plate III., No. 72) possesses a hinge-like process which closes up like a door when the animal contracts itself into its case. This very effectually protects it from assault. Both portions of the valve are capable of extension. Another group of ciliate infusoria also possess a limited number of cilia, but these, although restricted to the under surface of their bodies, have an unrestricted range of motion. The group are all free swimmers, belonging to the genus Oxytricha. They possess two separate alimentary orifices, neither of which are situated at the extremities or encased by a dense integument. Their locomotive organs consist either of setæ, vibratile cilia, or non-vibratile styles or uncini, variously situated, and all serving to make these infusorial animals very active (Plate III., Nos. 73 and 77). A typical species is the mussel-animalcule (Stylonychia, Fig. 338), common in all infusions and pools of water. Its body is oval and flattened, and about ¹⁄₁₀₀th of an inch in length. At one end a funnel-shaped depression or mouth, with a ciliated margin, leads to the inner part of the body, in which are two oval bodies, a nucleus and a contractile vacuole, which is seen to contract rhythmically. The creature can also stalk along by means of its cilia or setæ, and set up currents to the mouth. Plate III., Nos. 70, 71, 72, 73, and 74, are types of these interesting bodies.

Fig. 337.—Nodding-bell animalcule (*Epistyles operculata*) × 250 (Warne).

Fig. 338.—Mussel-animalcule (*Stylonychia mytilus*) under surface.

a. Mouth; *b.* Contractile vacuole; *c.* Nucleus. (Magnified 150 diameters.

Dr. Balbini believes a true sexual generation occurs among these organisms, but, with the exception of the Paramecium, this has not been seen to take place; even Gruber's more recent investigations appear to be inconclusive on this point. Conjugation, however, it is said takes place among some attached forms, as in the Stentors. These have been seen to put forth a bud from the body base, and soon after become free swimming bodies. The trumpet-animalcule (Stentor), a conspicuous member of the ciliata, is comparatively large, being about the ¹⁄₂₅th of an inch in length when extended to the full size. It is usually found attached to the under sides of duckweed, and is continually changing its form from that of a small knob when contracted, to the trumpet shape seen in Fig. 339, No. 6, when fully extended, and from which it derives its name. The long cilia projected from the upper part form a spiral within the margin of the open mouth leading to the digestive sac. A contractile vacuole lies to the right of the oral opening. New individuals are produced by the process of budding, and in the form of ciliated embryos from the nucleus. Stentors are commonly met with in fresh water, and are usually of a brilliant green colour. These little bodies will bear cutting up: if only a fragment of the nucleus be included in the section, the injury is soon repaired.

Rotifera, or *Wheel-animalcules* (Fig. 339).—In this group we have a higher type of animal, with a more complex organisation than those previously noticed. The great majority inhabit fresh water, and are readily developed in hay infusions, in bog-moss, in house-top gutters, everywhere if looked for after a shower of rain. The rotating organs from which these fascinating animalcula derive their name consist of two disc-like bodies whose margins are fringed with rows of cilia, which create currents toward the oral aperture, and which have given rise to the optical delusion of rotating wheels. The disposition of the cilia is so arranged as to bring food to the rotifer and conduct it to the mastax or digesting apparatus—a muscular bulb moved by a series of muscles—the gastric glands and stomach. The great transparency of the whole structure permits of the animal economy being easily studied. The body is covered with a horny envelope of two layers, and is divided into segmental divisions, which slide into each other telescopic fashion. Consequently, as the water dries up, the animal is for a long time rendered indestructible and capable of resisting varying temperatures and the action of caustic reagents.

Rotifers are oviparous, and their eggs are conspicuous and of three kinds. The common soft-shelled eggs produce females, the smaller and more spherical produce males. The ephippial, or summer eggs, are often beset with spines or bosses; these have only a membranous covering, and are hatched soon after they are laid, or before leaving the ova sac. The male rotifer is but a third of the length of the female, often without cilia, and appears to have no alimentary tract; indeed, the only internal organ is a large sperm sac. Rotifers have been divided by Dr. Hudson and the late Mr. Gosse in their charming work on these very interesting "Wheel-animalcules" into four orders, according to their powers of locomotion, as follows:—(1) Rhizota, the rooted; (2) Bdelloida, the leech-like, that swim and creep like a leech; (3) Ploïma, the sea-worthy, that only swim with their ciliary wreath; (4) Scirtopoda, the skippers, that swim with their cilia and skip with arthropodous limbs. These, again, are subdivided into families. With such hardy creatures as Philodina, Adineta, Brachionus, &c., creatures to whom extremes of cold, heat, and drought are the ordinary conditions of life, nothing can be easier to keep going throughout the year. Mr. C. F. Rousselet, who has so thoroughly succeeded in mounting Rotifers with their cilia fully extended, recently exhibited at one of the evening meetings of the Royal Microscopical Society, London, no less than four hundred specimens in a natural and perfect condition, the nervous system being seen more clearly from its successful staining throughout the body than in the living rotifer.

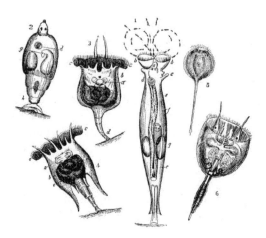

Fig. 339.

1. *Rotifer vulgaris* with its cilia; *b.* rotating; *c.* horn; *d.* œsophagus; *f.* outer case; *g.* ova, foot protruding through outer case. 2. Same in the contracted state and at rest, showing the segmentation of the body and development of young. 3. Pitcher-shaped Brachionus, furnished with two horny projections; *a.* mastax; *b.* shell; *c.* cilia, rotating disc; *d.* foot. 4. Baker's Brachionus, with six horny setæ; these are retracted when the cilia are in action; the letters relate to the same internal organs as in the former; the ova sac seen filled with eggs. 5 and 6. *B. ovalis*, closed, and with cilia displayed.

There is also a family of Rotatoria with a single rotatory organ, disposed around the margin of the case. This comprises at present a very small group. The Œcistes is a member of the family (Plate III., No. 69). A single ciliary wreath leads to the alimentary canal, and a pharyngeal bulb or mastax comprises the apparatus of nutrition. The visual organs are red, as in other rotifers, and the ovarium contains several ova, shown in No. 69. The envelope is a gelatinous transparent sheath, into which the animalcule can withdraw itself, its attachment to the bottom being by the end of the foot-like tail. The most interesting among this genus are the Floscularians. These creatures may undoubtedly be described as among the most beautiful and interesting of infusorial animals.

The Stephanoceros, "crowned animalcule," as it is termed, is about ⅟₃₆th of an inch in length, and enclosed in a transparent cylindrical flexible case, beyond which it protrudes five long arms in a graceful manner. These, touching at their points, give a form from which it derives its name. These arms are furnished with several rows of short cilia, which seize the food brought within their grasp until it can be swallowed. In addition to the rotatory organs, they have short flexible processes, or cornu, attached to the outside of one or more of their lobes. The water vascular system consists of two canals arising from a small pyriform contractile vesicle, situated below the stomach. The ova, after leaving the ova sac, remain quiescent until their cilia are developed. Floscularians, like Melicertans, have a certain affinity in form with Vorticellians and Stentors, and also with Campanulariæ, among polypes. Their cilia are less regular when in action than in other Rotatoria. When they retreat into their transparent cells they appear to fold themselves up. Their internal structure can be seen through the external case, and ova are observed enclosed in an ova sac; when thrown off they remain quiescent until the formation of their cilia. The whole family furnish interesting objects for microscopic investigation.

Melicerta ringens ("beaded Melicerta").—Of all the Melicerta, or "horny floscularia," this is the most beautiful. Its crystalline body is enclosed in a pellucid covering, wider at the top than the bottom, of a dark yellow or reddish-brown colour, which gradually becomes encrusted by zones of a variety of shapes, cemented together with a peculiar secretion that hardens in water. It derives its name from these pellets, which have the appearance of rows of beads. Mr. Gosse furnished an excellent account of the architectural instincts of *Melicerta ringens*: "An animalcule so minute as to be with difficulty appreciable by the naked eye, inhabiting a tube composed of pellets, which it forms and lays one by one. It is a mason who not only builds up his mansion brick by brick, but makes his bricks as he goes on, from substances which he collects around him, shaping them in a mould which he carries on his body.

"The pellets composing the case are very regularly placed in position; in a fine specimen, about the $\frac{1}{30}$th of an inch in length, when fully expanded, as many as fifteen longitudinal rows of pellets were counted, which gave about thirty-two rows in all. As it exposes itself more and more, suddenly two large rounded discs are expanded, around which, at the same instant, a wreath of cilia is seen performing surprising motions.

"On mixing carmine with the water, the course of the ciliary current is readily traced, and forms a fine spectacle. The particles are hurled round the margin of the disc, until they pass off in front through the great sinus, between the larger petals. If the pigment be abundant, the cloudy torrent for the most part rushes off, and prevents our seeing what takes place; but if the atoms be few, we see them swiftly glide along the facial surface, following the irregularities of outline with beautiful precision, dash round the projecting chin like a fleet of boats doubling a bold headland, and lodge themselves, one after another, in the little cup-like receptacle beneath. Mr. Gosse, believing that the pellets of the case might be prepared in the cup-like receptacle, watched the animal, and presently had the satisfaction of seeing it bend its head forward, as anticipated, and after a second or two raise it again; the little cup having in the meantime lost its contents. It immediately began to fill again; and when it was full, and the contents were consolidated by rotation, aided probably by the admixture of a salivary secretion, it was again bent down to the margin of the case, and emptied of its pellet. This process he saw repeated many times in succession, until a goodly array of dark-red pellets were laid upon the yellowish-brown ones, but very irregularly. After a certain number were deposited in one part, the animal would suddenly turn itself round in its case, and deposit some in another part. It took from two-and-a-half to three-and-a-half minutes to make and deposit a pellet."

Melicerta may be found in clear pools, mill-ponds, and other places through which a current of water gently flows. If a portion of water-weed be brought home and placed in a small glass zoophyte-trough, and carefully examined with a magnifying power of about fifty diameters, a few delicate-looking projections of a reddish-brown colour will probably be seen adhering to the plant; these are the tubular cases of Melicerta, which, after a short period of rest, will be seen to be animals of ¹⁄₁₂th of an inch or more in length.

Porifera. Spongiadæ.

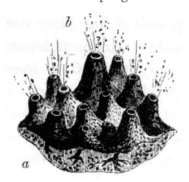

Fig. 340.—*Spongia panicea.*

Bread-crumb Sponge, showing currents entering surface *a*, and leaving by oscules *b*.

Sponges.—The term Porifera, or "canal-bearing zoophytes," was applied by the late Dr. Grant to designate the remarkable class of organisms known as sponges, met with in every sea, and numbering about two thousand species, varying in size from a pin's head to masses several feet in height; and weighing from a few grains to over a hundred pounds. Sponges assume an endless variety of shapes, as cups, vases, spheres, tubes, baskets, branched-like trees, but often as shapeless masses. When living they are all colours and all consistences, soft and gelatinous, fleshy, leathery or stony. A fuller knowledge of sponges was gained in 1825, when Dr. Robert Grant examined a fragment of living sponge under the microscope. On bringing it to the side of the glass cell in which he had preserved it, he beheld this living fountain pouring forth a torrent of liquid matter in rapid succession, and he was at once convinced that a current flowed out of the larger orifices. He introduced a small portion of fine chalk, and saw particles driven into the interior, and pass out again by different ways. To determine the cause of the currents, it was necessary to make a closer examination of the anatomy of the sponge. For this purpose he cut or peeled off thin sections, and saw that the whole substance was divided into flagellated chambers, enclosing spherical and other bodies, and perforated by pores. Each chamber proved to be about ¹⁄₅₀₀th of an inch in diameter, groups of them opening by a wider orifice into a common space, or canaliculus, and joining others to form canals terminating in larger oscular canals. The walls throughout are lined with flat cells, but in the flagellated chambers the living cells are more or less cylindrical, and each is provided at the free end with a whip-like appendage, or flagellum. Furthermore the upper margin was seen to be expanded into a thin hyaline collar, so that the whip appeared to have its origin in the centre of a basin or funnel. The currents of water traversing the body of the sponge are kept up by the movements of the flagella of the collar-cells. These beat the water in the flagellated chambers into the rootlets of the canals leading to the oscules. To replace this, water flows into the flagellated chambers from the rootlets of the canals passing down from the groups of pores in the skin. The currents entering the sponge bring in oxygenated sea-water and minute food particles, such as diatoms and infusorial organisms; the currents from the oscules contain an excess of carbonic acid of waste products, resulting from vital activity and indigestible remains. The cells lining the canals effect the exchange of gases, and take up food particles.

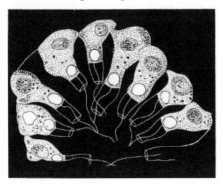

Fig. 341.—A section of a flagellate chamber of a Fresh-water Sponge, showing collar-cells (Vosmaer).

Professor Grant's careful and instructive researches were begun on the smaller kind of British sponges hanging down from rocks (*Spongia coalita*), and on which he gazed for "twenty-five minutes, until obliged to withdraw his eyes from fatigue." This sponge fixes itself by a root; and the currents enter through the stem and body, and leave principally by oscules placed on the branches.

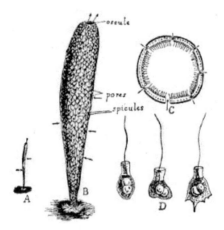

Fig. 342.—An Ascon Sponge.

A. Magnified × 20 diameters; B. × 80 diameters; C. Transverse section; D. Collar-cells, × 700 diameters. The embryo, an extremely minute oval cyst, is furnished with a flagellum for swimming; in the third it assumes an amœboid form (Warne.)

At present too little is known as to the physiology of digestion in sponges to permit of a definite statement on the subject. In specimens fed upon carmine the collar-cells have been found loaded with granules; in others, again, the flat cells lining the subdermal cavities have been found gorged with colour granules. From Bowerbank's monograph on the British Spongiadæ (1864 and 1874) nothing of importance can be gained on the subject; in fact, it relates almost entirely to the structure and organisation of sponges in their dried or preserved condition, and therefore is only of value for purposes of specific identification. One of the simplest of living sponges, the microscopic structure of which it is possible to trace, *Ascetta primordialis*, is found on seaweeds in the Mediterranean. In its simple unbranched condition it forms a minute white sac about one twenty-fifth of an inch in height, opening above by a wide round oscule and narrowing below to a stalk (Fig. 342). The walls are very thin and perforated by pores, through which the water passes into the interior. The walls of the sac are composed of two layers, an inner lining of collar-cells, and an outer layer consisting of a gelatinous matrix containing amœboid bodies and transparent three-rayed spicules. These serve to support the walls and as a frame-work for the pores, as in all the sponges. By eliminating the spicular skeleton, and by supposing the tube to be more globular, the "olynthus form" will be obtained, which has been regarded as the hypothetical ancestor of all sponges. A canal system arises when the walls grow thick or form folds, or give off pouches or tubes. From these channels arise incipient in-current canals, between the inside or lumen of the folds and that forming the out-current canal system.

There is a common ciliated Sycon found on seaweed round the British coast; it has the appearance of a white sac about an inch in height, with a crown of glassy spicules around the orifice. The vertical cavity of the sac is surrounded by a wall of closely-packed horizontal tubes, opening at their inner ends into the central cavity, but externally ending blindly. The central cavity of the sac is surrounded or lined with flat-cells, and the radial tubes with collar-cells, and the walls of the tubes are perforated. Here the spaces between and outside the densely-packed tubes are the in-current canals. In an equally common British sponge, Grantia, which forms small flat white bags, a rudimentary cortex covers the outer ends of the tubes. In Grantiopois, the cortex becomes quite thick; as the radial tubes in this species become more branched and the mesoderm thicker, so the passages or in-current canals become more complicated. Common silicious, sponges develop in a different manner from the calcareous ones, namely, from a hollow conical sac open at the top and with a flat base; the spherical flagellated chambers at a very early stage forming a mammillated layer in the walls. Plakina, one of the simplest silicious sponges, encrusts stones with a fleshy crust, consisting of a sac with a flat base attached to the stone in sucker-like fashion, and with the rest of the walls forming simple folds. The spaces between and outside the folds form the in-current, and those in the lumen of the folds the out-current, channels. Each of the flagellated chambers in the walls of the folds communicates with the in-current spaces through several pores, and opens into the out-current spaces by one large pore, the currents of water passing out by the central oscule. Here we have a general idea of the formation of all the commoner forms of sponges. In the more delicate species, as that of Venus' flowerbasket, the cells are formed by a trellis work of large spicules of silica. Groups of cells congregate in the ground substance and secrete a network of cylindrical fibres and spicules, which, although they remain to a certain extent separate, are always beautifully adapted for purposes of support. In addition to the support these afford, the skeleton spicules afford a means of defence against the attacks of small animals.[68]

A fairly good idea will be gained of the internal structure of sponges from the section made of a *Geodia Barretti*, Fig. 343.

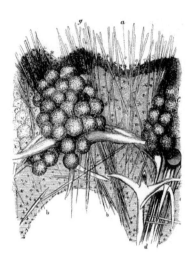

Fig. 343.—*Geodia Barretti* (Bowerbank).

A tangential section of geodia sponge exhibiting the radial disposition of the fasciculi of the skeleton, and a portion of the mesoderm of the sponge, magnified 50 diameters; *a.* intermarginal cavities; *b.* a basal intermarginal cavity; *c.* ova imbedded in the dermal crust of the sponge; *d.* large patentoternate spicula, the heads of which form areas for the valvular bases of the intermarginal cavities; *e.* recurvo-ternate defensive and aggressive spicula within the summits of the intercellular spaces of the sponge; *f.* portion of the interstitial membrane of sponge, crowded with minute stellate spicula; *g.* portions of the secondary system of external defensive spicula.

Reproduction.—As regards the modes of reproduction, both male and female cells are found in the mesoderm. The male cells generally give rise by division of the nucleus to masses of spermatozoa, each of which possesses a conical head and a long vibratile filament. The ova appear as large round cells, and when conglomerated in masses, resemble those of Micro-gromia, which, after fertilisation, undergo segmentation or division, first into two cells, and again dividing and sub-dividing, until a cluster or mass of cells results (as seen in Fig. 343). The outer layer of the egg-shaped embryo becomes more cylindrical in shape, and is now provided with cilia, and soon appears as an independent minute oval body. If a bread-crumb sponge be cut open in the autumn, the embryos will be seen as bright yellow spots within the body-substance. By keeping specimens in a vessel of water, the embryos will be seen to escape from the oscules, and swim freely about with the broad end forwards. After twenty-four hours of independent existence, the embryo remains stationary, and fixes itself by its broad end, which becomes flattened out. By a remarkable transformation, the larger granular cells of the interior burst out and grow over the outer flagellate layer of cells, and the latter become the collar-cells of the adult sponge. A minute sponge with one oscule results from the development of the fertilised ovum. An extensive crust with numerous oscules may be regarded either as a colony in which each oscule represents an individual, or simply as one individual in which the growth of the body necessitates the formation of new channels for the conveyance of food materials. The embryos of some of the fresh-water sponges (Spongillidæ) living in ponds, canals, lakes and rivers all over the world, as soon as they become fertilised undergo segmentation, and form oval ciliated bodies, in appearance somewhat resembling the gastrula of Monoxenia, one of the simplest kinds of corals. Fresh-water sponges are green in colour, due to the granular bodies which crowd the cells near the surface of the sponge; that this colour is not due to the formation of chlorophyll is seen on keeping them in a shady place, when they become pale grey or yellowish-brown, and if kept quite in the dark they entirely lose all colour.

PLATE XVI.

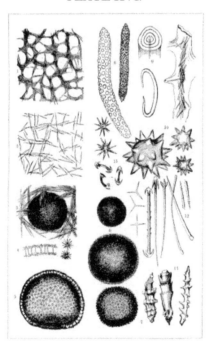

SKELETONS AND SPICULA OF SPONGES.

A few sponges possess no skeleton whatever, excepting the gelatinous ground substance; in some specimens the skeleton is mainly or entirely composed of foreign particles of sand or the remains of Foraminifera. Others are composed of calcium carbonate, and form the class Calcarea, the spicules of which are white, and opaque in mass; but on placing portions in hydrochloric acid, the skeleton is dissolved away with effervescence, and the spicules are left behind transparent and glassy. A great variety is seen in the different species, as will be gathered from the few typical forms shown in Plate XVI., and which even in their fossilised state remain unaltered, the silica which enters so largely into their composition being indestructible, the calcareous matter alone becoming separated in exposure to the action of air, or by boiling in hydrochloric acid. The only perceptible difference noticed is an increase in transparency, and this, on mounting them in Canada balsam, adds to their beauty when examined by polarised light.

Hyalonema, the "glass-rope" sponge of Japan, consists of a bundle of from 200 to 300 threads of transparent silica, glistening with a satiny lustre like the most brilliant spun glass; each thread is about eighteen inches long, in the middle the thickness of a knitting-needle, and gradually tapering towards either end to a fine point; the whole bundle coiled like a strand of rope into a lengthened spiral, the threads of the middle and lower portions remaining compactly coiled by a permanent twist of the individual threads; the upper portions of the coil frayed out, so that the glassy threads stand separate from each other. The spicules on the outside of the coil stretch its entire length, each taking about two and a half turns of the spiral. One of these long needles is about one-third of a line in diameter in the centre, gradually tapering towards either end. The spirally-twisted portion of the needle occupies rather more than the middle half of its entire length. In the lower portion of the coil, which is embedded in the sponge, the spicule becomes straight, and tapers down to an extreme tenuity, ultimately becoming so fine that it is scarcely possible to trace it to its termination.

Within the mesoderm, and in oscule, was noticed a deep brownish-orange coloured shrunken membrane; this was traced to a parasitic polyp. Since this was first observed on an early specimen of the Japanese glass-sponge, the same parasite has always been found growing on and in all these curious sponges. The surface of the stalk above the portion embedded in the mud is seen to be covered with a warty crust of parasitic polyps. All the specimens of Hyalonema in the European museums in 1860 had their stalks overgrown with Palythoa, while many had their bodies also covered with another parasite, and which, fortunately for the sponge, did not form a sandy crust. The polyps, having no skeleton, dry up entirely, and leave behind no trace except the stain first referred to. Unlike a parasite, however, the polyps do not feed upon the juices and soft parts of the sponge, nor indeed do they share its food, but simply settle upon the sponge and feed upon any food that may chance to come within their reach.

The dredgings of the *Challenger* brought to the surface many entirely new forms of glass-sponges and from great depths. One of the most beautiful, known as Carpenter's glass-sponge (Pheronema), is composed of concentric laminæ of silica deposited around a fine central axial canal. These form a gauze-like network throughout, but with no regularity of structure.

Clionæ.—Not the least wonderful circumstance connected with the history of sponges is the power possessed by certain species of boring into substances, the hardness of which might be considered as a sufficient protection against such apparently contemptible foes. Shells (both living and dead), coral, and even solid rocks are attacked by these humble destroyers, gradually broken up, and, no doubt, finally reduced to such a state as to render substances which would otherwise remain dead and useless in the economy of nature available for the supply of the necessities of other living creatures.

These boring sponges constitute the genus Cliona of Dr. Grant. They are branched in form, or consist of lobes united by delicate stems, and after having buried themselves in shells or other calcareous objects, preserve their communication with the water by means of perforations in the outer wall of the shell. The mechanism by which a creature of so low a type of organisation contrives to produce effects so remarkable is still doubtful, from the great difficulties which lie in the way of coming to any satisfactory conclusions upon the habits of an animal that works so completely in the dark as the *Cliona celata*. Mr. Hancock, in his valuable memoir upon the boring sponges, attributes their excavating power to the presence of the multitude of minute silicious crystalline particles adhering to the surface of the sponge; these he supposes are set in motion by ciliary action. In whatever way this action may be produced, however, there can be no doubt that these sponges are constantly and silently effecting the disintegration of submarine calcareous bodies—the shelly coverings, it may be, of animals far higher in organisation, and in many instances they prove themselves formidable enemies even to living molluscs, by boring completely through the shell. In this case the animal whose domicile it so unceremoniously invades has no alternative but to raise a wall of new shelly matter between himself and his unwelcome guest, and in this manner generally succeeds in barring him out.

From a close examination of the structural and developmental characters of the Spongideæ, it must be conceded that they belong rather to the flagellata Protozoa than to any other order. This was the view held by the late Professor Clark, and Mr. Saville Kent quite concurs in it.[69] Summing up the entire evidence adduced, scarcely a shadow of doubt is admissible concerning the intimate relationship that subsists between the Choano-flagellata and other flagellate Protozoa and that of sponges. The primary and essential element of the apparently complex sponge stock is the assemblage of collared flagellate zooids that inhabit its interstitial cavities under various plans of distribution. Individually these collared zooids correspond structurally and functionally in every detail with the collared units of such genera as Codosiga, Salpingœca, and Proto-spongia. The collar in either case presents the same structure and functions, exhibits the same circulatory currents or cyclosis, and acts in the same way for the capture of food. The body contains an identical centrally located spheroidal nucleus or endoplast, and a corresponding series of rhythmically pulsating contractile vesicles. The developmental reproductive phenomena are also strictly parallel. Both originate as simple Amœba or simple flagellate Monads, exhibiting no trace in their earliest stage of the subsequently acquired characteristic collar. Both again after a time withdraw their collar and flagellum, and assume the amœboid state; then, coalescing, enter upon a quiescent or encysted condition, and break up into a number of sporular bodies, and thus provide for the further existence and distribution of the species. The whole process again is much akin to that which obtains in the protophytic type, *Volvox globator*, which liberates from its interior free swimming gemmules that take the form of spherical aggregation of biflagellate daughter-cells. In their isolated state, on the other hand, the swarm gemmules of the sponge stock are directly comparable with the free swimming subspheroidal colony stock of the flagellate infusoria Synura, Syncrypta, and Uroglena, or with the attached subspheroidal clusters of Codosiga and Anthophysa.

ECHINODERMATA, HYDROZOA, POLYZOA, HELMINTHOIDA.

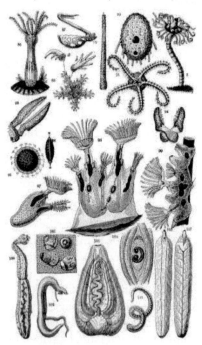

Tuffen West, del. Edmund Evans.

PLATE IV.

CHAPTER III.

Zoophytes, Cœlenterata, Medusæ, Corals, Hydrozoa.

Fig. 344.—Gorgonia Nobilis.

A study of the earliest growth of the Cœlenterata has shown that their internal cavities are nothing more than regular radiate out-growths of the internal structures. The result of this development is a condition which does not occur again in the whole of the animal kingdom. There is a system of cavities all in open communication one with another, no closed blood vascular system, and no specialised respiratory apparatus. Again, all the animals that constitute this large group are radiate in structure, that is, when viewed from above they are typically star-shaped, and if cut across, every horizontal section shows a symmetrical arrangement of the several parts around a centre. There are other radiate animals, as the Echinoderms, but while in these five is the fundamental number of rays, in the Cœlenterata the rays are a multiple of four, six and upwards. The skeleton or framework of each differs, and when the Cœlenterata form calcareous structures, these are quite different from the tests of the sea-urchins; and in all cases the anterior portion of the body is crowned with one or more circles of tentacles, which remain perfectly flexible and flower-like. The most highly-developed of the free forms are the sea-anemones and the jelly-fish. These have no hard or calcareous skeleton whatever, but withal they are, in the opinion of naturalists and microscopists, the most beautiful objects among Zoophytes.

In spite of their variety of forms, the Cœlenterata seem to be as incapable of higher development as do the Echinoderms, and they have failed to make headway in fresh water, but it is not improbable that some of the simplest forms of the whole group may have given rise to higher animal forms, while the sea anemones, corals, &c., being those descendants of the primitive simple form, have retained the original type of organization almost unchanged.

Fig. 345.—*Hydra viridis*, adhering to a stalk of *Anacharis alsinastrum*.

The type of the group is the Hydra, a fresh-water polyp, commonly found attached to the leaves and stems of many aquatic plants, or floating pieces of stick. Two species are well known to microscopists, the *H. viridis*, or green polyp, and the *H. vulgaris*, somewhat darker in colour, probably dependent upon the nature of its food. The third, less common species, the *H. fasca*, is distinguished from both by the length of its tentacles, which, when fully extended, greatly exceed those of either of the before-mentioned. The fresh-water group measures from one-eighth to the one-third of an inch in length, and form simple stocks of one, two or more branches. They almost exactly resemble in form the polyps of the Hydractinia, which are provided with a circle of tentacles. When placed in a vessel of water and left undisturbed they often attach themselves to the side, where they may be examined with a moderate power at leisure. They are then seen to spread out their tentacles like fine threads, and seize upon any small creature that may come in their way, and by the same means convey it to a mouth capable of great extension. All Hydra possess stinging-cells, by means of which they paralyse their prey. Many Hydra attain to a large size, and shoot out long poisonous filaments; they also possess smaller kinds of smooth cells, which appear to be employed for an entirely different purpose, but for what is not positively known. Hydra usually multiply by means of buds, an out-growth from the body, and these remain attached to the mother stalk for some time, often long enough to give rise to one or two smaller buds. Single eggs are also developed in the ectoderm beneath capsules, or wart-like prominences. The adult animal can be cut to pieces, and from each piece a new individual will be developed. This method of reproduction was first tried by the naturalist Trembley in 1739, whose experiments in this direction excited the greatest interest among the naturalists of the middle of the last century. *Hydra fusca* in various stages of development is given in outline in Fig. 346.

Fig. 346.

1, 2, 3. Hydra in various stages of development; 4. Group of *Stentor polymorphus*, many-shaped Stentor; 5. Englena; 6. Monads.

In the polyps belonging to this family the body-structure for the most part consists of a homogeneous aggregation of vesicular granules, held together by an intercellular sarcode, and capable of great extension and contraction, so that these animals can assume a variety of forms and extend their body and tentacles until the latter become almost invisible. It was the resemblance in this respect to the fabled Hydra that originated the name. Its organ of prehension is termed the *hasta*; this consists of a sac or opening at the terminal end of the tentacle, within which is seen a saucer-shaped vesicle, supporting a minute ovate body, which carries a sharp calcareous piece termed a *sagitta* or arrow. Although the fresh-water Hydra may be regarded as typical of this group of animals, marine fauna furnish a far more extensive group in the corals, jelly-fish, and sea-anemones.

A smaller group, the Ctenophora, although members of this sub-kingdom, have not yet found their true position; nevertheless they are interesting glassy, transparent creatures, either shaped like apples, melons, or Phrygian caps, or else forming bands of some considerable length; all are wonderfully transparent, with the single exception of the Beroë. These inhabit the open sea, and are only seen inshore when driven in by currents or strong winds. Their position in the water is usually more or less vertical, the mouth being turned downwards. The portion from which this group derives its name is the ribs, which are symmetrically arranged, and consist of rows of short transverse combs, each forming rows of cilia, which, as they wave to and fro, constitute a swimming or rowing plate, their activity in the water depending upon the will of the animal. They are also provided with an oral umbrella, and capturing filaments or tentacles with hair-like branches. These tentacles, attached to the sides of the animal, are capable of erection or withdrawal into pockets. Great variety is seen in these accessory organs of locomotion; for instance, the Cydippidæ (Plate XVII.) have only arms, but these are remarkable for their length, and serve for the purpose of capturing food as well as for steering. The most interesting, if not the most beautiful of the Ctenophora, are the Beroidæ; it is this family that bear a resemblance to the Phrygian cap (Plate XVII., *e*). The mouth is wide, but it appears to have no capturing tentacles, and yet their habits are carnivorous; they will even devour their own relations. Many of the genus are phosphorescent, and in place of stinging-cells have small spherical knobs beset with sticky globules, in which their food becomes entangled, and these are apparently in constant use.

PLATE XVII.

ZOOPHYTES, ASTEROIDS, NUDIBRANCHIS, ACALEPS, ECHINOIDS, CTENOPHORA, TUNICATA, AND CRUSTACEANS.

The Stinging Series, Cnidaria, comprise sea-anemones, corals, jelly-fish among marine animals, and Hydra among the fresh-water Cœlenterata; and derive their name from a remarkably curious feature, the so-called stinging capsules. These are not only offensive, but also defensive weapons with all the animals belonging to this group; the possession of which has converted the bell-like jelly-fish into a simple Cnidarian. The principal change is in the gelatinous layer between the outer wall and the inner digesting layer of the ectoderm. But without entering further into their structure and relations, the stinging-cells and batteries claim especial attention. These cells vary considerably in size without their characteristics being essentially changed. The protoplasm of the cell is modified into a tolerably firm substance, enclosing an oval or cylindrical vesicle. Closely associated with this is a pointed process, standing up far above the level of the outer covering, known as the *cnidocil*. Within the vesicle is found, either spirally rolled up or in an irregular tangle, a long filament or hollow tube, a prolongation of the vesicle, but turned outside in. This tube is more than twenty times as long as the cell, is pointed at the tip, and beset with two rows of fine spirally-arranged barbed hooks. When the cnidocil is touched or irritated, this filament is violently shot out, being then turned inside-out, like the fingers of a glove. So long as the thread remains rolled up within the vesicle the barbed hooks remain in their tube, but when shot out, they change to the outside. The rolled-up filament appears to be filled with some poisonous material, which is ejected when the tube is shot out, and where the point strikes a wound is inflicted, so that unless the prey is stronger than the attacker it cannot escape. The greater the struggle, the larger the number of capsules discharged in order to kill.

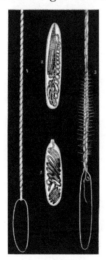

Fig. 347.—The Stinging Capsules of Cnidaria.

1 and 2. Retracted filaments; 3. Partly protruded; 4. Fully protruded. Magnified × 600. (Warne.)

Polypomedusæ.—Among the higher development of the stinging group is the jelly-fish. The Siphonophora, as represented by the Portuguese man-of-war, are in their turn the highest development of swimming-bells, and exhibit many modifications and combinations of individuals. The tentacles of the Physalia, the best known, are stiff with batteries of stinging-capsules, the sting of which is more like the shock of the electric current. The *Challenger* soundings brought to light some remarkably interesting forms, and these have furnished much work for the microscope, as all their larval forms are extremely curious. Among the Hydromedusæ there are many different life histories. Take the jelly-fish, the eggs of which have given up forming stocks, and are hatched out at once as Medusæ. There are others, the eggs of which form stocks; others, again, in which the sexual individuals do not swim away as jelly-fish. The last were at one time described under a new name, because of one or two curious forms being taken creeping on the ground. This creeping Medusa (*Clavatella prolifera*) has six arms, the tips of which are provided with true suckers, and on these it walks as on stilts, while from each arm a short stalk arises, the swollen end of which is beset with stinging capsules. It has an extensile mouth-tube, and feeds upon small crustaceans found on seaweeds.

Fig. 348.—*Plumularia primata. Doris tuberculata* seen clinging to a fucus.

Among the forms that swim away as jelly-fish a very curious example is presented in *Corymorpha mutans*. These swim about for a time, and then firmly attach themselves by numerous thread-like appendages, forced into the sand, and where the young prepare for their next metamorphosis. As an example of the stocks of those representatives which do not swim away as jelly-fish, take the beautifully-feathered, plant-like creatures found erect along the seashore, the Sertularia (Fig. 358, No. 12) and Plumularia. *Plumularia primata*, Fig. 348. Other members of these groups will be found in Plate IV., Nos. 95-99.

Fig. 349.—Group of female stock of *Hydractinia echinata*.

a, a. Nutritive individuals; *b, b.* Female individuals and groups of eggs. Highly magnified.—(Warne.)

In addition to the nutritive individuals, there are the egg-bearing; these do not become free-swimming individuals. One small family is neither branched nor feathered—the *Hydractinia echinata*, found in the North Sea and on the Norwegian coasts, where it attaches itself to the shells of gastropods, selecting those inhabited by hermit crabs. The part of the stock common to all the individuals is the skin-like portion which adheres to the surface of the shell. In some spiny processes are produced, and the nutritive canals running down the stems of the polyps are continued into the membrane belonging to the stock, as seen in Fig. 349.

The nutritive individuals are distinguished by long tentacles, mouths, and digestive canals. The females have no mouths, and are supplied with food through the system of canals running to them from the nutritive males. These reproductive members are furnished with stinging threads instead of tentacles for the protection of their ova. The ciliated larvæ, in a very short time, swim off to found new colonies.

Fig. 350.—Medusæ, Jelly-fish.

The free-swimming jelly-fish (Fig. 350, and Plate XVII., *c* and *d*) belong to the order Scyphomedusæ. These are characterised by their delicate colouring, and from the arrangement of their nervous system, which can only be made out by staining. Some new and curious forms were dredged from a depth of more than 6,000 feet off the coast of New Zealand, varying in size from an inch to twenty inches; many having from four to eight or ten eyes arranged along the margin.

Anthozoa.—From the free-swimming we turn to a group of permanently fixed polyp forms, the sea-anemones and corals. The development of Monoxenia commences with the egg, repeatedly dividing into many parts (Fig. 351, C, D, and E), by a process common to the animal kingdom, termed egg-segmentation, in this particular instance proceeding from an apparently hollow sphere, A, enclosing a single layer of cells, G. Each cell sends out a long cilia, or whip-like process, F, by means of which the larva turns about and swims in the body fluid of the parent polyp. One half of the sphere now becomes enfolded into the other half, H, and forms what is termed a *gastrula*, I, K. The gastrula stage of Monoxenia is of the simplest kind, the larva forming a sac, with walls consisting of two layers, an outer, or ectoderm, and an inner, or endoderm. The transition from the flat dish shape, H, to the sac with a narrow mouth is at once clear, and the knowledge that all the Cœlenterates proceed from similar larvæ, and that all the complications of their various systems are developed from a simple gastrula, throws much light on their anatomy. During these transitions the endoderm, whose cells multiply, continues as an uninterrupted lining to the stomach and its appendages, while the ectoderm yields the cuticular elements.

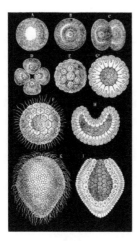

Fig. 351.—Stages in development of *Monoxenia Darwinii,* × 600.—(Warne.)

A third intermediate gelatinous layer, the *mesoglæa,* arises between the two layers in which muscles and connective interstitial tissue appear. In the mesoglæa of one species of coral calcification takes place; this internal calcification has but a small share in the work of the great rock-making corals, their most important calcification being external. In Monoxenia, although the transition from the gastrula larva to the adult animal has not been seen, there can be no doubt as to how this is carried out, the transformations having been watched throughout in other species. The larva attaches itself with the end opposite the mouth, the cilia disappear, and after the mouth-tube has been formed by the folding in of the anterior end along the longitudinal axis of the body, and has thus become marked off from the stomach, eight hollow tentacles rise round the mouth as outgrowths of the body cavity, or as direct continuations of the stomach.

Like all other corals, Monoxenia periodically multiply by means of eggs, which are formed either in the walls of the radiating partitions or septa, or along the free edges. These are ejected through the oral opening. As a rule, the polyps are either male or female; but in stock-forming species individuals of the two sexes are often mixed. Monoxenia may be taken as the simplest type of the regularly radiate polyps; in all the different organs being repeated in regular rings round a central axis; the mouth also is circular. From this interesting account, drawn by Haeckel, of a simple polyp, it will be at once seen what kind of radiate animal it is that builds up the coral reefs. "No garden on earth can match the gardens of the sea that circle the northern part of Australia. As the tide ebbs in azure sunset, coral-reefs peer out symmetrically arranged in beds and intersected by emerald pathways coursing through corals of all hues and tints fathoms deep in the channels."

In a growing polyp-stock the individuals usually remain in organic connection; that is to say, each first provides for itself and then shares its superfluity with others, sometimes by means of a continuous reticulated system of canals perforating the calcareous substance which often separates the members of one stock from another. The whole colony may thus be physiologically one creature with many mouths. There are others that remain single, as the inverted pyramidal-looking bodies, Fungidæ, commonly called "Sea-mushrooms," found in great variety. The colour of the polypidom is white, of a flattened round shape, made up of thin plates or scales, imbedded in a translucent jelly-like substance, and within is concealed a polyp; the footstalk, by means of which the animal is attached to the rock, is of a calcareous nature (Fig. 352, No. 1).

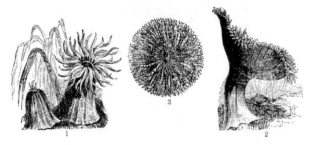

Fig. 352.—Sea-Anemones.

1. *Actinia rubra*, tentacles displayed and retracted; 2. *Heticictis bellis*; 3. *H. bellis*, seen from above.

Hexactinia (six-rayed polyps) are not limited to six rays, as the name given them may seem to imply; they are, in fact, very numerous in some of the largest and most gorgeous of the sea-anemones. All are distinguished by their solitary manner of life, their size, and their vivid and variedly beautiful colouring. The endoderm is firm, and when the animal withdraws its tentacles and shuts its body substance in, there is some difficulty in penetrating to the interior. It does not, however, secrete a calcareous skeleton inside or out, as do the true coral polyps. Among the Hexactinia the sea-anemone (Fig. 352) takes the first place.

These beautifully coloured creatures are, for the most part, found attached to the spot selected by the larvæ; a few species bore into the sand with the posterior part of the body, or build a sheath, which they inhabit. They are voracious feeders, and devour large pieces of flesh, and even mussel and oysters, sucking them in by means of their long grasping tentacles. Well-fed anemones change their skin frequently, during which process they remain closely retracted; the shed skin forms a loose girdle around the base. *Actinia bellis* not infrequently attach themselves to the shells of crabs and whelks, and are thus carried to pastures new.

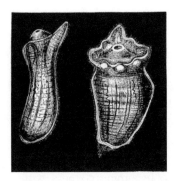

Fig. 353.—Larvæ of Sea-Anemones, *Actinia effœta*, highly magnified.

On account of the ease with which anemones are kept in captivity, their mode of reproduction can be closely observed. With but few exceptions they develop from eggs, and in the course of a few weeks are hatched into ciliated infusorial larvæ, presenting most curious and exquisite representations of jugs and jars, with cover lids (as seen in Fig. 353, *Actinia effœta*). These evince the handiwork of a master hand in the ceramic art. They are, however, of so translucent a nature as to permit of the internal structure being seen to consist of nerves and vessels, and which are rendered more apparent by staining. These settle down in a week or ten days, and then shed their cilia, the first tentacle appearing during the process of attachment.

In some species the young Actiniæ are seen to pass through their whole development within the body cavity of the parent. Most anemones are provided with several circles of more or less cylindrical tentacles, and there are a few specially beautiful species which, besides tentacles of the usual form, have, either within or without the ordinary circle of tentacles, lobed or leaf-like tactile and seizing organs. These belong to the family of the beautiful Crambactis of the Red Sea. Below these grasping tentacles comes a circle of thicker arms unlike the former, being spindle shaped. All the tentacles of the sea-anemones are hollow with a fine aperture at the tip, through which, on closing rapidly, it is seen to expel a jet of water.

True Corals.—It will have been noticed in the foregoing remarks that in the soft body-division of the Hexactinia there are both single individuals and colonies joined together to form stocks. The same diversity in this respect will be found among corals proper, with this difference, that the skeleton-forming polyps, by combining, build up substantial structures in the most secure and advantageous positions. Now it so happens that all the corals found about our coasts are generally small and solitary dwellers, one of the best known of which is the scarlet crisp coral, Flabellum, and is characterised by the slit-like form of the mouth. Viewed sideways it resembles a small fan fastened along the edges, and just inside a row of fully developed tentacles is seen protruding. An interesting form of budding occurs in these corals: the buds fall off, and in this budding condition the coral might pass, and indeed has been described as a different species of Flabellum. The colour of the coral is a beautifully transparent red. Remarkable as the solitary corals are, they are surpassed both in number and in form by those which form compound stocks, that is to say, in which the buds do not fall off, but go on building up coral islands and barrier reefs in the warmer seas. Some very few typical forms only are given in the group accompanying, shown in Fig. 358.

A different kind of stock is developed in a number of forms, some producing many buds, as in the Madrepores, in which selected polyps spring up above the rest, their sides also becoming covered with small buds, each one of which is a living, feeding, coral animal surrounded by a crown of tentacles. These Madrepores play a very important part in the building up of coral reefs.

Fig. 354. Developmental stages of Larvæ, *Astroides calycularis*, × 40.

Another massive coral, the *Astroides calycularis*, has a different mode of growth, the tubes not being fused together. When seen standing out these yellowish-red polyps have been mistaken for small anemones. The larvæ of this coral leave the egg while still in the large chambered body cavity of the parent, where they swim about for a time, till they escape through the mouth. They are worm-like in form, and swim by means of cilia, which are thicker at the foremost end. The mouth first appears after leaving the parent, but as they soon become exhausted by the effort they assume a contracted form, and attach themselves, as do anemones, by pressing the thicker end of the body against a rock, the whole contracting into a thick round disc, while longitudinal furrows become visible at the upper part where the mouth sinks in. At the end of these furrows twelve tentacles appear. The accompanying illustration shows the various stages through which the larvæ pass in rapid succession (Fig. 354); at the same time it has already commenced to secrete its calcareous skeleton. This is not formed as a connected whole but from a number of separate centres of secretion formed between the polyp and the substance to which it has attached itself, and which become gradually fused into a perfect skeleton. A section of the polyp at this stage forms an interesting microscopical object.

The so-called eight-rayed corals consist of the one genus Tubipora, the members of which are few in number and not varied in form (Fig. 358, No. 10). In the structure, however, of skeletons they are unique among extant corals. Each individual secretes a smooth-walled tube without calcification of the vertical septa. These tubes, like the pipes of an organ, stand almost parallel, and are united to form a stock by means of transverse platforms. The formation of buds does not appear to take place in this family.

Another of the eight-rayed corals is Gorgoniidæ. These are permanently fixed to the spot on which they are found, and form a bush-like growth, giving no idea of the living coral, as it rises in graceful branching colonies, in deep water, and represents a portion of *Gorgonia nobilis* with polyps expanded (Figs. 344 and 358, No. 9).

Other corals present numerous other departures from the types we have been considering, but so far modified in form as that of the Sea-pen, Veretillum (Fig. 355), the stock part of which is surrounded by polyps continued down a portion of the cylindrical stalk. The best known of the species is *Pennatula phosphorea* of the Mediterranean.

Fig. 355.

1. *Pennatula phosphorea*; 2. *Synapta chirodata*; 3. Anchor-shaped spiculum and plate from the ectoderm of same.

Pennatulidæ.—This family derives its name from *penna*, a quill. Their spicula also resemble a penholder in appearance, shown in Fig. 358, No. 3. The polyps are without colour, provided with eight rather long retractile tentacula, beautifully ciliated on the inner aspect with two series of short processes, and strengthened by these crystalline spicula, a row being carried up the stalk, together with a series of ciliated processes. The mouth, occupying the centre of the tentacula, is somewhat angular. The ova lie between the membranous part of the pinnæ; these are globular, of a yellowish colour, and by pressure can be made to pass through the mouth. Dr. Grant wrote:—"A more singular and beautiful spectacle could scarcely be conceived than that of a deep purple *Pennatula phosphorea*, with all its delicate transparent polyps expanded and emitting their usual brilliant phosphorescent light, sailing through the still and dark abyss, by the regular and synchronous pulsations of the minute fringed arms of the polyps."

The spicula are seen to be a continuous series of cones fitting into each other.

Bryozoa, Moss-animals.

The exact position in which the Bryozoa, or moss-animals, should be placed in the animal kingdom has not been finally determined. They were at one time associated with corals; then with sponges; but, on further acquaintance, it became evident that they did not belong to either. Naturalists also claimed them as Rotifers and Ciliata, but this claim met with no better reception. Since they appear to have no settled classification, there can be no objection to linking them once more to corals, as they apparently resemble these animals by always living in colonies, the individual members of which are joined in a number of different ways to form stocks, the individuals themselves, however, being very much smaller than those of corals proper. The advantage is that the structure of the Bryozoans can be more readily studied, as many of them live in transparent chambers or cells, the walls of which, although somewhat firmly agglutinated together, are flexible enough to fold up, as the animals instantly withdraw their bodies and close up the top on the slightest alarm (Fig. 356).

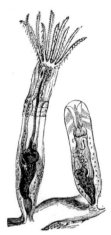

Fig. 356.—Paludicella, tentacles expanded and cell closed.

Fig. 357.—Sea-moss, Flustra, the body having been withdrawn from its cell.

The general structure of the Bryozoan individual, figured attached by its footstalk to a stem of wood, consists of a mouth at the anterior part of the body opening into a muscular pharynx in the alimentary canal, together occupying a considerable amount of space. The terminal portion turns upon itself towards the oral opening, its chief attachment being a short strand of tissue termed the funiculus (shown in Fig. 358, No. 11). In all adults two masses of cells are found attached to the wall of the chamber; the upper yields the eggs, within the lower the male elements are developed. Moss-animals are hermaphrodite, fertilisation being effected by the two elements mingling together in the body fluid. These are the essential points in the structure of the whole seventeen hundred species. Among the larger colonies a number of fresh-water genera are found attached to the roots and branches of aquatic plants, most of which, however, are inconspicuous. The beauty of these minute bodies can only be seen under the microscope. Many consist of delicate branching growths, the Sea-mats (Flustra), for instance; others again appear as attractive lace corals, between the open meshes of which multitudes of minute apertures crowned with tentacles are displayed. The several individuals of the genus Lepralia are arranged in rows, and further distinguished by the animals being developed only on one side of the stock. The marvellous variety of forms presented by these small animals is in a measure determined by the particular manner of their buddings. The greater number of fresh-water moss-animals belong to the order Phylactolæmata, so called because the mouth is provided with a tongue-shaped lid. The crown of tentacles is furnished with rows of cilia, and is horseshoe-shaped, the whole being surrounded at its base by an integument forming a kind of cup, which is either soft or horny. Those belonging to the wandering types (Cristatella, Plate IV., Nos. 95-98) form flattened elliptical colonies, some of which creep or move about on a kind of foot. A nervous system pervades the mass of polyps, while in each separate polyp a nerve ganglion is seen to be situated between the œsophagus and the posterior part of the alimentary canal. The colony nerve system regulates the movements of the stock.

Fig. 358.—Typical forms of Corals.

1. *Fungia agariciformis*; 2. Alcyonium, *Cydonium Mulleri*; 3. Cydonium, polyps protruding and tentacles expanded, others closed; 4. A stock viewed from above; 5. *Madrepore abrotanoide*; 6. Madrepore, slightly magnified, showing oral opening; 7. Corallidæ; 8. Coral, polyps protruding from cells; 9. *Gorgonia nobilis*, with polyps expanded; 10. *Tubipora musica*; 11. Tubes of same, with polyps expanded, one cut longitudinally to show internal structure; 12. Sertularia, polyps protruded, and withdrawn into their polypidoms.

Fig. 359.

1. *Coryne stauridia*; 2. A tentacle detached and magnified 200 diameters.

There are many beautifully formed freshwater polyps deserving of more than a passing notice, as the slender Coryne (*Coryne stauridia*), found adhering to the footstalk of a *Rhodymenia* (Fig. 359), about which it creeps in the form of a white thread. On placing both under the microscope, the thread-like body of the little animal appears cylindrical and tubular, perfectly transparent, and permeated by a central core, apparently cellular in texture, hollow, and within which a rather slow circulation of globules is perceived. The parent Coryne sends off numerous branches, the terminal head of which is oblong, cylindrical, and at the extreme end there are arranged four tentacles, long and slender, each being furnished with a nodular head. A magnified view of one detached is shown erect (Fig. 359, No. 2). This polyp is much infested by parasites, vorticella growing on it in immense numbers, forming aggregated clusters here and there, individuals of the parasitic colony adhering to each other, and projecting outwards in every direction.

Alcyonella, another fresh-water polyp, is found in the autumn of the year in all the London Docks adhering to pieces of floating timber. *A. stagnorum* partakes of the character of a sponge rather than that of a polyp. It is usually found in gelatinous colonies, and when stood aside for a short time these put forth a number of ciliated tentacles (shown in Fig. 360, magnified 100 diameters).

The ova contained within the sac, and viewed by transmitted light, appear as opaque spheres surrounded by a thin transparent margin; these increase in thickness as the ova is developed, and such of the ova as lie in contact seem to unite and form a statoblast. A rapid current in the water around each animal, drawing with it loose particles and floating animalcules, is seen moving with some velocity as in other ciliated bodies; and a zone of very minute vibrating cilia surrounds the transparent margin of each tentacle.

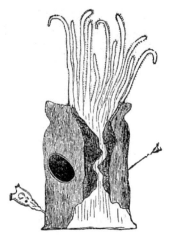

Fig. 360.—*Alcyonella fluviatella.*

Dr. Percival Wright discovered on the western coast of Ireland a new genus of Alcyonidæ, which he named after the well-known naturalist Harte, *Hartea elegans* (Plate IV., No. 86). This polyp is solitary, the body cylindrical, and fixed by its base to the rock; it has eight ciliated tentacles, which are knobbed at their base and most freely displayed. It is a very beautiful polyzoon of a clear white colour, and when fully expanded stands three-quarters of an inch high.

Lophopus crystallinus (Plate IV., No. 98) displays beautiful plumes of tentacles arranged in a double horseshoe-shaped series. When first observed these polyps resemble in many respects masses of the water snail ova, for which they are often mistaken. On placing these jelly-like masses into a glass trough with some of the clear water taken from the stream in which they are found, delicate tubes are seen to cautiously protrude, and the beautiful fringes of cilia are quickly brought into play. The organisation of *L. crystallinus* is simple, although it is provided with organs of digestion, circulation, respiration, and generation. The nervous[70] and muscular systems are well developed. This polyp increases both by budding and by ova, both of which conditions are shown in Plate IV., No. 98. The ova are enclosed in the transparent case of the parent. In Lophopus and some other fresh-water genera, Cristatella, Plumatella, and Alcyonella, the neural margin of the Lophopore is extended into two triangular arms, giving it the appearance of a deep crescent.

Another family presents a contrast: there is no lid to the mouth, and the tentacles are arranged in a circle on a disc. An important rise in organisation is found in the Gymnolæmata, especially in the lip-mouthed forms; the individuals belonging to this order vary in structure and fulfil different physiological functions. There are structures known as zoæcia, stolons, avicularia, vibracula, and ovicells, some of which are merely modified individuals. The zoæcia are the normal individuals of the colony, fully developed for most of the functions of life; the stolons have a much humbler function, but are indispensable—they are the root-like outgrowths of the stock, and serve for attaching the colony to foreign objects. The most remarkable are those known as *avicularia*, so called because they resemble the head of a bird. This process acts as a pair of forceps, the large upper blade of which is very like the skull and upper jaw of a bird, and the smaller lower blade (like the lower jaw) constantly opens and shuts by means of a complicated arrangement of muscles (shown in Fig. 361). These avicularia are movably attached by short muscles to the neck, and are found near the entrance to a zoæcium. They turn from side to side, snapping in all directions, catching at every particle of food that may come near; at length the morsel is drawn into the mouth by the cilia on the tentacles. From this very peculiar structure the Chilostomata were originally named bird's-head corallines, then specifically shepherd's-purse corallines, *Notamia bursaria*. Equally interesting, again, are the *vibracula*, long thread-like structures, attached by short footstalks. These keep up a constant whip-like motion, the object of which is not quite clear. The ovicells, or egg receptacles, are found at the lower ends of the zoœcia in the form of shields, helmets, or vesicles. In Plate IV., Nos. 95 and 96, a front and edge view of the statoblast is shown highly magnified.

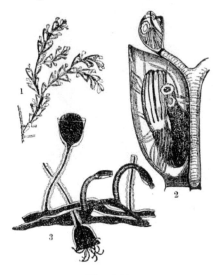

Fig. 361.

1. *Notamia bursaria*, shepherd's-purse Bryozoa; 2. Polyp magnified and withdrawn into its cell; 3. Portion of a colony of Hydroid polyps.

Another sub-order consists of the Cyclostomata, or round-mouthed Bryozoans, of which the Tubulipora is the typical form. The stocks are cup-shaped incrustations, the individuals radiating outwards, as in Plate IV., No. 92. *Tubularia dumortierii* is a very interesting form, the germinal bodies, statoblasts, being formed as cell masses on the strand, or funiculus, which also maintains the stomach in its place. They are round or oval in shape, and brown or yellow in colour, and consist of two valves fitted one upon the other like watch glasses, as shown in No. 96. A number of other statoblasts are shown, Nos. 97, 98, and 99. The edge running round No. 95 is seen to have barbed tips; the ring itself contains small air chambers, and is termed the swimming belt. It is, in fact, a perfect hydrostatic apparatus, giving support to the winter buds or statoblasts on the surface of the water. The barbed hooks apparently act as anchors, and by their means they catch on at points suitable for their development during the coming spring. As soon as the time comes, the two halves split apart and the germinal mass emerges forth. Out of these winter buds and statoblasts asexually produced individuals arise, which reproduce themselves sexually, their descendants again yielding winter germs. In short, an alternation of generations is a continually recurring process.

Fig. 362.—*Lingula pyramidata.*

Brachiopoda.—Here again we have to do with an enigmatical class· of arm-footed animals, of which the Lamp-shells may be regarded as typical. These have remained unaltered from the earliest geological epochs. Brachiopods are divided into two orders: those having shells without hinges, and those with shells hinged together. On the whole they possess less interest for the microscopists than many other animals, except in their earliest developmental stages of existence.

One of the most interesting of the hinge-class group, living chiefly near the shores of the warmer seas, is the Lingulidæ. The valves are almost exactly similar, but are not hinged together, and have no processes for the support of the thick fleshy spiral arms of the animals. In *L. pyramidata*, found around the Philippine Islands (Fig. 362), the stalk is nine times longer than the body. The animal does not attach itself by this, but moves about like a worm, making tubes out of sand, into which it can withdraw itself and disappear. The cilia at the mantle edge form a fine sieve, thus preventing foreign particles from entering the gills. Its internal structure possesses points of interest, and the parasitic growths covering the cartilaginous structure, miscalled a shell, are curious, and excite the attention of the naturalist.

Another bivalve so unlike a crustacean, among which it has been placed, I may venture to describe among Lamp-shells. I refer to the barnacle (Lepas) generally met with covering the bottoms of ships. These, as in the former genus, are more interesting to the microscopist in the early stage of existence, and also for the curious parasites known to infest them. The barnacle protrudes through its two valves six pairs of slender, bristly, two-branched filamentous limbs, which keep up a constant sweeping motion, and whereby it secures its supply of food (Fig. 363). When first hatched the young are in the Nauplius stage, being furnished with a median eye and three pairs of flagellated appendages. After enjoying a free life the larva moults and passes into a second stage, in which with its two eyes and compressed carapace (shown in Fig. 364) it so nearly resembles a Daphnia. Before these thoracic appendages entirely disappear they first change places, and then each is seen to be provided with a sucker; by this means the larva fixes itself to its permanent resting-place, while a cement gland pours out a secretion that glues it firmly to the point of attachment chosen. These Cirripedes are not true parasites, inasmuch as they do not extract nourishment from the body to which they are attached.

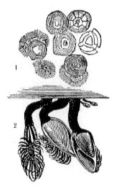

Fig. 363.

1. Spat of oyster, some ciliated; 2. Barnacles attached by footstalks.

One species, the Proteolepas, is in the adult stage a maggot-like, limbless, shell-less animal found living within the mantle chamber of other members of the same order, while the root-headed Cirripedes (*Peltogaster curvatus*, as Fig. 364, No. 1) live parasitically upon higher crustaceans.

Echinodermata.—This sub-kingdom includes the star-fishes, stone-lilies, sea-urchins, feather-stars, and sea-cucumbers, some of which have been already alluded to, and are so well known that they need no lengthy description, while of the fossil sea-urchins of our chalk formations, the Pentremites and Crinoids, whose silicious remains are so abundant and so familiar to naturalists and geologists, but little remains to be said. They are chiefly interesting to the microscopist from their calcareous and silicious appendages, known as spicula. In the sea-urchin, brittle-star, or feather-star, the outer body surface consists almost wholly of a deposit of calcium carbonate, combined in the form of little plates built up into a rigid "test," whereas in the star-fish it usually forms a kind of scaffolding, between the layers of which there stretches a firm leathery skin. Among the sea-cucumbers, the living specimens of which present extraordinary variations both in form and character, the deposit consists chiefly of small spicules which grate when the skin is cut with a knife. If a thin section of the skin is examined under the microscope, the spicules are seen to be profusely distributed in the middle layer. The same deposit takes place in the stalked column of a crinoid and in sea-urchins (Echinodermata), which has tended to preserve them in the fossilised state. Fig. 365 is selected as exhibiting to perfection the Medusa-headed Pentacrinoid. This echinoderm differs in two characters: first, its microscopic structure is that of a meshwork deposited in the spaces of a network of soft tissue; secondly, that each element, whether a spicule or a plate, is, despite its trellised structure, deposited around regular lines of crystallisation (shown in Plate IV., Nos. 89 and 90). Owing to these characteristics the minutest portion of an echinoderm skeleton is readily recognised, even when fossilised, under the microscope. Even the species of the sea-cucumber can be determined by the shape of their spicules.

Fig. 364.—Parasitic Barnacles.

1. *Peltogaster curvatus*; 2. Nauplius larva of Parthenopea; × 200.

Another noticeable feature in the radiate structure is that in many cases it gives to the animal a star-shape, to which the names of star-fish and brittle-star are given (see Plate IV., No. 91, and Plate XVII., *f* and *n*). The ordinary five-rayed star-fish is found everywhere around the English coasts. This constant arrangement of organs holds good in the majority of the echinoderms; it can be detected in the Holothurians, where, beside the feathery tentacles of the head, rows of shorter sucker-like processes will be found, which in some instances extend the whole length of the body, the fixed number of rows being also five in their internal organs. Hence these animals were formerly grouped under Radiata. But if a sea-cucumber or sea-urchin be dissected, a marked distinction will be found between them, in one portion of the organism in particular: the intestine is shut off from the rest of the body-cavity, often coiling round inside. Examine a star-fish or sea-urchin on the under-surface of the rays, and, passing in five bands from top to bottom, a number of small cylindrical processes are seen gently waving about; these lie in two rows with a clear space between them, and are termed in consequence *ambulacrum*. They end in sucker-like discs, which enable the animal to attach itself, or pull itself against strong currents.

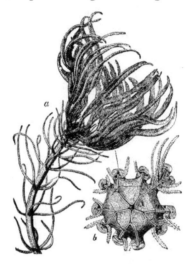

Fig. 365.—Medusa-headed Pentacrinoid.

a. Crown and part of stem; *b*. Upper surface of body, the arms broken away, showing the food grooves passing to the central mouth.—(Warne.)

Just one other special feature should be noticed: radial canals pass along under the ambulacra, and join a ring-canal around the mouth, well supplied by nerve cells.

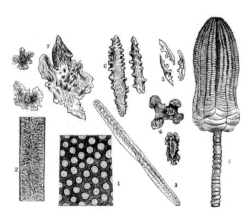

Fig. 366.

1. Transverse section of a branch of Myriapore; 2, and the others Section of the stem of *Virgularia mirabilis*; 3, Spiculum from the outer surface of Sea-pen; 4, Spicula from *Isis hippuris*; 5, from *Gorgonia elongata*; 6, from Alcyonium; 7, and from *Gorgonia umbraculum*; 8, Calcareous remains of a Crinoid.

Crinoids (stone-lilies), on the other hand, are formed of a series of flat rings, pierced through by a narrow canal. The ossicles, as they are termed, are joined by ligaments passing through their solid substance and endowed with muscular power; the central part serves for the passage of blood-vessels, and is surrounded by a sheath of nervous tissue that controls the movements of the stem, the latter being encrusted by a number of fine rootlets. The stems possess a limited power of bending. In the words of Professor Agassiz, "The stem itself passes slowly from a rigid vertical attitude to a curved or even a drooping position; the cirri move more rapidly than the arms, and the animal uses them as hooks to catch hold of objects, and on account of their sharp extremities they are well adapted to retain their hold of prey." The rosy-feather star-fish is often found clinging to a tube of the Sabella worm; the food of crinoids consists of foraminifera, diatoms, and the larvæ of crustaceans. There are so many curious features in connection with the Echinodermata that my readers may with advantage consult "The *Challenger* Reports" and Warne's "Natural History" on other points of interest.

Holothuroidea (sea-cucumbers) are elongated slug-like creatures, the skin being in structure similar to that of the slug, with a comparatively small amount of calcareous matter. Usually this occurs in small spicules, which assume very definite shapes, as the anchors of Synapta (Plate IV., No. 87, and in Fig. 355). There are also rings of calcareous plates around the gullet, five of which have the same relation to the radial water-vessels as the auricles round the jaws of a sea-urchin, and which likewise serve for the attachment of muscles. These plates are seen in Plate VIII., Nos. 171 and 172, as they appear coloured by selenite films under polarised light. Around the mouth in Cucumaria is a fringe of branched tentacles connected with the water-vascular ring; these appear to be used as a net to intercept floating organisms.

Correlated with the star-fishes is a small family based on the character of their pincer-like organs, called pedicellariæ, on the surface of the test (shown in Plate IV., Nos. 93 and 94, magnified × 25). Movable spines cover the surface of these echinoderms, varying in size from minute bristle-like structures to long rods. The pedicellariæ are, it is believed, derived from the smaller spines, and two of them are united at the base by muscles, slightly curved, and made to approach each other at their extremities. There is a gradual modification of this type through the whole series. Many uses have been assigned to them, as the holding of food, as they have been seen to hold to the fronds of seaweed and keep them steady until the spines and tube feet can be brought into action. The inner surface of the pedicellariæ are known to be the most sensitive, and the blades close on the minutest object touching the inner surface. Beside these peculiar bodies the surface of the skin has small tubular processes, and tubular feet with suckers at the end. At the extremity of each arm is a single tube-foot with an impaired tentacle, and above this again is a small eye coloured by red pigment.

Passing by many other points of interest in the Echinoidæ, the spines are seen to be attached to the test or shell by a ball and socket joint and well-arranged muscles, whereby the spines can be moved in any direction. The tubercles, however, do not cover the whole test, but are disposed chiefly in five broad zones extending from one pole to another. When a transverse section of a spine is examined by a medium power it is seen to be made up of a series of concentric and radiating layers (shown in Plate XVIII., Nos. 1 and 2), the centre being occupied by reticulated structure and structureless spots arranged at equal distances; these may be termed ribs or pillars. Passing towards the margin are other rows conveying the impression of a beautiful indented reticulated tissue. Many of the spines present no structure, while others exhibit a series of concentric rings of successive growth, which strongly remind one of the medullary rays of plants. When a vertical section of a spine is submitted to examination, it is seen to be composed of cones placed one above the other, the outer margin of each cone being formed by the series of pillars. In certain species of Echinus the number of cones is very considerable, while in others there are seldom more than one or two to be found; from these, transverse sections may when made show no concentric rings, only the external row of pillars.

The skeleton of echinoderms contains but a small amount of organic matter, as will be seen on dissolving out the calcareous portion in dilute nitric or hydrochloric acids. The residuum structure will appear to be meshes or areolæ, bounded by a substance having a fibrous appearance, intermingled with granulous matter; in fact, it bears a close resemblance to the areolar tissue of higher animals, and the test may be considered as formed, not by the consolidation of the cells of the ectoderm, as in the mollusc, but by the calcification of the fibro-areolar tissue of the endoderm. This calcification of a simple fibrous tissue by the deposit of a mineral substance, not in the meshes of areolæ but in intimate union with the organic basis, is a condition of much interest to the physiologist; it presents an example of a process which seems to have an important share in the formation and growth of bone, namely, in the progressive calcification of the fibrous tissue of the periosteum membrane covering of the bone.

The development of the sea-urchin from the fertilised egg first divides and then sub-divides, and in a short time the embryo issues forth with a small tuft of cilia, by means of which it swims off freely. The larvæ, in its full development, measures about one millimetre in diameter, and is a curious and remarkable creature.

The sub-kingdom Mollusca comprises some fifty thousand species, and fresh forms are being constantly discovered, the number of the aquatic genera being more than double that of the terrestrial species, for it matters not to what depth of ocean the dredge is let down, some new form is certain to be gathered. The *Challenger* expedition has enriched our knowledge of the deep-sea fauna to an enormous extent; so much so, that fifty volumes have already been published descriptive of animals brought to the surface. Nevertheless, we are told that the great coast lines of South America, Africa, Asia, and parts of Australia have been but imperfectly explored for smaller kinds of Mollusca.

Molluscs are soft-bodied, cold-blooded animals, without any internal skeleton, but this is compensated for by the external hardened shell, which at once serves the purpose of bones, and is a means of defence. These bodies are not divided into segments like those of worms and insects, but are enveloped in a muscular covering or skin, termed the mantle, the special function of which in most species is the formation and secretion of the shell. The foot, which serves the double purpose of locomotion and burrowing in the sand or rock, is an organ particularly characteristic of most molluscs. There are many departures from this rule, as, for instance, in the group Chitonidæ, where the shell takes the form of a series of eight adjacent plates; and in another, the Pholadidæ, there are one or more accessory pieces in addition to the two principal valves. Some are bivalved, others univalved, and concealed beneath the skin. All shells are mainly composed of carbonate of lime, with a small admixture of animal matter. Their microscopic examination reveals a great diversity of structure, as we shall presently see, and they are accordingly termed porcellaneous, nacreous, glassy, horny, and fibrous. Most molluscs have the power of repairing injuries to their shells;

many exhibit an outer coat of animal matter, termed the *peristracum*, the special function of which is to preserve the shell from atmospheric and chemical action of the carbonic acid in the water in which they dwell.

The shells of gastropods are enlarged with the growth of the mollusc by the addition of fresh layers to the margin. In some species the periodic formation of spines occurs; a typical case will be found among Muricidæ. The varied colours of shells are due to glands situated on the margin of the mantle, and beneath the peristracum; occasionally the inner layer of porcellaneous shells is of a different colour to the outer, as, for example, in the helmet-shells (Cassis), much used by carvers of shell cameos. Light and warmth, as in the vegetable kingdom, are the great factors in the production of brilliant colours. In cold climates land snails bury themselves in winter time in the ground or beneath decaying vegetable matter, and in hot seasons they close up the aperture of the shells with a temporary lid, called an *epiphragm*. These exhibit great tenacity of life, as, for instance, in the Egyptian desert-snail, *Helix desertorum*. The reproductive system is in all cases effected by means of eggs. The ova are usually enclosed in capsules, and deposited in masses, and the number of eggs contained in the squid and the whelk have been stated to be thirty or forty thousand. The ova of molluscs may be gradually developed into the adult, or there may be a free-swimming ciliated larval stage, or a special larval form, as in the fresh-water mussel. Most are provided with a more or less distinct head; both cephalopods and gastropods are furnished with eyes. In land snails these are found placed on projecting stalks. In most cases the utility of molluscs far outweighs the injury occasioned by a few species, as, for instance, the Teredo, and the burrowing habits of the Pholas and Saxicava, compact marble having been found bored through by them.

Mr. J. Robertson wrote me in 1866:—"Having, while residing here (Brighton), opportunities of studying the *Pholas dactylus*, I have endeavoured during the last six months to discover how this mollusc makes its hole or crypt in the chalk—by a chemical solvent? by absorption? by ciliary currents? or by rotatory motions? My observations, dissections, and experiments set at rest controversy on this point. Between twenty and thirty of these creatures have been at work in lumps of chalk in sea water in a finger glass and a pan, at my window for the last three months. The *Pholas dactylus* makes its hole by grating the chalk with its rasp-like valves, licking it up when pulverised with its foot, forcing it up through its principal or branchial siphon, and squirting it out in oblong nodules. The crypt protects the Pholas from Confervæ, often found growing parasitically not only outside the shell but even within the lips of the valves, thus preventing the action of the siphons. In the foot there is a spring, or style, which when removed is found to possess great elasticity, and this seems to be the mainspring of the motion of the Pholas."

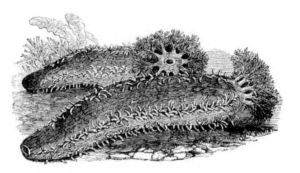

Fig. 367.—Hexabranchus.

I must pass by many groups and orders to more aberrant types, represented by the naked-gilled orders, Opisthobranchiata and Nudibranchiata. These gastropods constitute a large sub-order of extremely beautiful molluscs, remarkable in shape, and often brilliant in colour. The distinguishing character of these typical forms consists in the peculiar nature and situation of their breathing organs, which are exposed on the back of the animal or around the anterior part, and are not protected by the mantle. But the situation is varied, and the gills are sometimes placed on each side of the body, respiration being effected by the ciliated surface of the whole. For these and other reasons they have been placed in four groups. Nudibranchs are found in all parts of the world, and are most abundant in depths where the choicest seaweeds and corallines abound. Their fecundity is very great, as many as sixty thousand eggs being deposited by a single female at one time. They are eaten as a luxury where they most abound.

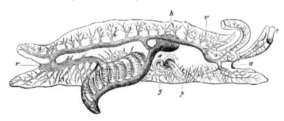

Fig. 368.—Longitudinal section of *Pleurobranchus aurantiacus*, showing circulation and gills or branchiæ.—(Warne.)

In the Opisthobranchs the branched veins as well as the auricle are placed behind the ventricle of the heart. They differ from Nudibranchs inasmuch as they are usually furnished with a pair of tentacles and labial palpi, or an expansion of the skin like the veil of the larval form. To clearly understand the character of the internal organisation of these curious animals, the longitudinal section given in Fig. 368 must be consulted: *p* is the foot; *a* the mouth, covered above with the veil-like expansion, over which are the tentacles, *c*; the branchial veins, *v*, carry the blood to the gills, from which it flows into the heart at *h*. This disposition is the opposite of that which characterises the Prosobranchus. Another anatomical peculiarity, which may here be referred to, is the direct communication of the system of blood vessels with the surrounding medium; a characteristic common to most other molluscs, and on which depends the changeable external appearance of the animal. In the illustration of Pleurobranchus here given, *g* indicates the opening of the duct which conveys water direct to the blood, and through which the blood vessels permeate the back and foot. Like the holes in the sponges, it can be filled or emptied at the will of the animal.

Although this, in the main, is the principle of the circulation in most of this order, one branch possesses no special breathing organs, respiration being carried on throughout the naked skin of the body.

With regard to the Nudibranchiata, the group having the most symmetrical form is the extensive family Dorididæ, characterised by differences in the branchiæ, the relative proportion of the mantle to the foot, and variations in the radula and jaws. The general aspect of the genus Doris, although drawn on a small scale, is represented in Plate XVII., Fig. *b*. The whole sub-order of Nudibranchs has become more generally known and admired since the publication of Alder and Hancock's monograph with its many attractive coloured illustrations.

These gastropods can be kept alive for some time in a small aquarium if the precaution is observed of often changing the water and adding a little fresh seaweed. Numerous curious microscopic forms of life may be found adhering to them.

Fig. 369.—*Aplysia dipilans.*

Tunicata.—The most remarkable group of animals belonging to this sub-order are the Ascidians. They derive their name from the test or tunic, a membranous consistence, in which they dwell, and which often includes calcareous spicules. The test has two orifices, within which is the mantle. Few microscopic spectacles are more interesting than the circulation along this network of muslin-like fabric, and that of the ciliary movement by which the fluid is kept moving. In the transparent species, as Clavelina and Perophora, the ciliary movement is seen to greater advantage. The animals are found adhering to the broad fronds of fuci near low water-mark. They thrive in tanks, and multiply both by fission and budding. Two species are figured in Plate XVII., Figs. *i* and *k*, the zooids of which were found arranged in clusters, as represented.

Aplysiidæ (sea-hares), so called on account of a slight resemblance to a crouching hare. The body form is elongated with a partially developed neck and head, oral and dorsal tentacles, and furnished beneath the mantle with a shelly plate to protect the branchiæ. The mouth is provided with horny jaws, and the gizzard is armed with spines, to prepare the food for digestion. The side lobes are thin and large, and are either folded over the back or used in swimming. Fig. 369 is a reduced drawing of *A. dipilans.*

The Pectinibranchs are known as violet sea-snails, Ianthinidæ and Scalariidæ. The radula consists of numerous rows of pointed teeth arranged in cross series, forming an angle in the middle. There is no central or rachidian tooth, and they have thin trochiform shells adapted for a pelagic life. They are mostly of a violet colour, from which they derive their name, the colour being more vivid on the underside, which is turned up towards the light when the animal is swimming near the surface of the sea (Fig. 370).

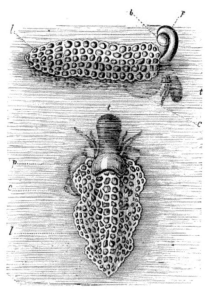

Fig. 370.—Ianthinia, Violet Sea-snail.—(Warne.)

The bubble *b*, drawn somewhat too large, is about to be joined to the anterior end of the float; *c.* Shell; *l.* Float; *p.* Foot; *t.* Head.

The most interesting feature in connection with these oceanic snails is the curious float which they construct to support their egg-capsules. It is a gelatinous raft, in fact, enclosing air-bubbles, which is attached to the foot, the egg capsules being suspended from its under-surface. They are unable to sink so long as they are in connection with their floats, and are therefore often cast on shore during storms, and furnish an endless series of microscopic specimens. The violet snails feed on various kinds of jelly-fish, and occur in shoals.

Pond Snails.—The three families, Limnœidæ, Physidæ, and Chilinidæ, form a special group of the pulminate, sessile-eyed fresh-water snails. The larger family of these belongs to the genus Limnœa, having a compressed and triangular head with two tentacles and eyes placed at their inner base. They are prolific and gregarious, and their ova are enclosed in transparent gelatinous capsules, deposited in continuous series, and firmly glued to submerged stems and leaves of aquatic plants. *L. stagnalis* is common in all ponds, marshes and slow-running rivers of Great Britain.

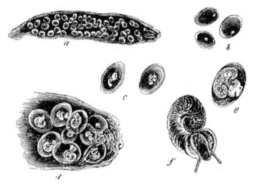

Fig. 371.—Ova and young of *Limnæus stagnalis.*

One of the species, *L. trancatula*, is the host of the liver-fluke so fatal to sheep. The fluke parasite passes one stage of its existence in the intestine of the pond snail.

Each ova-sac of Limnœa contains from fifty to sixty ova (represented in Fig. 371, at *a*). If examined with a low power soon after the eggs are deposited, they appear to consist simply of a pellucid protoplasmic substance. In about twenty-four hours a very minute yellowish spot, the nucleus, is discovered near the cell-wall. In another twenty-four hours the nucleus referred to is seen to have assumed a somewhat deeper colour and to contain within it a minute spot—a nucleolus.

On the fourth day the nucleus has changed its position, and is enlarged to double the size; a slightly magnified view is seen at *b*. On a closer examination a tranverse fissure is seen; this on the eighth day divides the small mass as at *c*, and the outer wall is thickened. The embryo becomes detached from the side of the cell, and moves with a rotatory motion around the interior; the direction of this motion is from the right to the left, and is always increased when sunlight falls upon it. The increase is gradual up to the eighteenth day, when the changes are more distinctly visible, and the ova crowd down to the mouth of the ova-sac, as at *d*. By employing a higher magnifying power a minute black spec, the future eye (*e*) and tentacles of the snail, is quite visible. Upon closely observing it, a fringe of cilia is noticed in motion near the edge of the shell. It is now apparent that the rotatory motion first observed must have been in a great measure due to this; and the current kept up in the fluid contents of the cell by the ciliary fringes. For days after the young animal has escaped from the egg, this ciliary motion is carried on, not alone by the fringe surrounding the mouth, but by cilia entirely surrounding the tentacles themselves, which whips up a supply of nourishment, and at the same time aeration of the blood is effected. From the twenty-sixth to the twenty-eighth day it appears actively engaged near the side of the egg, using force to break through the cell-wall, which at length it succeeds in accomplishing; leaving its shell in the ova-sac, and immediately attaching itself to the side of the glass its ciliary action recommences, and it appears to have advanced a stage, as at *f*. It is still some months before the embryo grows to the perfect form, Fig. 372; the animal is here shown with its sucker-like foot adhering closely to the glass of the aquarium. A single snail will deposit from two to three of these ova-sacs a week, producing, in the course of six weeks or two months, from 900 to 1,000 young.

Fig. 372.—*Limnæus stagnalis* (natural size).

The shell itself is deposited in minute cells, which take up a circular position around the axis; on its under-surface a hyaline membrane is secreted. The integument expands, and at various points an internal colouring-matter or pigment is deposited. The increase of the animal goes on until the expanded foot is formed, the outer edge of which is rounded off and turned over by condensed tissue in the form of a twisted wire; this encloses a network of small vessels filled with a fluid in constant and rapid motion. The course of the blood or fluid, as it passes from the heart, may be traced through the larger branches to the respiratory organs, consisting of branchial-fringes placed near the mouth; the blood may also be seen returning through other vessels. The heart, a strong muscular apparatus, is pear-shaped, and enclosed within a pericardium or extremely thin and pellucid enveloping membrane. The heart is seen to be furnished with muscular bands of considerable strength, the action of which appears like the alternate to-and-fro motion occasioned by drawing out a band of indiarubber, and which, although so minute, are clearly analogous to the muscular fibres of the mammal heart; it beats or contracts at the rate of about sixty times a minute, and is placed rather far back in the body, towards the axis of the shell. The nervous system is made up of ganglia, or nervous centres, and distributed throughout the various portions of the body.

The singular arrangement of the eye cannot be omitted; it appears at an early stage of life to be within the tentacle, and consequently capable of being retracted into it. In the adult animal the eye is situated at the base of the tentacle; and although it can be protruded at pleasure for a short distance, it seems to depend much upon the tentacle for protection as a coverlid—it invariably draws down the tentacle over the eye when that organ needs protection. The eye itself is pyriform, somewhat resembling the round figure of the human eye-ball, with its optic-nerve attached. In colour it is very dark, having a central pupillary-opening for the admission of light. The tentacle, which is cylindrical in the young animal, becomes flat and triangular in shape in the adult. The tentacles serve in some respect to distinguish species. In Limnœa they are, as I have said, compressed and triangular, with the eyes at their inner base. In Physa they are cylindrical and slender and without lateral mantle lobes. The development of the lingual membrane is delayed; consequently, the young animal does not early take to a vegetable sustenance: in place of teeth it has two rows of cilia, as before stated, which drop off when the teeth are fully formed. The lingual band bearing the teeth, or the "tongue," as it is termed, consists of several rows of cutting spines, pointed with silica.

It is a fact of some interest, physiologically, to know that if the young animal is kept in fresh water alone, without vegetable matter of any kind, it retains its cilia, and arrest of development follows, and it more slowly acquires gastric teeth, and attains to perfection in form or size. If, at the same time, it is confined within a narrow cell or space, it grows only to such a size as will enable it to move about freely; thus it is made to adapt itself to the necessities of a restricted state of existence. Some young animals in a narrow glass-cell, at the end of six months, were alive and well; the cilia were seen to be retained around the tentacles in constant activity, whilst other animals of the same brood and age, placed in a situation favourable to growth, attained their full size, and produced young, which grew in three weeks to the size of their elder relations.[71]

My experimental investigations were further extended to the development of the lingual membrane, or teeth, of Gastropoda, as well as the jaw and radula. In Limnœa, the teeth when fully developed resemble those of Helix; that is to say, in the fully grown animal are found several rows or bands of similar teeth, with simple obtuse cusps and a much suppressed central tooth. In the young snail a high power of the microscope is required to make them out. The dental band, however, in most Mollusca is disposed in longitudinal series, but varies a good deal in this respect, as will be seen on reference to my several papers, with illustrations of upwards of a hundred different species, published in "Linnæan Transactions" of 1866, and in the "Microscopical Society's Transactions" of 1868. By way of example I may say, in the Pulmonata the lingual band usually consists of a single median row, the laterals on each side being broad and similar. But in many other groups the teeth are arranged in three, five, or seven dissimilar series. Taking Nerita as a type, the broad teeth on each side of the median are termed *laterals*; and the numerous small teeth on the outside of the band, known as the *pleuræ*, are termed *uncini*.

Since the investigations of Lovén into the lingual dentition of the Mollusca, various observers have studied the subject, with great advantage to our knowledge of the affinities of these animals. That these investigations have proved of value is shown by the light which has been shed on the true position of many species. When once we have ascertained the homology of a genus, whose relations were otherwise somewhat doubtful, it is surprising how other characteristics, even of the shell, probably misunderstood before, concur to bear out the affinities indicated by the lingual band. These tooth-bearing membranes, armed with sharp cutting points, admirably adapted for the division of the food on which they feed, are most of them beautiful objects for the microscope.

 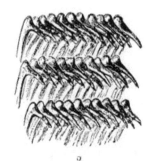

Fig. 373.

1. Palate of *Buccinum undatum*, common Whelk, seen under polarised light; 2. Palate of *Doris tuberculata*, Sea-slug.

The two ends of each longitudinal row of teeth are connected with muscles attached to the upper and lower surfaces of cartilaginous cushions; the alternate contractions and extensions of the muscles cause the bands of teeth to work backwards and forwards, after the fashion of a chain-saw, or rather of a rasp, upon any substance to which it is applied, and the resulting wear and tear of the anterior teeth are made good by a development of new teeth in the secreting sac in which the hinder end of the band is lodged. Besides the chain-saw-like motion of the band the lingual membrane has a kind of licking or scraping action as a whole. With the constant growth of the band new teeth are developed, when the teeth on the extreme portion of the band differ much in size and form from those in the median line.

As I have shown in the papers already referred to, that as each row is a repetition of the first, the arrangement of teeth admits of easy representation by a numerical formula, in which, when the uncini are very numerous, they are indicated by the sign ∞ (infinity), and the others by the proper figure. Thus, $\infty \cdot 5 \cdot 1 \cdot 5 \cdot \infty$, which, in the genus Trochus, signifies that each row consists of one median, flanked on both sides by five lateral teeth, and these again by a large number of uncini. When only three areas are found, the outer ones must be considered the pleuræ, inasmuch as there is frequently a manifest division in the membrane between them and the lateral areas.

Most of the Cephalopod molluscs are provided with well-developed teeth, and they are, as we know, carnivorous. The teeth of the cuttle-fish, *Sepia officinalis* (Plate V., No. 111), resemble those of the Pteropoda, and have the same formula, $3 \cdot 1 \cdot 3$. Sepia are also furnished with a retractile proboscis, and a prehensile spiny collar, apparently for the purpose of seizing and holding prey while the teeth are tearing it to pieces. In the squid Loligo (Plate V., No. 113) the median teeth are broad at the base, approach the tricuspid form with a prolonged acute central cusp, while the uncini are much prolonged and slightly curved. The lingual band increases in breadth towards the base, sometimes to twice that of the anterior portion. This band, mounted dry, forms an attractive object for black-ground illumination.

In another family, that of the rock-limpet, *Patella radiata*, the lingual band (Plate V., No. 116) well serves to distinguish it from the better-known common limpet. It is furnished with a remarkable long ribbon, studded by numerous rows of strong dark-brown tricuspid teeth. The lingual membrane when not in use lies folded up in the abdominal cavity. The teeth of Acmæa are somewhat differently arranged (Plate V., No. 117); their formula is $3 \cdot 1 \cdot 3$.

Testacella maugei, belonging to Pulmonifera, is slug-like in appearance, and subterranean in its habits, chiefly feeding on earth-worms. During winter and in dry weather it forms a kind of cocoon, and thus completely encloses itself in an opaque white mantle; in this way it protects itself from frost and cold. Its lingual membrane is large, and covered with about fifty rows of divergent teeth, gradually diminishing in size towards the median row; each tooth is barbed and pointed, broader towards the base, and with an articulating nipple set in the basement membrane. A few rows are represented slightly magnified (Plate V., No. 121). Their formula is 0 0 · 1 · 0 0.

TONGUES, ETC., OF GASTEROPODS.

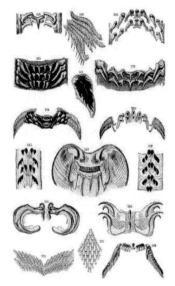

Tuffen West, del. W. F. Maples, ad. nat. del. Edmund Evans.

PLATE V.

The boat-shell, *Cymba olla*, belonging to the Velutinidæ, formula 0 · 1 · 0, or 1 · 1 · 1. The lingual band (Plate V., No. 118) is narrow and ribbon-like in its appearance, with numerous trident-shaped teeth set on a strong muscular membrane. The end of the band and its connection with the muscles at the extremity of the cartilaginous cushion is shown in the drawing. The blueish appearance is produced by a selenite film and polarised light. In *Scapander ligniarius* the band (Plate V., No. 119) is also narrow, but the teeth are bold and of extraordinary size; their formula is 1 · 0 · 1. This mollusc is said to be eyeless. *Pleurobranchus plumula* belongs to the same family; its teeth are simple, recurved, and convex, and arranged in numerous divergent rows, the medians of which are largest. The mandible (Plate V., No. 122) presents an exceedingly pretty tesselated appearance, and the numerous divergent rows of teeth are tricuspid.

The velvety-shell, *Velutina lævigata*, formula 3 · 1 · 3. The teeth (Plate V., No. 108) are small and fine; medians recurved, with a series of delicate denticulations on either side of the central cusp, which is much prolonged: 1st laterals, denticulate, with outer cusp prolonged; 2nd and 3rd laterals, simple curved or hooked-shaped. The mandible (No. 109), divided in the centre, forms two plates of divergent denticulations.

The ear-shell, *Haliotis tuberculatus*, is a well-known beautiful shell, much used for ornamental purposes. The lingual band (Plate V., No. 114), is well developed. The medians are flattened-out, recurved obtuse teeth; 1st laterals, trapezoidal or beam-like; uncini numerous, about sixty, denticulate, the few first pairs prolonged into strong pointed cusps.

The top-shell, *Turbo marmoratus*. After the outer layer of shell is removed, it presents a delicate pearly appearance. Its lingual band (No. 123) closely resembles Trochus; it is long and narrow, the median teeth are broadest, with five recurved laterals, and numerous rows of uncini, slender and hooked. A single row only is represented in the plate.

Cyclotus translucidus, a family of operculate land-shells, belongs to the Cyclostomatidæ. The teeth shown in No. 110, formula 3 · 1 · 3, are arranged in slightly divergent rows on a narrow band; they are more or less subquadrate, recurved, with their central cusps prolonged. *Cistula catenata*, one of the family Cyclophoridæ; its band (No. 115) formula, 2 · 1 · 2. Its teeth resemble those of Littorina. The lingual band of Cyclostomatidæ points out a near alliance to the Trochidæ; but this question can only be determined by an examination of several species, when it may, perhaps, be decided to give them rank as a sub-order. They are numerous enough; the West Indian islands alone furnish 200 species.

The length of the lingual band, and number of rows of teeth borne on it, vary greatly in different species. But it is among the Pulmonifera we meet with the most astonishing instances of large numbers of teeth. *Limax maximus* possesses 26,800, distributed through 180 rows of 160 each, the individual teeth measuring only one 10,000th of an inch. *Helix pomatia* has 21,000, and its comparatively dwarfed congener, *H. absoluta*, no less than 15,000.

Structure of the Shell of Mollusca.—In my opening sketch of the sub-order Mollusca an idea may have been gathered of the general character of the shell covering of these animals. The simplest form of shell occurs in the rudimentary oval plate of the common slug, *Limax rufus*. It is embedded in the shield situated at the back, near the head of the animal. In the Chitons, a small but singular group of molluscs allied to the univalve limpets, we have an ovoid shell, made up of eight segments, or movable plates, which give them a resemblance to enormous woodlice. These have been regarded as forming a transition series—a link between one division and the other. The shell in by far the greater portion of all the molluscs is developed from cells that in process of growth have become hardened by the deposition of calcareous matter in the interior. This earthy matter consists principally of calcium carbonate deposited in a crystalline state; and in certain shells, as in that of the oyster (Plate XVIII., Fig. 8), from the animal cell not having sufficiently controlled the mode of deposition of the earth particles, they have assumed the form of perfect rhomboidal crystals.[72]

PLATE XVIII.

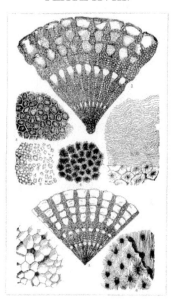

SECTIONS OF SHELL-STRUCTURE.

The shell of the wing-shells, *Pinna ingens* (Plate XVIII., No. 7), is composed of hexagonal cells, filled with partially translucent calcareous matter, the outer layer of which can be split up into prism-like columns. Figs. 3 and 6 are horizontal sections of the *Haliotis splendens*, with stellate pigment in a portion of the section, and wavy lines, as in the dentine of the human tooth, and of *Terebratulata rubicuna*, showing radiating perforations. Nos. 4 and 5, sections of the shell of a crab, show pigment granules beneath the articular layer and the general hexagonal structure of the next layer.

Some difference of opinion has been expressed with regard to the formation of pearls, but it is now generally understood to be a diseased condition. Pearls are matured on a nucleus, consisting of the same matter as that from which the new layers of shell proceed at the edge of the mussel or oyster. The finest kinds are formed in the body of the animal, or originate in the pearly-looking part of the shell. It is from the size, roundness, and brilliancy of pearls that their value is estimated.

The microscope discloses a difference in the structure of pearls: those having a prismatic cellular structure have a brown horny nucleus, surrounded by small imperfectly-formed prismatic cells; there is also a ring of horny matter, followed by other prisms, and so on, as represented in Fig. 374; and all transverse sections of pearls from oysters show the same successive rings of growth or deposit.

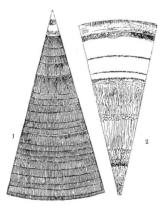

Fig. 374.

1. A transverse section of a Pearl from Oyster, showing its prismatic structure
2. A transverse section of another Pearl, showing its central cellular structure, with outside rings of true pearly matter. (Magnified 50 diameters.)

In a segment of a transverse section of a small purple pearl from a species of Mytilus (Fig. 375), all trace of prismatic structure has disappeared, and only a series of fine curved or radiating lines is seen. This pearl consists of a beautiful purple-coloured series of regular laminæ, many of which have a series of concentric zones, and are of a yellow tint. The most beautiful sections for microscopic examination are obtained from Scotch pearls.

Preparation of the Teeth and Shell of Mollusca for Microscopical Examination.—The method of preparing lingual membranes of Mollusca is as follows: Under a dissecting microscope, and with a large bull's eye lens, cut open and expose to view the floor of the mouth; pin back the cut edges throughout its length, and work out the dental band with knife and forceps. The band being detached, place it in a watch-glass, and boil in caustic potash solution for a few minutes. Having by this process freed the tongue from its integuments, remove it, wash it well, and place it for a short time in a dilute acid solution, either acetic or hydrochloric. Wash it well and float it upon a slide; with a fine sable brush open it out flat, and remove whatever dirt or fibre may be adhering to it. Lastly, place it in weak spirit and water, and there let it remain for a few days before mounting in formalin. Canada balsam renders them rather too pellucid, and the finer teeth are thereby lost.

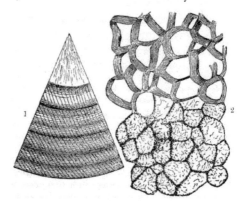

Fig. 375.

1. Transverse section of a small Pearl from a Mytilus; 2. Horizontal section magnified 240 diameters to show prismatic structure and transverse striæ.

The preparation of shell structure must be proceeded with with some amount of care and caution, or the delicate reticulated network membrane will be destroyed. If any acid solvent be used to remove the calcareous structure it should be much diluted, so that the action may proceed slowly rather than hastily. In the young hermit-crab, for example, where the calcareous and membranous portions of the shell are continuous, and the calcium carbonate in a relatively small proportion, a strong acid solution would entirely destroy the specimen. In the case of nacreous shells the process of cutting and grinding must also be proceeded with with some amount of caution. The operation should be examined as the process proceeds, and under polarised light. Sections of shell structure are usually mounted in Canada balsam. Under the heading *Technique* much useful information on this and kindred subjects will be found in the "Journal of the Royal Microscopical Society."

Annulosa, Worms, and Entozoa.

The Annulosa of Huxley embraces the lowest grade of articulated animals, most of which are now grouped with Metazoa, while some writers place them in a sub-kingdom Vermes. It appears to me then only possible to describe this heterogeneous group of worm-like animals among those which resemble each other in certain negative features, but not possessing any of the distinctive characters of those previously described. There are numerous species among Entozoa, every one of which is of the highest interest to mankind in general, and to animal life as a whole. To these I shall devote some attention, from the wide-spread importance attached to them. They are characterised by having a soft absorbent body with little or no colour, in consequence of being excluded from light, living within the bodies of animals and absorbing their vital juices, thereby inflicting a large amount of injury and death upon the whole vertebrate kingdom. They bear in this respect a close analogy to parasitic Fungi in the nature of their destructive action upon plant life, which I have fully discussed in a previous chapter.

The relations which obtain between parasites and their hosts are in all respects conditioned by their natural history; and without a detailed knowledge of the organisation, the development, and the mode of life of the different species, it is impossible to determine the nature and extent of the pathological conditions to which they give rise, and at the same time find means of protection against guests in every way so unwelcome.

The nutritive system of the entozoa must be regarded as in the lowest state of development, yet there are some among them of a higher grade, as will be seen as we proceed. All are remarkable alike for their vast productiveness and for their peculiar metamorphoses. For example, the greater number of the Tænia begin their lives as sexless, encysted larvæ, and on entering their final abode, segments are successively added, until the worm has finally reached the adult stage. Again, the tapeworm of the cat has its origin in the encysted larvæ found in the livers of the mouse and rat. Another species of entozoa inhabit the stomach of the stickle-back, and only attain their perfect form in the stomachs of aquatic birds that feed exclusively on fish. Another infests the mantle of pond-snails, and through their agency, the embryos pass into the stomach of sheep.

An almost endless number of similar transformations take place in other genera. The simplest form among internal parasites is the Gregarinæ, formerly grouped among Protozoa. They consist of a simple limiting membrane, with a mass of granular matter enclosed and surrounding a nucleus (Plate III., No. 53). These parasites pass through a crystoid stage in the body of one of the lower animals, usually the earthworm, *Lumbricus agricola*. In the more mature organism an envelope, differentiated from the protoplasm within, can be made out (No. 54); this affords an indication of greater differentiation in the subjacent layer of protoplasm. An anterior portion is in many cases separated by a constriction from the cylindrical or band-like body (No. 56). Gregarinæ multiply when encysted, and divide into a multitude of minute *pseudo-navicula*, so named from their resemblance in shape to a well-known form of Diatomaceæ. When a young pseudo-navicule escapes it behaves somewhat like an amœba, and if perchance it is swallowed by an appropriate host, it develops at once into the higher stage. The various forms are represented in Plate III., Nos. 53—61. Miescher, in 1843, described suchlike bodies, taken from the muscles of a mouse. A good account of specimens obtained from the muscles of a pig was published by the late Mr. Rainey in the "Philosophical Transactions," 1857. He regarded them as cestoid entozoa. They have been described under a variety of names, as worm-nodules, egg-sacs, eggs of the fluke, young measles, &c. M. Lieberkühn carefully traced the pseudo-naviculæ after leaving the perivisceral cavity of the earth-worm; he found large numbers of small corpuscles, exhibiting amœba-like movements, as well as pseudo-naviculæ, containing granules, formed in an encysted Gregarinæ. He imagines that these latter bodies burst, and that their contained granules develop into the amœbiform bodies which subsequently become Gregarinæ.

Professor Ray Lankester made a careful examination of more than a hundred worms for the purpose of studying these questions, but he succeeded in arriving at no other conclusion than that certain forms may be the by-products of encysted Gregarinæ. The *G. lumbricus* is one of those forms which are unilocular. The vesicle is not always very distinct, and is sometimes altogether absent; occasionally it contains no granules, sometimes several, one of which is generally nucleated. In other of these cysts a number of nucleated cells may be seen developing from the enclosed Gregarina, which gradually become fused together and broken up, until the entire mass is converted into nucleated bodies, often seen in different stages of development, assuming the form of a double cone, as that presented by certain species of Diatomaceæ. At length the cyst contains nothing but pseudo-naviculæ, sometimes enclosing granules; these gradually disappear, and finally the cyst bursts. Encystation seems to take place much more rarely among the bilocular forms of Gregarinæ than in the unilocular species found in the earthworm and other Annelids.[73]

Dr. J. Leidy published in the "Transactions of the Philadelphia Society," 1853, the results of his examinations of several new species of Gregarinæ. He described a double membrane "within the parietal tunic of the posterior sac, this being transparent, colourless, and marked by a most beautiful set of exceedingly regular parallel longitudinal lines."

Professor R. Leuckart is the latest writer on the parasites of animals, and to him we are indebted for a more systematic account of the whole group, and their life-history, than to any previous investigator. I can only attempt to give a mere outline of the developmental stages of a few typical forms of parasites, commencing with the cystic tapeworm, Tænia. These worms are ribbon-like in appearance, and are divided throughout the greater part of their length into segments, and their usual habitation is the intestinal cavity of vertebrate animals. The anterior extremity of a tænoid worm is usually called the head, and bears the organ by which the animal attaches itself to the mucous membrane of the creature which it infests. These organs are either suckers, or hooks, or both conjoined. In Tænia, four suckers are combined with a circlet of hooks, disposed around a median terminal prominence. The embryo passes through certain stages of development—viz., four forms or changes: but the embryo itself is very peculiar, consisting of an oval non-ciliated mass, provided with six hooks, three upon each side of the middle line. Tænia are found enclosed in various situations besides that of the alimentary canal: the eye, the brain, the muscular tissues, the liver, &c., of animals. The following cystic worms are usually included in this genera, *Cysticercus Anthocephalus, Cœnurus,* and *T. Echinococcus.* Plate IV., No. 100, shows an adult specimen of the latter with rostellum suckers, and three successive segments, the last of which is the ova sac. The water-vascular system is represented coloured by carmine. This parasite infests the human body as frequently as many other species. My accurately-drawn figure is copied from Cobbold's "Introduction to the Study of Entozoa."

Cysticercus fasciolaris is developed within the liver of white mice; *Cysticercus cellulosæ* in the muscles of the pig; hence we have the diseased state of pork familiarly known as "*measly pork.*" Should a lamb become infested with Tænia the final transformation will be different; within a fortnight symptoms of a disease known as "staggers" manifest themselves, and in the course of a few weeks the *Cœnurus cerebralis* will be developed within the brain. Von Siebold pointed out the bearing of this fact upon the important practical problem of the prevention of "staggers." Others belonging to the same class of parasites are quite as remarkable in their preference for the alimentary canal of fishes. The Echinorhynchus is developed in the intestinal canal of the flounder, *Triænophorus nodulus* in the liver of the salmon. Thus, by careful and repeated observation with the microscope, a close connection is found to exist between the cystic and cestoid entozoa.

The Echinococcus (Plate IV., No. 101) infests the human liver. These parasites are always found in cysts, and in closed cavities in the interior of the body. They are united in fours by a very short stalk or pedicle, common to the whole. By an increase of magnification the contents of a cyst present the several structures represented in Fig. 376.

Echinorhynchus, or spiny-headed threadworms, constitute a group of entozoa which undergo a metamorphosis hardly, perhaps, less remarkable than that known to take place in other Nematode worms. Leuckart instituted, in 1861, a series of experiments with the ova of *Echinorhynchus proteus* found parasitic upon the *Gammarus pulex.* The ova of *E. proteus* resemble in form and structure those of allied species. They are of a fusiform shape, surrounded with two membranes, an *external* of a more albuminous nature, and an *internal* chitinous one. When the eggs reach the intestine the outer of these membranes is absent, being in fact digested, while the inner remains intact until ruptured by the embryo.

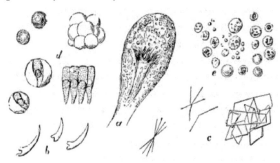

Fig. 376.—Cystic Disease of Liver (Human).

a. Cyst with Echinococcus enclosed; *b.* detached hooklets from the head of Echinococcus, magnified 250 diameters; *c.* crystals found in cyst, chiefly cholesterine; *d.* cylindrical epithelium, some enclosed in structureless vesicles; *e.* Puro-muculent granules, fat and blood corpuscles.

The typical Threadworm belonging to the order Nematoidea infest the intestines of children, and are a source of much suffering. The egg is elliptical, and contains a mass of granular protoplasm, the external wall of which soon becomes marked out into a layer of cells. The mouth of the worm appears as a depression at the end of the blunt head. When the muscular system and alimentary canal are developed the embryo hatches out, some few of which are free living forms; most of them lead a parasitic life. Their reproduction is enormous, representing thousands of eggs and embryos.

Of the non-parasitic species of thread-worm, the common vinegar eel, Anguillula,[74] affords an example. This is found in polluted water, bog-moss, and moist earth, as well as in vinegar; also in the alimentary canal of the pond-snail, the frog, fish, &c. Another species is met with in the ears of wheat affected with a blight termed the "cockle"; another, the *A. glutinis,* in sour paste. If grains of the affected wheat are soaked in water for an hour or two before they are cut open, the so called "eels" will be found. The paste-eel makes its appearance spontaneously just as the pasty mass is turning sour; the means of securing a supply for microscopical examination consists in allowing a portion of the paste in which they show themselves to dry up, and laying it by for stock; if at any time a portion of this is introduced into a little fresh-made paste, and the whole kept warm and moist for a few hours, it will be found to swarm with these wriggling little worms. A small portion of paste spread over the face of a Coddington lens is a ready way of viewing them.

Trichina spiralis.—One of the smallest and most dangerous of all human internal parasites is *T. spiralis,* since it finds its way into the muscles

- 514 -

throughout the human body. The young animal presents the form of a spirally-coiled worm in the interior of a minute oval-shaped cyst (Plate IV., No. 104), a mere speck scarcely visible to the naked eye. In the muscular structure it resembles a small millet seed, somewhat calcareous in composition. The history of the development of Trichina in the human muscle is briefly that in a few hours after the ingestion of infected pork, Trichina, disengaged from the muscle, will be found in the stomach: hence they pass into the small intestine, where they are further developed. Continuing their migrations, they penetrate far into the interior of the primitive muscular fasciculi, where they will be found, in about three days after ingestion, in considerable numbers, and so far developed that the young entozoa have almost attained a size equal to that of the full-grown Trichina (Plate IV., No. 105). They quickly advance into the interior of the muscular fasciculi, where they live and multiply in continuous series, while the surrounding structures as well as the muscular tissue undergo a process of histolysis. The destructive nature of the parasite is very great.

The number of progeny produced by one female may amount to several thousands, and as soon as they leave the egg they either penetrate through the blood-vessels, or are carried on by the circulation, and ultimately become lodged in the muscles situated in the most distant parts of the body. Here, as already explained, they become encysted.

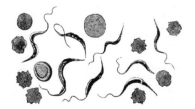

Fig. 377.—Monads in Rat's Blood, stained with methyl violet, showing membrane under different aspects; blood-corpuscles, some crenated and others with stained discs (× 1,200).—(Crookshank.)

Professor Virchow draws the following conclusions:—"1. The ingestion of pig's flesh, fresh or badly dressed, containing Trichinæ, is attended with the greatest danger, and may prove the proximate cause of death. 2. The Trichinæ maintain their living properties in decomposed flesh; they resist immersion in water for weeks together, and when encysted may, without injury to their vitality, be plunged in a sufficiently dilute solution of chromic acid for at least ten days. 3. On the contrary, they perish and are deprived of all noxious influence in ham which has been well smoked, kept a sufficient length of time, and then well boiled before it is consumed."

A more minute Filarian worm has been detected in the human blood-vessels, known as *Filaria sanguinis hominis*. This worm carries on its work of destruction throughout the night; during the day it remains perfectly passive. It increases rapidly, and produces swellings of the glandular structures of the body, somewhat after the nature of those characteristic of the Bombay plague, with a slight difference, that after death the swellings are seen to be due to the vast accumulations of the *Filaria sanguinis* blocking the blood-vessels. The accompanying Fig. 377 shows a similar infiltration of monads in the blood of rats dying of plague in Bombay.

Trematode Worms.—In the order Trematoda, to which the fluke belongs, the body is unsegmented, and to the naked eye smooth throughout, with a blood circulatory system, and two suctorial discs at the hinder end. There is a distinct digestive canal, usually forked, furnished with only one aperture, the mouth. The excretory organs open out as in tape worms, and the male and female organs co-exist in the same individual.

The Fluke (shown in Plate IV., No. 103) is cone-shaped, and is the *Amphistome conicum* of Rudolphi. This parasite is common in oxen, sheep, and deer, and it has also been found in the Dorcas antelope. It invariably takes up its abode in the first stomach, or rumen, attaching itself to the papillated folds of the mucous membrane. In the full-grown, adult stage, it rarely exceeds half an inch in length. It is certainly one of the most remarkable in form and organisation of any of the internal parasites.

The larger fluke (*Fasciola hepatica*) often attains to an inch or more in size. It is not only of frequent occurrence in all varieties of grazing cattle, but has likewise been found in the horse, the ass, and also in the hare and rabbit and other animals. Its occurrence in man has been recorded by more than one observer. The oral sucker forming the mouth leads to a short œsophagus, which very soon divides into two primary stomachal or intestinal trunks, the latter in their turn sending off branches; the whole together forming that attractive dendritic system of vessels so often compared to plant-venation. This remarkably-formed digestive apparatus is represented in Plate IV., Nos. 106 and 107, *Fasciola gigantea* of Cobbold, and should be contrasted with the somewhat similarly racemose character of the water-vascular system. Let it be expressly noted, however, that in the digestive system the majority of the tubes branch out in a direction obliquely downwards, whereas those of the vascular system slope obliquely upwards. A further comparison of the disposition of these two systems of structure, with the same systems figured and described as characteristic of the Amphistoma, will at once serve to demonstrate the important differences which subsist between the several members of the two genera, if we turn to the consideration of the habits of *Fasciola hepatica*, which, in so far as they relate to excitation of the liver disease in sheep, acquire the highest practical importance. Intelligent cattle-breeders, agriculturists, and veterinarians have all along observed that the *rot*, as this disease is commonly called, is particularly prevalent after long-continued wet weather, and more especially so if there have been a succession of wet seasons; and from this circumstance they have very naturally inferred that the humidity of the atmosphere, coupled with a moist condition of the soil, forms the sole cause of the malady. Co-ordinating with these facts, it has likewise been noticed that the flocks grazing in low pastures and marshy districts are much more liable to the invasion of this endemic disease than are those pasturing on higher and drier grounds; a noteworthy exception occurring in the case of those flocks feeding in the salt-water marshes on our eastern shores. Plate IV., No. 106, *Fasciola gigantea*: the anterior surface is exposed to display oral and ventral suckers, and the dendriform digestive apparatus injected with ultra-marine; No. 107 shows the dorsal aspect of the specimen and the multiramose character of the water-vascular system, the vessels being injected with vermilion.

In their larval condition the Amphistoma live in or upon the body of the pond-snail. This we infer from the circumstance that the larvæ, or cercariæ, of a closely-allied species, the *Amphistoma subclavatum*, are known to infest the alimentary canal of frogs and newts, and have also been found on the body of the Planorbis by myself. The cercariæ larvæ are taken, it is believed, by the sheep and the cattle while drinking. The earliest embryotic stage in which I have found the embryo fluke is represented at Fig. 378, No. 1. In the year 1854, whilst observing the habits of Limnœa and other water-snails, I brought home specimens from the ornamental water in the Botanic Gardens; upon these were discovered thousands of minute thread-like worms, subsequently met with on other embryos, and at first taken to be simple infusorial animals, but upon placing them in a glass vessel these minute bodies were observed to detach themselves and commence a free-swimming existence. A fringe of cilia was seen to surround the flask-shaped body (No. 1).

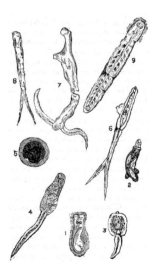

Fig. 378.—Forms of Cercaria; stages in the development of the Fluke.

1. An infusorial embryo; 2. a Trematode embryo having quite recently escaped from the egg; 3. embryo cercaria; 4. fully-formed cercaria, showing alimentary canal and sucker-like head; 5. encysted form of same; 6. *Cercaria furcata*, with the nervous system and forked tail displayed; 7. in the act of breaking up; 8. tail portion half an hour after division; 9. parasitic worm of another species of Trematoda. (Magnified from 10 to 25 diameters.)

The study of these embryos throws a flood of light upon the obscure history of Cercariæ. After a short period of wandering, their embryos fasten upon the water-snail, and compel it to act as a wet-nurse, and prepare it for a further and higher stage of life. The earliest condition in which I have discovered them concealed about the body of the water-snail is shown at No. 2; in appearance, a simple elongated sac filled with ova or germs, and which in a short time develop into the caudate worms already spoken of; their tails gradually attaining to the length of the mature embryos, Nos. 3 and 4, the latter being a full-grown *Cercaria ephemera*.

Diesing described no less than twelve species of Cercariæ, some of the most curious of which live on the puddle-snail, in colonies of thousands. All throw off their tails at the moment of changing into a fluke. On placing some *Cercaria furcata* (Nos. 6 and 7) under the microscope, they were seen to plunge about in frantic attempts to escape from confinement. Suddenly I saw them shed their tails and their bodies divide into two parts, each half swimming about as vigorously as before, quite indifferent as to the severance, and apparently dying from exhaustion. Those represented in Nos. 6 and 7 have a highly-organised nervous system, forming a continuous circuit throughout the body and tail. The mouth is furnished with a sucker and hooklets, which can be projected out some distance, while a digestive apparatus and ventral opening or sucker can be differentiated. The tail is bifurcated and articulated with the body by a sort of ball-and-socket joint, and when broken off, the convexity of one part is seen to accurately fit into the concavity of the other; it lashes about this appendage with considerable dexterity, rarely attaching itself to any of the small aquatic plants.[75]

There is yet another Filarian worm, a pest to the poultry-yard, the Gape-worm, *Sclerostoma syngamus*. This parasite is widely distributed, and is invested with special interest, since it produces disease, and kills annually thousands of young chickens, pheasants, partridges, and many of the larger kinds of wild birds. The worms find their way into the windpipe or tracheæ, through the drinking water, while in the embryotic or cercarian stage of existence, and their increase is so rapid, the birds quickly die of suffocation. The female gape-worm often attains to a considerable size, and when full grown resembles the well-known mud-worm of the Thames (*Gordius aquaticus*). She measures full six-eighths of an inch in length, while the male only measures one-eighth. So insignificantly small is he that the female carries him about tucked into a side pocket. The ova sac occupies a considerable portion of the internal body space, and is always found loaded with eggs in all stages of development, numbering some five hundred or a thousand. In shape these are ovoid. On cutting open the windpipe of chicken and partridges, I have found their tracheæ literally swarming with the gape-worm.[76]

A remarkable form of the Trematode worm is *Bilharzia hæmatobra* of Cobbold, *Distomia hæmatobium* of other authors (Plate IV., No. 102). This genus of fluke, discovered by Dr. Bilharz in the human portal system of blood vessels, gives rise to a very serious state of disease among the Egyptians. So common is the occurrence of this worm, that this physician expressed his belief that half the grown-up population of Egypt suffer from it. Griesinger conjectures that the young of the parasite exist in the waters of the Nile, and in the fish which abound. Dr. Cobbold thinks "it more probable that the larvæ, in the form of cercariæ, rediæ, and sporocysts, will be found in certain gasteropod mollusca proper to the locality." The anatomy of this fluke is fully described by Küchenmeister in his book on parasites, by Leuckart,[77] and by Cobbold. The eggs and embryos of Bilharzia are peculiar in possessing the power of altering their forms in both stages of life; and it is more than probable that the embryo form has been mistaken for some extraordinary form of ciliated infusorial animal, its movements being quick and lively. We cannot fail to notice the curious form of the male animal, and, unlike the Filarian previously described, it is he who carries the female about and feeds her. The whip-like appendage seen in the figure is a portion of the body of the female. The disease produced by this parasite is said to be more virulent in the summer months, probably owing to the greater abundance of cercarian larvæ at this period of the year.

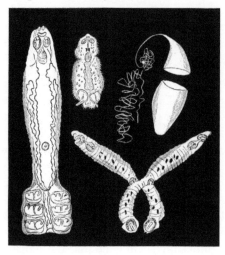

Fig. 379.—The double parasitic worm (*Diplozoum paradoxum*).

There are also double parasitic worms, which may be described as a sub-order of Trematoda, differing very much from those previously described. These live on the gills of several species of fresh-water fish, the gudgeon and minnow, for instance. Among them is a most remarkable creature well deserving the name of *Diplozoum paradoxum* which has been bestowed upon it. It consists of two complete mature similar halves, each possessing every attribute of a perfect animal (*a*). Each of the pointed front ends has a mouth aperture, and close to it two small sucking discs; while each individual has a separate intestine, consisting of a medium tube and innumerable side-branches. At the hinder end of the body are two suckers sunk in a depression, and protected by four hard buckle-shaped organs. The eggs are elongated, and provided at one end with a fine thread-like appendage (*b*). In this egg the young (*c*)—which at the time of hatching is only about one-hundredth of an inch—takes about a fortnight to develop. It is covered with cilia, has two eyes and two suckers; after quitting the egg, the larvæ are very lively and restless in their movements, gliding about and then swimming off with rapidity. If unable to find the fish into which they are destined to live, they grow feeble and perish, but if successful they grow into the Diporpa (*d*), which is flattened and lancet-shaped, and bears a small sucking disc on the under surface and a conical excrescence on the back. After living in this state for some weeks, and gaining nourishment by sucking the blood from the fish's gills, the worms begin to join together in pairs, one specimen seizing the conical excrescence of another by its ventrical sucker; then, by a truly acrobatic feat, the second twists itself to the dorsal excrescence of the first, and in this state an inseparable fusion takes place between the suckers and the excrescences involved in the adhesion.[78]

In the group Vermes, the more highly-organised Annelida must be included. These, for the most part, live either in fresh or salt water. The Annelids are various, while the Planaria, a genus of Turbellaria, are very common in pools, and resemble minute leeches; their motion is continuous and gliding, and they are always found crawling over the surfaces of aquatic plants and animals, both in fresh and salt water. The body has the flattened sole-like shape of the *Trematode entozoa* (Fig. 378, No. 9), the mouth is surrounded by a circular sucker; this is applied to the surface of the plant from which the animal draws its nourishment; it is also furnished with a rather long proboscis, which is probably employed for a similar purpose.

Planariæ multiply by eggs, and by spontaneous fissuration in a transverse direction, each segment becoming a perfect animal. Professor Agassiz believes that the infusorial animals, Paramæcium and Kolpoda, are simply planarian larvæ.

Hirudinidæ, the leech tribe, are usually believed to form a link between the Annelida on the one hand, and the Trematoda on the other; their affinities place them closer with the latter than the former. Although deprived of the characteristic setæ of the Annelida, and exhibiting no sectional divisions, they are provided with a sucker-like mouth possessed by Trematoda, but they present no resemblance to them in their reproductive organs. On the other hand, in the arrangement of the nervous system and in their vascular system, the Hirudinidæ resemble Annelida. The head in most of the Annelida is distinctly marked, and furnished with eyes, tentacles, mouth, and teeth, and in some instances with auditory vesicles, containing otolithes. The nervous system consists of a series of ganglia running along the ventral portion of the animal, and communicating with a central mass of brain.

Hirudina medicinalis puts forth a claim for special attention on the ground of services rendered to mankind. The whole of the family live by sucking the blood of other animals; and for this purpose the mouth of the leech is furnished with a number of strong horny teeth, by which they cut through the skin. In the common leech three rows of teeth exist, arranged in a triangular, or rather triradiate form, a structure that accounts for the peculiar appearance of leech bites. The most interesting part of the anatomy of the leech to microscopists is certainly the structure of the mouth (Fig. 380). This is a muscular dilatable orifice, within which three beautiful little semi-circular saws are situated, arranged so that their edges meet in the centre. It is by means of these saws that the leech makes the incisions whence blood is to be procured, an operation which is performed in the following manner. No sooner is the sucker firmly fixed to the skin, than the mouth becomes slightly everted, and the edges of the saws are thus made to press upon the tense skin, a sawing movement being at the same time given to each, whereby it is made gradually to pierce the surface, and cut its way to the capillary blood-vessels beneath.

Fig. 380.—Mouth of Leech.

In Clepsinidæ the body is of a leech-like form, but very much narrowed in front, and the mouth is furnished with a prehensile proboscis. These animals live in fresh water, where they may often be seen creeping over aquatic plants. Their prey is the pond-snail.

Tubicola.—The worms belonging to this series of branchiferous Annelida are all marine, and distinguished by their invariable habit of forming a tube or case, within which the soft parts of the animal can be entirely retracted. This tube is usually attached to stones or other submarine bodies. Externally it is composed of various foreign materials, sand, crystalline bodies, and the *débris* of shells; internally it is lined with a smooth coating of sarcode, sometimes of a harder consistency. The Tubicola generally live in societies, winding their tubes into a mass which often attains a considerable size; only a few are solitary in their habits. They retain their position in their cases by means of tufts of bristles and spines; the latter, in the tubicular Annelids, are usually hooked, so that by applying them to the walls of the case, the animal is enabled to oppose a considerable resistance to any effort made to withdraw it. In the best known family of the order (Sabellia), the branchiæ are placed in the head, and form a circle of plumes, or a tuft of branched organs. The Serpulidæ form irregularly twisted calcareous tubes, and often grow together in large masses, when they secure themselves to shells and similar objects; other species, Terebellidæ, which build their cases of sand and stones, appear to prefer a life of solitude. The best known form is *Terebella littoralis.*[79] The curious little spiral shells seen upon the fronds of seaweeds are formed by an animal belonging to the Spirorbis.

Fig. 381.—Serpula with extended tentacles and body protruding from calcareous case.

If the animals be placed in a vessel of sea-water a very pleasing spectacle will soon be witnessed. The top part of the tube is seen to open, and the creature cautiously protrudes a fringe of tentacles; these gradually spread out two beautiful fan-like rows of tentacles, surrounded by cilia of a rich purple or red colour. These serve the double purpose of breathing and feeding organs. When withdrawn from its calcareous case, the soft body is seen to be constructed of a series of rings, with a terminal prehensile foot by which it attaches itself.

Many Annelids are without tubes or cells of any kind, simply burying their bodies in the sand near tidal mark. The Arenicola, lob-worm, is a well-known specimen of the class; its body is so transparent that the circulating fluids can be distinctly seen under a moderate magnifying power. Two kinds of fluids flow through the vessels, one nearly colourless, the other red; the vessels through which the latter circulate are described as blood-vessels.

Not very much interest attaches to the developmental stage of the Annelida. They issue forth from ova, and the embryo so closely resemble ciliated polypes, that competent observers have mistaken them for animals belonging to a lower class; a few hours' careful watching is sufficient to dispel a belief of the kind, when the embryonic, globular, or shapeless mass is seen to assume a form of segmentation, and soon the various internal organs become more and more developed, eye spots appear, and the young animal arrives at the adult stage of its existence.

Crustacea.

The crustaceans comprise a large assemblage of Arthropods, presenting great diversity of structure. Some of the parasitic species have become so simplified in organisation that they appear to present no relationship with the higher members of the class, yet it is certain that all the species, whether terrestrial or aquatic, belong to the same stock, and may have had origin in the same fundamental plan of structure. Essentially, the body consists of a large number of segments, to each of which is attached a pair of two-branched appendages; the external branch is termed the exopodite and the internal the endopodite. Five segments at the front end of the body unite to form a head, the appendages of the first two being situated in front of the mouth, and performing the office of feelers or antennæ, while those of the remaining three segments are transformed into jaws, the first pair of jaws being the mandibles and the following two pairs the maxillæ. The rest of the appendages are variously modified and to some are attached respiratory organs in the form of gills. Crustaceans are broadly divided from Centipedes, Millipedes, Insects, &c., by the presence of two pairs instead of one pair of antennæ, and by the possession of branchial and not tubular (tracheal) respiratory organs. Arachnida and some other species are again widely separated. The majority of the young on leaving the egg are quite unlike the parent, and only acquires their definite form after undergoing a series of changes. The earliest stage, which has been called the Nauplius, already referred to in connection with the barnacle, is a minute body showing no trace of segmentation, and provided with a single eye, and three pairs of swimming appendages, which become the two pairs of antennæ and the mandibles of the adult. This stage is by no means of invariable occurrence, but is chiefly characteristic of the lowest members, the Entomostraca, and is rare in the higher, Malacostraca. The typical crustaceans are shrimps, crayfish, &c., so familiarly described by Huxley. The zoæa stage of the crab, a minute transparent creature, which undergoes several changes, swims about flapping its long jointed abdomen, like some of the Entomostraca, and the shrimp in particular. The larva of crayfish, the so-called glass-crab, is very peculiar and interesting. The sessile-eyed series, in which the compound eyes are never mounted on a movable stalk, and to which the Isopoda belong, exhibits great diversity of structure as well as of habits and habitat. Some live in fresh water, most are marine, while others live on land and take to a parasitic life.

Fig. 382.—Male Gnathia, enlarged.

This genus contains Gnathia, in which the male and female are so dissimilar, that they are frequently referred to as members of two families. In the adult male the mandibles are powerful and prominent, and the head is large, squared, and as wide as the thorax. In the female, on the contrary, the head is curiously small and triangular, without visible mandibles, and the thorax is much dilated. The creatures are about one-sixth of an inch long, and of a greyish colour, and the destruction they bring about is due to their habit of boring into timber below water mark. Fig. 382 represents an enlarged view of the male Gnathia. These crustaceans are vegetarians, and feed on wood. Other members of the group, known as fish lice, are much larger in size, and chiefly infest the cetacea, and bear in addition two large eyes. By means of their powerful fore feet the Cymothordæ attach themselves to both marine and fresh-water fish, showing a preference for the inside of the mouth of their host.

Fig. 383.—1. Cypris; 2. Cyclops; 3. *Branchipus grubei.*

The bar-footed group Copepoda are free living, and the thorax bears four or five swimming feet; the abdomen is without appendages. The best known fresh-water form is Cyclops, the structure of which serves as a type of the order. The body is, as is well known to microscopists, broad in front and tapering behind, being thus, when viewed swimming, pear-shaped in outline. The dorsal elements of the head are fused to form a carapace, which bears a single eye, from which circumstance it derives its name. The eggs are carried by the female in a couple of ova-sacs attached to the last segment of the thorax, and so prolific are these creatures that a female will produce over four thousand million young. The young when hatched is an oval Nauplius, which after two or three moults acquires the adult state. In the family of the Apodidæ we have an equally well-known crustacean, the Branchipus. In the Branchipodidæ the body is also elongated, but there are no appendages to the abdomen, which consists of nine segments, while there are eleven pairs of thoracic appendages. The head shield is not developed backwards, and the large separated eyes are supported on distinct stalks. In the male the second antennæ are converted into claspers. These crustaceans swim upside down (Fig. 383).

Cladocera (*Daphniadæ* of Dr. Baird).—The water-flea (*Daphnia pulex*) may be taken as the best known example of the order. The body of this little active animal is narrowed in front, and at the posterior end, where the carapace is deeply notched, is the tip of the abdomen bearing the pair of rigid barbed setæ from which the genus takes its name. At the front of the head is a large compound eye and two pairs of branched plumed appendages, antennæ. The first pair of these are small and simple. The jaws consist of the mandibles and the first pair of maxillæ, the second pair of maxillæ being obsolete in the adult. The thorax comprises five segments, each bearing a pair of leaf-like swimming limbs. The abdomen consists of three segments, and is destitute of limbs. The males are usually smaller than the females, and much rarer, being rarely met with before the end of summer.

Eggs are laid both in summer and winter, and are passed into a brood-pouch, separating the upper surface of the thorax from the backward extension of the carapace. Here the summer eggs hatch, but the winter set are enclosed in a kind of capsule developed from the carapace. This capsule, termed the *ephippium*, is cast off with the next moult of the mother's integument (a process necessary for the gradual growth of the crustacean), and falling to the bottom of the water, gives exit to the embryos, which hatch in its interior, and the young born from these "ephippial" eggs produce young, which in their turn become mothers. It appears, then, the winter eggs are enclosed in capsules of more than usual hardness to enable them to withstand any degree of cold that might otherwise prove fatal to the parent. Dr. Baird found, on examining ponds that had been again filled up by rain after remaining two months dry, numerous specimens of Daphnia and *Cyclops quadricornis* in all stages of growth.[80]

We learn also from his investigations that the Daphnia have many enemies. "The larva of the *Corethra plumicornis*, known to microscopical observers as the skeleton larva, is exceedingly rapacious of Daphnia. Pritchard says they are the choice food of a species of Nais; and Dr. Parnell states that the Lochleven trout owes its superior sweetness and richness of flavour to its food, which consists of small shell-fish and Entomostraca." These crustaceans abound in fresh and salt water. Artemiæ are formed exclusively in salt water, in salt marshes, and in water highly charged with salt. Myriads of these Entomostraca are found in the salterns at Lymington, in the open tanks or reservoirs where the brine is deposited previous to boiling. A pint of the fluid contains about a quarter of a pound of salt, and this concentrated solution destroys most other marine animals. During the fine days in summer Artemiæ may be observed in immense numbers near the surface of the water, and, as they are frequently of a lively red colour, the water appears tinged with the same hue. The movements of this little animal are peculiar. It swims about on its back, and by means of its tail, its feet being at the same time in constant motion. They are both oviparous and ovoviviparous, according to the season of the year. At certain periods they only lay eggs, while during the hot summer months they produce their young alive. In about fifteen days the eggs are expelled in numbers varying from 50 to 150. As is the case with many of the Entomostraca, the young present a very different appearance from the adult animals; and they are so exactly like the young of *Chirocephalus*, that with difficulty are they distinguishable one from the other. The ova of other species are furnished with thick capsules, and imbedded in a dark opaque substance, presenting a minutely cellular appearance, and occupying the interspace between the body of the animal and the back of the shell; this is called the ephippium. The shell is often beautifully transparent, sometimes spotted with pigment; it consists of a substance known as chitine, impregnated with a variable amount of calcium carbonate, which produces a copious effervescence on the addition of a small quantity of a strong acid to the water in which the shell is immersed. When boiled, Artemiæ turn red as their congeners, lobsters. Their shells may be said to consist of two valves united at the back, resembling the bivalve shell of a mussel, or simply folded at the back to appear like a bivalve, but are really not so; or they may consist of a number of rings or segments. The body of Cypris presents a reticulated appearance, somewhat resembling cell structure. Entomostraca should be narcotised and prepared for examination under the microscope as directed by Mr. Rousselet at pages 345, 346.

INSECTS' EGGS, ETC.

Tuffen West, del. Edmund Evans.

PLATE VI.

CHAPTER IV.

Arthropoda—Insecta.

Distinctive Characters of Insects.—The term Insect, although originally and according to the meaning of the word correctly employed in a wide sense to embrace all those articulate creatures in which the body is externally divided into a number of segments, including, of course, flies, butterflies, beetles, bugs, spiders, scorpions, crabs, shrimps, &c., is now by common consent used in a much more restricted sense to apply only to such of these animals as have six walking legs. Insects belong to a class of Arthropoda, and are distinguished by having the head, chest, and abdomen distinctly marked out and separable; by having not more than three pairs of legs in the adult state; by having the legs borne by the thoracic segments only; by having usually two pairs of wings; by the possession of tracheæ, or air-tubes, as respiratory organs; and by being provided with a single pair of antennæ, or feelers. The insect class is one exhibiting uniformity of type and structure. Extreme variations are no doubt seen within certain limits, but these variations are sharply marked off from the groups we have been previously considering. The examination of insects may be pursued according to a defined order, and it will be found that no class of animals will afford the microscopist a more wonderful field of observation and a greater variety of interesting objects than that of the insect tribes.

In the insect, as in the crustacean, the hard parts of the body form an outer and protecting covering, and also serve for the attachment of muscles. The casing, however, in insects is purely of a chitinous, or horny nature, and has in its composition only a trace of calcium carbonate. Each somite, or joint of the body, is usually composed of six pieces; the upper, or dorsal half of each segment is named the tergum, the lower half the sternum, the side pieces pleura, the sternum being further sub-divided into epimeral and espisternal pieces. The body as a whole consists of some twenty segments, of which five or six form the head, the thorax of three joints, while the abdomen may number from nine to eleven. The head segments are united to form apparently a single mass, and the appendages of this region are modified for sensory purposes, and also serve as cutting and masticatory organs. The appendages of the head, examined in order, will be found to consist of eyes, antennæ, or feelers, and organs of the mouth. The antennæ of insects rarely exceed two in number, but these present great variations in form and size. In their simplest form they exist as straight jointed filaments, but in many insects they are forked, in others club-shaped, while in others they mimic forms of vegetation, and for the most part are extremely interesting objects for the microscope.

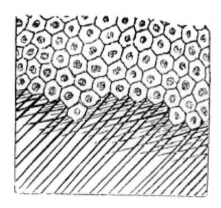

Fig. 384.—Vertical section of cornea of Eye of Fly.

The principal use of these antennæ is that of organs of touch, but it is quite probable that they may subserve other functions, as of taste or even hearing. The eyes of insects consist of either a pair of *ocelli*, or of a great number, when they are termed compound eyes, formed of an aggregation of external hexagonal facets and lenses, and nerve filaments, all of which have a distinct connection with the mass of ganglia recognised as the brain, as will be seen in Fig. 384, a section of the eye of a fly. The number of facets varies very greatly in these compound eyes; ants, for example, have fifty facets, flies two thousand or more, and butterflies as many. Dr. Hooke counted seven thousand, and Leuwenhoeck as many as twelve thousand in the eye of a dragon fly. The eyes of some insects are supported on short stalks or pedicles, but these are never movable, as, for example, in Stalk-eyed crustaceans.

The organs of the mouth in insects present a striking homology or similarity in their fundamental structure. Two chief types of mouth are found. The biting or masticatory, as in beetles, includes a labium or upper lip, a pair of mandibles or lower jaws, a pair of lesser jaws or maxillæ, which bear one or two pairs of palpi, and a lower lip or labium, also with palpi. This latter and primitive condition of the labium is seen in Orthropterous insects and some Neuroptera. Other structures occurring in those of the mouth are the ligula, this being sometimes divided, as in bees, into three lobes, of which the two outer are the paraglossæ and the middle process the lingua or tongue. There is a second form of mouth, termed the suctorial. This is seen in Lepidoptera (butterflies), and is adapted for extracting the pollen and juices of flowers, and in which the palpi are greatly developed, and form two hairy pads or cushions, between which the proboscis is coiled up when at rest. Thus we find in the Lepidoptera the same fundamental condition of mouth as in some Coleoptera. In Hymenoptera (wasps and bees), a variety of mouth is found which presents a combination of the masticatory with the suctorial types. The labium and mandibles exist as in the beetle, the maxillæ being developed to form long sheaths protecting the labium, which now takes the form of a tongue. In Hemiptera (bugs and their allies), the mandibles and maxillæ exist as sharp lancets, while the labium forms a protective sheath. In the Diptera (flies, gnats, &c.), the labium undergoes a great development, and forms a very prominent tongue, the other parts of the mouth being developed simply as sheaths to the labium. See Figs. 389 and 390.

The thorax or chest of insects consists of three segments, named from before backwards: the prothorax, mesothorax, and metathorax. The first bears the anterior pair of legs; the mesothorax, the second pair of legs and the first pair of wings; and the metathorax, the third pair of legs and second pair of wings. The last joints of the leg constitute the tarsus or foot-claws. The nervures of the wings are in reality hollow tubes, and are extensions of the spiracles, or respiratory apertures.

The muscles of insects lie concealed beneath the integument; they are not gathered into distinct bundles as in the higher animals, although they exhibit in many cases a striated or striped structure. This is well seen in some of the beetle tribe, the water-beetle in particular. In certain larvæ the muscles are exceedingly complicated. Lyonnet found in the larva of the goat-moth, two hundred and twenty-eight muscles in the head alone, and in the whole body no less than three thousand nine hundred and ninety-three. The muscular power of insects is, relatively to the size of the body, very great. The flea, for instance, leaps two hundred times its own height. There are beetles weighing a few grammes that will escape from a pressure of from twenty to thirty ounces.

Professor Schäfer infers that the structure of the wing-muscles of insects furnishes the key to the comprehension of the more intricate muscular structure of vertebrates. The sarcode element, however, is not made up of a bundle of rods, but of a continuous sarcous element, readily made out by staining with hæmatoxylin. This substance is then seen to be pierced by minute tubular canals, and the longitudinal striation of muscle is due to this canalisation. The whole is connected and enclosed by a membrane of extreme delicacy.

The digestive system of insects varies with their habits and food. In Stylops, bee-parasites, and in young bees living on fluids, the intestine ends in a blind sac. There are three coats of structure throughout the digestive system. The œsophagus or gullet is provided with a crop in flies, bees, and butterflies; a true analogue of the gizzard in birds. There is in some respects a curious likeness between the conformation of the digestive organs of birds and that of insects. No true liver, but salivary glands in the mouth have been made out; the heart lies dorsally, and consists of a pulsating sac divided into compartments, and the fluid flows through it towards the head, whence it circulates freely to other parts of the body. Each trachea is an elastic tube formed of two delicate membranes, between which the spiral filament is coiled up, and is of sufficient density to prevent the collapse of the tube by the movements of the body. These tracheæ are distributed throughout the muscular tissue and the whole of the body. Thus the insect, like the bird, may be said to breathe in every part of the body, and is in this way rendered light and buoyant for flight. The air is admitted to the tracheæ by apertures termed spiracles, which the insect can close at will, and these are distributed to the number of eleven on each side of the body. The nervous system consists of a chain of ganglia or nerve-knots, which unite towards the head to form a single cord, as seen in the section made through the spider (Fig. 409).

The reproduction of all insects takes place by ova, and they are diæceous—that is, have two distinct sexes. In some few instances, as that of Aphides, or plant-lice, we have the peculiar phenomenon of parthenogenesis, the process of reproduction being performed by imperfect wingless females. These bring forth living young ones, which begin to feed the moment they are born, and constitute a viviparous brood; in other cases females lay eggs, and the process proceeds in the ordinary way, and nearly all the year round. The former is provided with a lancet-like beak for piercing and sucking the juices of the leaf, and a pair of curious honey-tubes. Insects generally undergo a transformation or metamorphosis in passing from the egg to the adult stage. While within the egg the body may be seen to become segmented, and in the course of time—in such insects as flies, bees, beetles, and butterflies—issue forth from the egg as larvæ, or caterpillars. This worm-like creature makes for itself an investing case or cocoon, in which it passes into the pupa stage of its existence. Within the pupa case a wonderful transformation takes place; the larval body being literally broken down by the process of histolysis, while its elements are rebuilt and transformed into that of the *imago*, or perfect insect. In grasshoppers, crickets, dragon-flies, bugs, &c., the metamorphosis is incomplete (hemimetabolic). Some few lower insect forms (lice, spring-tails, &c.) undergo no change of the kind, and in no way differ from the adult except in size. These are termed ametabolic insects. Others again, as the cockchafer and gold beetle, pass three years in the larval stage. Development in all cases is arrested or retarded by cold. Reaumur kept a butterfly pupa for two years in an ice-house, and it exhibited no tendency towards a change until removed to a warm temperature.

From the short natural history of insect life I have endeavoured to sketch out, it will have been surmised that insects offer a wide field of research, and an almost endless number of objects of interest for the microscope. The variety of material is great, and the structure and adaptation of means to an end is of the most fascinating kind. Most cabinets abound in preparations gathered together with some care and mounted with all the skill at the command of the collector, affording, as a rule, as endless an amount of pleasure to the tyro as to the more practised entomologist. It may be surmised, then, that to enter fully into a description of the several parts of insect structure would require a volume[81] of very large bulk, and occupy months and years. I will, therefore, take some points of interest in the structural characteristics of insects, and take them in the order in which they have already been brought to notice. The head, eyes, and other appendages of these insects we are more or less acquainted with.

Fig. 385.—A tangential or side section of Eye of Fly, with palp or pads protruded.

We will take for examination a typical member of Muscidæ, a family embracing a large and varied assortment of species, among which the house-fly and the blow-fly are the best known forms. *Musca domestica* needs no description. An interesting part of the house-fly to the microscopist is the wonderful component parts of the head. On examination we find a couple of protuberances, more or less prominent, and situated symmetrically one on each side. Their outline at the base is for the most part oval, elliptical, circular, or truncated; while their curved surfaces are spherical, spheroidal, or pyriform. These horny, round, and naked parts are the corneæ of the compound eye of the fly, and they are appropriately so termed, from the analogy they bear to the larger transparent tunics in the higher classes of animals. They differ, however, from the latter, as when viewed by the microscope they display a large number of hexagonal facets, which constitute the medium for the admission of light to several hundred simple eyes. Under an ordinary lens, and by reflected light, the entire surface of one cornea presents a beautiful reticulation, like very fine wire gauze, with minute papilla, or at least a slight elevation, in the centre of each mesh. These are resolved, however, by the aid of a compound microscope, and with a power of from 80 to 100 diameters, into an almost incredible number (when compared with the space they occupy) of minute, regular, geometrical hexagons, well defined, and capable of being computed with tolerable ease, their exceeding minuteness being taken into consideration.

Fig. 386 represents a vertical section of the eye, showing the hexagonal faceted arrangement of cylindrical tubes.

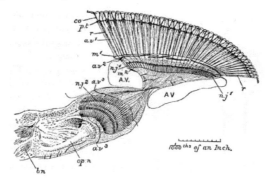

Fig. 386.—Section of Eye of Fly.

l. Lenses; *co.* Cones; *pl.* Pigment layer, consisting of rings round the rods; *r.r.* Rods; *a.v¹.* Air vessels between the rods; *m¹.* Membrane on which the rods and air vessels rest; *a.v².* Shorter lengths of air vessels which form a layer above the first nerve junction; *n.j¹.* First nerve junction; *m².* Membrane on which it stands; A. V., A. V. Large air vessel surrounding the eye; *n.j².* Second nerve junction; *a.v³.* Air vessels; *op. n.* Optic nerve; *b.n.* Brain substance. (Magnified × 160.)

In this section it appears to be questionable whether the normal shape of the lenses is not round, assuming the hexagonal shape during the process of growth in consequence of their agglomeration. The corneal surface can be peeled off, and if carefully flattened out and mounted it will be seen that each lens is not a simple lens, but a double-convex compound one, composed of two plano-convex lenses of different densities or refracting power joined together.

Experiments made on the eyes of insects, and also of crustaceæ, show that in the insect a real and reversed image of external bodies is formed in each ommatidium; it coincides with the internal face of the crystalline cone in immediate contact with the retina. Although small, the retinal image is distinct and subtends an angle of nearly forty-five. In the same way in the crustacean, the crystalline lens forms on the retinula a reversed image, but the refractive media have a longer focus, and the retinal membrane is not connected with the lens, the interval being filled up by a substance analogous to the vitreous of vertebrates. In both cases it would appear that light does not act directly on the rods; these latter can only receive impressions through the intermediary retinal cells. The retinal images of arthropods, as might have

- 533 -

been surmised, are much less perfect than those of the higher orders; on the other hand, their eyes seem to be better adapted for seeing objects in relief and the movements of bodies. The shyness of butterflies and moths is certainly an inherited instinct as a protection against danger from their many enemies.

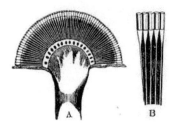

Fig. 387.

A. Vertical section of Eye of *Melolontha vulgans*, Cockchafer; B. A few facets more highly magnified, showing facets and pigment layer.

In the accompanying Fig. 387, A is a vertical section of the eye of *Melolontha vulgans*, the fan-like arrangement of the facets, together with the transparent pyramidal gathering of the retinal rods proceeding towards the brain; B is a few of the corneal tubes more highly magnified, the darker portion representing the pigment layer of the corneal tubes. In Plate VI., No. 133, the under surface of the head and mouth of the "Tsetse" fly, *Glossina morsitans*, is shown. The proboscis of this fly is long and prominent, and the antennæ are peculiar, inasmuch as the third segment is long, and produced almost as far as the flagellum, which is furnished with barbed hairs along its outer surface only. Although this fly barely equals the blow-fly in size, it is one of the greatest pests to the domestic cattle of Equatorial Africa. The palpi, although arising from two roots, are seen joined together when the fly is at rest, but when in the act of piercing or sucking they divide and the sheath is thrown directly upwards. The palpi are furnished on their convex sides with long and sharply-pointed dark-brown setæ or hairs, while the inner concave sides, which are brought into contact with the proboscis, are perfectly smooth and fleshy. Three circular openings seem to indicate the tubular nature of what in the house-fly is a fleshy, expanded, and highly-developed muscular proboscis (seen in Fig. 388, *Musca domestica*). The proboscis (labium) forms the chief part of the organ, dilates into wonderful muscular lips, and enables the insect to employ the tongue as a prehensile organ. The lips are covered with rows of minute setæ, directed a little backwards and arranged rather closely together.

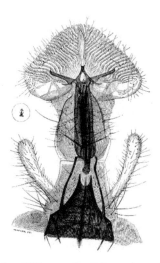

Fig. 388.—Proboscis of House-fly, *Musca domestica*. (The small circle indicates the object about the natural size.)

There are very many rows of these minute hairs on each of the lips, and from being arranged in a similar direction are employed by the insect in scraping or tearing delicate surfaces. These hairs are tests for the best of high powers. It is by means of these that it teases human beings in the heat of summer, when it alights on the hand or face, to sip the perspiration as it exudes from the skin. The fluid ascends the proboscis, partly by a sucking action, assisted by the muscles of the lips themselves, which are of a spiral form, arranged around a highly elastic, tendinous, and ligamentous structure, with other retractile additions for rapidity and facility of motion.

Fig. 389.—Spiral structure of Tongue of House-fly, from a micro-photograph made with a Zeiss 16 mm. and apochromatic projection eye-piece × 150.

The beautiful form of the spiral structure of the tongue should be viewed under a high magnifying power, when it will be seen that no continuing spiral structure really exists; each ring, apparently detached, does not extend quite round; their action is that of sucking tubes. Fluids are evidently drawn up through the entire fissure caused by the opening between the ends of the whole series of rings. It may well be pronounced a marvellous structure. The mounting of the tongue must be done with a considerable amount of care to show this structure, imperfectly represented in my woodcut.

These insects are of some service in the economy of nature, by their consumption of decaying animal matter, found about in quantities ordinarily imperceptible to most people, and that would not be removed by ordinary means during hot weather. It was asserted by Linnæus that three flies would consume a dead horse as quickly as a lion. This was, of course, said with reference to the offspring of such three flies; and it is quite possible the assertion may be correct, since the young begin to eat as soon as hatched, and a female blow-fly will produce twenty thousand living larvæ (one of which is   represented in Plate VI., No. 141). In twenty-four hours, each will have increased in weight two hundred times, in five days it attains to its full size, and changes into the pupa, and then to the perfect insect.

Fig. 390.—Tongue, Proboscis, and piercing apparatus of Drone-fly (*Eristalis tenax*).

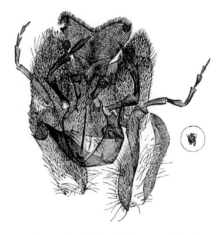

Fig. 391.—Under-surface of a Wasp's Tongue, Feelers, &c. (Seen within the circle is the tongue about life-size.)

In the drone-fly (*Eristalis tenax*), the mouth organs are larger than in the house-fly, and differ in many respects. The tongue is split up for a certain distance, and then again united, as represented in Fig. 390. The labium, mandibles, and maxillæ are converted into well-developed lancet-shaped organs; these both pierce the skin of animals, and form tubes by which their blood may be sucked up. Next to the maxillary palpi a couple of lancets are seen to project out; these again are associated with two other instruments, one resembling in appearance a two-edged sword, and a peculiar one with pincers or cutting teeth at the extremity. It is very peculiar, and resembles an instrument used in surgery for enlarging the wound, and in this case to increase the flow of blood. This remarkable compound piercing apparatus of the drone-fly is of exquisite finish, and must strike the observer with amazement, while it greatly transcends the work of human mechanism. The fleshy tongue itself projects some distance from the apparatus described, and is furnished with setæ or hairs, shorter and fewer in number than those of the house-fly, and while its spiral structure is not so fully developed, its retractor, muscles, and ligaments are even more so.

The further development of the mouth organs must be looked for in other members of the insect tribe, when it will be seen many assume a more or less modified form of structure, that, for example, in Hymenoptera (the bee and wasp), in which insects the mouth and tongue are divided into lobes which are used to extract the nectary (as Linnæus termed it) from the plants on which they feed. The tongue in most species is capable of extension and contraction.

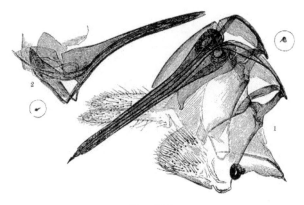

Fig. 392.

1. Sting of Wasp (*Vespa vulgaris*), with its muscular attachments and palpi for cleansing the apparatus; 2. Sting of Bee.

In Fig. 391 the under-surface of the wasp's tongue is shown, together with its two pairs of antennæ, and pair of brushes on either side, for brushing off the gathered pollen and honey from the broad tongue. It is amply provided with muscular structure. The antennæ, or feelers, are as curious in form as they are delicate in structure. Those of the male differ from those of the female.

Both the bee and the wasp are armed with an exceedingly venomous sting, as is well known. This structure takes the form of a well-adapted mechanical contrivance, and is a weapon of offence as well as of defence. The sting consists of two barbed needle-points, of a sufficient length to pierce the flesh to some depth. From the peculiar arrangement of their serrated edges their immediate withdrawal cannot take place, and it is this circumstance, with the drop of poison injected into the open wound, that renders their sting of the most painful and irritating kind. The gland containing the poison is contained in a minute sac situated at the root of the piercing apparatus. In Fig. 392 is shown the sting of the wasp and the bee.

Very many insects are provided with instruments for boring into the bark or solid wood itself. The female Cynip bores into the oak-apple for the purpose of depositing her egg. The larva, when full grown, eats its way out of the nut, and drops to the ground, where it attains the form of the perfect fly (Fig. 393).

Fig. 393.—Female Gall-fly and Larva.

There are numbers of species living exclusively upon the leaves of plants, to which they do much damage by the excrescences or galls they form. Each tree seems to be infested by its own species of gall-mite, the so-called *nail-gall* of the lime being caused by a species named *Phytoptus tibiæ*. These galls take the form of a pointed column, standing erect on the upper side of the leaf. Galls of much the same structure occur in the sycamore, maple, elm, and various fruit trees.

The gnat (*Culex pipiens*) is furnished with a sting curiously constructed (Fig. 394), and enclosed in a perfectly clothed sheath covered throughout by scales or feathers. This is folded up when not in use. The mouth is provided with a complete set of lancets for piercing the flesh; after having inflicted a severe wound, it injects an acid poison through the proboscis. The scales of the gnat vary in structure accordingly as these are found on the wing, the body, or the proboscis. A magnified wing is shown at No. 2, Fig. 394, and a magnified scale from the proboscis at No. 3. In Fig. 405, Nos. 3 and 5, more highly magnified wing and body scales are given. The proboscis is protected on either side by antennæ and feelers.

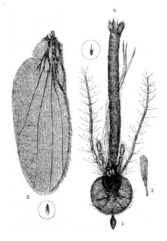

Fig. 394.

1. Head of *Culex pipiens*, female Gnat, detached from body; 2. Wing, showing nervature and fringed edges; 3. Scale from Proboscis; 4. Proboscis and Lancets. The reticulated markings on each side of the head show the proportionate space occupied by the eyes.

The giant-tailed wasp, *Sirax gigas*, is furnished with an even more curious mechanical boring apparatus (Fig. 395) than its congeners. This is a boring ovipositor, skilfully contrived for piercing the bark of trees, in which the insect deposits her eggs, and where the larva, when hatched, will find an ample supply of food to carry it through this stage of existence. The boring tube, it will be seen, is a perfect muscular structure (*c, c, a,* and *x*); in short, it is an endless form of drill, well known to the mechanic, such as is employed in fine work for drilling holes. The females are of some size, and may be surprised and taken in the act of boring through the bark of the pine tree, for which they have a preference.

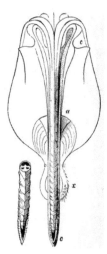

Fig. 395.—Boring apparatus of Giant-tailed Wasp (*Sirex gigas*), × 350.

There is also a species of the broad-bodied saw-fly, *Lyda campestris*. These bore the Scotch fir, and deposit their eggs. The larvæ from these eggs, when hatched out, feed upon the pine-needles, first spinning a fine web to conceal their work of depredation. A better known saw-fly, *Abraxas grossulariata*, plays havoc among our gooseberry trees. The female is provided with a curious mechanical apparatus as an ovipositor, with which she cuts into the thicker under-leaf of the plant. This penetrating and cutting tool consists of a double-saw (Fig. 396) of elaborate construction, which when not in use is kept concealed in a long narrow case situated beneath the abdomen. It is further protected by two horny plates. The saws pass out through a deep groove so arranged that the saws work side by side backwards and forwards, without a possibility of running out of the groove. When the cut is made, the four are drawn together and form a central canal, through which an egg is forced into the leaf. The cutting edges of the saws are provided with about eighteen or twenty teeth; these have sharp points of extreme delicacy, and together make a serrated edge of the exact form given to the finest and best-made surgical saws of the present day. In the summer-time the proceedings of the female insect may be witnessed, and the method of using this curious instrument seen, by the aid of a hand magnifier. These insects are not easily alarmed when busy at work.

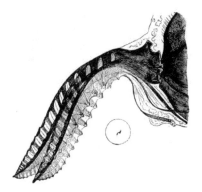

Fig. 396.—Saws of the Gooseberry-fly (*Abraxas grossulariata*).

Before bringing my remarks on proboscides of insects to a conclusion, attention must be given to that of the honey bee (*Apis mellifica*), and its curious accessories. The mouth of bees exhibits a combination of the suctorial and the masticatory form of oral apparatus. Thus the labial, or upper lip, and the mandibles, or large pair of jaws, are well developed, while the maxillæ, or lesser pair, are elongated to form a tubular organ, through which, together with the tongue, the flower juices, "honey-dew," may be sucked up. The labium, lower lip, is also rather prolonged, and the palpi, or organs of touch, with which it is endowed form a useful protective apparatus. The mandibles are employed by bees in the construction of their abodes, while the suctorial portion of the mouth is devoted to the reception of nourishment and to prehension. The sting of the bee, already noticed, is in fact an ovipositor, the female alone being provided with this weapon as an egg-depositing organ, although better known as an *aculeus* or sting; but it forms no part of the oral apparatus (as shown in Fig. 397). The proboscis itself will be seen to be curiously divided; the divisions are elegant and regular, beset with numerous setæ or hairs. The two horny outside lancets are spear-shaped and partially set with short hairs; at the base of each is a hinge articulation; this permits of considerable motion in several directions, and is much used by the busy insect for forcing open the more internal parts of flowers, thus facilitating the introduction of the proboscis. The two shorter feelers are closely connected with the proboscis, and terminate in three-jointed articulations. The structure of the proboscis is so arranged that it can be enlarged at the base, and thus made to contain a greater quantity of the collected honey-dew; at the same time it is in this cavity the nectar appears to be converted into pure honey. The proboscis tapers off to a little nipple-like extremity, and at its base is seen two shorter and stronger mandibles, from between which is protruded a long and narrow lance-like tongue, the whole being most curiously connected by a series of strong muscles and ligaments. The basal or first joint of the hind leg in the neuter or working bee is developed into an enlarged form of pocket, used by the insect for conveying the pollen of flowers and the propolis to the hive. Indeed, both the tibia and the first joint of the tarsus are broadened out into plates, but the two sides of the plates are differently furnished. On one side is a thick coating of hairs, those on the tarsus taking the form of a brush, evidently used for brushing out the pollen, as these special developments are not found on the hind legs of the drones or of the queen.

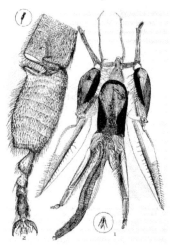

Fig. 397.

1. Honey bee's tongue; 2. Leg of worker bee. (The small circles show the objects about the natural size.)

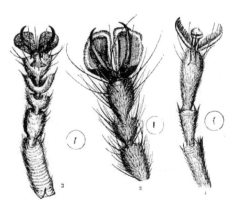

Fig. 398.

1. Foot and leg of Ophion; 2. Foot and leg of Flesh-fly; 3. Foot and leg of Drone-fly, with pad or sucker appendage.

The wax used in the formation of cells is a secretion that exudes through certain portions of the body of the bee, since it is found in little pouches situated on the under part of the body, but it is not brought home ready for use. The walls of the cells are strengthened when completed by a kind of varnish, already referred to as the propolis, collected from the buds of poplar and lime trees, and this is spread over the walls of the cell by that wonderful pair of broad spatulæ, represented in the drawing.

Many interesting variations will be found in the legs and feet of flies, as well as in those of other orders of insects (Lepidoptera). One or two typical forms are represented in Plate VI., and in Fig. 398.

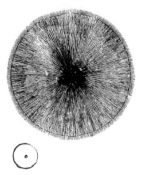

Fig. 399.—Sucker on the leg of Water-beetle. (The dot in the circle represents the object natural size.)

The tarsus, or foot of the fly (Fig. 398), consists of a deeply bifid, membranous structure, *pulvillus*; anterior to its attachment to the fifth tarsal joint, or the upper surface, are seated two claws, or "tarsal ungues"; these are freely movable in every direction. These ungues differ greatly in their outline, size, and relative development to the tarsi, and to the bodies of the insects possessing them, and in their covering; most are naked over their entire surface, having however a hexagonal network at their bases, which indicates a rudimentary condition of minute scale-like hairs, such as are common on some part of the integument of all insects. Flexor and extensor muscles are attached to both ungues and flaps; the flaps are either corrugated or arranged on the ridge and furrow plan, in other cases they are perfectly smooth on their free surface, while others are covered with minute scale-like hairs. The thickness of the divided membrane on the blow-fly does not exceed the $\frac{1}{2000}$th of an inch at the margin; they somewhat increase in thickness towards the point of attachment. Projecting from the flap are organs which have been termed "hairs," "hair-like appendages," "trumpet-shaped hairs." These are doubtless the immediate agents in holding on to a smooth surface, as that of glass, and are termed "tenent-hairs," in allusion to their office. The under surface of left forefoot of *Musca vomitoria* is shown with tenent-hairs (Plate VI., No. 140); *a* and *b* are more magnified hairs, *a* from below, *b* from the side. No. 142 is the left forefoot of *Amara communis*, showing the under surface and form of tenent appendages, one of which is seen more magnified at *a*; No. 143, under surface of left forefoot, *Ephydra riparia*. This fly is met with in immense numbers on the surface water in salt marshes. It does not possess the power of climbing glass; this is explained by the structure of the tenent-hairs; the central tactile organ is also very peculiar, the whole acting as a float, one to each foot, to enable the fly to rest on the surface of the water; *a* is one of the external hairs, No. 135, under surface of left forefoot of *Cassida viridis* (tortoise-beetle), showing the bifurcate tenent appendages, one of which is given at *a* more magnified. These, in ground beetles, are met with only in males, and are used for sexual purposes. The delicacy of the structure of these hairs in the fly and the elastic membranous expansion of the foot are marvellous. When the fly is climbing, a minute quantity of some glutinous fluid is exuded, so that the tubular nature of the tenent-hairs hardly admits of a doubt.

"At the root of the pulvillus, or its under surface, is a process, which in some instances is short and thick, in others long and curved, and tapering to its extremity (Scatophaga), setose (Empis), plumose (Hippoboscidæ), or, in one remarkable example (Ephydra), closely resembling in its appearance the very rudimentary pulvillus with which it is associated. Just at the base of the fifth tarsal joint, on its under surface, there is present, in Eristalis, a pair of short, very slightly curved hairs, which point almost directly downwards."[82]

Tenent-hairs are usually present in some modification or other. It is really difficult to name a beetle which has not some form of them; the only one I yet know that seems to me really to possess nothing of the kind is a species of Helops, living on sandy heaths. I suppose the dense cushion of hairs on the tarsi to be for the protection, simply, of the joints to which they are attached. I have detected them on the tarsal joints of species of Ephydra, and on the first basal tarsal joint of the drone of the hive-bee. A very rudimentary form of tenent-hairs is present on the under surface of some of the tree-bugs (Pentatomidæ), which have in addition a large, deeply-cleft organ at the extremity of the tarsus; this appears to be a true sucker.

When walking on a rough surface, the foot represents that of a Coleopterous insect without any tenent appendages. The ungues are always attached to the last joint of an insect's tarsus. They are not attached to the fifth tarsal joint of a Dipterous insect, neither are they attached to the fifth tarsal joint of a Hymenopterous insect, but to the terminal sucker, which again, in this great order, is a sixth tarsal joint, membranous, flexible, elastic in the highest degree, retractile to almost its fullest extent within the fifth tarsal joint—a joint modified to an extraordinary degree for special purposes.

In plantula of Lucanus, with its pair of minute claws, the ungues are hairs modified for special purposes; and they have the structure of true hairs. The sustentacula of Epeira, the analogous structures on the entire under surface of the last tarsal joints in Pholcus, the condition of the parts in the hind limbs of Notonecta, in both its mature and earlier conditions, as well as in Sarcoptes, Psoroptes, and some other Acari, all may be cited in proof of this fact. The various orders of insects have, for the most part, each their own type of foot. Thus there is the Coleopterous type, the Hymenopterous type, the Dipterous type, the Homopterous type, &c.; each so very distinctive, that in critical instances they will sometimes serve at once to show to which order an insect should be referred. Thus, amongst all the Diptera, I have as yet met with but one subdivision which presents an exception to the structure described. This exception is furnished by the Tipulidæ, which have the Hymenopterous foot. With hardly an exception, then, I believe the form of foot described will be found universal among the Diptera.

It may be desirable to add a few words on the best plan of conducting observations on the feet of insects. Their action should be studied by placing the insect under the influence of chloroform. It is of advantage to carefully preserve the parts examined, and for this purpose Deane's medium or glycerine jelly suits very well; some of the more delicate preparations, however, can only be kept unchanged in a solution of chloride of zinc. The plan of soaking in caustic potash, crushing, washing, putting into spirits of wine and then into turpentine, and lastly into Canada balsam, is perfectly useless, excepting in rare instances where points connected with the structure of the integument have to be made out. Of course, the parts should be viewed from above, from below, and in profile, in order to gain exact ideas of their relations. The binocular microscope diminishes the difficulties which formerly had to be encountered, as by its aid many parts may be clearly viewed without preparation of any kind.

Fig. 400.

1. Antenna of the Silkworm-moth; 2. Tongue of Butterfly; 3. A portion of tongue highly magnified, showing its muscular fibre; 4. Tracheæ of silkworm; 5. Foot of silkworm. (The small circles enclose each object somewhat near the natural size.)

Moths and butterflies supply the microscopist with some of the most beautiful objects for examination. What can be more wonderful in its adaptation than the antenna of the moth (represented in Fig. 400, No. 1), with a thin, finger-like extremity almost supplying the insect with a perfect and useful hand, moved throughout its extent by a muscular apparatus of the most exquisite construction. The tongue of butterfly (No. 2) is evidently made for the purpose of dipping into the interior of flowers and extracting the juices; this act is assisted by a series of fine muscles. An enlarged view of a portion is given at No. 3; see Plate VI., Nos. 132 and 133, antennæ of Vapour Moth.

Fig. 401.—Breathing aperture or spiracle of silkworm. (In the circle it is shown about the natural size.)

Fig. 402.—Magnified portions of the trachea of the Hydrophilus, showing spiral tubes.

The inconceivably delicate structure of the maxillæ or tongues (for there are two) of the butterfly, rolled up like the trunk of an elephant, and capable, like it, of every variety of movement, has been carefully examined and described by Mr. Newport. "Each maxilla is convex on its outer surface, but concave on its inner; so that when the two are united they form a tube, *haustellium*, by their union, through which fluids may be drawn into the mouth. The inner or concave surface, which forms the tube, is lined with a very smooth membrane, and extends throughout the whole length of the organ; while that of each maxilla is hollow in its interior, apparently forming a tube 'in itself,' but this is not so; the mistake has arisen from the existence of large tracheæ, or breathing tubes, in the interior of the proboscis. In some species the extremity of the haustellium is studded externally with a number of minute papillæ, or fringes—as in *Vanessa atalanta*—in which they become small elongated barrel-shaped bodies, terminated by smaller papillæ at their extremities. On alighting on a flower, the insect makes a powerful expiratory effort, by which the air is expelled from the interior air-tubes, and from those with which they are connected in the head and body; and at the moment of applying its proboscis to the food, it makes an inspiratory effort, by which the central canal in the proboscis is dilated, and the food ascends it at the same instant to supply the vacuum produced; and thus it passes into the mouth and stomach, the constant ascent of the fluid being assisted by the action of the muscles of the proboscis, which continues during the whole time that the insect is feeding. By this combined agency of the acts of respiration and the muscles of the proboscis we are also enabled to understand the manner in which the humming-bird sphynx extracts in an instant the honey from a flower while hovering over it, without alighting; and which it certainly would be unable to do were the ascent of the fluid entirely dependent upon the action of the muscles of the organ."

The trachæal or respiratory system of insects varies, or rather is found to exist in modified forms to suit their varied conditions of life. While in the larval stage the breathing apertures are seen to recur at intervals on each side of the abdomen (as that of the silkworm, Fig. 401), thus ensuring a continuous supply of air to the circulating fluids throughout the whole body. These spiracles are usually nine or ten in number, and consist of a membranous ring of an oval form. The air-tubes are exquisitely composed of two thin membranes, between which a delicate elastic thread or spiral fibre is interposed, forming a cylindrical opening and keeping the tube in a distended condition, thus mechanically preserving the sides from collapse or pressure in their passage through the air, which otherwise might occasion suffocation. Fig. 402 represents the double spiral arrangement of a portion of a trachea of Hydrophilus, which ensures both elasticity and strength.

There are other points of interest confined to the water-beetle tribe, among the more striking of which is the foreleg of the *Dytiscus marginalis*. Here the first three joints of the tarsus are expanded into a broad surface, and fringed throughout with curved hairs. From the surface of these spring a number of short hairs, with cup-like discs at their extremities, one of which is seen highly magnified in Plate VI., No. 142. These are so cup-like in form that they have been hitherto described as "suckers," but it is believed they are simply a special apparatus for the development of the hairs seen on the leg and foot of the beetle. Another curious example occurs in the Gyrinus, or whirligig-beetle. The front pair of legs are of the ordinary kind, but the under pair are furnished with expanding paddles. The trochanter, femur, and tibia, are flat plates of a triangular shape, pointed at their outer angles, from which the apex springs. But the tarsus is jointed on the inner angle of the furthermost end of the tibia, and each of its four joints expands into a flat paddle blade. In the accompanying Fig. 403 one paddle is seen expanded, the other closed.

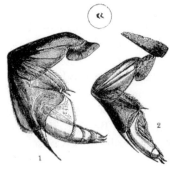

Fig. 403.

1. Leg of Gyrinus, Whirligig, paddle shown expanded. 2. Paddle closed up.

These paddles are adapted with much precision to ensure the most effectual application of the propelling power; as the beetle strikes out in the act of swimming, the membranous expansion described enables it to move about with great rapidity; upon the legs being drawn back towards the body, the membrane closes up, and thus offers no resistance to the water. The eyes are not the least curious part of the merry little beetle: the upper section is fitted for seeing in the air, and is adapted to the upper or superior part of the head; the lower portion, for seeing under the water, being placed at a lower angle, a thin division only separating the two.

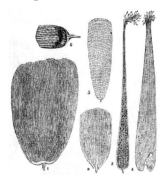

Fig. 404.—Scales from Butterflies' and Moths' wings, magnified 200 diameters.

1. Scale of *Morpho menelaus*; 2. Large scale of *Polyommatus argiolus*, azure blue; 3. *Hipparchia janira argiolus*; 4. *Pontia brassica*; 5. *Podura plumbea*; 6. Small scale of azure blue.

Wings of Insects.—These exhibit variety of form and structure, as well as of beauty of colouring. At an early period the orders of insects were mainly founded upon these interesting appendages. The Orthoptera were the straight wings; the Neuroptera the nerved; the Trichoptera the hairy wings; the Coleoptera the cased or sheathed wings; the Diptera the two wings; the Hymenoptera the married wings; and the Lepidoptera the scaled wings. A number of wings are small and membranous, and may be mounted dry for examination under the microscope. Others are better seen mounted in benzol-balsam. The elytra, iridescent wing cases of the diamond, and other beetles, as well as the wings of the more highly coloured butterflies, make pretty objects mounted dry for opaque illumination by the Lieberkühn or reflector. The thicker horny cases of other members of the beetle tribe require long soaking, as described in a former chapter.

The wings of moths and butterflies are covered with scales or feathers, carefully overlapping each other, as tiles are made to cover the tops of houses. The iridescent variety of colouring on insects' wings arises from the peculiar wavy arrangement of the scales. Figs. 404 and 405 are magnified representations of a few of them. No. 1, a scale of the *Morpho menelaus*, taken from the side of the wing, is of a pale-blue colour; it measures about ¹⁄₁₂₀th of an inch in length, and exhibits a series of longitudinal striæ or lines, between which are disposed cross-lines or other striæ, giving it very much an appearance of brick-work (better seen in Fig. 405, No. 1).

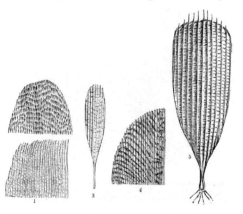

Fig. 405.—Portions of Scales, magnified 500 diameters.

1. Portion of scale of *Morpho menelaus;* 2. Portion of large scale of *Podura plumbea;* 3. Scale from the wing of Gnat, its two layers being represented; 4. Portion of a large scale of *Lepisma Saccharina;* 5. Body scale of Gnat, magnified 650 diameters.

Polyommatus argiolus, azure-blue (Fig. 404, Nos. 2 and 6), are large and small scales taken from the under-side of the wing of this beautiful blue butterfly; the small scale is covered with a series of spots, and exhibits both longitudinal and transverse striæ, these should be clearly defined, and the spots separated by a quarter-inch object-glass. No. 3, *Hipparchia janira*, is a scale from the meadow-brown butterfly: on this brown spots, having an irregular shape with longitudinal striæ, are seen. No. 4, *Pontia brassica*, cabbage butterfly, was at one time taken to be an excellent criterion of the penetration and definition of an object glass. It is seen to have a free extremity or brush-like appendage. With a fairly good power, the longitudinal markings appear like rows of small beads. Chevalier selected for his test object the scale of the *Pontia brassica*. Mohl and Schacht extolled *Hipparchia janira* as a good test of penetration in an objective of moderate angular aperture. Amici's test object is *Navicula rhomboides*, the display of the lines forming the test.

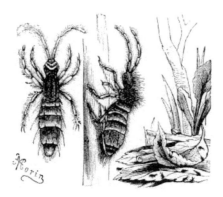

Fig. 406.—*Podura villosa*, male and female, highly magnified.

The *Tinea vestianella*, clothes-moth, is furnished with unique scales. Small and destructive as this moth is, it suffers much from a parasitic mite, and from which it is unable to free itself.

The Podura scale (Fig. 405), with its delicate transparent membrane and curiously inserted "notes of admiration," as they were called, was long believed to be an excellent test object for the highest powers of the microscope, but I believe it is no longer regarded in that light: indeed, most insect scales have declined in the value and estimation of the skilled microscopist. This is in part due to the improvements made in the objective. The high-angled glasses have cleared up obscure points in the structural characters of the minuter forms of life, and the scales of insects are no longer found to be difficult test objects for the modern objective of a Zeiss or a Powell to resolve. Nevertheless, the scale of the Podura belonging to the order Thysanura, a curious little insect commonly known by the name of springtail, usually found living in most obscure places, and too small to attract attention, is not likely to be entirely thrust aside. The springtails (Collembola) are furnished on the under-side of the first abdominal segment with a curious tube or sucker, from the orifice of which glandular process a secreted viscid matter is protruded; they are remarkable also from the fact that in most of them no trace of a tracheal system has yet been discovered. The eyes when present are in the form of simple or grouped ocelli, the antennæ number six joints, and the abdomen has but six segments, often only three. The forked tail is a curious process turned forward and attached to one of the tender segments and held in position under the body; when released it springs back and bounds up to a very considerable height. Fig. 406 represents *Podura villosa*. There are several species, one of which (*P. aquatica*) is found floating in patches on pools of water on bright summer days.

Lepisma saccharina belongs to the same genus as Podura. This minute springtail derives its name from having been discovered in old sugar-casks. It has a spindle-shaped body covered with silvery scales, long used as test objects. The sides of the abdomen are furnished with a series of appendages with long bristle-like setæ, or hairs, at their extremities. The head is concealed under a prothorax, the antennæ are long, and the maxillary palpi are either five or seven-jointed, and very conspicuous, to enable them to cut the dry wood on which they principally feed. The scales must be mounted under thin cover-glasses; oblique illumination shows up some portions to advantage, while central light from an achromatic condenser and a wide-angled objective renders their markings more distinct. Portion of a scale more highly magnified is shown in Fig. 405.

Eggs of Insects (Plate VI., Nos. 124-139).—In form, colour, and variety of design, the eggs of insects are more surprisingly varied than those of the feathered tribes; but as from extreme smallness they escape observation, an acquaintance with their structure is not so familiar as it might be. Although the eggs of the bird tribe differ much in their external characteristics, they closely resemble each other while yet a part of the ovarian ova, and prior to their detachment from the ovary. At one period of their formation all eggs consist of three similar parts:—1st. The internal nucleated cell, or germinal vesicle, with its macula; 2nd. The vitellus, or yolk-substance; and 3rd. The vesicular envelope, or vitelline membrane. The germinal vesicle is the first produced, then the yolk substance, which gradually envelops it, and the vitelline membrane, the latest formed, incloses the whole. The chemical constituents of the egg are the same in all cases, albumen, fatty matters, and a proportion of a substance precipitable by water. The production of the chorion, or shell membrane, does not take place till the ovum has attained nearly its full size, and it then appears to proceed, in part at least, from the consolidation over the whole surface of one or more layers of an albuminous fluid secreted from the wall of the oviduct.

The embryo cell is so directly connected with the germinal vesicle that at a certain period it disappears altogether, and is absorbed into the germinal yolk, or rather becomes the nucleus of the embryo, when a greater degree of compactness is observed in the yolk, and all that remains of the germinal vesicle is one or more highly refracting fat globules and albuminoid bodies. Towards the end of the period of incubation, the head of the young caterpillar is said to lie towards the dot or opening in the lid, termed the micropyle,[83] from its resemblance to a small gate, or opening through which the larva emerges forth as a butterfly.

The germinal vesicle is comparatively large and well-marked while the egg is yet in the ova-sac. By preparing sections after Dr. Halifax's method,[84] we find that the germinal vesicle in the bee's egg is not situated immediately near or even below the so-called micropyle, but rather more to the side of the egg;

just in the position which the head of the embryo is subsequently found to occupy at maturity.

The egg membrane, or envelope, of all the Lepidoptera is composed of three separate and distinct layers: an external slightly raised coat, tough and hard in its character, a middle one of united cells, and a fine transparent vitelline lining membrane, perfectly smooth and homogeneous in structure, imparting solidity, and giving a fine iridescent hue to the surface. The germinal vesicle is of a proportionately large size for the egg, and its macula is at first single, then multiple. In the egg of the silkworm the outer membrane is comprised of an inner reticulated membrane of non-nucleated cells, in the outer layer the cells are arranged in an irregular circular form, also non-nucleated, with minute interstitial setæ or hairs projecting outward.

The outer surface of the egg-shell of *Coccus Persicæ* is covered by minute rings, of which the ends somewhat overlap. These rings are thought to be identical in their character with the whitish substance which exudes through pores on the under-side of the body; it is more than probable that a succession of layers of rings fully accounts for the beautiful prismatic hues they present viewed as opaque objects under the microscope, and illuminated by Lieberkühn or side-condenser. This white substance, it should be observed, forms a part of the intimate structure of the egg-shell, and is in nowise affected by methylated spirit or dilute acids. Sir John Lubbock[85] states that in the greenish eggs of Phryganea, "the colour is due to the yolk-globules themselves. In Coccus, however, this is not so; the yolk-globules are slightly yellow, and the green hue of the egg is owing to the green granules, which are minute oil globules. When, however, the egg arrives at maturity, and the upper chamber has been removed by absorption, these green granules will be found to be replaced by dark-green globules, regular in size, and about $\frac{1}{8000}$th of an inch in diameter, and which appear to be in no way the same in the yolk of Phryganea eggs." Another curious fact has been noticed, which partially bears on the question of colour: the production of parasite bodies within the eggs of some insects. In the Coccus, for instance, parasitic cells of a green colour occur, "shaped like a string of sausages, in length about the $\frac{1}{2000}$th of an inch by about the $\frac{1}{7000}$th in breadth."

The eggs of moths and butterflies present many varying tints of colour; in speaking of this quality I do not restrict the term solely to those prismatic changes to which allusion has been made, and which are liable to constant mutations according to the accident of the rays of light thrown upon them; but I more particularly refer to the several natural transitions of colour, the prevailing tints of which are yellow, white, grey, and a light-brown. In some eggs the yellow, white, and grey are delicately blended, and, when viewed with a magnifying power of about fifty diameters, and by the aid of the side-reflector (parabolic-reflector), exhibit many beautiful combinations. The more delicate opalescent, or rather iridescent, tints appear on the eggs of insects, while those of the feathered tribes furnish no like example. The egg of the mottled umber moth, *Erannis defoliaria* (Plate VI., No. 137), is in every way very beautiful. It is in shape ovoid, with regular hexagonal reticulations, each corner being studded with a knob or button; the space within the hexagon is finely punctated, and the play of colours is exquisitely delicate. In this egg no micropyle can be seen. The egg of the thorn moth, *Ennomos erosaria* (Plate VI., No. 138), is of an elongated brick-looking form, one end of which is slightly tapered off, while the other, in which the lid is placed, is flattened and surrounded by a beautifully white-beaded border, having for its centre a slightly raised reticulated micropyle. The empty egg-shell gives a fine opalescent play of colours, while that containing the young worm is of a brownish-yellow.

The egg of the straw-belle moth, *Aspillates gilvaria* (Plate VI., No. 139), is delicately tinted, somewhat long and narrow, with sides slightly flattened or rounded off, and irregularly serrated. The top is convex, and the base a little indented, in which are seen the lid and micropyle. The young worm, however, usually makes its way through the upper convex side: the indentation represented in the drawing shows the place of exit.

An example of those eggs possessing a good deal of natural colour is presented in that of the common puss-moth, *Cerura vinula*, a large spheroidal-shaped egg, having, under the microscope, the appearance of a fine ripe orange; the micropyle exactly corresponds to the depression left in this fruit on the removal of the stalk. The surface is finely reticulated, and the natural colour a deep orange.

The egg of the mottled rustic moth, *Caradina morpheus* (No. 124), is subconical, and equally divided throughout by a series of ribs, which terminate in a well-marked geometrically-formed lid. The egg of the tortoise-shell butterfly, *Vanessa urticæ* (No. 125), is ovoid and divided into segments, the ribs turning in towards the micropyle. The common footman, *Lithosia campanula* (No. 126), produces a perfectly globular egg covered with fine reticulations of a delicate buff colour. The egg of the shark moth, *Cucullia umbratica* (No. 127), is subconical in form, with ribs and cross-bars passing up from a flattened base to the summit, and turning over to form the lid. No. 136 is the egg of blue argus butterfly, *Polyommatus argus*. That of the small emerald moth, *Jodis Vernaria* (No. 134), is an egg of singular form and beauty—an oval, flattened on both sides, of silvery iridescence, and covered throughout with minute reticulations and dots. It is particularly translucent, so much so that the yellow-brown worm is readily seen curled up within. The lid or micropyle is not detected until the larva eats its way out of the shell. It should be noted that the series of eggs in Plate VII. are somewhat over-coloured, and consequently lose much of their natural transparency. The eggs of flies and parasites also present much variety in form, colour, and construction. Many of their eggs are provided with a veritable lid, which opens up with a hinge-like articulation. This lid is seen in the egg of bot-fly, Plate VI., No. 144, from which the larva is just escaping; No. 146, egg of Scatophaga; No. 147, egg of parasite of magpie.[86] Still more remarkable in the delicate and beautiful forms are some of the parasities which infest birds in particular: Plate VI., No. 145, the egg of parasite of pheasant; No. 147, that of the magpie, while that of the peacock is curiously interesting. In Fig. 407 the larvæ of the horn-bill are seen just about to emerge from their eggs.

Fig. 407.—Larvæ of the Hornbill emerging from eggs.

The larvæ of most Hymenoptera are footless grubs, furnished with a soft head, and exhibiting but little, if any, advance upon those of Diptera (Plate VI., No. 141). In the saw-fly, however, the larva, instead of being as above described, a mere footless maggot, presents the closest resemblance to the caterpillar of the Lepidoptera; it is provided with a distinct head, with six thoracic legs, and in most cases from twelve to sixteen pro-legs are appended to the abdominal segments.

One other conspicuous object represented in Plate VI., No. 128, is the maple Aphis, also known as the leaf-insect, averaging in size about the one-fiftieth of an inch in length. Although recognised and described under the name of the leaf-insect, nothing was known of its origin and history, with the exception of what the Rev. J. Thornton published in 1852, and to whom we owe its re-discovery on the leaves of the maple. Subsequently it attracted the attention of the Dutch naturalist, Van der Hoeven, who regarded it as the larval form of a species of Aphis, and named it Periphyllus. It has more recently engaged the attention of Dr. Balbiani and M. Siguoret, whose united investigations will be found in "Comptes Rendus," 1867. These observers assigned it definitely to Aphis. A brown species is also met with during a great part of the year feeding upon the young shoots of the maple. The female produces two kinds of young, as do all the genus Aphis, one normal the other abnormal; the first are alone capable of reproducing their species, while the latter retain their original form, which is not changed throughout their existence. They increase so slowly in size that it may appear doubtful whether they eat, the mouth being rudimentary; they undergo no change; do not acquire wings, and their antennæ always retain the five joints peculiar to all young Aphides before the first moult. Neither are they all of the same colour, some being of a bright green, as represented in Plate VI., while others are of a darker, or brownish-green colour. The brown-green embryos differ from the adult female only in those characters analogous to all other species, and this chiefly with regard to the minute hairs, which are long and simple. In the green embryos, in the place of setæ, the body is surrounded by transparent lamellæ, oblong in shape. These scales not only cover the body, but also the anterior portion of the head, the first joint of the antennæ, and the outer edge of the tibiæ of the first pair of legs. The dorsal surface in these insects is covered with a mosaic of hexagonal plates, very closely resembling the plates of the carapace of the tortoise. In this particular my artist has fallen into a slight error. Another peculiarity is that the body is much flattened out, and looks so much like a scale on the surface of the leaf that it requires considerable practice, as well as quickness of sight, to detect the young maple Aphis. One of the lamellæ is seen highly magnified at *c*, and a tenent-hair at *b*. The antennæ, tapering off towards the apex, are serrate on both edges, and terminate in a fine lancet (shown at *a*), with which it penetrates the leaf of the plant. Beneath the insertions of the antennæ is a complex form of sucking mouth, and on either side of the head are two brilliant scarlet-coloured eyes.

Aphides, as is well known, live upon the juices of plants, which they suck, and when they occur in great numbers cause considerable damage to the gardener and farmer. Many plants are liable to be attacked by swarms of these insects, when their leaves curl up, they grow sickly, and their produce is either greatly reduced or utterly ruined. One striking instance is presented in the devastation caused by the hop-fly (*Aphis humuli*).

Fig. 408.—*Aphrophora spumaria*, Cuckoo-spit.

a. The frothy substance; *b*. The pupa.

The *Aphrophora bifasciata*, common frog-hopper, is a well-known garden pest. The antennæ of this insect are placed between the eyes, and the scutellum is not covered; the eyes, never more than two in number, are occasionally wanting. These pests are furnished with long hind legs, that enable them to perform most extraordinary leaping feats. The best-known British species is the cuckoo-spit, froth-fly (Fig. 408). The names cuckoo-spit and froth-fly both allude to the peculiar habit of the insect, while in the larva state, of enveloping itself in a kind of frothy secretion, somewhat resembling saliva.

Arachnidæ.—In this class of insects, spiders, scorpions, and mites are included, all of which belong to a sub-class of Arthropoda, and are appropriately placed between the Crustacea on the one hand and the Insecta on the other. The highest Crustaceans have ten feet, the Arachnidæ eight, and insects six. The Arachnidæ are wingless, have no antennæ, and breathe by means of tracheal tubes, or pulmonary sacs, these performing the function of lungs. As a rule they have several simple eyes, have no proper metamorphosis, and they are essentially predaceous, the females being larger than the males. Most of the Arachnidæ live on insects, and may therefore be regarded in the light of a friend to the florist and gardener.

The *Epeira diadema* is the best known member of the species; in summer spiders abound on every shrub, and spin out their wonderful webs from branch to branch.

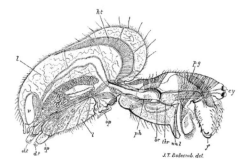

Fig. 409.—A lengthways section through the body of female *Epeira diadema*.

Explanation of reference.—*ey.* Eyes; *p.g.* Poison gland; *ht.* Heart; *in.* Intestine, alimentary canal; *l.* Liver; *r.* Rectum or cloaca; *dt.* and *sp.* Discharge tubes of spinnerets; *o.* Slit, or air opening; *ov.* Ovipositor; *ph.* Pharynx; *br.* Brain; *thr.* Throat, or gullet, filled with eggs; *un. l.* Under lip; *m.* Mouth; *f.* Fang, or claw; *j.* Jaw. The gills, or breathing apparatus are situated at the air opening, *o*; and the silk glands are above this. (Magnified 20 diameters.)

The body, seen in my illustration, Fig. 409, in section, consists of two parts; the foremost is the cephalothorax, or head, upon which is mounted four pairs of eyes (two of which are seen in section), while to the thorax is attached eight jointed well-developed legs terminating in feet, with claws adapted for climbing and holding on. The other half consists, of the abdomen, together with spinnerets and glands, which secrete the fluid out of which the web is spun, and this, although it hardens to some extent on exposure to the air, retains its viscid nature for the purpose of entangling its prey. The spinnerets are the most interesting feature in the anatomy of the Epeira (Figs. 410 and 411).

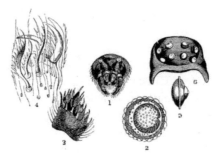

Fig. 410.

1. Spinnerets of Spider; 2. Extreme end of one of the upper pair of spinnerets; 3. End of under pair of spinnerets; 4. Foot of Spider; 5. Side view of eye; 6. The arrangement of the four pairs of eyes.

Five kinds of spinning glands are found in spiders. The glandulæ aciniformes are those which consist of a proper tunica and an epithelium; these exhibit in all parts the same reaction to staining agents. The glandulæ pyriformes consist of a tunica proper and an epithelium, which in their lower parts (or those near the efferent ducts) stain more deeply than the upper. The glandulæ ampullaceæ and glandulæ tubuliformes have similar coverings, the latter terminating in a large spool. The glandulæ aggregatæ have a wide and branched lumen, the efferent duct of which is provided with cells and an accessory piece, which draws out to a tip. All the glands have secreting portions, which serve as collecting cavities for the spinning material. The spools are two-jointed basal and one-jointed accessory pieces. In addition to the five glands enumerated, there are also lobate and cribelleum glands; these are variously distributed, and exercise different functions, one set preparing the so-called moist filaments from the moist droplets, another spins the egg-cocoon, as nearly all spiders envelop their eggs in a covering of silken threads and store them up in some sheltered place awaiting the warm weather of spring to hatch them out. The bag that holds the eggs is not one of the least curious efforts of skill and care. The mother uses her body as a gauge to measure her work, precisely as a bird uses her body to gauge the size and form of its nest. The spider first spreads a thin coating of silk as a foundation, taking care to have this circular by turning its body round during the process. In the same manner it spins a raised border round this till it takes the form of a cup; it is at this stage of the work the female begins to lay her eggs in the cup, and not content to fill it up to the brim, she also piles up a heap as high as the cup is deep. Here, then, is a cup full of eggs, the under half covered and protected by the silken sides of the cup, but the upper still exposed to the air and the cold. She now sets to work to cover this; the process is similar to the preceding—that is, she weaves a thick web of silk all round the top, and instead of a cup-shaped nest, like those of the bird tribe, the whole partakes of the form of a ball much larger than the body of the spider.

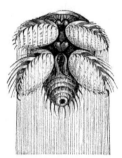

Fig. 411.—Spinnerets of Spider greatly enlarged.

The eight legs and feet of the spider (one only is represented Fig. 410, No. 4) are curiously constructed. Each foot, when magnified, is seen to be armed with strong horny claws, with serrations on their under-surface. By this arrangement the spider is enabled to regulate the issue of its web from the spinnerets. In addition, a remarkable comb-like claw is provided for the purpose of separating certain threads which enter into the composition of the delicate web, so that everything is arranged and planned in the most geometrical order, while the mouth or jaws with their two movable poison-fangs convert the Arachnidæ into formidable and dangerous foes. The maternal industry and instincts of spiders, the ballooning habits of others, the cave dwellers, with their limited vision, combined with an increased delicacy of touch and hearing, their disguise of feigned death when a strong enemy approaches, are all of the most interesting character.

One of the more remarkable, the *Argyroneta aquatica* (diving spider), weaves itself a curious little bell-shaped globule, which it takes with it to the bottom of the water, whither it retires to devour its prey. Notwithstanding its aquatic habits, this, like the rest of its species, is fitted only for aerial respiration; it therefore carries down, entangled amongst the hairs of its body, a small bubble of air. This contrivance presents us with the earliest form of diving-bell.

Mites and Ticks constitute a group which for diversity of structure, number of species and individuals, and minuteness of size, has no equal. The typical genus of the family—Ixodidæ—being wholly parasitic in their habits, are so modified in organisation, so marked by degeneration, that some authors have proposed to remove them into a class by themselves. One leading character distinguishes the whole: the abdomen rarely presents a trace of segmentation, but is confluent with the cephalothorax, the fusion between the two being so complete that, as in the harvest spiders belonging to Palpatores, the anterior sternal plates of the abdomen are thrust far forward between the coxæ of the cephalothoracic limbs. As in Arachnidæ, however, the mouth is adapted for sucking, but the jaws are often partially united, and form, with a plate termed the *epistome* and the labium, a beak. The mandibles are either pincer-like, or simply pointed at the tip, forming piercing organs; the palpi have their basal segments, or maxillæ, united, which form a conspicuous plate, or *hypostomes*, constituting the floor of the mouth. These organs are often seen to be separated from the rest of the cephalothorax by a membranous joint, and constitute a kind of head, the *capitulum*. In most cases no trace of special respiratory organs can be found. Another characteristic of value in separating ticks from harvest-spiders is that in the former the young undergo a metamorphosis in the course of growth, being hatched as six-footed larvæ, and acquiring later in life a fourth pair of legs.

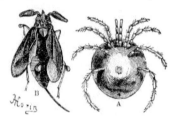

Fig. 412.

A. *Atax spinipes*, water mite seen from below; B. Water Scorpion infested by Atax.

The Acariæ include a number of families, all distinguished by the position of the respiratory stigmata and the form of the mandibles and palpi. In the velvety mites (Trombidiidæ), the integument is soft and covered with variously-coloured fine hairs, and the legs are adapted for walking, running or swimming. The latter live in fresh-water ponds, creeping over the leaves of aquatic plants. The fresh-water mites (*Atax spinipes*, Fig. 412) swim about freely by means of vigorous strokes of their legs, which act as oars. In the adult the body is more or less spherical, and usually of a bright red or greenish colour. The males of one species have a curious blunt tail-like prolongation from the hinder end of the abdomen. The eggs are laid in the spring on the stems of water plants, and the six-footed larvæ when hatched attach themselves to water-bugs (Nepa) or water-beetles (Dytiscus) by means of a large sucker developed on the front of the head.

Fig. 413.—*Ixodes ricinus* or Sheep-tick (under surface). The small circle encloses one life-size.

Of all the Acari, the best known and most troublesome are those belonging to the family Ixodidæ; these infest the whole animal creation. They are furnished with a long cylindrical beak, armed with recurved hooks, formed of the two mandibles above and the long slender labium below. They have no eyes, nor apparently any dermaploptic sense, but there are various seemingly sensitive setæ distributed over the body and on the appendages. The whole of the mites will be found suitable objects for the study of development, as the process is slow and their eggs do not require much care. The segmentation of the eggs differs; some of the cells are distinguished by their large nuclei, which stain feebly by carmine. During the cleavage of the egg no division of the so-called yolk has been observed, but later on this breaks up into several minute pieces.

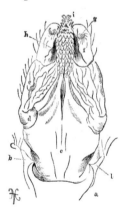

Fig 414.—Mouth organs of Sheep-tick.

c. Capitulum; *d, e, f, g.* Segments of palpi; *h.* Labial process; *i.* Spiny beak formed of fused mandibles.—(Warne.)

The accompanying Fig. 413 shows the under surface of the body and the mouth parts of the common English dog and sheep tick, *Ixodes ricinus*, with its six formidable legs. The upper surface is shown in Fig. 415; the head (*capitulum*) and mouth organs in Fig. 414, *c, d, e, f, g,* together with the four segments of the palpi; *h* the labial process armed with hooks forming the lower side of the beak, and *i* indicating the tips of the two mandibles forming the upper side, and projecting beyond the apex of the labium. By means of this beak, which is thrust to its base into the integument, the tick adheres firmly to its host, and in detaching them care must be taken that the head is not left behind buried in the skin. This tick is found in all stages of growth; the females, gorging themselves with blood, swell up to the size of a pea, as seen in Fig. 413, but the male, formerly regarded as a distinct species, is of a much smaller size. In distribution these pests are almost cosmopolitan, and in tropical countries they grow to much greater dimensions, the females sometimes attaining the size of a large gooseberry.

The family of true mites is that of the Sarcoptidæ; these are either free or parasitic. They have no breathing organs; the palpi are basally fused to the rostrum, the mandibles are pincer-like, and the tarsi are often furnished at their tips with a sucker. The most familiar is the cheese mite, Tyroglyphus, which feeds upon decaying matter.

Fig. 415.

1. Female Sheep-tick; 2. Rat-tick; 3. Head of Cat-flea; 4. Larva of Flea. (The life size is given in circles.)

The well-known cheese mite attains to a size plainly visible to the naked eye, but when first hatched out from the egg (shown in its several stages of development in Fig. 417), requires a moderate amount of magnification. Its growth, however, is rapid and the young begin to feed as soon as they leave the egg. The body is partially covered over by setæ, or hairs, and the feet terminate in hooklets, as seen in the full-grown acarus. The mandibles are cutting, but as a rule they prefer soft and partially-decayed kinds of food. It also feeds upon damaged flour, sugar, and other domestic articles. The *Dermestes lardarius*, one of the minute beetle tribe (Fig. 418), commits even greater depredations among insect and other collections during the larval stage of its existence.

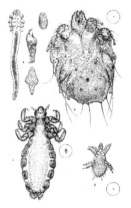

Fig. 416.

Tyroglyphus. 1. *Pediculus vulgaris* × 50 diameters; 2. *Acarus destructor* under surface; 3. *Sarcoptes scabiei*, Itch-insect, magnified 350 diameters; 4. *Demodex folliculorum* from the human skin in various stages of growth, from the egg upwards, magnified 400 diameters. (The small circles enclose the objects of the natural size.)

Fig. 417.—The Cheese Mite, *Acarus domesticus*, seen in its several stages of development.

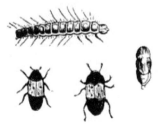

Fig. 418.—*Dermestes lardarius*: larva, pupa, and imago. (Natural size.)

Birds suffer much from mites living parasitically upon them belonging to Sarcoptidæ; these likewise infest mankind, and give rise to a disease known as the itch (Fig. 416, No. 3). This malady and the irritation accompanying it are caused by the mite excavating tunnels under the skin. In these the eggs are laid and hatched, and the young then start burrowing on their own account; their burrows are traced as whitish lines on the surface of the skin.

Fig. 416, No. 4, *Demodex folliculorum*, is another remarkable parasite found beneath the skin; this is usually obtained from a spot where the sebaceous follicles or fat glands are abundant, such as the forehead, the side of the nose, and the angles between the nose and lip. If the part where a little black spot or a pustule is seen be squeezed rather hard, the oily matter there accumulated will be forced out in a globular form. This minute mite is less than one-fiftieth of an inch in length; if it be laid on a glass slide, and a small quantity of glycerine added to cause the separation of the harder portions, the parasite in all probability will float out, and, by means of a fine-pointed pencil or brush, can be transferred to a clean slide and mounted in Canada balsam. An allied species is found in the skin of dogs suffering from mange.

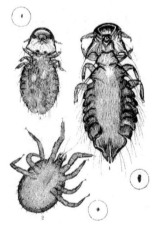

Fig. 419.

1. Parasite of Turkey; 2. Acarus of common Fowl, under surface; 3. Parasite of Pheasant. (The small circles enclose each about life size.)

The Stylopidæ are remarkable parasites, living upon the bodies of wasps, bees, and bugs, and present a type of structure quite distinct from beetles or the ticks described. The male (*Xenos peckii*, Fig. 420) is a winged insect with coarsely faceted eyes, large fan-shaped wings, extremely small inconspicuous elytra, the two first thoracic rings short, while the metathorax is elongated and covers the base of the abdomen, and the hind legs are placed a long way behind the middle pair. The female, on the other hand, is a grub-like creature, without legs, wings, or eyes; she never leaves the body of her host, and from her eggs active little larvæ develop and get carried into the nests of bees and wasps.

Fig. 420.—*Xenos peckii.* 1. Male; 2. Female.

Mites are very numerous, differ in form, and are interesting objects under the microscope. The body of the common flea (Fig. 421) is divided into distinct segments, those about the thorax being separated. Although apterous, the flea has the rudiments of four wings in the form of horny plates on both sides of the thoracic segments. Its mouth consists of a pair of sword-shaped mandibles, finely serrated; these, with a sharp, penetrating, needle-like organ, constitute the formidable weapons with which it pierces through the skin.

The neck is distinctly separated, and the body covered with scales, the edges of which are beset with short setæ; from the head project a short pair of antennæ, below which are a proboscis and a lance-shaped cutting apparatus. On each side of the head a large compound eye is placed; it has six many-jointed powerful legs, terminating in two-hooked claws; a pair of long hind legs are kept folded up when the insect is at rest, which, in the act of jumping, it suddenly straightens out with great muscular force. The female flea (Fig. 421) lays a great number of eggs, sticking them together with a glutinous secretion; the flea infesting the dog or cat glues its eggs to the roots of the hairs. In about four days the eggs are hatched out, and a small white larva or grub is seen crawling about, and feeding most actively. Plate VI., No. 141, is a magnified view of one covered with short hairs. After nine or ten days the larva assumes the pupa form; this it retains four days, and in nine days more it becomes a perfect flea. The head of the flea found in the cat (Fig. 415, No. 3) somewhat differs in form from that of the species infesting the human being; its jaws are furnished with more formidable-looking mandibles, and from between the first and second joints behind the head short strong spines project.

Fig. 421.

1. Female Flea; 2. Male Flea. (The small circles enclose fleas of about life size.)

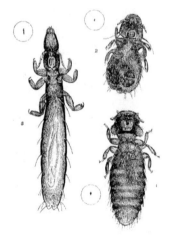

Fig. 422.

1. Parasite of Eagle; 2. Parasite of Vulture; 3. Parasite of Pigeon, *Sarcoptes palumbinus*. (The circles enclose each about life size.)

Two small and obscure groups of the mites and ticks have been associated with the latter, but for no better reason than that their affinities are unknown. The first of these are the Tardigrada, or bear animalcules, which comprise microscopical animals living in damp, sandy, and mossy places; the body is long and oval in shape, and possesses four pairs of bud-like unjointed appendages, each tipped with claws: the last pair of legs project from the hinder part of the body. The mouth is much subdued, and only a trace of jaws is found as a pair of stylets; there appear to be no organs of respiration or circulation, and, unlike what obtains in all true Arachnida, the sexes are united in each individual. These curious infusorial creatures have been found by myself in an infusion of cow manure.

Injurious Insects.—In describing some of the more interesting points in connection with insect life, I have only quite incidentally referred to the destructive habits of the larger number of insects and the ravages annually inflicted, chiefly by the smaller parasitical tribes, upon our cultivated crops of all kinds.

Here we have a wide field of research open to the microscopist, whose investigations must be carried out systematically, day by day, and for which a moderate power will effectually serve his purpose.

There are some ten or twelve species of injurious insects that attack the hop plant. By way of example, I will select one of the least known among them, the hop-flea, or beetle (*Haltica concinna*). This is sufficiently minute to require the aid of the microscope, and very closely resembles the turnip-flea proper, *H. nemorum*. Under the microscope the former will be seen to differ considerably. Its colour is brassy, whereas the colour of its congener is dusky or black, and its wing-cases are striped. They both have wonderful powers of jumping. *H. concinna* has a curious toothed formation of the tibia, with a set of spines, while the tibia of the turnip-flea is without any curve. It presents other points of difference. The hop-flea is, in fact, a winged beetle, and passes the winter in the perfect state under clods, tufts of grass, or weeds outside the hop-plantation, and here it lays its eggs. In the early spring the larvæ are hatched out as a little white maggot, which immediately makes its way to the hop-plant and burrows into the young leaves and feeds upon its tissues. Here we have an insect taken at random from among thousands of others of the most destructive kinds which annually destroy crops of enormous value to the nation.

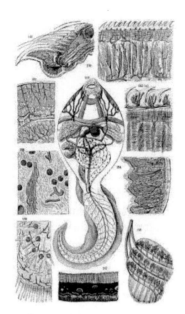

Tuffen West, del. Edmund Evans.

PLATE VII.

CHAPTER V.

Vertebrata.

The most complicated condition in which matter exists is where, under the influence of life, it forms bodies with a structure of tubes and cavities in which fluids are incessantly in motion, and producing continuous changes. These have been rightly designated "organised bodies," because of the various organs they contain. The two principal classes into which organised bodies have been divided are recognised as vegetable and animal. It was Bichat who taught that our animal life is double, while our organic life is single. In organic life, to stop is to die; and the life we have in common with vegetables never sleeps, and if the circulation of the fluids within the animal body ceases for a few seconds, it ceases for ever. In the vertebrate body, however, the combination of organs attains to the highest development, in striking contrast with that of the class we have previously considered, the Invertebrata, the animal kingdom being divided into Vertebrates and Invertebrates.

The Vertebrata are distinguished from all other animals by the circumstance that a transverse and a vertical section of the body exhibits two cavities completely separated from one another by a partition. A still more characteristic feature separates the one from the other; it is the specialisation of the chief nervous centres, and their peculiar relation to the other systems of the body.

The dorsal cavity of the body contains the cerebro-spinal nervous system, the ventral, the alimentary canal, the heart, and usually a double chain of ganglia; these pass under the name of the sympathetic system. It is very probable that this sympathetic nervous system represents, wholly or partially, the principal nervous system of the Annulosa and Mollusca. In any case, the central parts of the cerebro-spinal nervous system—*i.e.*, the brain and the spinal cord—would appear to be unrepresented among invertebrate animals. Likewise, in the partition between the cerebro-spinal and visceral tubes, certain structures which are not represented in Invertebrates are contained. During the embryonic condition of all Vertebrates, the centre of the partition is occupied by an elongated cellular cylindrical mass, the notochord, or chorda dorsalis. This structure persists throughout the life in some Vertebrata, but in most it is more or less completely replaced by a jointed, partly fibrous, cartilaginous, and bony vertical column. All vertebrate animals have a complete vascular system. In the thorax and abdomen, in place of a single perivisceral cavity, in communication with the vascular system, and serving as a blood-sinus, there are one or more serous sacs. These invest the principal viscera, and may or may not communicate with the exterior, recalling in the latter case the atrial cavities of the Mollusca. In all Vertebrata, except Amphioxus, there is a single valvular heart, and all possess a hepatic portal system, the blood of the alimentary canal never being wholly returned directly to the heart by the ordinary veins, but being more or less completely collected into a trunk (the portal vein), which ramifies through and supplies the liver.

With reference to one other point of importance, the development of the ova of Vertebrates, these have the same primary composition as those of other animals, consisting of a germinal vesicle containing one or more germinal nuclei, and included within a vitellus. But as this forms a part of general anatomy, and as my object is simply the investigation of the fundamental and microscopical structure of animal organisms, I shall not further pursue the morphological part of the subject, especially as so many excellent text-books are within reach of the student who desires to fully acquaint himself with precise information.

Notwithstanding, then, the apparent diversity in the structure of the vertebrate and the invertebrate and the various tissues of which animals and vegetables are constituted, microscopical research has satisfactorily demonstrated that all textures have their origin in cells; in fact, when the formative process is complete, the animal cell is seen to consist of the same parts and almost the same chemical constituents as the typical cell of the plant—namely, a definite cell-wall enclosing cell contents, of which the nature may be diverse, but the cell nucleus is precisely the same and is the actual seat and origin of all formative activity. The cell and nucleus grow by assimilation or intersusception, that is, by inflowing of nutrition among all parts, the new replacing the old, yet maintaining its original structure and composition. That which was once thought special to animals is now found to be common to both plants and animals: they are found to be alike fundamentally in internal structure, and in the discharge of the mysterious processes of reproduction and of nutrition, although the latter forms a convenient line of separation. Life in plants goes on indefinitely; cuttings may be taken without injury to their vigour and duration of life. The same may be said of some of the lower forms of invertebrate life; for example, the hydra, the anemone, and some other well-known animals, may be cut up, divided into several parts, each one of which will form a new animal, provided a nucleus be included in the section. Nevertheless, the organisation of the amœba and the hydra is as complete for its purpose as that of man for his, and the evidence of continuity forbids the drawing of hard and fast lines, as was formerly done between the two kingdoms, the animal and vegetable. The amount of similarity or agreement in the organisation of animals is various. Animals indeed differ from each other in slight points only, for the discovery of which the microscope must be brought into requisition. Living matter in its earliest stage and simplest form appears to the naked eye as a homogeneous structure, but when placed under the highest powers of the microscope, it is seen not to be so.

But perhaps the most marked feature of the age has been the increasing attention given to the study of the lower forms of life, using their simpler structures and more diffuse phenomena to elucidate the more general properties of living matter. To understand life we must understand protoplasm. Of this there can be no doubt, as we have seen in a previous chapter that a whole family, the Monera, consists of this simple living, microscopic, jelly-like substance, which has not even begun to be differentiated, as in the amœba, which has as yet no special organs, and every speck becomes a mouth or a stomach, and which can be turned inside out and shoot out tongues of jelly to move and feel with. "Reproduction is the faculty most characteristic of life, and sharply distinguishes the organic from the inorganic." It is, then, the corpuscles of protoplasm, called cells (cellulæ), which have so much interest for the physiologist, and these, like the cytods, may form independent organisms, which are then termed unicellular. Again, cells form other cells, and a multicellular organism results, and goes on increasing in geometrical progression. In the Vertebrata the cell retains its characteristic spheroidal shape, as seen in Fig. 423, and undergoes division by virtue of its living protoplasmic mass.

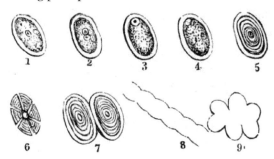

Fig. 423.

1. Newly formed cell structure; 2. Division of the nucleus; 3. It changes its situation in the cell; 4. Subdivides and breaks up; 5. Cell-walls increase in thickness; 6. Branch out into stellate cells; 7. Two cells coalesce; 8 and 9. Become multicellular.

Epithelial Cells.—All free surfaces of the human body, both internal and external, are to a very considerable extent covered by epithelium cells. These cells are everywhere the same, but with modifications in shape and arrangement. Epithelial cells are nucleated and always joined by their surfaces or edges, without, on the external surfaces, the intervention of connective tissue.

There are four essential varieties:—1. Tesselated; 2. Columnar; 3. Spheroidal; 4. Ciliated; in all of which the nucleus remains remarkably uniform in its characters, is either round or oval, and flattened out, measuring 1/6000th to 1/4000th of an inch in diameter. They are insoluble in acetic acid, colourless, or slightly tinted by the structure with which they are in contact, and usually contain one or more nucleoli with a few minute irregular granules, as represented in Fig. 424.

The simplest and most commonly distributed variety is the tesselated, known also as the scaly, squamous, pavement, and flattened epithelium, always arranged in single layers, lining serous cavities, many parts of the mucous membrane, and the interior of ducts and blood vessels. Upon the external surface of the body it occurs in superimposed layers, forming the "stratified epidermis." To obtain specimens of lamellar epithelium it is only necessary to collect a little saliva, or pass a glass slide over the lining membrane of the cheek, cover it with a thin cover glass, and examine it with a 1/4-inch objective. Pavement epithelium is the elementary structure of hair, nails, and horn.

PLATE XIX.

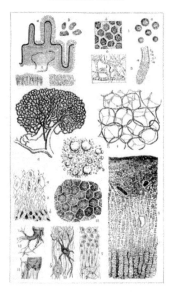

ANIMAL TISSUES.

Columnar epithelium exists upon the mucous membrane of the stomach, on the villi of the intestines, and in the several canals. It occupies either a vertical or horizontal position, and may be detached in rows, as shown in Plate XIX., No. 2, a section taken from the intestine of a rabbit. This variety, when more highly magnified, as in Fig. 424, is seen to consist of club-shaped nucleated cells, the thicker end being turned towards the surface. The protoplasm of the cell is granular, and the presence of minute vacuoles and fatty globules occupy a great part of the space. The nucleus is now seen to contain a fine network. At times the outer end of the cell is distended, as in Fig. 3. This form of columnar epithelium (known as the "goblet" cell) presents a close and remarkable resemblance to the cilio-flagellate "collared" infusorial monad in its extended "wine-glass" form.

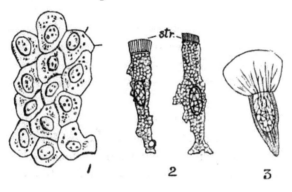

Fig. 424.

No. 1. Pavement epithelium, taken from an internal membrane; 2. Columnar epithelium, from the intestine of a rabbit, showing central fat globules, and at str a fine ciliated border; 3. A so-called "goblet"-cell.

Spheroidal epithelium is confined to the closed cavities of the body, and in the internal structure of the ducts of secreting glands. The cells are, for the most part, circular, although some are flattened out at the sides in which they are in contact with each other (Plate XIX., No. 1*a*). Specimens of this form may be taken from the internal surface of one of the lower animals with a scalpel. The collected matter must be placed in a drop of distilled water and examined with a high power.

Ciliated epithelium is characterised by the presence of those fine hair-like filaments (cilia) attached to the free surface of the cell. During life, and for some time after death, the cilia are seen to retain their constant waving motion. The cilia all move in one direction and rhythmically, thus giving rise to the appearance of a succession of undulations. Ciliated epithelium is found lining the mucous membrane of the air passages and nasal ducts, and wherever it is necessary to urge on a secretion by mechanical means, ciliated epithelium exists. Specimens for examination are easily obtained from the oyster, and with care will show the characteristic motion. A portion of a gill separated from the mollusc will live on for a considerable time if kept in a little of its natural secretion. The parameciæ, rotifera, and all the ciliata, are furnished with cilia as a means of locomotion and obtaining sustenance. By snipping off a small piece from the gills of the mussel, always accessible to the microscopist, and covering it over with thin glass to prevent evaporation of the animal juices, its cilia will continue to work for hours.

Lymph and Blood, Fig. 425 B, *a a.*—There are other cells in the animal body which possess a certain amount of resemblance to those confined to the more superficial structures—*i.e.*, the lymph, chyle, and blood. These fluids present in one respect a physical uniformity of composition, and a resemblance in the size of their characteristic corpuscles. Chyle contains besides the corpuscles of lymph, a quantity of minute granules which imparts a white colour to the fluid. Intermixed are oil globules, free nuclei, and sometimes a few red blood discs. Chyle may be had for microscopic examination by squeezing a little juice from the lymphatic gland of a sheep just slaughtered.

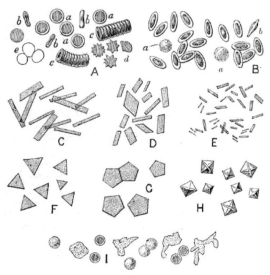

Fig. 425.—Human Blood Corpuscles and Crystals.

A. *a a.* Red blood corpuscles lying flat on the warm stage; *b b.* in profile; *c c.* arranged in rouleaux; *d.* crenated; *e.* rendered spherical by water; I. leucocytes and white amœboid corpuscles; B. Blood discs of fowl, red and white, others seen in convexity and with a nucleus. Blood Crystals.—C. Hæmatin from human blood; D. Hæmatoidin; E. Hæmin; F. Tetrahedral; G. Pentagonal; H. Octahedral crystals from blood of mouse.

Blood Corpuscles or cells vary considerably in mammals, birds, reptiles, and fishes. Fig. 102 (page 143) is a microphotograph of a drop of blood magnified 3,500 times; and Fig. 425, A, shows both red and white discs drawn to scale, magnified 1,200 diameters. The red corpuscles of human blood are distinguished by their clearly defined outlines and dark centres. Each disc is biconcave in form, and hence the whole surface cannot be focussed at the same time. When the circumference is well illuminated the centre is dark, but by bringing the objective nearer to the object, the concavity of the disc is brought into focus. It generally happens that blood corpuscles, on being first drawn, run together, and present the appearance of rolls of coins; or they may be scattered about over the field. There is a considerable difference in the form of the discs; they are circular in all mammals, except the camel, dromedary, and llama, these being oval. In profile blood corpuscles are biconcave, their investing membrane is homogeneous and elastic, and will readily move along the smallest capillary vessels. There is no trace of a nucleus in the blood-discs of the adult Mammalia, while in size they bear no proportion to the bulk of the animal in whose blood-vessels they circulate. The corpuscles of Mammalia in general are like those of man in form and size, being either a little larger or smaller. The most marked exception is the blood of the musk-deer, in which the corpuscles are of extreme smallness, about the $\frac{1}{12000}$th of an inch in diameter. In the elephant they are large, about $\frac{1}{2700}$th of an inch in diameter. The goat, among common animals, has very small corpuscles, but they are, withal, twice as large as those of the musk-deer. In the *Menobranchus lateralis* they are of a much larger size than in any animal, being the $\frac{1}{350}$th of an inch; in the proteus, the $\frac{1}{400}$th of an inch in the longest diameter; in the salamander, or water-newt, $\frac{1}{600}$th; in the frog, $\frac{1}{900}$th; lizards, $\frac{1}{1400}$th; in birds, $\frac{1}{1700}$th; and in man, $\frac{1}{3200}$th of an inch. Of fishes, the cartilaginous have the largest corpuscles; in gold-fish, they are about the $\frac{1}{1700}$th of an inch in their longest diameter.

The large size of the blood discs in reptiles, especially in the Batrachia, has been of great service to physiologists by enabling them to ascertain many particulars regarding structure which could not have been otherwise determined with certainty. The value of the spectroscope in the chemical examination of the blood has been already referred to. See page 252.

White corpuscles or leucocytes (Fig. 425, I) differ materially from the red. They are large, spheroidal, finely granular masses of about $\frac{1}{2800}$th of an inch in diameter. In a cubic millimètre of human blood there are about 10,000 white corpuscles. They have a lower specific gravity than the red, have no cell-wall, and their substance mainly consists of protoplasm. The internal granular appearance is now believed to be due to a fine intercellular network having small dots at the intersections of the web. In the meshes of the net a hyaline substance is interspersed. They possess one or more nuclei; these are seen on the application of a few drops of acetic acid. When examined in a perfectly fresh state, especially if the glass slide be placed on the warm stage of the microscope, they exhibit a spontaneous change of shape, amœba-like, such movements being accordingly termed amœboid. The movements referred to consist in the protrusion of processes of protoplasm which are retracted and other processes protruded as represented (Fig. 425, I). Both in human blood and in newts there are colourless corpuscles which contain coarser granules than others; these are called granular corpuscles. Some are shown near the amœboid bodies. The white corpuscles are readily found in various tissues of the body, as in the lymphatic glands. In inflammatory diseases these *leucocytes* pass through the walls of the capillaries into the tissues, and form morbid products, pus-cells.

Sections of blood discs are made by dipping a fine needle in a drop of blood as it exudes from a prick of the finger and drawing thin lines across the glass slip, allowing time to dry, and then cutting the lines across in all directions with a razor. The loosened portions should be removed with a camel's-hair brush.

In birds, the blood discs are oval in shape and possess a nucleus, shown in Fig. 425 B, in the blood of the fowl; this is rendered more apparent on adding a drop of acetic acid. The blood of fishes is also oval and nucleated, rather more pointed than that of birds. In reptiles generally the red blood discs are large, oval, nucleated bodies, the white corpuscles still preserving their invariable circular form and granular appearance. In the salamander and proteus the discs attain to their greatest size. In the former they measure $\frac{1}{700}$th of an inch, and in the latter $\frac{1}{400}$th.

Blood Crystals.—In addition to the elements described, the blood contains various crystalline forms, represented in Fig. 425, C to H. In connection with the micro-spectroscope (p. 253), the spectra of certain blood crystals are given; although varying in different animals, sufficient uniformity prevails as to render them characteristic. The crystals are formed when a little blood is mixed with water on the slide, allowing a short time for crystallisation. Near the edge of the cover-glass, where crystals begin to form, they are more distinct, but a high power is required for their examination. In human blood the crystals are prismatic; in that of the guinea-pig, tetrahedral; in the blood of the mouse, octahedral. Other forms may be obtained by the aid of chemical reagents.

In human blood there are at least three distinct forms of crystals: *Hæmatin* is formed in normal blood, is made visible on the addition of a little water to blood, or by agitation with ether, so as to dissolve the cell-wall of the blood corpuscles, and allow the contents to escape. A drop of blood will furnish crystals large enough to be seen with a moderate power. *Hæmatoidin* crystals are abnormal products, found in connection with certain diseased conditions. These crystals are seen as represented at D. *Hæmin* crystals must be regarded as artificial chemical products, the result of treating blood with glacial acetic acid; the acicular crystals at E, reddish-brown in colour, are artificially produced.

Fig. 426.

1. White fibrous or non-elastic tissue; 2. Yellow fibrous elastic tissue.

Basement Membrane—Connective Tissue System.—Connective or areolar tissue is present almost throughout the whole of the human body, and serves to connect the various organs with one another, as well as to bind together the several parts. The muscles are surrounded by a connective tissue sheath; this penetrates into their substance, and binds together fasciculi and fibres. The same tissue is present in the skin and the mucous membranes; it also forms a sheath for the arteries, veins, and nerves. It is plentifully supplied by blood-vessels, and nerves pass through its substance. Microscopically, four different elements can be clearly made out:—1. Connective tissue cells or corpuscles; 2. White fibrous tissue; 3. Yellow fibrous tissue; 4. Ground substance.

On examining the connective tissue cells of young animals, various cells will be seen with fine granular contents, together with nuclei, lying in spaces in the ground substance, some branched, others flattened or rounded. Even tissues supposed to be homogeneous in structure, are on staining seen to have connective tissue cells, such as those represented in a section of the cornea of the eye (see p. 31). In this case the connective tissue cells are termed corneal corpuscles; the branched cells, it will be noticed, are united by branches.

The cells in the fibrous tissue of tendons are square or oblong, and form continuous rows. White fibrous tissue is distributed throughout the animal body, but in a variety of forms; it is found in the skin and other membranes, and in all parts where strength and flexibility are necessary. The structure of white and yellow fibrous tissues is shown in Figs. 426 and 427.

Fig. 427.

1. White fibrous tissue lining the interior of the egg shell, with the calcium carbonate removed by immersion in hydrochloric acid; 2. White fibrous tissue, from the sclerotic coat of the eye.

White fibrous tissue presents silver-lustre bundles, running for the most part in parallel directions through and over the muscles and tendons. For examination under the microscope, obtain a fragment of fresh meat cut in the longitudinal direction; place it in water, and tease it out with needles as directed in a former chapter. The smallest fragment will suffice for examination under a quarter or one-sixth inch objective. These filaments are exceedingly minute, measuring $\frac{1}{3000}$th to $\frac{1}{2500}$th of an inch in diameter, and do not interlace through the bundles, although they intersect each other occasionally. Transverse sections may be made by drying a piece of tendon until it becomes sufficiently firm to cut with a razor or microtome, and mounted as a permanent specimen. From the cut ends of the fibres small dark points will be seen, especially in the denser structure of the tendons; these are termed "connective tissue corpuscles."

Yellow elastic fibrous tissue is remarkable in contradistinction to the white for its elasticity and capability of extension. It is found on the coats of blood-vessels, between the vertebral arches, and in quadrupeds it forms a strong elastic band, extending from the occiput, throughout the spines of the vertebra, and enabling the animal to support the head in the pendent position, without muscular exertion. These fibres can only be separated from each other with difficulty, and their elasticity is shown by a tendency to curl up. These yellow fibres are somewhat coarser than the white, and they remain unaffected by acetic acid of the ordinary strength. Elastic tissue is a constituent of the skin, mucous, and serous membranes, and of the areolar or cellular tissue.

In order to microscopically examine this structure, take a small portion of the strong ligament of the neck of the ox, place it as before in water, and tease it out with needles; place a fragment on a glass slip, cover with a thin cover-glass, and submit it to a high magnifying power. Transverse sections made as directed in the case of white tissue will be seen to be hexagonal in form.

Adipose Tissue.—Fat is found in many situations in the animal body, and on examination is seen to consist entirely of vesicles, distributed through a delicate membrane of connective tissue, shown in Plate XIX., Nos. 4 and 5. On pressure, the circular or oval form of the cells becomes polyhedral; occasionally the fatty acids in the interior of the vesicles crystallise, and give rise to a star-like appearance. For the examination of adipose tissue, take a portion of the mesentery of any small animal—a mouse, or rat.

Retiform Tissue.—Adenoid, or retiform tissue, consists of a delicate network of connective tissue corpuscles, joining their branches together. This forms the stroma or framework of lymphoid tissue. It is found in connection with all the lymphatic glands, spleen, &c. Plate XIX., No. 3, *a b*, shows small sections of a lymphatic, together with capillary vessels.

Muscular Fibre.—There are two varieties of muscular fibre in the body—*i.e.*, striated, and non-striated. The striated is formed in muscles attached to bony structures, as those of the arm and leg, and in some of the soft structures, as the tongue, palate, œsophagus, in short, all muscles under the control of the will. Striped muscle is of a dull red colour and marked with peculiar longitudinal furrows on its surface. Voluntary muscle consists of:—1, a connective tissue sheath; 2, fasciculi; 3, fibres and sarcolemma; 4, discs, fibrilla and sarcous elements. These are shown in connection with other tissues in Plate XIX., Nos. 11 and 12, and also in Fig. 428 (1, 2, 3).

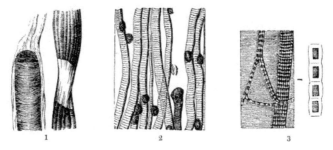

Fig. 428.

1. Muscular fibre broken across, the fragments connected by the connective tissue membrane × 100; 2. Fibre broken up into irregular distinct bands: a few blood corpuscles distributed about × 200; 3. A fasciculus of muscular fibre from leg of pig × 600.

In Plate XIX., Fig. 11, the muscular fibre taken from the tongue of a lamb shows the continuity of the upper portion with the connective tissue membrane. In Fig. 12, a branching-out bundle of muscular fibre, taken from the upper lip of the rat, is seen to end in stellate connective cells. The delicate homogeneous sheath that binds the fibres together is termed *sarcolemma*. This is readily seen in prepared muscle of the frog and water-beetle, less plainly in man. Each muscle is provided with a sheath of connective tissue; this surrounds it, binds the fasciculi together, and supports the blood-vessels; it is called the *perimysium*, and sends fine prolongations in between the fibres, termed *endomysium*. The intervals seen on high amplification between the dark striæ are called Kruse's membrane. On breaking up the striated structure it is resolvable into fibrillæ and furthermore into discs.

Fig. 429.

1. Vertical section of epidermis; 2. Pigment cells from a lower layer of cutis.

Among mammalia the pig furnishes the best examples of muscle fibrillæ; among insects the water-beetle and the thorax of the housefly. A power of 600 or 800 diameters is required to separate the fibrillæ. Blood-vessels are well supplied with striated muscle, but none of their minuter branches penetrate the sarcolemma. The involuntary or non-striated variety of muscular fibre exists in all parts of the body where movements occur independently of the will, also in the ciliary muscle and the iris of the eye, as well as in the middle coats of the arteries. Non-striated fibres are pale in colour, prismatic in shape, and easily flattened by pressure. In size, they vary from ⅟₇₀₀₀th to ⅟₃₅₀₀th of an inch in diameter, and are marked at short intervals by oblong corpuscles.

The Integument or Skin consists of epidermis or cuticle, dermis, corium or cutis vera, sweat-glands, nails, hairs, sebaceous glands, and numerous nerves and vessels. The epidermis forms a protective covering over the whole surface of the body, and is moulded on to the surface of the corium beneath, covering the ridges, depressions and papillæ. It is made up of three principal layers: the horny layer or *stratium corneum*, the most superficial, this consists of layers of flattened cells, which are without a nucleus; the *stratum lucidum*, composed of layers of nucleated cells, more or less indistinct in section; the *rete mucosum* or malpighian layer; is composed in its upper part of layers of "prickle cells" and its inferior of a single stratum of columnar cells. Pigment is principally found in the lowest layer, Fig. 429.

The gradations of colour in the skin are due to the granular contents of the pigment cells. This is seen on steeping sections cut from the skin of a negro in chlorine; the colour is discharged. In Plate XIX., No. 13, the pigment cells of the choroid coat of eye are shown. Here the pigment is darker in colour, and its function is the absorption of light and the prevention of disturbing effects occasioned by circles of dispersion.

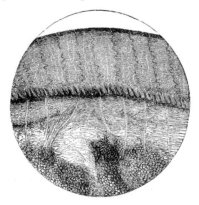

Fig. 430.—Vertical section of skin and subcutaneous tissues, showing the sweat-glands and fat-globules, ducts passing upwards to the epidermis or external cuticle. Magnified 250 diameters.

The Dermis, or true skin, consists of an interlacing network of connective tissue, yellow elastic tissue corpuscles, vessels, and nerves. There are also small muscular fibres in connection with the hair follicles, and beneath the subcutaneous tissues contain an abundant supply of fat adipose tissue. Numerous ridges are seen on the surface, especially on the palm of the hand and sole of the foot, caused by rows of little elevations of the cutis vera, termed papillæ. These are more or less conical, and contain a capillary loop, nerve, and touch corpuscle, which serve to increase the sensitiveness of the part, lodging a touch corpuscle in a favourable position for receiving sensations of touch, Fig. 430.

Sweat glands are situated in the subcutaneous tissue, and consist of fine tubes, which form the duct (seen in the section, Fig. 430); these are continuous with a blind extremity, coiled up into a ball one-sixtieth of an inch in diameter, and surrounded by a plexus of capillaries to form the gland (Fig. 431, No. 2). Between the layer of columnar cells and the limiting membrane is a layer of non-striated muscle, and beneath the rite mucosum there are several layers of polyhedral cells, and an external and internal limiting membrane; the epithelium of the duct is at its mouth continuous with the epithelium of the epidermis.

 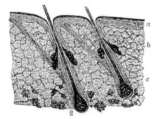

Fig. 431.

1. Blood vessels of papillæ supplied to cutis; 2. Perpendicular section through the scalp, with two hair-sacs; *a.* epidermis; *b.* cutis; *c.* muscles of the hair follicles.

Nails consist of a root and body, the lunular of which is the whitish portion of the body near the root, where the skin beneath is less vascular than any other portion of the finger. The nail closely resembles the epidermis, and consists of hard and thin layers of cells on the surface, and round, moist cells beneath. Posteriorly the nail fits into a groove which lodges its root. The part to which the nail is attached is known as the nail-bed. The stratified appearance produced by the coalescence of the cells, and their lying over each other, is shown in Plate VII., No. 149, the toe of the mouse; while the special arrangement of tissue is better seen under polarised light (Plate VIII., No. 174).

Hairs consist of a shaft and root. The shaft is cylindrical, and covered with a layer of imbricated scales, arranged with their edges upwards. The substance of the hair consists of fibres, or elongated fusiform cells, in which nuclei are seen. There are present in some hairs (Fig. 432) small air spaces or lacunæ. In the coarser hair of the body there is a pith (medulla), occupied by small angular cells and fat granules.

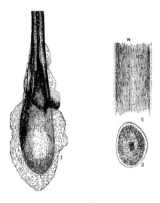

Fig. 432.

1. Single Hair-root and Shaft; 2. Vertical section, showing fibrous character of the hair together with colouring matter, external edges serrated; 3. Transverse section of human hair, medullary substance, and central pith.

The root of the hair is seen to dilate that it may fit more firmly into the skin hair-follicle. The latter consists of two coats, an outer and an inner, continuous with the epidermis, and this is called the root sheath. The outer portion consists of three layers, formed of connective tissue, blood-vessels, and nerves. The inner, or epidermic, coat comes away when the hair is pulled out, and hence is called the root sheath. This again is made up of two layers, the outer of which corresponds with the horny layer, and is composed of flattened cells. The bulbous root of the hair is connected with the papilla. In the cat the tactile nasal hairs are very large. Small bundles of involuntary muscular fibres connect the corium with the root, so that in contracting they elevate or expand the hair.

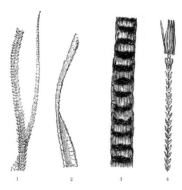

Fig. 433.

1. Jointed hairs of Indian bat; 2. Hair of flying-fox, showing imbricated scales; 3. Hair of mouse, showing pigment layers; 4. Hair of a small beetle (Dermestes). × 250.

The hair of the lower animals presents a diversity of structure, especially on the outer surface, and with reference to the arrangement of the scales. The hair of the Indian bat, for instance, consists of a shaft invested with erectile scales, placed at regular intervals; these stand out from the shaft, as in Fig. 433, No. 1. This form of scale varies considerably in the different species of these animals, and a portion of hair near the root is nearly divested of scales. Many of the scales are not unlike those of certain of the insect tribe, seen in that of Dermestes, No. 3, while the hair of the mouse has a series of transverse imbricated scales arranged as tiles on a house, due to accumulated pigment. Hairs taken from various animals form interesting objects of study for the microscope, as already noticed. Other hairs are shown in Fig. 434. No. 1 is a transverse section of a hair from the ant-eater; the central part consists of air-cells, the outer of a granular pith. No. 2 is a transverse section of hair of peccary, with a diversified arrangement of the cortical envelope, sending outward a set of radial prolongations and air-cells; this kind of structure is also found in the quills of the porcupine. No. 3 is a transverse section of a hair of the elephant, which shows a combination of a number of tubes united together, somewhat resembling the arrangement of the hoof-horn of some of the ruminants, and the denser horny growth on the snout of the rhinoceros, No. 4. The curious modification of these horny structures is seen in the horns of other animals, and which may be likened to a bundle of hairs. On making a transverse section, as in Fig. 434, and submitting it to polarised light, on rotating the analyser, the dark central spot shown is replaced by a bright one with a play of colours due to the interference of light (Plate VIII., No. 178). The scales of fish are also of interest (Fig. 435). These have been shown to afford an unerring guide in the classification of fishes and in the examination of their fossil remains. As a class of objects for the microscope, they are found to be both curious and beautiful. Plate VIII., No. 176, is a scale of the grayling, seen under polarised light.

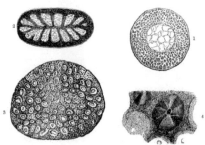

Fig. 434.

1. Hair of ant-eater; 2. Hair of peccary; 3. Hair of elephant; 4. Horn of Rhinoceros.

Fig. 435.—Fish Scale (Sole).

Of the harder outgrowths of the dermal structures, the teeth afford the chief example among animals. The rough anatomy of the tooth in mankind consists of a crown, that projects from the gum; a root, or fangs, fixed in a socket of the jawbone, and a short intermediary neck. Each tooth is supplied with an artery and nerve, and has a central cavity filled with a soft, vascular, sensitive substance, the pulp. On making a vertical section of a tooth, we recognise the several structures in the order of, pulp, crusta, petrosa, dentine, and enamel. A section through a human molar tooth (shown in Fig. 436) will convey some idea of the arrangement of the denser structures referred to above.

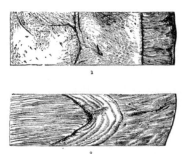

Fig. 436.—Sections of Human Molar Tooth (magnified 50 diameters). 1. Vertical section; 2. Horizontal section.

Blandin was the first to demonstrate that teeth are developed in the mucous membrane, similar to that of hair and nails. Teeth are formed in grooves of the mucous membrane, and subsequently converted into closed sacs by a process of involution, and their final adhesion to the jaw is a later process. It is very generally conceded that teeth belong to the *muco-dermoid*, and not to the periosteal, series of tissues; that, instead of standing in close relation to the endo-skeleton, they are part of the dermal or exo-skeleton; their true analogues being the hair, and some other epidermic appendages. Huxley proved that, although teeth are developed in two ways, they are mere varieties of the usual mode in the animal kingdom. In the first, which is typified by the mackerel and the frog, the pulp is never free, but from the first is inclosed within the capsule, seeming to sink down as fast as it grows. In the other, the pulp projects freely at one period above the surface of the mucous membrane, becoming subsequently included within a capsule formed by the involution of the latter; this occurs in the human subject. The skate offers a sort of intermediate structure.

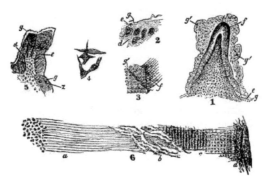

Fig. 437.

1. Section of a cusp of the posterior molar of a child. The inner outline represents it before the addition of acetic acid—the outer afterwards, when Nasmyth's membrane *g* is seen raised up in folds; *f.* the enamel organ; *c.* the dentine; the central portion being filled with pulp. 2. Edge of the pulp of a molar cusp, showing the first rudiment of the dentine, commencing in a perfectly transparent layer between the nuclei of the pulp and the *membrana preformativa.* 3. Nasmyth's membrane detached from the subjacent enamel by acetic acid. 4. Stellate-cells of the enamel organ. 5. Tooth of frog, acted on by dilute hydrochloric acid, so as to dissolve out the enamel and free Nasmyth's membrane. The structure of the dentine *e* is rendered indistinct. At the base, Nasmyth's membrane is continued over the bony substance at *z*, in which the nuclei of the lacunæ are visible. (After Huxley.) 6. Decalcified tooth-structure; *a.* the dentine; *b.* enamel organ; *c.* enamel; *d.* Nasmyth's membrane.

The *enamel* forms a continuous layer, and invests the crown of the tooth; it is thickest upon the masticating surface, and decreases towards the neck, where it usually terminates. The external surface of the enamel appears smooth, but is always marked by delicate elevations and transverse ridges, and covered by a fine membrane (Nasmyth's membrane), containing calcareous matter. This membrane is separable after being subjected to hydrochloric acid; it then appears like a network of areolar tissue, shown in Fig. 438, No. 6; Huxley's *"calcified membrana,"* which commence at the pulp cavity, and pass up to the enamel.

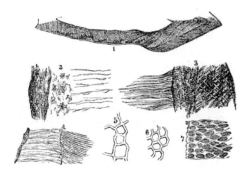

Fig. 438.—Tooth Structure.

1. Longitudinal section of superior canine tooth, exhibiting general arrangement, and contour markings, slightly magnified; 2 and 3. Portions from same, highly magnified, showing the relative position of bone-cells, cementum at 2, dentine fibres, and commencement of enamel at 3; 4. Dentine fibres decalcified; 5. Nasmyth's membrane separated and the calcareous matter dissolved out with dilute acid; 6. Cells of the pulp lying between it and the ivory; 7. A transverse section of enamel, showing the sheaths of fibres, contents removed, and magnified 300 diameters.

Czermak discovered that the curious appearances of globular conglomerate formations in the substance of dentine depend on its mode of *calcification* and the presence of earthy material; and he attributed the contour lines to the same cause. Contour markings vary in intensity and number; they are most abundant in the root, and most marked in the crown. Vertical sections exhibit them the best; as Fig. 440, No. 1. In preparing a specimen, first make the section accurately, then decalcify it by submersion in dilute hydrochloric acid; dry it and mount in Canada balsam; place the specimen in the hot chamber for some time to soak in the fluid resin before it cools. The white opacity at the extremity of the contour markings gives the appearance of rings to the tooth-fang.

"The tooth-substance appears," says Czermak, "on its inner surface, not as a symmetrical whole, but consisting of balls of various diameter, which are fused together into a mass with one another in different degrees, and in which the dentine tubes in contact with the germ cavity terminate. By reflected light, *dark-ground* illumination, one perceives this stalactite-like condition of the inner surface of the tooth-substance very distinctly, by means of the varied illumination of the globular elevations, and by the shadows which they cast." To see this structure to advantage the preparation should be made from a tooth root, the growth of which is not complete. With such preparations, the ground-substance of the last formed layer of the tooth-substance is seen to be, at least partly, in the form of globular masses, fused together with those of the penultimate layers.

The cementum is the cortical layer of osseous tissue, forming an outer coating to the fangs, which it sometimes cements together. Its internal surface is intimately united with the *dentine*, and in many teeth it would appear as if the earliest determined arrangement of the fibres of the dentine started from the *canaliculi*, as they radiate from the lacunæ in the cement. The inter-lacunar layer is often striated, and exhibits a laminated structure: sometimes it appears as if Haversian canals were running in a perpendicular direction to the pulp cavity. The *canaliculi* frequently run out into numerous branches, connecting one with another, and anastomising with the ends of the dentine fibres. The thick layers of cement which occur in old teeth show immense quantities of aggregated lacunæ of an irregular and elongated form.

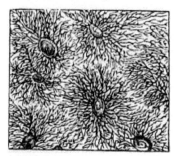

Fig. 439.—Transverse section of Tooth of Pristis, showing orifices of medullary canals, with systems of radiating fibres (*tubuli*) analogous to the Haversian canals in true bone.

Compact Tissues, Cartilage and Bone.—Cartilage is a bluish or yellowish-white, semi-transparent, elastic substance, without vessels or nerves, and surrounded by a membrane, termed pericondrium, of a dense fibrous nature. That kind, however, known as articular cartilage, receives a layer of epithelium from the synovial membrane, but this is confined to marginal portions, in consequence of the central wear which occurs as soon as the parts are subjected to friction, during the movement of the limbs. Cartilage covers the ends of all bones in apposition to form joints, and thus lessens the effects of concussion. Besides the ordinary kind of cartilage, temporary and permanent, there are two modifications of the tissue, confined to certain portions of the body: cellular cartilage, composed of cells lying close together, in a mesh formed of fine fibres; and fibro-cartilage, cells distributed in a matrix of fibrous tissue.

Examined with a low power, cartilage appears to be homogeneous in structure, studded over with numerous round, oval, oblong, semilunar, and irregular-shaped corpuscles, as seen in Plate XIX., No. 8, a vertical section of animal cartilage, arranged in columns, and condensed at the lower surface previous to its conversion into bone. The greater opacity of this portion is owing to the increase of osseous fibres, and the multiplication of oil globules, and the intercellular spaces becoming filled with vessels. No. 9 shows a small transverse section of the same, with a further change of the cartilage cells at *a* into bone cells, and at *b* with the characteristic canaliculi and lacunæ. No. 7 further shows a section of the large tendon fixed to the back of the heel of the foot, near the juncture of the tendo-Archillis with the cartilage. For the examination of these several changes a high power is necessary, and for the purpose pieces taken from the ox may be easily obtained from the butcher, and fine sections cut with a razor parallel to the surface.

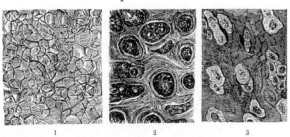

Fig. 440.

1. Cartilage from a mouse's ear closely resembling vegetable tissue ×200; 2. Cartilage from rabbit's ear, with nucleated cells embedded in matrix; 3. Cartilage from the end of a human rib ×300.

The better specimens for microscopical examination are those taken from very young animals, in whom the ossific process is still incomplete. In order to examine cellular cartilage, the ear of the mouse should be taken and just dried sufficiently to enable fine sections to be cut by the microtome transversely (Fig. 440).

Cartilage forms the entire skeleton of a certain number of fishes, as the skate, lamprey, ray, shark, &c., the cells of which are embedded in a matrix of granular matter, which has been properly termed intercellular. The nearest approach to ossification of cartilage in fishes is that of the cuttle-fish; in this stellate cells are freely distributed, as shown in Fig. 441, No. 3.

Fig. 441.

1. Cartilage from the head of the skate, cells filled with nuclei; 2. Cartilage from frog, oblong cells with nuclei; 3. Cartilage from cuttle-fish, with stellate cells, × 200.

White fibro-cartilage occurs between the bodies of the vertebræ as a connecting medium. In this kind the cells are more widely distributed, specimens of which may be taken from the central portion of an interarticular disc of any animal. The oval or circular corpuscles will be seen surrounded by an abundance of fibrous tissue.

An acquaintance with the degeneration of the textures with which we have been dealing may be of service to the student, as he may, in the course of his examination, meet with an abnormal condition altogether different to those described. The process of degeneration is usually a slow one, except in the case of fatty infiltration, an example of which is furnished by the fatty degeneration of the liver in Strasburg geese. Muscular tissue is very prone to fatty degeneration, and fatty heart is often met with. Calcareous degeneration of the muscles, ligaments, and cartilages, as well as morbid deposits, are not at all uncommon in these structures. In Plate XIX., No. 9, a small section is given of an enchondroma, and in which the round or ovoid cells of the cartilage are seen degenerated and converted into granular masses of a calcareous nature. Fig. 442 is a somewhat more highly magnified section of a calcareous or morbid growth, taken from a human subject in which a morbid growth was seen to be gradually destroying the bone and cartilage cells.

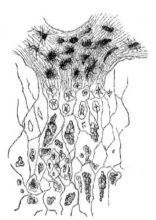

Fig. 442.—Cartilage taken from a diseased finger, in which both cartilage and bone were in a state of degeneration.

Bone.—Bone is a hard unyielding structure, and which in the vertebrata forms the skeleton of the adult. It is the framework for the support of the soft tissues of the body, and forms various cavities for the reception of important organs, as the brain, spinal cord, eyes, heart and lungs, and acts as levers for the action of the muscles and joints. The partial elasticity of bone is seen in the ribs, and the rebound when the skull is dropped on the ground. Bone consists of earthy and animal matters intimately combined; the removal of either, however, does not destroy the form of the bone, if the process of separation be carefully conducted. The earthy constituents may all be dissolved out by hydrochloric acid, but the form of the bone is preserved in its minute particular, and in this state sections may be cut for microscopical examination. If allowed to become dry it shrivels, and assumes the density of horn. The interior of a bone is of a spongy or cancellated structure, particularly at the ends. The outer portion of the bone is more dense than the internal part. The study of bone should commence with sections of the softened structure. Directions for making sections of bone are given in the chapter on Practical Microscopy.

PLATE XX

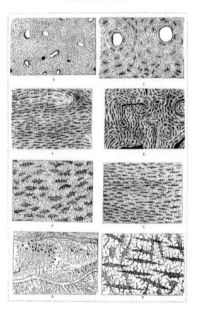

VERTEBRATA, BONE STRUCTURE.

The intimate structure of bone will be studied in connection with Plate XX. Two series of lamellæ may be demonstrated in bone after maceration in acid, a larger system surrounding the medullary canal, and a smaller surrounding the Haversian canals, both of which are seen in Nos. 1 and 2. In macerating bones, the lamellæ of the layer concentric system may be peeled off in layers; these are seen to be pierced with fine apertures, caused by the canaliculi. In some parts larger apertures are seen through which bundles of fibres pass, pinning, as it were, the several layers together; these are the perforating fibres. The outermost of the layers, being near the periosteum, the membrane covering the bone, are termed periosteal layers; the innermost, being close to the canal, are called medullary layers. No. 1 is a transverse section of a flat bone, the clavicle, and it shows the Haversian canals, varying in size from $\frac{1}{2000}$th to $\frac{1}{200}$th of an inch in diameter, the largest being near the medullary canal. In shape they are round, oval, or oblong, according to the line of section. Each canal is surrounded by rings, none of which are complete, and running one into the other at various parts. Under a higher power, those irregular shaped bodies termed lacunæ, with fine radiating fibres, are seen to be smaller canals, canaliculi.

By means of this complete and intricate distribution of the canals of the Haversian system, the nutritive fluids pass into the most compact parts of the osseous tissue. Longitudinal sections of the long bones show these canals as continuous branching-out cells.

In many of the lower animals the bony structure differs from those of man, as will be seen in Plate XX. No. 3 shows a transverse section of the femur, or leg-bone of an ostrich, magnified ninety-five times, in which the Haversian canals are much smaller and more numerous, and many of them run in the transverse direction. No. 4, again, is a transverse section of the humerus, or fore-arm bone of a turtle (*Chelonia mydas*). This exhibits traces of Haversian canals, with a slight tendency to a concentric arrangement of bone-cells around them, the bone-cells being large and numerous, and occur, for the most part, in parallel rows. In No. 5, a horizontal section of the lower jaw-bone of a conger-eel exhibits a single plane of bone-cells arranged in parallel lines. There are no Haversian canals present, and when this specimen is contrasted with that of No. 4, it will be noticed that the canaliculi given off from each of the bone-cells of this fish are very few in number in comparison with that of the reptile. No. 6 is a section of a portion of the cranium of a siren (*Siren lacertina*), remarkable for the large size of the bone-cells, and of the canaliculi, which are larger in this animal than in any other yet examined; and as in the preceding specimen, no Haversian canals are present. No. 7 is a section of bone taken from the exterior of the shaft of the humerus of a Pterodactyle; this exhibits the elongated bone-cells characteristic of the order Reptilia. No. 8 is a horizontal section of a scale, or flattened spine, from the skin of a Trygon, or sting ray; this exhibits large Haversian canals, with numerous wavy parallel tubes, like those of dentine, communicating with them. This specimen shows, besides wavy tubes, numerous bone-cells, whose canaliculi communicate with the tubes, as in dentine.

The following points may be noted with regard to the several sections of bone described. That of the bird, for instance, contrasted with that of the mammal, exhibits the following peculiarities: the Haversian canals are more abundant, much smaller, and often run in a direction at right angles to that of the shaft, by which means the concentric laminated arrangement is in some cases lost; the direction of the canals follows the curve of the bone; the bone-cells are much smaller and more numerous; while the number of canaliculi sent off from the cells is less than in those of mammals. No. 3 is the average length of a bone-cell of the ostrich, $\frac{1}{2000}$th of an inch, in breadth $\frac{1}{6000}$th.

In the Reptilia, the bones may be either hollow, cancellated, or solid; and their specific gravity is less than that of birds or mammals. The short bones of most of the chelonian reptiles are solid, and the long bones are either hollow or cancellated; the ribs of the serpent-tribe are hollow, the medullary cavity performing the office of a Haversian canal; the bone-cells are accordingly arranged in concentric circles around their canals. The vertebræ of these animals are solid; and the bone, like that of certain birds, is remarkable for density and whiteness. When a transverse section is taken from one of the long bones, and contrasted with that of a mammal or bird, the difference will be noticed; there are very few, if any, Haversian canals, and these are large; and at one view, in the section, No. 7, the canals and bone-cells are arranged both vertically and longitudinally. The bone-cells are remarkable for the great size to which they attain; in the turtle they are $\frac{1}{375}$th of an inch in length, the canaliculi are extremely numerous, and are of a size proportionate to that of the bone-cell.

In fishes a greater variation occurs in the minute structure of the skeleton than in either of the three preceding classes. A rare structure is that of the sword of the sword-fish (Istiophorus). In this, Haversian canals and a concentric laminated arrangement of the bone are found, but no bone-cells. The Haversian canals, when they are present, are of large size, and very numerous, and then the bone-cells are, generally speaking, either absent or but few in number, their place being occupied by tubes or canaliculi, which are often of a very large size. The bone-cells are remarkable for their graduate figure, and the canaliculi derived from them are comparatively few in number. In a thin section of the scale of an osseous fish, the cells lie nearly all in one plane, and the anastomoses of the canaliculi are more distinctly seen; in the hard scales of many, as the Lepidosteus and Calicthys, and in spines of the Siluridæ, the bone-cells are well differentiated. In the true bony scales comprising the exo-skeleton of cartilaginous fishes the bone-cells are seen in great numbers.

Now, if we proceed at once to the application of the facts which have been laid down, and make a fragment of bone of an extinct animal the subject of investigation, it will be found that the bone-cells in Mammalia are tolerably uniform in size; and if we take $\frac{1}{2000}$th of an inch as a standard, the bone-cells of birds fall below that standard; but the bone-cells of reptiles are much above either of the two preceding, while those of fishes are essentially different, both in size and shape, and are not likely to be mistaken for one or the other; so that the determination of a minute yet characteristic fragment of fishes' bone is a task easily performed. If the portion of bone does not exhibit bone-cells, but presents either one or other of the characters indicated, the task of discrimination is equally easy. We have now the mammal, the bird, and the reptile to deal with. In consequence of the very great size of the cells and their canaliculi in the reptile, a portion of bone of one of these animals can readily be distinguished from that of a bird, or a mammal. The only difficulty lies between these two last; but, notwithstanding that on a cursory glance the bone of a bird appears very like that of a mammal, there are certain points in their minute structure in which they differ; and one is the difference in size of the bone-cells. To determine accurately, therefore, between the two, we must, if the section be a transverse one, also note the comparative sizes of the Haversian canals, and the tortuosity of their course; for the diameter of the canal bears a certain proportion to the size of the bone-cells, and after close examination the eye will readily detect differences.

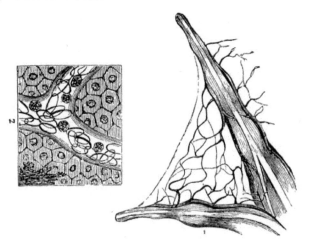

Fig. 443.

1. A portion of the web of frog's foot, spread out and slightly magnified to show distribution of blood-vessels; 2. Is a portion magnified 250 diameters to show the ovoid form of the blood discs in a vessel, beneath which hexagonal nucleated epithelium cells appear.

Arteries and Veins.—The circulation of the animal frame is maintained by arteries, veins, and capillaries. The arteries are elastic and contractile tubes; these convey the blood from the heart to the capillaries. The larger arteries are exceedingly elastic, but feebly contractile on account of the muscular tissue in their walls. The veins ramify throughout the body, are more numerous than the arteries, and of greater capacity. They usually accompany the arteries and correspond to them in structure, the larger veins possessing semi-lunar valves; these project into their interiors, and thus prevent the regurgitation of the blood. They have four coats, consisting of areolar tissue, yellow fibres combined with muscular fibres, and white fibrous tissue, two layers of yellow fibres arranged longitudinally, and a single layer of epithelial cells. Intermediate between the arteries and veins there are exceedingly fine tubes, termed capillaries, in which the arteries terminate, and from which the veins arise. These are composed of a fine homogeneous membrane, with here and there a nucleus. The capillary circulation of the blood is readily seen in the tail of the newt and the foot of the frog, Fig. 443.

Fig. 444.—A network of capillaries.

A network of capillaries conveying blood to the lungs, and ramifying throughout the structure, is shown in Fig. 444, and in Plate XIX., No. 6, the termination of a capillary of a blood-vessel in the fat-cells of the human body. Plate VII. illustrates the distribution of the arteries and veins to various parts of the animal body. This coloured plate, however, is designed to show the value of injected preparations in the delineation of animal structures. By thus artificially restoring the blood and distending the tissues, a much better idea is obtained of the relative condition of parts, the appearance presented by the erectile papillæ, &c. In the section of foot of mouse (No. 149), the bone is seen surrounded by its vascular supply, arterial and venous; in No. 150, the papillæ of the tongue are distended and seen erect; in No. 152, a vertical section of the fungi-form papillæ on the tongue of cat, with capillary loops passing into them, is demonstrated; in No. 151, the vertical section of brain of a rat, the vascular supply is shown; No. 153, the malpighian tufts (circular bodies) and arteries ramifying about the structure; in No. 154, the vertical section through the intestine of the rat, shows villi (arteries and veins) surmounted by epithelium, and supported on a layer of the mucous membrane; in No. 155, the vascular supply sent to the roots of the whisker of the nose of the mouse; in No. 157, a tangential section cut through the several textures, the sclerotic coat and retina of the eye of a cat is clearly made out although not highly magnified; again, in No. 156, the beautiful vascular arrangement of the internal gill of the tadpole could scarcely be so strikingly illustrated in any other way; while in the central, No. 158, the vascular system throughout the whole of the body of a fully developed tadpole, with the way in which the blood is carried from the remotest part of the tail to the heart, and sent to the gills, the brain, &c., it is quite unnecessary to enlarge upon. These are seen under a low power, but for the purpose of studying the basement membrane, together with the intimate association and termination of the nerves accompanying the arteries and veins, it is absolutely necessary to resort to a staining process, and cutting fine sections with the microtome. Small portions of a nerve may be cut off with fine scissors, teased out with needles, and a drop of acetic acid added to render the sheath more transparent; in a few seconds the connective tissue corpuscles will be brought into view. For the microscopical examination of nerve-fibrillæ take a small section from the leg of a frog, and tease it out in blood serum or white of egg. In size the fibrillæ vary, even in the same nerve, from the $\frac{1}{12000}$th to the $\frac{1}{1500}$th of an inch in diameter.

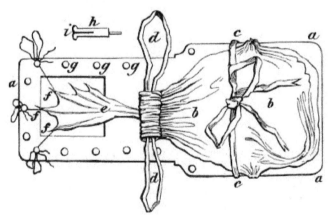

Fig. 445.

To show the circulation of the blood in the frog's foot, and without causing the animal pain or much inconvenience, it is better to enclose it in a black silk bag, and draw out the foot as shown at *a a a*, Fig. 445. The bag provided should be from three to four inches in length, and two and a half inches broad, shown at *b b*, having a piece of tape, *c c*, sewn to each side, about midway between the mouth and the bottom, and the mouth itself capable of being closed by a drawing-in string, *d d*. Into this bag the frog is placed, and only the leg which is about to be examined kept outside; the string *d d* must then be drawn sufficiently tight around the small part of the leg to prevent the foot from being pulled into the bag, but not to stop the circulation; three short pieces of thread, *f f f*, are now passed around the three principal toes; and the bag with the frog must be fastened to the plate *a a* by means of the tapes *c c*. When this is accomplished, the threads *f f f* are passed either through some of the holes in the edge of the plate, three of which are shown at *g g g*, in order to keep the web open; or, what answers better, in a series of pegs of the shape represented by *h*, each having a slit, *i*, extending more than halfway down it; the threads are wound round these two or three times, and then the end is secured by putting it into the slit *i*. The plate is now ready to be adapted to the stage of the microscope: the square opening over which the foot is secured must be brought over the aperture in the stage through which the light passes from the mirror.

The tadpole circulation is readily seen by placing the creature on its back, when we immediately observe the beating heart, a bulbous-looking cavity, formed of delicate, transparent tissue, through which the blood alternately enters by one orifice and leaves by a more distant exit. The heart, it will be noticed, is enclosed within its pericardium, this being the more delicate part of the creature's organisation. The binocular microscope should be used for viewing the circulation. Passing along the course of the great blood-vessels to the right and left of the heart, the eye is arrested by a large oval body, of a more complicated structure. This is the inner gill, formed of delicate, transparent tissue, traversed by arteries, and a network of blood-vessels. It is almost unnecessary to say the tadpole has a respiratory and circulatory system resembling those of fishes.

In nearly all fish the heart has but two cavities, an auricle and ventricle; the blood is returned by the veins to the auricle, passes into the ventricle, and is then transmitted to the gills, where, being exposed to the air contained in the water, it becomes deprived of carbonic acid, aerated, and rendered fit to breathe. In the reptile we find a modification of plan. The heart has three cavities, two auricles and one ventricle; by this contrivance there is a perpetual mixture in the heart of the impure carbonized blood which has already circulated through the body, and flows into the ventricle from the *right* auricle, with the purer aerated blood returned from the lungs, which flows at the same instant into the ventricle from the *left* auricle.

For the purpose of subsequent observations the tadpole should be selected at a period in which the skin is perfectly transparent, otherwise the appearances already described of the form and situation of the heart, and the three great arterial trunks (proceeding right and left), will not be clearly made out. The anatomical arrangement of the vessels will be seen to be closely connected with the corresponding gill, the upper one (the *cephalic*) running along the upper edge of the gill, giving off, in its course, a branch which ascends to the mouth, with its accompanying vein; this is termed the *labial* artery and vein. The cephalic artery continues its course around the gill, until it suddenly curves upwards and backwards, and reaches the upper surface of the head, when it dips down between the eye and the brain.

It must not be supposed that this can be made out in the average tadpole, the obstacle to which is the large coil of intestines, usually distended with dark-coloured food. This must first be reduced by making your tadpole live on plain water for some days. Plate VII., No. 158, affords a view of the vessels obtained under the influence of low diet, and whereby we are enabled to trace the course of the three large arteries. The third trunk, traversing the lung, is seen to emerge from the lower edge and descend into the abdomen to form the great abdominal aorta. A small half-starved tadpole shows the heart beating and the blood circulating, but the latter is quite colourless, not a single red globule visible anywhere. The heart is a colourless globe, the gills two transparent ovals, and the intestines a colourless, transparent coil. Through the empty coil the artery is seen on either side leaving the gills, and converging towards the spine, and uniting to form the abdominal aorta, the large central vessel coloured red in the figure. After the aorta has supplied the abdominal viscera, a prolongation, or *caudal* artery is seen descending to the tail, the all-important organ of locomotion in the tadpole. This artery, entering the root of the tail, is imbedded deeply in the flesh, whence it emerges, and then continues its course, closely accompanied by the vein, to within a short distance of the extremity, where, being reduced to a state of extreme fineness, it terminates in a capillary loop, composed of the end of the artery and the beginning of the vein. The artery, in its course, gives off branches continually to supply the neighbouring tissue. The blood-current in the tail is often seen, even in the main artery or vein, to be sluggish. This occurs independently of the heart, which will continue to beat as usual; it happens, because the circulation in the tail depends very much on the motion of the organ. When this is suspended (as in the confined tadpole under the microscope), the blood moves sluggishly, or stops, till the tail regains its freedom and motion, when the activity of the current is restored.

Having traced the arterial system which conveys the blood from the heart to the extremities, we will now note its return by the veins back again to the heart.

The caudal vein runs near the artery during the greater part of its course, with its stream of blood *towards* the heart. This stream is swollen by perpetual tributaries from numerous vessels. As the vein approaches the root of the tail it is inclined towards the artery, and diverges from it at the point of entering the abdomen. Here it approaches the kidneys and sends off branches, while the main trunk continues its course onward; and, passing upwards behind a coil of intestine, it approaches the liver, and runs in a curved course along the margin of that organ. The blood is now seen to enter the vena cava by several channels, that converge towards the great vein as it passes in close proximity to the organ. Beyond the liver the vena cava continues its course upwards and inwards to its termination in the sinus venosus or rudimentary auricle of the heart. This termination is the junction of not less than six distinct venous trunks, incessantly pouring their blood into the heart. The circulation in the fringed lips forms a most complicated network of vessels, out of which proceeds a vein corresponding to the artery already traced. This descends in a direct course till it joins the principal vein of the head, which corresponds to the *jugular* in the mammalia.

Thus it will be seen the blood is driven by the heart into each inner gill through three large blood-vessels, which arise directly from the *truncus arteriosus*, and may be called the *afferent vessels of the gill*. In Plate VII., No. 156, an enlarged view of a gill is shown.

On closer examination "each *internal gill* or entire branchial organ is seen to consist of cartilaginous arches, with a piece of additional framework of a triangular form, stretching beyond the arches, composed of semi-transparent, gelatinous-looking material. These form the framework of the organ and support upon their upper surface the three rows of crests with their vascular network, and the main arterial and venous trunks lying parallel to and between them. The three systemic arteries arising, right and left, from the *truncus arteriosus*, enter each gill on its cardiac side, and then follow the course of the crests, lying in close proximity to them. The upper of these branchial arteries runs alone on the outside of the upper crest, and another branch leaving the trunk and passing into the network of the crest, whence a returning vessel may be traced carrying back the blood *across* the branchial artery, and to a vessel lying close to and taking the same course as the artery itself. Carrying the eye along the latter vessel we find, at a short distance from the first of these crest branches, a second, leaving the main trunk and entering the crest, when a corresponding returning vessel conveys the blood across the arterial trunk into the vessel lying beside it, as in the former instance. A number of these branches may be traced from one crest to the other. But it is now seen that the trunk from which these arterial branches spring diminishes in size as it proceeds in its course (like the gill artery in fishes), while the vessel running parallel to it and receiving the stream as it returns from the crest enlarges to some extent. Thus, the artery or *afferent* vessel which brings the blood to the gill is large at its entrance, but gradually diminishes and dwindles to a point at the opposite end of the crest; while the venous or *efferent* vessel, beginning as a mere radical, gradually enlarges, and thus becomes the trunk that conveys the blood out of the gill to its ultimate destination. This vessel is the *upper branchial vein* so long as it remains in contact with the gill; subsequently it changes its name on leaving the gill and as it passes upwards for distribution to the head, when it is designated the *cephalic artery.* The *middle branchial artery and vein* proceed in like manner in connection with the middle crest, and the *lower artery and vein* in connection with the lower crest. The middle and lower venous trunks, having reached the extremity of the crests, curve downwards and inwards, and leave the gill. The former trunk, converging towards the spine, meets its fellow, and with it forms the *ventral aorta.* The latter gives origin to the *pulmonary artery*, and supplies also the integuments of the neck. Curious and interesting is the final stage of the metamorphosis, when the waning tadpole and incipient frog coexist, and are actually seen together in the same subject. The dwindling gills and the shrinking tail—the last remnants of the tadpole form—are yet seen, in company with the coloured, spotted skin, the newly formed and slender legs, the flat head, the wide and toothless mouth, and the crouching attitude of the all but perfect reptile."[87]

To observe the circulation and how it is carried on during life in the gills, the outer covering must be carefully raised, or even stripped off. This will be better accomplished by putting the tadpole under the influence of cocaine or chloroform—a drop of the fluid is sufficient for the purpose.

The metamorphosis in the embryo of the frog is by no means exceptional. The ascidian begins life in the form of a tadpole, with a muscular tail; subsequently it fixes itself by its head to a rock, and its tail disappears. The changes the tadpole of the frog passes through are in every respect, except in one or two minor details, similar to those of adult amphibia which pass their whole lives in water. The newly-hatched flat-fish is symmetrical, an eye being placed on each side of its head, with the adults of other fishes. The fœtal whale has well-developed hind limbs, and which, after passing into a condition almost perfect in proportion to the rest of the body, gradually dwindle away again to the merest rudimentary structures. In all these, and a number of similar cases, it is seen that the earlier condition of existing animals represents, and is in agreement with that of its adult ancestor of a remote period in the past. Collected facts bearing upon this question have been made the groundwork of a theory of hereditary properties in the germ, and a disposition to go through the same phases of life as the parent.

CHAPTER VI.

The Mineral and Geological Kingdoms.

The structure of rocks and the formation of crystals will be found to furnish an endless supply of instructive material for the microscope. In sciences of pure observation, as those of mineralogy and geology, the facts to be observed are of several different kinds, and where so many observers are at work all over the world, constant progress will necessarily be made, as well as continued correction required from change and improvement in the methods of observation. It would be impossible to give even a slight sketch of what has been done in the two departments of nature referred to during the past few years. Mineralogical and geological research have derived very great advantage from having been assigned to professional teaching. But, as Professor Bonney reminds us, the progress made in geological work in particular, has been directly due to the revelations of the microscope. It called forth an instrument of special construction for the purpose, the petrological microscope (Fig. 79), well equipped with Nicol's prisms, and numerous other appliances demanded for the important investigations.

"Upon the history of the two main groups of rocks the microscope has thrown much light. For the igneous rocks it has simplified their classification and determined their mutual relations; while for the rudimentary group, it has shown the true nature of their constituents, and pointed out the sources from which they were derived. But it is in helping to elucidate the problem of the metamorphic rocks, of which much less was known, that the microscope has been of the most service. It has likewise greatly assisted in the attempt to determine the history and mutual relation of these rocks. One of the most important results within the last few years has been the demonstration that without exception these crystallin schists are very old, all probably older than the first rocks in which traces of life have been found. The conclusion arrived at, is that "the environment necessary for changing an ordinary sediment into a crystalline schist existed generally only in the earliest ages, and but very rarely and locally, if ever, since palæozoic time began."

The crystalline schists then are the relics still preserved to us of the early days of the earth's history, when the temperature near the surface was still high. Since that time the zone for marked mineralogical changes has been continually sinking, until at the present day it has reached a depth practically unattainable. "The subterranean laboratory still exists, but the way to it was virtually closed at a comparatively early period in the earth's history." Greater progress has been made since the microscope was pressed into the service of geology, and inspires the hope that we shall yet learn something more of the earliest ages, when the mystery of life began.

"It may be regarded as one of the most remarkable results of geological science, that an acquaintance with organic forms is at least as necessary for a geologist as a knowledge of minerals, and that a correct knowledge of organic remains (portions of fossil plants and animals) should prove a more certain and unerring guide in unravelling the structure of complicated districts of countries, than the most wide and general acquaintance with inorganic substances. The cause of this, however, is obvious, as the mineral substances produced at any one period of a vast succession of ages, do not appear to have had any essential difference from those formed under like circumstances at another. The animals and plants, however, living at one period of the earth's history were widely different from those living at other periods. There has been a continuous succession of different races of living beings on the earth following each other in a certain regular and ascertainable order, and when that order has been determined, it is equally certain that we can at once assign to its proper period of production, and therefore to its proper place in the series of rocks, any portion of earthy matter we may meet with containing any one, or even any recognisable fragment of one, of these once living beings."

The method of preparing sections of minerals and rocks for microscopic examination will be found at pp. 241, 307-309. The sections, it is almost needless to say, must be prepared thin enough to permit the use of transmitted light, as well as for that of polarised light: that is to say, they should range from about $\frac{1}{100}$th to $\frac{1}{1000}$th of an inch. Almost any lapidary will cut sections of any choice specimen.[88] The formation of crystals, and the method of preparing them for examination, has also been fully explained in the chapter on polarised light, pp. 219 et seq., and illustrated on Plate VIII. It is well known in micro-chemistry that "almost every substance, simple or compound, capable of existing in the solid state, assumes, under favourable conditions, a distinct geometrical figure, usually bounded by plane surfaces and having angles of constant value.

Much useful information may be gained upon micro-crystallography, as well as on almost everything having any relation to the *technique* of the microscope, in the "Journal of the Royal Microscopical Society." To the June number (1898) Mr. T. Charters White contributes an article on crystals, and reminds us that the presence of much or little moisture will modify and alter forms, as much and as often as varying degrees of temperature. At the same time he offers a few useful suggestions for the purpose of securing better results, for which purpose he employs hippuric acid, hydroquinine, and picric acid alone or in combination with hippuric acid, and an aqueous solution of bichromate of potassium, crystallised in a tolerably thick emulsion of gum arabic. This is the only aqueous solution; the other solvents have been methylated spirit, acetone, and absolute alcohol, taking these three solvents as types of the greatest volatility, because in making certain crystals it is necessary that the solvent should evaporate quickly, otherwise the crystals will assume their original forms. It is further desirable to make saturated, or even super-saturated solutions of the three chemicals named, as the colours produced under polarised light are of a deeper and richer character than they are if made from weaker solutions. Of the three chemicals named he prefers hippuric acid, for reasons stated, that it is the most manageable, and allows of more time being taken in modifying the formation of the crystals. It is also advisable to slightly warm the glass slide before the drop of fluid is applied. On the whole, picric acid appears to furnish a greater variety of crystals when used in combination with bichromate of potassium and a solution of gum arabic.

APPENDICES AND TABLES USEFUL TO THE MICROSCOPIST.

ILLUMINATION ARRANGEMENTS OF THE MICROSCOPE.

A doubt has of late been expressed among practical microscopists as to the value of the illumination arrangements of the lamp and the microscope, so as to secure the more perfect definition of the flagellate organ of the monas and other minute forms of infusorial life. We have been told that better results will be obtained by turning the mirror aside, and so disposing the microscope and lamp in the horizontal position, that the central rays of light from the mirror-edge of the lamp-flame shall pass through the optical axis of the achromatic condenser, the focus of which must be accurately brought upon the field of view by means of the substage centring screws and rack-work, and in such a manner, that by employing a 1-inch objective, a sharply-defined image of the lamp-flame, edge-on, is projected on to the centre of the field in association with the specimen under examination. If the 1-inch objective be now replaced by a 1-12th or 1-16th inch immersion and once again focussed into place, and a slight re-adjustment of the centring made, it will be found that the field is brilliantly illuminated, and the most minute portions of infusorial life are well defined, and with a sharpness otherwise unattainable. At the same time the graduating or iris diaphragm must be brought into use.

Dr. Clifford Mercer, the President of the American Microscopical Society, who has quite recently reinvestigated the question of illumination, utterly condemns the narrow cone, as well as that of oblique light in all such investigations, and considers the 3-4ths axil cone as the most suitable method for microscopical illumination, and he bases his resolving limit accordingly. Some important experiments are brought forward by Dr. Mercer, which at the same time demonstrate the correctness of Lord Rayleigh's limit of resolution (referred to in a previous chapter, p. 44), for circular apertures as contrasted with that calculated by the late Sir George Airy.

With regard to the Abbé Theory, Dr. Mercer says: "Resolution in the Abbé Theory may be said to increase by bounds. So long as the central image of the source of light alone is to be seen at the back of the objective, resolution is not present. The aperture may be increased without change in the contraction of the diffraction pattern, and in accompanying resolution, so long as the central image alone is to be seen at the back of the objective; but the moment the increase in aperture is sufficient to uncover or admit one flanking spectrum image, resolution is present. With greater increase in aperture, no improvement in the picture as to the contraction of the diffraction pattern is to be seen until another spectrum image is uncovered or admitted. Dr. Mercer gives his reasons for considering that the advantageous reduction in a cone of light between an object and the objective should not exceed, in the case of first-class objectives, one-fourth to one-third (never more than one-half) of the diameter of the cone. On the other hand, with full cone illumination, resolution increases continuously, and not by jumps or by periodic accessions. With regard to the use of oblique light, he says his Photos 2, 3, and 4[89] are a pictorial warning for a second time against the use of oblique illumination in ordinary work us a means of increasing, or of attempting to exhaust the resolving power of the microscope. At the same time it becomes evident that every substage should be provided with a means by which its condenser may be accurately centred, and that every student using the microscope should be familiar with a method of centring his substage condenser.

Dr. Mercer summarises the results of his experiments thus:—

1. "Diffraction rays on leaving an object may be considered in the same category with other rays changed in direction by an object.

2. "The diffraction phenomena seen in a projected image are essentially the effect of changes in light *above* the objective, due to a function of aperture, and not to changes *below* the objective, due to diffraction of light in the plane of the object.

3. "Diffraction in the plane of the object does, under some circumstances, furnish light to certain parts of an aperture from which primary rays are absent, and this enables aperture to more fully determine the character of the projected image, resulting in a more nearly truthful image, or, on the other hand, in false appearances. This is the gist of the Abbé phenomena of microscopic vision.

4. "But such phenomena are not peculiar to microscopic vision, notwithstanding Professor Abbé's claim to the contrary.

5. "With any positive lens similar and more brilliant results may be got by utilising corresponding pencils of primary rays, instead of isolated pencils of diffracted rays.

6. "Still more trustworthy results may be got by using primary rays in place of the isolated pencils of primary rays.

7. "An advantage peculiar to using narrow cone illumination with an objective of wide aperture (the only illumination admissible in the Abbé theory), consists in giving, under suitable conditions, approximately the acme of resolving power simultaneously in each several diameters. Thus a circular

aperture is approximately squared or made rectangular as to resolving power in several of its diameters simultaneously.

8. "Special attention is called to the fact that the Abbé theory deals with complex objects; for only such objects are subject to resolution. Single particles and uniform areas are outside its domain. These latter, however, are microscopic objects, and all objects are essentially different shaped aggregations of points. An isolated point-like particle, no matter what its minuteness, may be seen if it present sufficient contrast with the surrounding microscopic field. The size of the disc image is no less than a limit determined finally by aperture. That limit in size varying inversely with aperture, determines the limit of resolving power. This is the gist of the theory of microscopic vision which harmonises with our experimental study of aperture."

APPENDIX B.

MICRO-PHOTOGRAPHY.

Owing in some measure to the more complete knowledge of the subject gained by the experience of years, and the extreme value of micro-photography in the delineation of bacteria, and perhaps in a measure to the advent of the perfected dry-plate process, photography is being rapidly pressed forward in conjunction with the microscope. In the course of the year [1898] no less than six, more or less, new forms of micro-photographic apparatus have appeared; two are simple, one for daylight, one for lamp, one for electric, and one for lime-light illumination. Passing over the simpler forms, for a notice of which I am unable to find room, there is one piece of new apparatus, that of Mr. E. B. Stringer, which is not only new, but is in every way adapted to the work of micro-photography. It is in fact a well-arranged camera, fitted with a powerful condensing arrangement, each portion of which is capable of being independently centred and controlled. Indeed, the specially interesting feature of the apparatus is the control of the gas and the beautiful and uniformally illuminating disc of zircon, about a quarter of an inch in diameter.

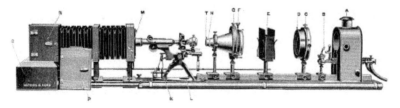

Fig. 446.—Mr. E. B. Stringer's Improved Micro-photography Apparatus.

B. Oxyhydrogen jet with zirconium cylinder, covered by the cowl A when working.

C. Doublet parallelising condenser, with centering screws.
D. Iris diaphragm.
E. Holder for trough and light-filtering media.
F. Plano-convex lens, 4¼ins. diameter, with centering screws G
H. Plano-concave lens, with iris diaphragm T.
K. Connecting pulleys between focussing rod of camera and fine adjustment of Microscope.
L. Triangular frame in which Microscope feet are placed.
M. Flap shutter.
N. Door through which image is observed on card screen, etc.
O. Solid block of mahogany on which camera body is fixed and supported.
P. Dark slide.

This efficient photo-micrographic apparatus (Fig. 446) is made by Messrs. W. Watson & Sons, under the instructions of Mr. E. B. Stringer. The illuminating condensing system is mounted on a square brass bar, the illuminant being oxygen-hydrogen light burning on zirconium. Immediately in front of this is a condenser, c, four and a half inches diameter, with an iris diaphragm, D, immediately in front of it. The holder, E, carries the light filtering media through which the beam passes and enters the condenser, F. It then goes through a tank of water contained in the cone, F to H, and emerges a practically parallel beam of great intensity through a plano-concave lens, h, of such a diameter as to exactly fill the back lens of the substage condenser. There is an iris diaphragm, T, for cutting off stray light.

The whole of the apparatus is fitted with centring screws and clamps, and after having been once adjusted it is ready for use at any moment without preparation. By means of this apparatus, instantaneous pictures can be taken of living rotifers, so brilliant is the illumination, while photographs of such fine objects as the flagella of bacteria cannot be secured with the same amount of certainty by any other microphotographic apparatus with which I have made myself acquainted.

APPENDIX C.

FORMULÆ AND METHODS:—CEMENTING, CLEARING, HARDENING AND MOUNTING.[90]

CLEARING AGENTS.

The object of employing a clearing agent is to replace the alcohol in the dehydrated section by a liquid which has a refractive index about the same as the balsam into which it is to be placed, and which will readily mix with it.

OIL OF BERGAMOT will clear quickly from 90 per cent. of alcohol. Clove oil clears more rapidly, but it dissolves out aniline colours to a considerable extent. Xylol is without action on aniline colours. This strength of alcohol is chosen because of its being that of the methylated spirit sold in London, and which is much used in washing and dehydrating on account of its cheapness.

OIL OF CEDAR WOOD, although an essential oil, resembles xylol, but evaporates slowly. It has very little solvent action on the aniline colours. It clears rapidly from absolute alcohol, but not well from 90 per cent. Sections can be left in it for several days. It is a convenient medium in which to examine tissues before mounting them permanently. It clears celloidin without dissolving it; and as a connecting fluid between the object and objective nothing better has been discovered.

Other clearing agents have been tried, but as they dissolve out the aniline colours, are no longer used.

CEMENTS.

GROVE'S MASTIC AND BISMUTH.—Dissolve gum mastic in chloroform, and thicken with nitrate of bismuth. The solution of mastic should be nearly saturated.

GROVE'S OXIDE OF ZINC, DAMMAR, AND DRYING OIL.—Rub up well-ground oxide of zinc, 2 ozs., with drying oil, to the consistence of thick paint. Then add an equal quantity of gum dammar, previously dissolved in benzoline, and of the thickness of syrup. Strain through close-meshed muslin. Keep in well-corked bottle, and, if necessary, thin with benzoline.

ISINGLASS CEMENT.—Heat the isinglass in a covered vessel on the water-bath with a little glacial acetic acid, until it is thoroughly softened and forms a stiff mass, then gradually add more acid until it produces a thick solution which is of uniform consistence, and just fluid while hot. Then run into wide-mouth bottles and close with good corks.

KITTON'S CEMENT of white lead and red lead in powder, and litharge powder in equal parts. Grind together with a little turpentine, until thoroughly incorporated, and mix with gold size. The mixture should be thin enough to use with a brush; in using, one coat should be allowed to dry before applying another. No more cement should be mixed with the gold size than is required for immediate use, as it sets quickly, and becomes unworkable.

KRÖNIG'S CEMENT.—Gradually add ordinary resin, 7 to 9 parts, to melted beeswax, 2 parts, then steam and cool.

SHELLAC CEMENT.—Dissolve shellac in an equal weight of methylated spirit, then pour off the clear portion and add a few drops of balsam and castor oil.

MARINE GLUE.—Dissolve indiarubber in mineral naphtha, and add twice the quantity of powdered shellac; or make chloroform the solvent, and use mastic instead of shellac. For casting battery trays, use a composition of 4 parts resin and 1 of gutta percha, with a little boiled oil.

SELIER (*Cleaning Glass Slides*).—New slides or cover-glasses must be placed for a few hours in a mixture of 1 part of potassium bichromate, 1 of sulphuric acid, and 25 of water. Subsequently wash with water and wipe dry with a linen rag, after draining off the excess of moisture. Covers that have been used should be previously immersed for a few days in a mixture of equal parts of alcohol and hydrochloric acid. Scrape old slides free of mounting medium before immersing them in the bichromate solution.

ELSCHING'S CELLOIDIN SOLUTION.—Allow the celloidin shavings to swell up for 24 hours in the necessary quantity of absolute alcohol, then add the proper amount of ether.

KOCH'S COPAL.—Stain small pieces of material in bulk, and dehydrate with alcohol, then immerse in a thin solution of copal in chloroform. Evaporate with a gentle heat until the solution is so far concentrated as to draw out into threads that are brittle on cooling. Then remove the objects and leave on a tile for a few days to dry. Sections may then be cut by means of a fine saw. If objects are imbedded unstained, remove copal from sections by soaking in chloroform, decalcify if necessary, and stain.

EULENSTEIN'S CEMENT.—Mix equal parts of Brunswick black and gold size with a very little Canada balsam.

DECALCIFYING AND BLEACHING.

In the case of bony structures, or tissues so impregnated with calcium salts, the material should be decalcified by an acid capable of dissolving out the mineral matter. Hydrochloric acid with alcohol is in more general use. The older the bone the stronger will be the acid required, nitric with alcohol and chromic acid. Picric acid is preferred for foetal bone.

ANDEER, J. J., finds an aqueous solution of phloroglucin acts as a powerful decalcifying agent on the bones of animals, but is without action on the most delicate organic tissue. If treatment with hydrochloric acid be employed as well, the residual "ossein" will be without a trace of either calcium phosphate or carbonate.

EBNER'S FLUIDS.—(1) Mix 100 C.c. of cold saturated aqueous solution of sodium chloride, 100 C.c. of water, and 4 C.c. of hydrochloric acid. Preparations are placed in the fluid, and 1 to 2 C.c. of hydrochloric acid added daily until they are soft. (2) Mix 2·5 parts of hydrochloric acid (sp. gr. 1·16) with 500 of alcohol (90 per cent.), 100 of water, and 2·5 of sodium chloride.

FOL'S LIQUID.—Mix 70 volumes of 1 per cent. chromic acid, 3 of nitric acid, and 200 of water.

MAYER'S DESILIFICATION PROCESS.—Place the objects in alcohol contained in a glass vessel coated internally with paraffin, then add hydrofluoric acid drop by drop until desilification is complete, avoiding the fumes meanwhile.

MARSH'S CHLORINE METHOD.—Chlorine is generated in a small bottle by treating crystals of potassium chlorate with strong HCl., and the gas is led through a piece of glass tubing, bent twice at right angles, to the bottom of a bottle containing the sections immersed in water.

RANVIER'S FLUID.—Use 50 per cent. hydrochloric acid with the addition of sodium chloride to counteract its swelling action.

SQUIRE'S FLUID.—(1) Mix 95 parts of glycerine with 5 parts of hydrochloric acid; used for softening teeth. (2) Use a 4 per cent. aqueous solution of arsenic acid at a temperature of 30° to 40° C. After softening tissues in this solution, keep them in alcohol.

WALDEYER.—To a 0·1 per cent. solution of palladium chloride, add one-tenth its volume of hydrochloric acid.

HARDENING, FREEZING, AND EMBEDDING.

ALTMANN (*Fixing Solution*).—A mixture of equal parts of 5 per cent. potassium bichromate solution and 2 per cent. osmic acid.

ALCOHOL.—Strengths of alcoholic solutions, as given by Squire, will be found of practical value. Absolute alcohol (sp. gr. O·797) containing about 98 per cent. of ethylic alcohol is taken as the basis in most instances. Alcohol of 90 per cent. (sp. gr. 0·823) is prepared by mixing 14 volumes of absolute alcohol and 1 volume of distilled water; 84 per cent. alcohol (sp. gr. 0·838) is rectified spirit B.P.; 70 per cent. alcohol (sp. gr. 0·872) may be obtained by adding 1 volume of distilled water to 3 volumes of absolute alcohol, 6 volumes of rectified spirit, or 4 volumes of methylated spirit; 50 per cent. alcohol (sp. gr. 0·918) is prepared by adding 4 volumes of distilled water to 5 volumes of absolute alcohol, 3 volumes of water to 5 volumes of rectified spirit, or 3·5 volumes of water to 5 volumes of methylated spirit. Absolute alcohol, 75 C.c., mixed with acetic acid, 25 C.c., serves as an excellent fixing agent for nuclei. Immerse tissues in it for 6 to 12 hours, then transfer to 90 per cent. alcohol until hardened, afterwards preserving in 70 per cent. alcohol till wanted.

BETZ'S HARDENING FLUID.—A mixture of equal parts of sulphuric ether and alcohol. This is used for hardening the brain of insects prior to cutting sections.

COLE'S FREEZING PROCESS.—Dissolve picked gum acacia, 4 ozs., in distilled water, 6 ozs., and to each 5 parts of the resulting mucilage add 3 parts of syrup made by dissolving loaf sugar, 1 lb., in distilled water, 1 pint. To each ounce of the medium add 5 grains of pure carbolic acid, and soak the tissues in it prior to freezing. For tissues liable to come to pieces, mix 4 parts of syrup with 5 of mucilage.

FLEMMING'S FIXING SOLUTION.—Osmic acid (1 per cent. solution), 80 C.c.; chromic acid (10 per cent. solution), 15 C.c.; glacial acetic acid, 10 C.c.; distilled water, 95 C.c.

FOL'S FIXING—Osmic acid (1 per cent. solution), 4 C.c.; chromic acid (10 per cent. solution), 5 C.c.; glacial acetic acid, 10 C.c.; distilled water, 181 C.c.

FISCHER'S IMBEDDING MASS.—Dissolve 15 parts of transparent soap in 17·5 parts of 96 per cent. alcohol.

KLEIN'S HARDENING.—Mix 1 C.c. of 10 per cent. chromic acid solution with 60 C.c. of water, and add 30 C.c. of 90 per cent. alcohol.

MÜLLER'S FLUID FORMULA, see page 288.—This solution is sometimes mixed with one-third its volume of 90 per cent. alcohol, its hardening action being then much more rapid.

RABL'S HARDENING FLUID.—Chromic acid solution (10 per cent.), 7 C.c.; water, 200 C.c.; formic acid (sp. gr. 1·2), 5 drops.

ROLLETT'S FREEZING PROCESS.—Small portions of tissue placed on the stage of microtome, after immersion in the white of an egg, then frozen and cut with a very cold knife.

RYDER (*Double Embedding*).—After the celloidin bath, soak objects in chloroform, then remove into a mixture of chloroform and paraffin, heated to not more than 40° C., and finally into a bath of pure paraffin.

STRICKER (*Imbedding Mass*).—Prepare the objects in alcohol and imbed in a concentrated solution in gum arabic in a paper case, then throw the whole into alcohol and cut after 2 or 3 days.

WEBB (*Dextrin Freezing*).—A thick solution of dextrin (1:40) in aqueous solution of carbolic acid is used for imbedding, and subsequently frozen.

MOUNTING MEDIA.

Sections are usually mounted in balsam, dammar, glycerine, &c., but it is not a necessity that the cover-glass should be fixed or cemented down. Some cements (caoutchouc by preference) should be employed when glycerine or aqueous (Farrant's) media are used.

ALLEGER'S GELATINE PROCESS.—Add a few drops of formalin to each gramme of 0·5 to 1 per cent. gelatine solution. After mounting the section in this, apply heat to the slide until the paraffin is softened, and allow the superfluous gelatine to drain from the edge of the slide.

APÁTHY'S MOUNTING MEDIUM.—Picked gum arabic, 50 Gm.; cane-sugar, 50 Gm.; distilled water, 50 Gm.; dissolve over a warm bath and add 0·05 Gm. of thymol. This medium sets very hard, and combined with a paper cell it may be used for ringing glycerine mounts.

COLE'S SLOW OR EXPOSURE METHOD OF MOUNTING.—Dissolve dried Canada balsam, 3 ozs., in benzole, 3 fl. ozs., and filter. Apply a clean cover-glass to a slide that has been moistened by breathing on it, and place a few drops of the balsam solution on the cover-glass. Then remove a section from turpentine, and put it into the balsam. Put aside for 12 hours to allow the benzole to evaporate, and having warmed a slide and added a drop of fresh balsam solution to that on the cover-glass, bring the fluid balsam in contact with the warmed slide. Press the cover down carefully to avoid the inclusion of air bubbles, and when the excess of balsam is squeezed out, put the slide aside to cool, after which it may be cleaned with a camel-hair brush or soft rag moistened with methylated spirit.

FARRANT'S SOLUTION.—Take of gum arabic 5 parts; water 5 parts; when the gum is fairly dissolved add 10 parts of a 5 per cent. solution of carbolic acid.

FLEMMING'S GLYCERINE PRESERVATIVE.—Mix equal parts of alcohol, glycerine, and water. Lee recommends the addition of 0·5 to 0·75 per cent. of acetic acid.

LEE'S TURPENTINE COLOPHONIUM MOUNTING MEDIUM.—This is highly recommended for general work, and is prepared by adding small pieces of colophonium to rectified oil of turpentine, heating in a stove, and when the solution is sufficiently thick filtering twice in the stove.

SEAMAN (*Glycerine Jelly*).—Dissolve isinglass in water so as to make a jelly that remains stiff at the ordinary temperature of the room, and add one-tenth part of glycerine, together with a little solution of borax, carbolic acid, or camphor water. Filter through muslin whilst warm and add a little alcohol.

SEILER (*Alcohol Balsam*).—Heat Canada balsam until it becomes brittle when cold, then dissolve in warm absolute alcohol and filter through absorbent cotton-wool. This is chiefly useful as a mounting medium for objects stained with carmine.

SQUIRE (*Farrant's Medium*).—Dissolve in 200 C.c. of distilled water 1 Gm. of arsenious acid and 130 Gm. of gum arabic, then add 100 C.c. of glycerine.

Filter through fine Swedish filter paper upon which has been deposited a thin layer of talc.

SQUIRE (*Glycerine and Gum*).—Dissolve 130 Gm. of gum arabic in 200 C.c. of chloroform water (1 in 200), then add 100 C.c. of glycerine and filter.

SQUIRE (*Glycerine Jelly*).—Soak 100 Gm. of French gelatine in chloroform water, drain when soft, and dissolve with heat in 750 Gm. of glycerine. Add 400 Gm. of chloroform water, with which has been incorporated about 50 Gm. of fresh egg albumen, mix thoroughly, and heat to boiling point for about 5 minutes. Make up the total weight to 1550 Gm. with chloroform water and filter in a warm chamber.

SQUIRE (*Canada Balsam*).—Dry the balsam over a water bath until brittle when cooled, then to each 200 Gm. add 100 C.c. of benzole or rather less xylol.

SQUIRE (*Dammar Solution*).—(1) Dissolve 100 Gm. of dammar in 100 C.c. of benzole. (2) Dissolve 100 Gm. of dammar in 200 C.c. of turpentine oil, and add 50 Gm. of mastic dissolved in 200 C.c. of chloroform.

SQUIRE (*Potassium Acetate Solution*).—Dissolve 250 Gm. of potassium acetate in 100 C.c. of water, by the aid of gentle heat, and filter. This is used as a mounting medium.

SQUIRE (*Treatment of Sections*).—Imbed tissues to be cut in paraffin melting between 45° and 50° C., according to the temperature of the room and the nature of the material. Afterwards preserve the sections, prior to staining and mounting, in 50 per cent. alcohol, or in a mixture of equal volumes of glycerine and thymol water (1 in 1500). Sections may be conveniently washed in alcohol, dehydrated, and cleared, in small wide-mouthed bottles.

TOPPING'S SOLUTION.—Mix 1 part of absolute alcohol with 5 parts of water, or 4 parts of water and 1 part of aluminium acetate. Add an equal volume of glycerine before use.

STAINS AND STAINING METHODS.

APÁTHY'S HÆMATOXYLIN STAIN.—After staining in 1 per cent. solution of hæmatoxylin in 70 or 80 per cent. alcohol, wash out in 1 per cent. solution of potassium bichromate in alcohol of the same strength. The bichromate solution should be freshly made by mixing 1 part of a 5 per cent. aqueous solution with about 4 parts of 80 to 90 per cent. alcohol.

ALFEROW (*Silver Staining*).—An acid solution of silver picrate, lactate, acetate, or citrate, is prepared by adding to 800 C.c. of the solution 10 to 15 drops of a concentrated solution of the acid of the salt taken.

BETHE'S STAIN FOR CHITIN.—Place series of mounted sections on slides in a freshly prepared 10 per cent. solution of aniline hydrochloride, containing 1 drop of hydrochloric acid for each 10 C.c., for 3 or 4 minutes, then rinse in water, and put the slide with sections downwards in a 10 per cent. solution of potassium bichromate. The process may be repeated if the stain is not sufficiently intense, but the sections must be well rinsed with water after each immersion.

BEALE'S AMMONIA CARMINE.—Carmine, 10 grs.; strong solution of ammonia, 30 mins.; distilled water, 2 ozs.; alcohol, 0·5 oz.; glycerine, 2 ozs. Dissolve the carmine in the ammonia by the aid of heat, boil for a few seconds, and let the solution cool. Then allow the excess of ammonia to evaporate, add the other ingredients, and filter. If any carmine should deposit on keeping add one or two drops of ammonia solution to redissolve it.

BENDA'S COPPER HÆMATOXYLIN.—Harden the material with chromic acid or Flemming's solution and leave sections for 24 hours in a 5 per cent. solution of neutral copper acetate at a temperature of about 40° C., wash out well with distilled water, and stain to a dark grey or blackish tint in a saturated aqueous hæmatoxylin solution. Decolourise the sections in 0·2 per cent. hydrochloric acid until light yellow, put back into the copper solution until they turn bluish-grey, then wash, dehydrate, clear, and mount in balsam.

BISMARCK BROWN.—Vesuvine 0·5 Gm., rectified spirit 2, and distilled water 80 C.c.; or a concentrated alcoholic solution may be kept ready for dilution.

BOCHMER'S HÆMATOXYLIN.—Dissolve (a) crystallised hæmatoxylin, 1 Gm., in absolute alcohol, 10 C.c., and (b) alum ammonia, 10 Gm., in distilled water, 200 C.c. Mix the two solutions, and allow to ripen for some days before use. Filter after standing a week. Wash out with aqueous solution of alum (0·5 per cent.) or with acids.

CALBERLA'S INDULIN STAIN.—Dilute a concentrated aqueous solution with 6 volumes of water and stain sections for 5 to 20 minutes. Afterwards wash in water or alcohol, and examine in glycerine or clove oil.

CALBERLA'S MACERATING MIXTURE (for nerve and muscle of embryos).— Dissolve potassium chloride, 0·4 Gm., sodium chloride, 0·3 Gm., sodium phosphate, 0·2 Gm., and calcium chloride, 0·2 Gm., in water, 100 Gm., saturated with carbon dioxide just before using. Mix one volume of this solution with half a volume of Müller's solution and one volume of water. The Müller's solution may be replaced by a 2·5 per cent. solution of ammonium chromate. Tissues macerated in this mixture are isolated by teasing and shaking, and mount specimens in concentrated potassium acetate solution.

CANOY'S SALT SOLUTION.—Add a trace of osmic acid to a 0·75 per cent. solution of sodium chloride in water.

CHENZINSKY'S METHYLENE BLUE AND EOSINE.—Mix saturated aqueous solution of methylene blue, 40 parts, with 0·5 per cent. solution of eosine in 70 per cent. alcohol, 20 parts, and distilled water or glycerine, 40 parts.

COHNHEIM'S GOLD METHOD.—Place pieces of tissue in 0·5 per cent. gold chloride solution until quite yellow, then expose to light in water acidulated with acetic acid until the gold is thoroughly reduced. Mount specimens in acidulated glycerine.

CROOKSHANK'S METHOD OF STAINING FLAGELLA.—Cover-glass preparations are stained with a drop of concentrated alcoholic solution of gentian violet, then rinsed in water, allowed to dry, and mounted in balsam.

CZOKER'S ALUM COCHINEAL.—Dissolve alum 1 Gm. in distilled water, 100 C.c., add powdered cochineal, 1 Gm., and boil; evaporate down to half of its original bulk, filter, and add ½ C.c. of liquid carbolic acid.

DELAFIELD'S HÆMATOXYLIN.—Dissolve hæmatoxylin, 4 Gm., in absolute alcohol, 25 C.c., and add the solution to 400 C.c. of a saturated aqueous solution of ammonia alum. Expose the mixture to light and air for 3 or 4 days, then filter and add glycerine, 100 C.c., and methylic alcohol, 100 C.c. Again expose the solution to light until it becomes dark-coloured, then filter and preserve in a stoppered bottle.

EHRLICH'S ACID HÆMATOXYLIN.—Dissolve hæmatoxylin, 2 Gm., in absolute alcohol, 100 C.c., and add glycerine, 100 C.c., distilled water, 100 C.c., ammonia alum, 2 Gm., glacial acetic acid, 10 C.c. Expose to daylight for at least a month before use, removing the stopper at intervals.

EHRLICH'S HÆMATOXYLIN (AMMONIATED).—Dissolve ammonium carbonate, 0·4 Gm., and hæmatoxylin, 2 Gm., in proof spirit, 40 C.c., and expose to the air in a shallow dish for 24 hours. Then make up the volume to 40 C.c. with proof spirit (warming if necessary to re-dissolve any separate crystals), and add ammonia alum, 2 Gm., dissolved in distilled water, 80 C.c., together with glycerine, 100 C.c., rectified spirit, 80 C.c., and glacial acetic acid, 10 C.c.

EHRLICH-BIONDI MIXTURE (or Ehrlich-Biondi-Heidenheim mixture).—Dissolve (a) methyl green, 0·5 Gm., in distilled water, 100 C.c.; (b) acid fuchsine, 0·5 Gm., in distilled water, 40 C.c.; (c) orange, 2 Gm., in distilled water, 200 C.c. Mix the three solutions and filter before use. Stain sections for 12 hours, then wash, dehydrate, clear, and mount.

EHRLICH-WEIGERT-KOCH'S   GENTIAN-VIOLET-ANILINE-WATER.—
Aniline water, 100 C.c., concentrated alcoholic solution of gentian violet, 11
C.c.; absolute alcohol, 10 C.c.

EVERARD, DEMOOR, AND MASSART'S HÆMATOXYLIN-EOSINE.—Dissolve
alum, 20 Gm., in water, 200 Gm., by the aid of heat, then filter, and after 24
hours add a solution of hæmatoxylin, 1 Gm., in alcohol, 10 Gm. Let the
solution stand for 8 days, again filter, and mix with an equal volume of the
following solution:—Eosine, 1 Gm., alcohol, 25 Gm., water, 75 Gm.,
glycerine, 50 Gm.

FLEMMING'S GENTIAN VIOLET METHOD.—Use a concentrated alcoholic
solution of Gentian Violet diluted with about one half its bulk of water.
Differentiate the stained objects in alcohol acidulated with about 0·5 per
cent. of hydrochloric acid, followed by pure alcohol and clove oil.

FLEMMING'S ORANGE METHOD.—Stain for days or weeks in strong
alcoholic safranine solution diluted with half its bulk of aniline water
(saturated); then rinse in distilled water, differentiate in absolute alcohol
containing 0·1 per cent. of hydrochloric acid, stain for 1 to 3 hours in strong
aqueous gentian violet solution, again wash in distilled water, and finally treat
with concentrated aqueous solution of Orange. After a few minutes transfer
sections to absolute alcohol, then clear in clove or bergamot oil, and mount
in dammar or balsam.

FOL'S FERRIC CHLORIDE FIXING AND STAINING PROCESS.—Preparations
are treated with tincture of ferric chloride diluted with 5 to 10 times its bulk
of 70 per cent. alcohol, and then transfer for 24 hours to alcohol containing
a trace of gallic acid.

FREY'S FUCHSINE SOLUTION.—A solution of 0·01 Gm. of crystallised
fuchsine, 20 to 25 drops absolute alcohol, and 15 C.c. of water.

FRIEDLAENDER'S STAINING METHODS.—Cover-glass preparations are
treated for 3 minutes with a 1 per cent. solution of acetic acid, and allowed
to dry after removal of excess of liquid by filter paper. Next place them in
gentian violet aniline water (aniline water, 100 C.c., concentrated alcoholic
solution of gentian violet, 11 C.c.; absolute alcohol, 10 C.c.) for half a minute,
wash in water, mount and dry in balsam. Sections are kept for 24 hours in a
warm place, in the following solution:—Concentrated alcoholic solution of
gentian violet, 50 C.c.; distilled water, 100 C.c.; glacial acetic acid, 10 C.c.
Then treat for 1 or 2 minutes with 0·1 per cent. acetic acid, dehydrate, clear,
and mount in balsam.

GAFFKY'S STAINING METHODS.—Sections of material hardened in alcohol
are left for 20 to 24 hours in a deep blue opaque solution, freshly made by
adding saturated alcoholic solution of methylene blue to distilled water. Then

wash in distilled water, dehydrate in absolute alcohol, clear in turpentine oil, and mount in balsam.

GIACOMI'S STAINING METHOD.—Stain cover-glass preparations for a few minutes in a hot solution of fuchsine, then place in water containing a few drops of ferric chloride solution, and afterwards decolourise in strong ferric chloride solution. If any precipitate be formed with the iron solution, complete the decolourisation in alcohol. Counterstain with vesuvine.

GIBBES' DOUBLE STAINING METHOD.—Well mix magenta, 2 Gm., and methylene blue, 1 Gm., then add slowly aniline oil, 3 C.c., dissolve in rectified spirit, 15 C.c. Subsequently add 15 C.c. of distilled water and keep the stain in a stoppered bottle. Cover-glass preparations are placed for 4 minutes in the slightly heated stain and sections left for some hours in the stain at the ordinary temperature. Afterwards, wash in methylated spirit until no more colour comes away, then dehydrate, clear in cedar oil, and mount in balsam.

GIBBES' MAGENTA STAIN.—Mix magenta, 2 Gm.; aniline oil, 3 Gm.; rectified spirit, 20 C.c.; and distilled water, 20 C.c.

GOLGI'S SUBLIMATED METHOD.—Small cubes of tissue are hardened for 15 to 30 days in Müller's fluid, which should be frequently changed. Then transfer for 8 to 10 days to 0·25 to 1 per cent. aqueous mercuric chloride solution, which must be changed, as it becomes coloured. If desired, treat subsequently with weak sodium sulphide solution to darken the stain and make it sharper. After cutting sections from material thus prepared they must be well washed with water.

GRAM'S STAIN FOR BACTERIA.—This is prepared by shaking 15 drops of aniline oil with 15 Gm. of water, filtering the solution and adding to the filtrate 4 to 5 drops of saturated alcoholic solution of gentian violet. Or shake 3·3 C.c. of aniline with 100 C.c. of distilled water and, after filtering, add 11 C.c. of concentrated alcoholic solution of gentian violet and 10 C.c. of absolute alcohol. After preparations have been stained for 1 to 3 minutes in one of the above they are quickly rinsed in absolute alcohol and then placed in Gram's solution of iodine in potassium iodine (iodine, 1 Gm.; potassium iodine, 2 Gm.; water, 300 C.c.), until they have acquired a brown colour. This takes about 1 to 3 minutes, and they are next washed in 90 per cent. alcohol until they become pale yellow, then dehydrated, cleared, and mounted in balsam. Counterstain with eosine or vesuvine if desired.

GRAM'S SOLUTION.—Iodine, 1 Gm.; potassium iodine, 2 Gm.; distilled water, 300 Gm.

GRENACHER'S ALUM CARMINE.—Dissolve 5 Gm. of ammonium alum in 100 C.c. of distilled water, add 1 Gm. of carmine, and boil for 20 minutes, filter when cool, and add distilled water to make up to 100 C.c.

GRENACHER'S ALCOHOLIC BORAX CARMINE.—Dissolve 4 Gm. of borax in 100 C.c. of distilled water, then add 3 Gm. of carmine, and heat gently. Finally, add 100 C.c. of 70 per cent. alcohol, filter the solution, if necessary, before use. Pieces of tissues are stained in this for 1 to 3 days, and then transferred to 70 per cent. alcohol, containing 0·5 to 1 per cent. of hydrochloric acid.

HEIDENHAIN'S HÆMATOXYLIN METHOD.—Dissolve (a) hæmatoxylin, 1 Gm., in distilled water, 300 C.c.; (b) potassium chromate, 1 Gm., in distilled water, 200 C.c. Small pieces of tissue hardened in alcohol or picric acid are placed in (a) for 12 to 24 hours, and then transferred for a similar length of time to (b). Wash thoroughly in water, dehydrate in alcohol, and imbed in paraffin.

HENLE'S STAIN (for nervous tissue).—Sections are left in palladium chloride solution (1:300 to 1:600) till they are of a straw colour, then rinsed in water and stained with strong ammonia carmine.

HENNEGUY'S ALUM CARMINE.—Excess of carmine is boiled in saturated solution of potash alum, and 10 per cent. of glacial acetic acid added on cooling. Allow to settle for some days, and then filter.

HENNEGUY'S PERMANGANATE METHOD.—Treat sections for 5 minutes with 1 per cent. potassium permanganate solution, then wash in water and stain with safranine, rubin, gentian violet, vesuvine, preference being given to a safranine solution prepared with aniline water.

HERMANN'S PLATINO-ACETO-OSMIC MIXTURE.—Mix 15 parts of 1 per cent. platinic chloride solution, 1 part of glacial acetic acid, and 2 or 4 parts of 2 per cent. osmic acid.

HERTWIG'S MACERATING FLUID.—Mix equal parts of 0·05 per cent. osmic acid, and 0·2 per cent. acetic acid. Medusæ are treated with this mixture for 2 or 3 minutes, then washed in 0·1 per cent. acetic acid until free from osmic acid. Leave them for 24 hours in the dilute acetic acid, then wash in water, stain with Beale's carmine, and mount in glycerine. For Actiniæ use 0·04 per cent. osmic acid and make both solutions with sea water. Wash out with 0·2 per cent. acetic acid, and stain with picro-carmine.

HESSERT'S METHOD FOR STAINING FLAGELLA.—Fix the film by treating cover-glass preparations with a saturated alcoholic solution of mercuric chloride, wash, and stain for 30 or 40 minutes in a hot 10 per cent. aqueous solution of saturated alcoholic solution of fuchsine.

HOFFMANN'S BLUE STAIN.—Dissolve 1 Gm. of Hoffmann's blue in 20 C.c. of rectified spirit and 80 C.c. of distilled water, then add 0·5 C.c. of glacial acetic acid. As a nuclear stain immerse sections for 10 minutes or more, rinse in water, wash in 90 per cent. alcohol, dehydrate, clear, and mount in balsam. To stain sieve areas, less time is required, 5 to 10 minutes, rinse in distilled water, and mount in glycerine; or dehydrate, clear, and mount in balsam.

HOYER'S SHELLAC INJECTION MASS.—Dissolve shellac in 80 per cent. alcohol to the consistency of a thin syrup, and strain through muslin of medium thickness. Colour with aniline colours in alcoholic solution, or by means of vermilion or other pigment suspended in alcohol.

HOYER'S SILVER NITRATE GELATINE MASS.—Mix a concentrated solution of gelatine with an equal volume of a 4 per cent. silver nitrate solution and warm, then add a very small quantity of aqueous pyrogallic acid solution to reduce the silver salt, and add chloral and glycerine as in the carmine gelatine mass.

HOYER'S SILVER STAIN.—Add ammonia to a solution of silver nitrate of known strength, until the precipitate formed just re-dissolves, then dilute the solution until it contains 0·75 to 0·50 per cent. of the salt.

KAISER'S BISMARCK BROWN STAIN. Sections are stained for 48 hours, at a temperature of 60 C., in a saturated solution of Bismarck brown in 60 per cent. alcohol, and washed out in 60 per cent. alcohol containing 2 per cent. of H.C.L., or 3 per cent. of acetic acid.

KAISER'S NERVE STAIN.—This is a modification of Weigert's process. The material is hardened in Müller's solution for 2 or 3 days, then cut into slices 2 to 4 Mm. thick, and treated with the solution for 5 or 6 days more. Subsequently immerse in Marchi's solution for 8 days, then wash, pass through alcohol, and imbed in celloidin. Sections are mordanted for 5 minutes in the following mixture:—Solutions of ferric chloride, 1 part; distilled water, 1 part; rectified spirit, 8 parts. Next wash in Weigert's hæmatoxylin, and warm in a fresh quantity of the same for a few minutes, wash with water, differentiate in Pal's solution, and neutralise the oxalic acid by washing in water containing a little ammonia.

KAISER'S STAIN FOR THE SPINAL CORD.—Sections are stained for a few hours in solution of náphthylamine brown, 1 part, in water, 200 parts, and alcohol, 100 parts. Afterwards wash with alcohol and clear with origanum oil.

KALLIN'S NEUROLOGICAL METHOD.—Dissolve hydroquinone, 5 Gm., sodium sulphite, 40 Gm., and potassium carbonate, 75 Gm., in 25 Gm. of distilled water. At the time of using, dilute this solution with one-third to one-half its bulk of absolute alcohol; immerse sections of silvered material for several minutes until reduction is complete. Then place them in 70 per cent. alcohol for 10 to 15 minutes, and subsequently leave in aqueous solution of sodium hyposulphite (1:5) for 24 hours or more. Finally dehydrate and mount. Carmine may be used as an afterstain.

KLEINENBERG'S SOLUTION (*Improved Formula*).—Hæmatoxylin, 2½ Gm.; crystallised calcium chloride, 20 Gm. in 10 C.c. of distilled water; alum, 3 Gm. in 16 C.c. of distilled water; rectified spirit, 240 C.c. Dissolve the calcium chloride and alum in their respective quantities of water by the aid of heat; mix the solutions and immediately dilute with rectified spirit; after an hour filter and add the hæmatoxylin. This makes a good working solution which keeps well. Of course it contains the alumina in solution, not as alum but aluminium chloride. If in special cases the colour is considered too strong, the dilution (when staining in bulk) must be made with some of the solution to which hæmatoxylin has not been added.

KOCH'S METHOD FOR STAINING FLAGELLA.—Immerse cover-glass preparations in a 1 per cent. aqueous solution of hæmatoxylin, then transfer to a 5 per cent. solution of chromic acid or to Müller's fluid; dry and mount in balsam.

KOCH-EHRLICH, BACILLI.—Place sections, or cover-glass preparations, for at least 12 hours in gentian violet, or fuchsine aniline water (aniline water, 100 C.c.; concentrated alcoholic solution of gentian violet, or fuchsine, 11 C.c.; absolute alcohol, 10 C.c.), then immerse in a mixture of pure nitric acid (sp. gr. 1·42), 10 C.c., and distilled water, 30 C.c., for some seconds. Rinse in 60 per cent. alcohol for a few minutes, and then counterstain with vesuvine (vesuvine, 0·5 Gm.; rectified spirit, 20 C.c.; distilled water, 80 C.c.) after gentian violet; or methylene blue (methylene blue, 0·25 Gm.; rectified spirit, 20 C.c.; distilled water, 80 C.c.) after fuchsine. Finally rinse in water, dehydrate, clear, and mount in balsam. According to Squire, who points out that nitric acid is apt to injure delicate sections, Watson Cheyne recommends that sections should be transferred from fuchsine aniline water to distilled water, then rinsed in alcohol, and placed in the following contrast stain for 1 or 2 hours:—Saturated alcoholic solution of methylene blue, 20 C.c.; distilled water, 100 C.c.; formic acid (sp. gr. 1·2), 1 C.c.

KÜHNE'S CARBOLIC METHYLENE BLUE.—Rub up 1·5 Gm. of methylene blue with 10 C.c. of absolute alcohol, and add 100 C.c. of a 5 per cent. aqueous solution of carbolic acid.

KÜHNE'S METHYL VIOLET SOLUTION.—Dissolve 1 Gm. of methyl violet in 90 C.c. of distilled water and 100 C.c. of alcohol.

KÜHNE'S ANILINE OIL SOLUTIONS.—Rub up as much methylene blue, methyl green, or safranine as will go upon the point of a knife, with 10 C.c. of aniline, and allow to settle.

KÜHNE'S CARBOLIC FUCHSINE OR BLACK BROWN.—Dissolve 1 Gm. of fuchsine or black brown in 10 C.c. of absolute alcohol, and add 100 C.c. of a 5 per cent. aqueous solution of carbolic acid.

KÜHNE'S MODIFICATION OF GRAM'S METHOD.—Stain nuclei with carmine, then treat sections for 5 minutes in methyl violet solution, diluted one-sixth with a 1 per cent. aqueous solution of ammonium carbonate, or in a solution of Victoria blue, 0·25 Gm., in rectified spirit, 20 C.c., and distilled water, 80 C.c. Next rinse thoroughly in water and transfer to Grain's solution for 2 to 3 minutes; again rinse in water and extract excess of stain with solution of yellow fluorescine, 1 Gm., in absolute alcohol, 50 C.c. Finally, pass through pure alcohol, aniline, terebene, and xylol, and mount in balsam.

LÖFFLER'S SOLUTION.—Concentrated alcoholic solution of methylene blue, 30 C.c.; solution of (caustic potash) potassium hydrate (1:10,000), 100 C.c. Mix and filter shortly before use. Sections are stained for a few minutes (tubercle sections for some hours), and excess of stain can be removed by immersion for a few seconds in 0·5 per cent. acetic acid. Dehydrate in absolute alcohol, clear in cedar oil, and mount in balsam. Löffler found that most bacteria stained better in this solution than in the weaker solutions used by Koch for turbercle bacillus.

LAVDOWSKY'S BILBERRY JUICE STAIN.—Well wash the fresh berries of *Vaccinium myrtillus*, then express the juice and mix with twice its bulk of distilled water, mixed with a little 90 per cent. alcohol. Heat for a short time and filter whilst warm. Dilute the stain with 2 or 3 volumes of distilled water before use.

LEE'S FORMALDEHYDE SOLUTIONS.—(1) Mix 1 part of 40 per cent. formaldehyde solution with two parts of 1 per cent. chromic acid solution, and add 4 per cent. of acetic acid. (2) Mix 1 part of 40 per cent. formaldehyde solution with 4 parts of 1 per cent. platinic chloride solution, and add 2 per cent. of acetic acid.

LEE'S OSMIC ACID AND PYROGALLOL STAIN.—Fix the tissues in Hermann's mixture or Flemming's mixture for half an hour, then place in a weak solution of pyrogallol, which may be prepared with alcohol in some cases. Safranine may be used as a second stain.

MARTINOTTI'S PICRO-NIGROSINE STAIN.—Pathological objects are stained for 2 or 3 hours or days, in a saturated solution of nigrosine in saturated alcoholic picric acid solution. Then wash out in a mixture of 1 part of formic acid with 2 parts of alcohol until the grey matter appears clearly differentiated from the white to the naked eye.

MAYER'S ALUMINIUM CHLORIDE CARMINE.—Dissolve 1 Gm. of carminic acid and 3 Gm. of aluminium chloride in 200 C.c. of water.

MAYER'S BERLIN BLUE INJECTION.—Add a solution of 10 C.c. of tincture of ferric chloride in 500 C.c. of water, to a solution of 20 Gm. of potassium ferrocyanide in 500 C.c. of water, allow to stand for 12 hours, decant, wash the deposit for 1 or 2 days with distilled water until the washings come through dark blue, then dissolve the blue in about a litre of water.

MAYER'S CARMALUM.—Dissolve 1 Gm. of carminic acid and 10 Gm. of alum in 200 C.c. of distilled water; decant, or filter, and add a few crystals of thymol, 0·1 per cent. of salicylic acid, or 0·5 per cent. of sodium salicylate. A weaker solution contains 3 to 5 times as much alum and 5 times as much water.

MERBEL'S CARMINE AND INDIGO FLUIDS (give a blue and red stain, and are very selective).—To prepare the red fluid, take—Carmine, 2 dr.; borax, 2 dr.; distilled water, 4 ozs. For the blue fluid, take—Indigo carmine, 2 dr.; borax, 2 dr.; distilled water, 4 ozs. Mix each in a mortar, and allow it to stand, then pour off the supernatant fluid. If the sections have been hardened in chromic acid, picric acid, or a bichromate, they must be washed in water till no tinge appears. Place them in alcohol for fifteen or twenty minutes, then in the two fluids mixed in equal proportions, after which wash them in a saturated aqueous solution of oxalic acid, where they should remain a rather shorter time than in the staining fluids. When sufficiently bleached, wash them in water, to get rid of the acid, then pass them through spirit and oil of cloves, and mount in balsam or dammar.

MITROPHANOW'S GOLD PROCESS FOR PRICKLE-CELLS AND INTERCELLULAR CANALS.—Wash the tail of an axolotl larva with distilled water, place for an hour in a watch-glassful of 0·25 per cent. solution of gold chloride, containing 1 drop of hydrochloric acid; wash, and reduce in a mixture of 1 part of formic acid with 6 parts of water.

MITROPHANOW'S MACERATION METHOD FOR EPITHELIUM.—Fix the embryo for 15 minutes in 3 per cent. nitric acid; then place for an hour in a mixture of alcohol, 1 volume, and water 2 volumes, and finally treat with stronger alcohol for 24 hours to separate the epidermis.

MÜLLER'S BERLIN BLUE FOR INJECTIONS.—Precipitate a concentrated solution of Berlin blue by means of 90 per cent. alcohol. The precipitate is very finely divided, whilst the fluid is perfectly neutral and much easier to prepare than that of Beale.

NEILSEN'S SOLUTION OF METHYL VIOLET.—Dissolve fuchsine, 1 part, in alcohol, 10 parts, and add a 5 per cent. watery solution of carbolic acid, 100 parts.

NEISSER'S DOUBLE-STAINING FOR SPORE-BEARING BACILLI.—Cover-glass preparations are immersed for 20 minutes in fuchsine aniline water (concentrated alcoholic solution of fuchsine, 11 C.c.; absolute alcohol, 10 C.c.; aniline water, 100 C.c.; then heat to 80° or 90° C.; next rinse in water, alcohol, or weak acid, according to the nature of the bacilli, counterstain with aqueous solution of methylene blue, rinse in water, dry and mount in balsam). The spores are stained red and the rest of the bacilli blue.

NISSL'S FUCHSINE STAIN FOR NERVE CELLS.—(1) Fresh material in pieces measuring 1 C.c. are hardened in a "chromic solution in 70 per cent. alcohol" for 2 days, then transferred to absolute alcohol for 5 days, and afterwards cut. Stain the sections singly in a saturated solution of fuchsine, warming in a deep watch-glass until vapours begin to be given off. Next plunge the section into absolute alcohol for 1 or 2 minutes, then place it on a slide, flood with clove oil, and when no more colour is given off, drain and mount in balsam.

OHLMACHER'S FORMALDEHYDE STAINING.—Formalin in a 2 to 4 per cent. solution is used as a mordant for tar colours. The tissues may be mordanted separately by treatment for 1 minute or longer, or the formalin may be added to the stain. Dissolve 1 Gm. of fuchsine in 10 C.c. of absolute alcohol, and add to 100 C.c. of 4 per cent. formalin solution. Or, add saturated alcoholic solution of gentian violet or methyl violet 5 B. to the formalin solution, in the proportion of 1:10. In the case of methylene blue, dissolve 1 G.m. in 100 C.c. of the formalin solution. Sections stain in half a minute, and are said to resist alcohol much more than if formalin were not used.

OPPITZ'S SILVER STAINING.—Reduction is very rapidly effected by placing the preparations for 2 or 3 minutes in a 0·25 to 0·5 per cent. solution of chloride of tin.

PAL'S HÆMATOXYLIN STAIN.—Dissolve 0·75 Gm. of hæmatoxylin in 90 C.c. of distilled water and 10 C.c. of absolute alcohol. Just before use add saturated solution of lithium carbonate in the proportion of 3 drops to each 10 C.c. of hæmatoxylin solution. (See Weigert.)

PAL'S HÆMATOXYLIN METHOD.—Proceed at first as in Weigert's process for nerve fibre, omitting the copper bath, and stain in Pal's hæmatoxylin solution (see above) for 5 or 6 hours. Then wash the sections in distilled water (containing a trace of lithium carbonate if the sections are not deep blue), next treat for 15 to 30 seconds with a 0·25 per cent. potassium permanganate solution, rinse in water, and decolourise in Pal's bleaching solution. (If black spots appear replace in the permanganate solution, again bleach, and wash for 15 minutes in water.) The grey substance of the sections is decolourised in a few sections; the sections should then be well washed out, and may be double-stained with picro-carmine or acetic acid carmine (see Schneider), Magdala red, or eosine. The nuclei may be stained with alum carmine. Finally dehydrate, clear, and mount.

PAL-EXNER'S OSMIC ACID METHOD.—Spinal cord or brain in 0·25 inch cubes is immersed in 0·5 per cent. osmic acid solution for 2 days, the solution being changed each day; then wash in water, transfer to absolute alcohol, and imbed in celloidin or paraffin. Place sections as cut in glycerine, then wash in water, treat with potassium permanganate and Pal's solution, as in Pal's hæmatoxylin method, counter-stain with carmine, dehydrate, clear, and mount in balsam.

PLANT'S METHOD OF STAINING ACTINOMYCOSIS.—Sections are placed for 10 minutes in Gibbes' magenta solution or carbolic fuchsine, at 45° C.; next they are rinsed in water and placed in saturated aqueous solution of picric acid, mixed with an equal volume of absolute alcohol, for 5 or 10 minutes; they are then washed once more, passed through 50 per cent. alcohol into absolute alcohol, cleared in cedar oil, and mounted in balsam.

RANVIER'S LEMON JUICE METHOD.—Soak pieces of fresh tissue in fresh lemon juice until transparent (5 to 10 minutes), then rapidly wash in distilled water, treat for 10 to 60 minutes with 1 per cent. gold chloride solution, again wash and expose to light in a bottle containing 50 C.c. of distilled water and 2 drops of acetic acid. Reduction is complete in 24 to 48 hours. If it is not desired to retain the superficial epithelium, reduction may be more completely effected in the dark, by treatment with formic acid (sp. gr. 1·2), diluted with 3 times its volume of water. The lemon juice in the above process may be replaced by an aqueous solution of citric acid (40 grains in each ounce).

RANVIER'S PICRO-CARMINE.—Carmine, 1 part; distilled water, 10 parts; solution of ammonia, 3 parts; mix and add of a cold saturated solution of picric acid 200 parts.

RENAUT'S HÆMATOXYLIC EOSINE.—Mix 30 C.c. of concentrated aqueous solution of eosine, 40 C.c. of saturated alcoholic solution of hæmatoxylin (which has been kept for some time and precipitated), and 130 C.c. of saturated solution of potash alum in glycerine (sp. gr. 1·26). Stand for 5 or 6 weeks in a partially covered vessel, protected from dust, until the alcohol is evaporated, and then filter. The filtrate can be diluted with glycerine if desired. Mount objects in this fluid diluted with 1 or 2 volumes of glycerine, or, stain separately for some days or weeks and mount in balsam, after washing in alcohol charged with a sufficient quantity of eosine.

RANVIER AND VIGNAL'S OSMIUM MIXTURE.—Fix tissues in a freshly-prepared mixture of equal volumes of 1 per cent. osmic acid and 90 per cent. alcohol, then wash out in 80 per cent. alcohol, next with water, and stain for 48 hours with picro-carmine or hæmatoxylin. This method has been applied to the histology of insects.

RENAUT'S GLYCERINE HÆMATOXYLIN.—To a saturated solution of potash alum in glycerine, add a saturated solution of homatoxylin in 90 per cent. alcohol drop by drop, so as to form a deeply coloured solution. Expose to daylight for a week, and then filter. This solution, like Renaut's hæmatoxylic cosine, may be used for mounting unstained sections, which after some time absorb the colour from the liquid and become stained.

SAFRANINE.—Safranine, 0·5 Gm.; rectified spirit, 20 C.c.; distilled water, 80 C.c.

SCHÄFER'S ACID LOGWOOD SOLUTION is especially useful for certain structures, as tendon, cells, &c. It is thus prepared:—A 1 per cent. solution of acetic acid is coloured by the addition of 1·3 of its volume of logwood solution.

SCHÄFER'S ANILINE DYES, whether in aqueous or alcoholic solutions, give good results, and are prepared as follows:—Roseanilin or magenta (1 gr. to 1 oz. of alcohol), red; acetate of mauvein (4 gr., alcohol 1 oz., acid nitric 2 drops), blue; aniline black (2 gr., water 1 oz.), grey-black; Nicholson's soluble blue (1-6 gr., alcohol 1 oz., and nitric 2 m.), blue. These stains should be used weak; and after sections are stained they should be passed through alcohol and oil of cloves as rapidly as possible; otherwise the colour will dissolve out before they can be mounted in balsam.

SCHULTZE (*Staining Bacilli*).—Stain sections and cover-glass preparations for some hours in aqueous methylene blue solution, differentiate in 0·5 per cent. acetic acid, dehydrate in alcohol, clear in cedar oil, and mount in balsam.

SCLAVO'S STAIN FOR FLAGELLA.—Leave the preparations for 1 minute in a solution of 1 Gm. of tannin in 100 C.c. of 50 per cent. alcohol; wash in distilled water; transfer for 1 minute to 50 per cent. phospho-molybdic acid; again wash, and stain for 3 to 5 minutes in a hot saturated solution of fuchsine in aniline water. Then wash in water, dry on filter paper, and mount in balsam.

SQUIRE'S PICRO-CARMINE.—(1) Dissolve 1 Gm. of carmine with a gentle heat in 3 C.c. of strong solution of ammonia, and 5 C.c. of distilled water, then add 200 C.c. of saturated aqueous solution of picric acid, heat to boiling, and filter. (2) Dissolve 10 Gm. of carmine in a solution of 1 Gm. of caustic soda in 1000 C.c. of distilled water; boil, filter and make up to 1000 C.c. with water. Mix the solution with an equal quantity of water, and add 1 per cent. aqueous solution of picric acid so long as the turbidity produced disappears on agitation.

SQUIRE'S BLUEING OF SECTIONS.—After staining with hæmatoxylin, treat for a few seconds with a solution of sodium bicarbonate (1:1000) in distilled water.

VALENTINE (*Fuchsine*).—Ether shaken with a solution containing fuchsine is coloured violet after adding ferrous iodide, but not before.

VICTORIA BLUE.—Victoria blue, 0·25 Gm.; rectified spirit, 20 C.c.; distilled water, 80 C.c.

WEDL'S ORSEILLE OR ORCHELLA STAIN.—Mix 5 C.c. of acetic acid, 20 C.c. of absolute alcohol, and 40 C.c. of distilled water; then add sufficient archil, from which excess of ammonia has been driven off, to form a dark reddish fluid.

WEIGERT'S HÆMATOXYLIN.—Dissolve 1 part of hæmatoxylin in 10 parts of absolute alcohol; then add 90 parts of distilled water and 1 part of aqueous solution (1:70) of lithium carbonate.

WEIGERT (*Gram's Method*).—In this modification aniline is substituted for alcohol, in order to avoid prolonged washing with the latter, and the process is conducted on a slide. The section is placed on a slide, stained with a few drops of gentian violet aniline water, prepared as in Gram's method, the excess of fluid removed, and a few drops of Gram's solution applied. Subsequently remove the liquid by gently blotting it off, then wash the section by allowing aniline to flow' backwards and forwards over it, and when colour ceases to come away, repeat the operation with xylol for about 1 minute, then mount in balsam.

WEIGERT (*Staining in Actinomycosis*).—Immerse sections for 1 hour in Wedl's Orseille stain, then quickly rinse with alcohol and counterstain with gentian violet. If it be desired to stain the mycelium also, afterwards submit the sections to Weigert's modification of Gram's method. See page 335.

WEIGERT (*Staining Brain Tissue*).—Pieces of brain and spinal cord are hardened in bichromate solution, followed by alcohol, then imbedded in celloidin or gum. If imbedded in celloidin, the pieces are subsequently taken from the spirit in which they are immersed, and placed for one or two days in saturated aqueous solution of copper acetate, diluted with an equal bulk of water, the mixture being kept at about 40° C. Afterwards transfer the pieces to 80 per cent. alcohol until required for cutting. Or, the sections can be cut first, and then treated with copper acetate. To stain the sections, after being well washed in 90 per cent. alcohol, they are transferred to Weigert's hæmatoxylin and left from a few hours to two days, according to the differentiation required. When opaque and of a deep blue-black colour, they should be well washed for two or three days in distilled water. Next decolourise for 0·5 to 2 hours in a solution of 2 Gm. of borax and 2·5 Gm. of potassium ferrocyanide in 200 C.c. of water. As soon as the grey and white substances are sharply defined, again wash the sections in water for half an hour, then dehydrate, clear, and mount in balsam.

WOODHEAD'S METHOD OF STAINING TUBERCLE BACILLI.—Take a small quantity of sputum rich in bacilli, and spread it out by pressure between two cover-glasses, so that a fairly thin film remains on each. Then carefully slip one over the other until they come apart. Thoroughly dry the covers, and pass them rapidly three times through the flame of a spirit lamp, care being taken not to scorch the film, then float them face downwards on the staining solution, which has been previously prepared and filtered into a watch-glass. The stain should consist of saturated alcoholic solution of basic fuchsine, 1 part; absolute alcohol or rectified spirit, 10 parts; carbolic acid solution (5 per cent.), 10 parts. Leave the preparations in the watch-glass for 12 to 24 hours, unless time is an object. In the latter case heat the fluid gently until vapour is given off, then drop the films on the surface, and leave them for 3 to 5 minutes only. Next transfer the covers to an aqueous solution of sulphuric acid (25 per cent.), and when decolourisation is complete, as evidenced by the pink colouration not returning when the specimens are plunged into a bowl of tap-water containing a single drop of ammonia solution, thoroughly rinse in the slightly alkaline water and counter-stain in an aqueous solution of methylene blue. Finally, wash in water, carefully dry and mount in Canada balsam. The bacilli should stand out as bright red rods on a blue background of cells.

ZIEHL-NEELSEN (*Staining Bacilli*).—Sections are removed from weak spirit into Neelsen's carbolic fuchsine and left for 10 or 15 minutes; next decolourise in sulphuric acid (sp. gr. 1·84) or nitric acid (sp. gr. 1·42) diluted with 3 volumes of water, rinse in 60 per cent. alcohol, and wash in a large volume of water to remove the acid. Tubercle and leprosy bacilli are the only micro-organisms that can retain the stain after treatment with acid. If the presence of traces of nitrous acid in the nitric acid be suspected, Squire recommends the use of saturated aqueous solution of sulphanilic acid mixed with one-third its bulk of nitric acid. The sulphanilic acid destroys any free nitrous acid, which would otherwise exercise a bleaching action on the fuchsine-stained bacilli. The sections may be counterstained with a solution of 0·5 Gm. of methyl green (or 0·25 Gm. of methylene blue) in 20 C.c. of rectified spirit and 80 C.c. of distilled water. Finally dehydrate in absolute alcohol, clear in cedar oil, and mount in balsam.

APPENDIX D.

THE METRIC SYSTEM OF WEIGHTS AND MEASURES.

The initial unit of the Metric System is the Metre or unit of length, which represents one ten millionth part of the earth's quadrant, or one forty-millionth part of the circumference of the earth around the poles. The multiples and sub-divisions of this and all the other units are obtained by the use of decimals, and for this reason the system is also known as the *decimal system.* The multiples are designated by the Greek prefixes, *deca* = 10; *hecto* = 100; *kilo* = 1000; *myria* = 10,000. For the sub-divisions Latin prefixes are employed, as follows: *deci* = ¹⁄₁₀; *centi* = ¹⁄₁₀₀; *milli* = ¹⁄₁₀₀₀. Thus for measures of length we have the following expressions, showing the abbreviations commonly employed, and the equivalents in the ordinary English standards of measurement—

1 Myriametre,	Mm.	=	10,000.0	M.	=	6.2137	miles.
1 Kilometre,	Km.	=	1,000.0	M.	=	0.6213	mile.
1 Hectometre,	Hm.	=	100.0	M.	=	109.362	yards.
1 Decametre,	Dm.	=	10.0	M.	=	32.8086	feet.
1 Metre,	M.	=	1.0	M.	=	39.3704	inches.
1 Decimetre,	dm.	=	0.1	M.	=	3.9370	"
1 Centimetre,	cm.	=	0.01	M.	=	0.3937	"
1 Millimetre,	mm.	=	0.001	M.	=	0.0393	"

From the unit of linear measure of metre is derived the unit of the measure of capacity or LITRE. This represents the cube of one-tenth part of a metre, or a cubic decimetre, and its multiples and sub-divisions with their corresponding equivalents in Imperial fluid measure are as follows:—

1 Myrialitre,	Ml.	=	10,000.0	L. =	2200.9667	imperial gallons.[91]
1 Kilolitre,	Kl.	=	1,000.0	" =	220.0966	imperial gallons.
1 Hectolitre	Hl.	=	100.0	" =	22.0096	imperial gallons.
1 Decalitre,	Dl.	=	10.0	" =	2.2009	imperial gallons.
1 Litre,	L.	=	1.0	" =	35.2154	fluid ounces imperial.
1 Decilitre,	dl.	=	0.1	" =	3.5215	fluid ounces imperial.

1 Centilitre,	cl.	=	0.01	"	=	0.3521	fluid ounces imperial.
1 Millilitre,	ml.	=	0.001	"	=	0.0352	fluid ounces imperial.
or							
1 Cubic Centimetre,	ccm.	=	0.001	L.	=	0.0352	fluid ounces imperial.

The unit of weight in the metric system is the GRAMME. This is also derived from the metre, and represents the weight of one cubic centimetre, of water, or the quantity of distilled water, at its maximum density, 4° C. (39·2° F.), which would fill the cube of one-hundredth part of a metre. The relative value of the gramme, together with its multiples and sub-divisions, as compared with the English standards of weight, may be seen from the following table:—

1 Myriagramme,	Mg.	=	10,000.0	Gm. =	22.0461	pounds.
1 Kilogramme,	Kg.	=	1,000.0	" =	2.2046	"
1 Hectogramme,	Hg.	=	100.0	" =	3.5273	ounces avoir.
1 Decagramme,	Dg.	=	10.0	" =	154.3235	grains.
1 Gramme,	Gm.	=	1.0	" =	15.4323	"
1 Decigramme,	dg.	=	0.1	" =	1.5432	"
1 Centigramme,	cg.	=	0.01	" =	0.1543	"
1 Milligramme,	mg.	=	0.001	" =	0.0154	"

The expression *micro-millimetre* is used for microscopic measurements, and denotes the thousandth part of a millimetre. Of the measures of capacity, the terms most commonly employed are the litre and the cubic centimetre. Thus a decalitre may also be expressed as 10 litres, a centilitre as 10 cubic centimetres, etc. Of the metric weights the gramme and its fractional parts, with their respective prefixes, are much used in analytical work. The kilogramme is largely employed in commercial transactions, and is commonly abbreviated *kilo*.

As a comparison of the values of some of the more frequently employed expressions of the metric and English systems, the following may be found convenient for reference:—

1   mm. (millimetre) = $\frac{1}{25}$ of an inch.

1   cm. (centimetre) = $\frac{2}{5}$ of an inch.

1   inch = 25 millimetres or 2½ centimetres.

1   mg. (milligramme) = 0.01543 grain (or approx. $\frac{1}{64}$ grain).

1   gm. (gramme) = 15.4324 grains.

1   Kg. ("Kilo" or kilogramme) = 2 lbs. 3¼ ozs. av.

1   pound avoir. = 453,592 grammes.

1   ounce avoir. = 28,350 grammes.

1   grain = 0.06479 gramme or 64.79 milligrammes.

1   cc. (cubic centimetre) = 16.9 minims Imperial measure.

1   L. (litre) = 35.21 fluid ounces Imperial measure, or 33.815 fluid ounces Wine measure.

1   fluid ounce Imperial measure = 28.350 grammes.

1   pint Imperial measure = 567.0 grammes.

1   gallon Imperial measure = 4.536 litres, or 10 lbs. avoir. of pure water at 62° F. and under an atmospheric pressure of 30 inches of mercury.

It may be well to bear in mind that on the Continent liquids are always weighed, not measured.

APPENDIX E.

COMPARISON BETWEEN THE CENTIGRADE AND FAHRENHEIT THERMOMETERS.

F.	C.	F.	C.
212	100	86	30
200	93.3	84	28.9
150	65.6	82	27.8

112	44.4	80	26.7
110	43.3	78	25.6
108	42.2	76	24.4
106	41.1	74	23.3
105	40.5	72	22.2
104	40	70	21.1
103	39.4	68	20
102	38.9	66	18.9
101	38.3	64	17.8
100	37.8	62	16.7
99	37.2	60	15.6
98	36.7	58	14.4
96	35.6	56	13.3
94	34.4	54	12.2
92	33.3	52	11.1
90	32.2	32	0
88	31.1	25	-3.9

Dr. Culpeper's Microscope 1738.

FOOTNOTES:

1 My earliest acquaintance with the Microscope occurred in the thirties, when I fortunately became possessed of a Culpeper-Scarlet instrument, figured in the title-page.

2 At the time this was written, scarcely a book of the kind had been published at a price within the reach of the student.

3 For fuller information, see the Cantor Lectures on the Microscope, by the late John Mayall, F.R.M.S., "Society of Arts Journal," 1885.

4 "A Practical Treatise on the Use of the Microscope." London, 1855.

5 For further information, I must refer my readers to Parkinson's "Treatise on Optics;" Herschel's "Familiar Lectures on Light;" "Cyclopædia Britannica;" Everett's translation of Deschanel's "Physics;" and Nägeli and Schwendener's "Theory and Practice of the Microscope," translated by Frank Crisp, LL.D.

6 The cornea of the eye is not so entirely the simple transparent structure as it at first sight may appear to be. It is composed of several layers, the most important of which is the nerve layer, consisting of innumerable ganglionic stellate plexus of cells held together by a network, as seen in Fig. 21, a small section stained by chloride of gold, and magnified 300 diameters. Beneath the nucleated nerve cells is a second layer of stellate cells, varying a little in their form. These nerve and stellate cells serve the purpose of maintaining the cornea in health, and must play a significant part in the dioptric system.

7 The standard condition of perfect vision is termed *emmetropia*.

8 *Landolt*, "The Accommodation and Refraction of the Eye," 1886.

9 μ = $\cdot001$ of a millimetre. This measurement is now universally employed in microscopy.

10 Diffraction effects may be observed without a microscope, indeed, the more striking are seen in connection with telescopic vision. A beautiful series of phenomena in illustration of the diffraction of light may be produced as follows: Draw on a large sheet of paper a series of geometrical figures, arranged at equal distances in a circle. A collodion photographic picture of these being taken, a series of small transparent apertures in the elsewhere opaque film will result. This film is then mounted, so that it may be in turn brought before the centre of a small hand telescope, previously adjusted to view an image of the sun. In this way we have an apparatus of the most compact form, and by means of

which a series of fifty or more phenomena may be brought into view in a few minutes. These pictures being very small (occupying on an average area one-tenth of an inch in diameter), inaccuracies of surface and substance of the glass may be neglected. A film of Canada balsam with which the glass is cemented over the picture produces no disturbance. There is a manifest advantage in the figures being small, as the size of the image is in inverse proportion to the size of the aperture.

11 Carpenter, "The Microscope," p. 65, 1891.

12 "Phil. Mag.," viii., p. 167 (1896).

13 Professor Stokes wrote me in the following flattering terms:— "What you have submitted to me on the subject of apertures is so sound, clear, and succinct, that I have nothing to add to it. The method adapted as you have explained respecting the immersion system, I consider to be perfectly satisfactory." Subsequently, and at my request, Sir George Stokes contributed a valuable paper on the subject to the "Transactions of the Royal Microscopical Society," 1876, on "The Theoretical Limit of Aperture."

14 "On the Estimation of Aperture in the Microscope," "Journal of the Royal Microscopical Society," series ii. vol. i.; "Notes on Aperture, Microscopic Vision, and the Value of Wide-angled Immersion Objectives," 1881.

15 *Numerical aperture* is generally used in the sense in which it was introduced in 1873 by Professor Abbe, on the basis of his theoretical investigations. Numerical aperture represents the ratio between the radius of the effective aperture (p) of the system on the side where the image is formed—more accurately the radius of the emerging pencils measured in the upper focal plane of the objective—and the equivalent focal length (f) of the latter, *i.e.*,

$$\text{Numerical aperture} = p/f.$$

This ratio is equal to the product of the sine of half the angle of aperture u of the incident pencils and the refractive index n of the medium, situated in front of the objective. With dry lenses n has therefore the value 1; with immersion lenses it is equal to the refractive index of the particular immersion fluid:

$$\text{Numerical aperture} = n \, \text{Sin} \, u.$$

The numerical aperture of a lens determines all its essential qualities; the brightness of the image increases with a given magnification and, other things being equal, as the square of the aperture; the resolving and defining powers are directly related to it, the focal depth of differentiation of depths varies inversely as the aperture, and so forth. (Abbe, "The Estimation of Aperture," "Journal of the Royal Microscopical Society," 1881, p. 389.)

16 "Journal of the Royal Microscopical Society."

17 "Journal Roy. Micros. Soc.," p. 19, 1878, and p. 20, 1880.

18 "The Magnifying Power of Short Spaces" has been ably elucidated by John Gorham, Esq., M.R.C.S. "Journal of Microscopical Society," October, 1854.

19 The late Mr. Coddington, of Cambridge, who had a high opinion of the value of this lens, had one of these grooved spheres executed by Mr. Carey, who gave it the name of the Coddington Lens, supposing that it was invented by the person who employed him, whereas Mr. Coddington never laid claim to it, and the circumstance of his having one made was not known until nine years after it was described by Sir David Brewster in the "Edinburgh Journal."

20 "Journal of the Royal Microscopical Society, 1890," p. 420.

21 "Journal of the Royal Microscopical Society, 1880," p. 1050.

22 Apo-chromatic, from the Greek, signifying freedom from colour.

23 Prof. Abbe "On Stephenson's System of Homogeneous Immersion for Microscope Objectives," "Journal of the Royal Microscopical Society," II. (1879), p. 256, and on "The Essence of Homogeneous Immersion," Ibid., I. (1881), p. 131.

24 Reichert, in his catalogue, does not clearly indicate what the initial powers of his eye-pieces are.

25 Messrs. Ross have two series of eye-pieces, both Huyghenian. One series is for use with the English 10-inch tube-body, and is distinguished by Roman letters, and the other by numerals, and made as is usual on the Continent, and for use with the shorter tube-body 6½-inch. The initial powers given in the table are for the 10-inch tube, and for the shorter must be read as follows:—

1 2 3 4   }
                 with 6½-inch tube.
4 6 8 12 }

26 This centring-glass consists of a tubular cap with a minute aperture, containing two plano-convex lenses, so adjusted that the image of the

aperture in the object-glass and the images of the aperture of the lenses and the diaphragms contained in the tube which holds the illuminating combination, may be all in focus at the same time, so that by the same adjustment they may be brought sufficiently near to recognise their centricity.

27 Summary of the value of parabolic illumination and immersion illuminators, by the late Mr. J. Mayall, will be found on p. 27, "Journal of the Royal Microscopical Society" (1879).

28 Messrs. Baker and Swift have constructed lamps with removal and fixed achromatic bull's-eye lenses in gymbal, and changeable tinted glass screens. Either of these will add to the usefulness of the lamp in bacteriological research work. Baker's is constructed on the Herschel doublet formula, and should therefore be free from aberration. It is mounted on a heavy brass tripod foot, has vertical and horizontal movements by rack and pinion, brass reservoir, with screw opening for filling, metal chimney to take $3 \times 1\frac{1}{2}$-inch glass slip, removable frame for carrying tinted glass screens, &c.

29 "Journal of the Royal Microscopical Society," p. 365, 1896.

30 Dr. G. A. Piersoll, "American Annual of Photography," 1890.

31 "Journal of the Royal Microscopical Society," 1892, p. 684.

32 "Journal of the Royal Microscopical Society," p. 578, 1897.

33 Herapath's test-fluid is a mixture of three drachms of pure acetic acid, one drachm of alcohol, and three drops of sulphuric acid.

34 "Journal of the Royal Microscopic Society," 1867.

35 Born in 1787, at Straubing, a small town in Bavaria.

36 Dr. Thudicum's "Tenth Report of the Medical Officer of the Privy Council, 1867." Mr. Sorby "On Some Improvements in the Spectrum Method of Detecting Blood." "Journal of the Royal Microscopical Society," 1871.

37 "On the Reduction and Oxidation of the Colouring-matter of the Blood" ("Proc. of the Royal Soc." vol. xiii. p. 355). The oxidising solution is made as follows:—To a solution of proto-sulphate of iron, enough tartaric acid is added to prevent precipitation by alkalies. A small quantity of this solution, made slightly alkaline by ammonia or carbonate of soda, is to be added to the weak solution of blood in water.

38 "Journal of the Royal Microscopical Society," 1869.

39 Professor Sylvanus Thompson, "On the Measurement of Lenses," "Journal of the Royal Microscopical Society," 1892, p. 109.

40 "Journal of the Royal Microscopical Society," 2nd Series, Vol. iv., p. 542.

41 Mr. J. F. Smith, "On the Structure of the Valve of Pleurosigma Pellucida," "Quekett Club Trans."

42 "Quarterly Journal of Microscopical Science," New Series, Vol. viii., 1878.

43 It is quite possible also for the student to make his own microscope stand. Mr. Field in the "English Mechanic," pp. 171 et seq., 1897, furnishes numerous working drawings for the construction of a high-class stand, together with patterns for the metal work.

44 "Modern Microscopy," by Martin J. Cole.

45 With regard to the use of absolute alcohol, this re-agent requires to be used with caution; all minute details are lost, and it causes irregular shrinking of the finer tissues, while fibrous tissue is brought into undue prominence at the expense of the cellular elements. Consequently in certain biological laboratories the method of hardening in alcohol has been abandoned in favour of other re-agents.

46 "Journal of Anatomy and Physiology," XX. 1881, p. 349.

47 "Journal of the Quekett Club," July, 1893, and March, 1895.

48 Mr. John Hood, 50, Dallfield Walk, Dundee, offers a weekly supply of infusorial life for a small annual subscription, or a single tube by post at the trifling cost of one shilling.

49 Professor Marshall Ward, F.R.S., "Address to the Botanical Section of the British Association, 1897."

50 "British Medical Journal," March 26, 1859; "Medical Times and Gazette" and "Popular Science Review," 1862.

51 "Parasitic Diseases," "Journ. of the Royal Micros. Soc. of Lond.," 1859-60.

52 There are several other kinds of bacteria infesting milk, some of which are motile, others non-motile, producing acidity and colouring matter, as *B. prodigiosus*, red-milk; *B. synxanthus*, yellow milk; *B. lactis aerogens*, which are pathogenic; *B. lactis albus*, which coagulate milk; and another form, which is productive of slimy or ropy-milk.

53 "Parasitic Diseases of the Skin," 1859-73, p. 30. Bailliere, Tindal, and Cox.

54 "Organic Germ Theory of Disease," "Medical Times and Gazette," p. 685, 1870.

55 F. Cohn on the "Natural History of *Protococcus pluvialis.*"

56 Pritchard's "Infusoria," p. 24, Plate I., 4th edition.

57 In order to detect the presence of starch-grains in plants, the tissue must be kept in alcohol exposed to light, until the whole of the chlorophyll is dissolved out; it must then be treated for several hours in a strong solution of potash. After neutralisation with acetic acid, the tissue may be treated with iodine, which colours it blue, or with coralline solution, which colours it pink.

58 Verhandl. d. Natur. Hist. Jahr. xx. p. 1. "Micros. Jour. Science," vol. iii., p. 120.

59 For instance, where the yellow Palmella is found the Chlorococcus will assume a yellow tinge in its soridial stage. Viewed by transmitted light the sori are seen as opaque balls, with an irregular outline.

60 "Contributions to the Knowledge of the Development of the Gonidia of Lichens." By J. Braxton Hicks, M.D., "Quarterly Journal of Microscopical Science," vol. viii., 860, p. 239.

61 Berkeley's "Introduction to Cryptogamic Botany," 1857.

62 For more detailed information on the structure and classification of unicellular plants, and cryptogams, the reader is referred to Ralfs' "British Desmidaceæ"; Smith's "British Diatomaceæ"; Goebel's "Outlines of Classification and Special Morphology"; Berkeley's "Cryptogamic Botany"; De Bary's "Comparative Anatomy of the Phaneragams and Ferns"; Professor Marshall Ward's "Sach's Physiology of Plants," and numerous memoirs on Fungi; and Bower and Sidney Vine's "Course of Practical Instruction in Botany," a most instructive book on the histology of plants.

63 "A Manual of the Infusoria," by W. Saville Kent, F.L.S., &c., 1880.

64 "Journal of the Linn. Society," vol. viii., p. 202; vol. ix., p. 147, 1865 and 1866.

65 Among the more important works on Foraminifera for consultation will be found D'Orbigny's "Foraminiferes Fossiles du Bassin Tertiaire de Vienne" (Autriche); Schultze, "Ueber den Organismus der Polythalamien," 1854; Carpenter and Williamson's "Researches on the

Foraminifera," "Phil. Trans. 1856;" Parker and Rupert-Jones in the "Annals of Natural History." Specimens of Foraminifera may be obtained by shaking dried sponges; but if required alive they must be dredged for, or picked off the fronds of living seaweeds, over the surface of which they are, by the aid of a lens, seen to move.

66 W. Saville Kent, F.L.S., Op. Cit., p. 335.

67 Difficulties formerly associated with the microscopic examination of flagellate forms of infusorial life have been overcome by improvements in the objectives, by the knowledge gained of the monad groups, and by the exhaustive researches of Drs. Drysdale and Dallinger, whose joint investigations were published in the Journal of the Royal Microscopical Society, 1873-75. By employing the highest and most perfectly constructed powers of the microscope, and devoting an enormous amount of time and attention to unravelling mysteries so long associated with the production of the lowly organised flagellate organisms, monads, and patiently watching hour by hour, the life-history of numerous species of these minute infusorial animalcules were obtained. Not only was it discovered that these organisms increased indefinitely by fission, but that under certain conditions two or more individuals were united into encystments, and whose contents broke up into a greater or less number of spore-like bodies, were speedily developed into the parent type. In the examination of these minute bodies, it has been found that talc-films, that is, talc split into extremely fine laminæ, offer the best kind of cover, in fact, supersede ordinary glass covers, and possess an advantage, that of bending readily, thus permitting the objective to be brought close down upon the object.

68 R. Kirkpatrick, Warne, Op. Cit., pp. 532-3.

69 Saville Kent, *op. cit.*, p. 191.

70 Fritz Müller first demonstrated a nervous system in the Polyzoa:— "The nervous system of each branch consisting of—1st, a considerable sized ganglion situated at its origin; 2nd, of a nervous trunk running the entire length of the branch, at the upper part of which it subdivides into branches, going to the ganglia of the internodes arising at this part; and 3rd, of a rich nervous plexus resting on the trunk, and connecting the ganglia just mentioned, as well as the basal ganglia of the individual polypides." For further account, see paper in the "Micros. Journ.," vol. i., New Series, p. 330.

71 I have ventured to devote some considerable space to the development of the pond-snail, and for an obvious reason, that of

making it perfectly clear to my readers that my microscopical investigations of Limnœa, made in 1853, were published in the "Journal of the Microscopical Society," June, 1854, and republished in extenso in the several editions of this book, dating from the last mentioned period. Nevertheless, the fringe of cilia was, it appears, rediscovered in 1874, just twenty years after my paper was published. It is almost unnecessary to add that Carpenter gravely errs in his statement "that the existence of the fringe of cilia in the embryo snail had been overlooked until 1874."

72 Mr. George Rainey many years ago made us acquainted with the fact that certain of the appearances presented by the shell or other hard structures of animals, and which had hitherto been referred to as cell-development, are really governed by the physical laws which govern the aggregation of certain crystalline salts when exposed to the action of vegetable and animal substances in a state of solution. Mr. Rainey furnished a process for obtaining artificially a crystalline substance which shall so closely resemble shell structure that it can barely be distinguished from it. The chemical substances to be used in the preparation of the artificial shell, or calculi, are a soluble compound of lime and carbonate of potash or soda, dissolved in separate portions of water, and mixed with some viscid vegetable or animal substance, as gum or albumen, and mixing the several solutions together. The mechanical conditions required are that such a quantity of each of the viscid materials in each solution shall be of about the same density as that of the nascent carbonate of lime, and at perfect rest. This state of rest will require from two to three weeks or longer. Mr. Rainey shows the analogy or identity of his artificially formed crystals with those found in natural products both in animals and vegetables, chiefly confining himself to the structure and formation of shells and bone, pigmental and other cells, and the structure and development of the crystalline lenses, which he contends are all formed upon precisely the same physical principles as the artificial crystals.

73 E. Ray Lankester, "On the Gregarinæ found in the common Earthworm."—"Micros. Trans." vol. iii. p. 83.

74 For the fullest information of marine, land, and fresh-water species, consult Dr. Bastian's "Monograph on the Anguillulidæ"; "Lin. Soc. Trans." vol. xxv. p. 75; the "Anguillula Aceti," by the author, in the "Popular Science Review," January, 1863.

75 "Cercaria parasitic on Limnœa," "Jour. Royal Micros. Soc." 1870.

76 See my paper "The Natural History of a Nematode Worm," "Journ. of Microscopy and Natural History," October, 1888.

77 "The Parasites of Man and the Diseases which proceed from them," by Professor Rudolf Leuckart, 1886.

78 R. J. Pocock, "On Worms" (Warne, Op. cit.), p. 465.

79 An interesting account of the formation of the tubes of Serpula is given by Mr. Watson, "Jour. Micros. Soc.," vol. 1890, p. 685.

80 Dr. Baird, "Natural History of British Entomostraca," printed for the Ray Society, 1850.

81 See Mr. B. T. Lowne's exhaustive treatise on "The Anatomy and Physiology of the Blow-fly," a volume of 750 pages and 52 plates, 1891.

82 Tuffen West, "Trans. Linn. Soc.," vol. xxiii., p. 393.

83 The term micropyle (a little gate) has heretofore only been used in its relation with the vegetable kingdom: it is used to denote the opening or foramen towards which the radicle is always pointed.

84 Dr. Halifax adopts the method of killing the insect with chloroform; he then immerses it in a bath of hot wax, in which it is allowed to remain until the wax becomes cold and hard; with a sharp knife sections are easily made in the required direction without in the least disturbing any of the more fragile parts, or internal organs of the specimen.

85 "Phil. Trans.," 1859, p. 341.

86 See my paper on "The Eggs of Insects," in "The Intellectual Observer," Oct. 1867, in which other varieties of eggs are given.

87 W. U. Whitney, "Transactions of the Microscopical Society" for 1861 and 1867.

88 Mr. F. G. Cuttell, 52, New Compton Street, Soho, cuts and prepares excellent sections.

89 Published with his paper in detail, "Aperture as a Factor in Microscopic Vision," "Journal of Royal Micros. Soc.," June, 1808, pp. 334 *et seq.*

90 "Squire's Methods and Formulæ;" "Modern Microscopy," Cross and M. F. Cole; "The Microscopists' Vade Mecum," A. B. Lee; "Bacteriology." Professor Dr. E. Crookshank, Messrs. Baird and Tattock, Cross Street, Hatton Garden, supply all Scientific Apparatus for Bacteriological Work.

91 The imperial gallon contains 277.27384 cubic inches, and the imperial pint 20 fluid ounces, whereas the wine gallon has 231 cubic

inches and the pint 16 fluid ounces. In wine measure 1 litre = 33.815 fluid ounces.

Booksophile
Your Local Online Bookstore

Buy Books Online from
www.Booksophile.com

Explore our collection of books written in various languages and uncommon topics from different parts of the world, including history, art and culture, poems, autobiography and bibliographies, cooking, action & adventure, world war, fiction, science, and law.

Add to your bookshelf or gift to another lover of books - first editions of some of the most celebrated books ever published. From classic literature to bestsellers, you will find many first editions that were presumed to be out-of-print.

Free shipping globally for orders worth US$ 100.00.

Use code "Shop_10" to avail additional 10% on first order.

Visit today
www.booksophile.com

Ingram Content Group UK Ltd.
Milton Keynes UK
UKHW010811060623
422954UK00004B/407